Managing California's Water

From Conflict to Reconciliation

Ellen Hanak • Jay Lund • Ariel Dinar
Brian Gray • Richard Howitt • Jeffrey Mount
Peter Moyle • Barton "Buzz" Thompson

Supported with funding from S. D. Bechtel, Jr. Foundation, The David and Lucile Packard Foundation, Pisces Foundation, Resources Legacy Fund, and Santa Ana Watershed Project Authority

PUBLIC POLICY
INSTITUTE OF CALIFORNIA

Managing California's Water
From Conflict to Reconciliation

Ellen Hanak, Jay Lund, Ariel Dinar,
Brian Gray, Richard Howitt, Jeffrey Mount,
Peter Moyle, Barton "Buzz" Thompson

San Francisco, CA

Library of Congress Cataloging-in-Publication Data are available for this publication.

ISBN 978-1-58213-141-2

Manufactured in the United States of America.

Cover image: The California Aqueduct and the federal Delta-Mendota Canal, side by side.
Photo by California Department of Water Recources.

Contents

Figures

Tables

Boxes

Abbreviations

AB	Assembly Bill
af	acre-feet
CALFED	state-federal program for the San Francisco Bay and Sacramento–San Joaquin Delta
CALVIN	California Value Integrated Network Model
CEQA	California Environmental Quality Act
CESA	California Endangered Species Act
CPUC	California Public Utilities Commission
CVP	Central Valley Project
CVPIA	Central Valley Project Improvement Act
CWA	Clean Water Act
DFG	Department of Fish and Game
DWR	Department of Water Resources
EIR	Environmental Impact Report
EPA	Environmental Protection Agency
ESA	Endangered Species Act
EWA	Environmental Water Account
FERC	Federal Energy Regulatory Commission
FGC	Fish and Game Commission
FIFRA	Federal Insecticide, Fungicide, and Rodenticide Act
GCM	Global Circulation Models
GO bonds	general obligation bonds
gpcd	gallons per capita per day
HCP	Habitat Conservation Plan
IID	Imperial Irrigation District
IPCC	Intergovernmental Panel on Climate Change
IRWM	Integrated Regional Water Management
ISO	independent system operator
LAO	Legislative Analyst's Office

maf	million acre-feet
MCL	maximum concentration level
mg/l	milligrams per liter
NCCP	Natural Community Conservation Plan
NFIP	National Flood Insurance Program
NMFS	National Marine Fisheries Service (also known as NOAA Fisheries Service)
PCB	polychlorinated biphenyl
PGC	public goods charge
PIER	Public Interest Energy Research
PVID	Palo Verde Irrigation District
REACH	Registration, Evaluation, Authorization and Restriction of Chemical Substances
ROD	Record of Decision
SAFCA	Sacramento Area Flood Control Agency
SB	Senate Bill
SWP	State Water Project
SWRCB	State Water Resources Control Board
taf	thousand acre-feet
TMDL	total maximum daily load
TSCA	Toxic Substances Control Act
USBR	U.S. Bureau of Reclamation
USFWS	U.S. Fish and Wildlife Service
UWMP	Urban Water Management Plan

Preface and Acknowledgments

> The best is the enemy of the good.
> Voltaire, *Philosophical Dictionary*

California has always had water conflicts, and as a semiarid state it always will. It is easy in these troubled times to assert that California is doomed, for this and other reasons, and that nothing can be done about it. But California has thrived more than almost any other part of the world despite scarce water supplies, and there is little reason why prosperity cannot continue, despite new challenges, with suitable adaptations in policy and management. California is now at a crossroads for water management, with crises looming on numerous fronts.

In this book, we explore solutions for the modern era, when water management must become more balanced and flexible to support both economic prosperity and environmental sustainability. We start by reviewing the history of how California has adapted to changes and conflicts in water management in the past—slowly, controversially, and imperfectly—but with remarkable success. We then lay out a variety of promising principles and directions for improving water management in California for contemporary and anticipated future conditions.

Many will find our proposals difficult, impossible, or even misguided. However, given the many enormous and seemingly impossible changes that have occurred in the past half century—the creation of the European Union, the fall of the Berlin Wall, the rapid rise of Asian economies, and the economic and social transformations from information technology—we should be open and hopeful about the prospects for progress on water problems in California, which seem small by comparison. California already has made great strides on other difficult environmental or resource issues such as climate change and marine reserves. The reforms we recommend will not satisfy or improve conditions for everyone, and many will seem unrealistic in the near term, but we believe they form a basis for a robust, sustainable trajectory for California.

We write from the perspectives of eight independent authors who are long acquainted with water policy and management in California, with experience in a wide range of areas, including biology, economics, engineering, geology, and law. We have sought to integrate these perspectives into a coherent whole, because real problems and real solutions are not confined to our individual disciplines. It is also more rewarding to work in this way.

Many people have helped us greatly in this work. We received excellent research support from a team of researchers and graduate students at the University of California–Davis Center for Watershed Sciences, the Public Policy Institute of California, Stanford University Law School, and the University of California–Riverside Water Science and Policy Center. Robyn Suddeth helped keep us organized. Josue Medellin-Azuara and Joshua Viers oversaw new technical and data analysis and the development of new maps. Shannon Brown, Anna Fryjoff-Hung, and Davin Reed developed the maps presented throughout. Rachel Ragatz developed new results using the CALVIN model, presented in Chapter 6. Marisol Cuellar-Mejia, J. Aapris Frisbie, Bryce Kaufman, Getachew Nigatu, Joshua Patashnik, Rachel Ragatz, Davin Reed, and Elizabeth Stryjewski provided general research support, and they collected and helped us to digest much of the data presented herein. Sarah Null coordinated interviews with over 100 policy experts and was assisted by Eleanor Bartolomeo, Nathan Burley, Christina Buck, Daphne Korthamar, and others already mentioned. A synthesis of these interviews is provided in an online appendix to this book (Null et al. 2011—add weblink).

Our work benefited greatly from the insights of these policy experts, as well as from the counsel of a candid and constructive advisory group that included Curt Aikens, Joya Banerjee, Ginny Cahill, Celeste Cantú, Martha Davis, Mike Eaton, Jim Fiedler, Randy Fiorini, Bob Fisher, Ron Gastelum, Brandon Goshi, Les Grober, Laura Harnish, Allison Harvey Turner, Bill Hauck, Kai Lee, Steve Macaulay, Michael Mantell, Doug Obegi, Bill Phillimore, Tim Quinn, Betsy Rieke, Justice Ron Robie, Spreck Rosekranz, Mary Scoonover, Christa Shaw, Steve Thompson, Tim Washburn, and Terry Young.

Additional helpful discussions, technical advice, and assistance with data sources came from Art Baggett, Melody Baldwin, Dylan Beaudette, Damian Bickett, Diana Brooks, Chris Brown, Mike Byrne, Steve Canal, Steve Chedester, Michael Colvin, Steve Cowdin, Michael Deas, Stuart Drown, Farhad Farnam, William Fleenor, William Forsythe, Congressman John Garamendi, Teresa Geimer, Mark Gowdy, Peter Green, Darwin Hall, Michael Hanemann, Quinn Hart, Bill Hasenkamp, Tom Hawkins, Steve Hatchett, Kris Higgs, Ray Hoagland, Steve Hirsch, Richard Juricich, Tariq Kadir, Rami Kahlon, Eric Kauffman, Chuck Keene, Mark Lubell, Michael Mierzwa, Dan Nelson, Toby O'Geen, Nickolas Perez, Halla Razar, Jim Rich, Ken Robbins, Nancy Saracino,

Andy Sawyer, Jane Schafer-Kramer, Mary Scruggs, Eric Senter, Greg Smith, Frances Spivy-Weber, Evelyn Tipton, Cynthia Truelove, and Diane Vaughan.

We thank reviewers of an earlier draft for their sage and detailed comments and suggestions. These include Stuart Drown, Steve Hatchett, Michael Hanemann, Bruce Herbold, John Leshy, Dean Misczynski, Justice Ron Robie, Lynette Ubois, and Terry Young. We also received excellent editorial and production support from Patricia Bedrosian, Gary Bjork, Todd Duft, Janice Fong, Eileen La Russo, Kate Reber, Mary Severance, and Lynette Ubois.

Last, but not least, we thank the organizations that funded this work. Stephen D. Bechtel, Jr. made the initial suggestion that a broad analysis of California water policy would be useful at this juncture in California's history. The S. D. Bechtel, Jr. Foundation, the David and Lucile Packard Foundation, the Pisces Foundation, the Resources Legacy Fund, and the Santa Ana Watershed Project Authority provided generous financial support.

We alone are responsible for the recommendations in this book and any errors herein.

California water features

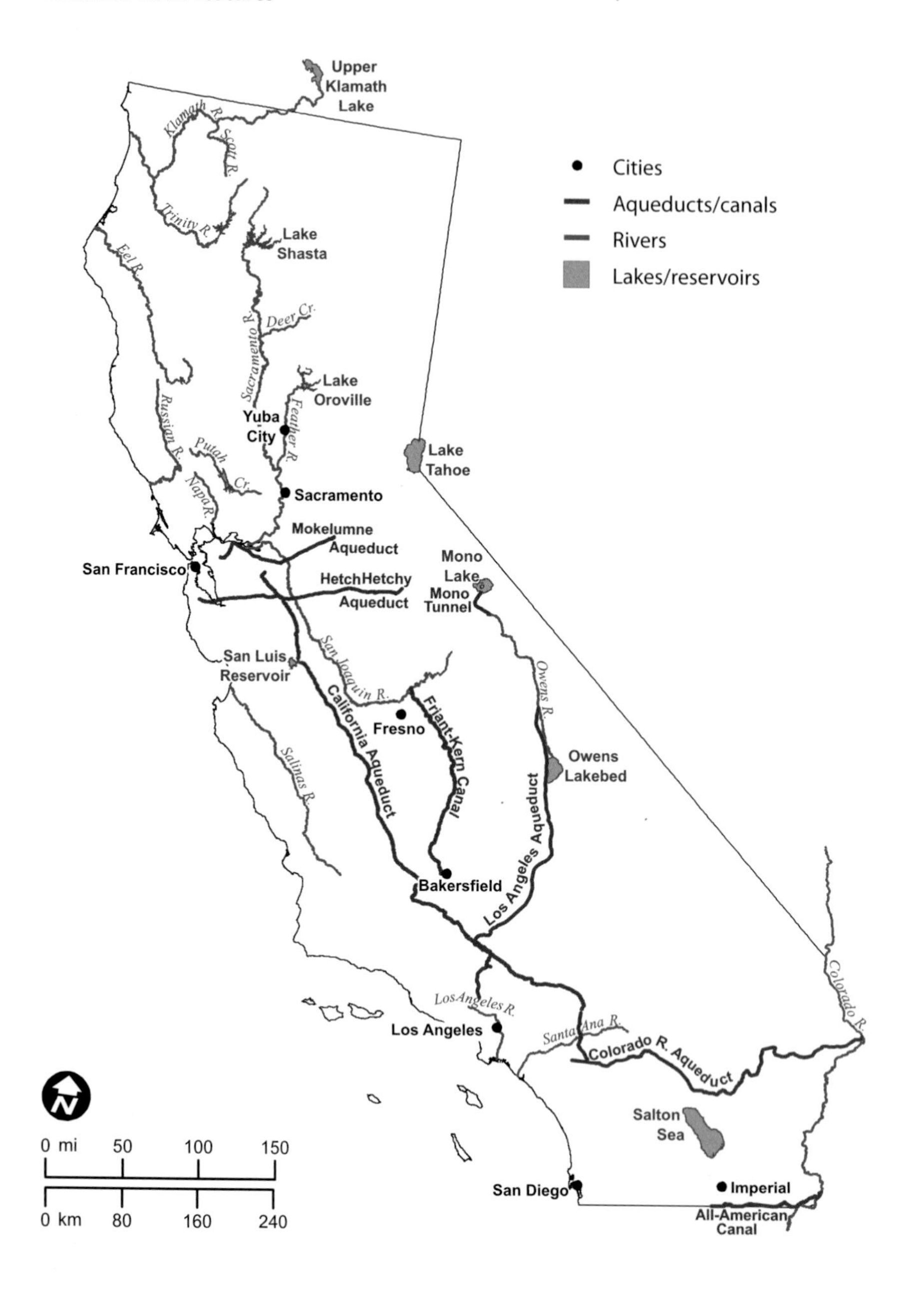

California counties

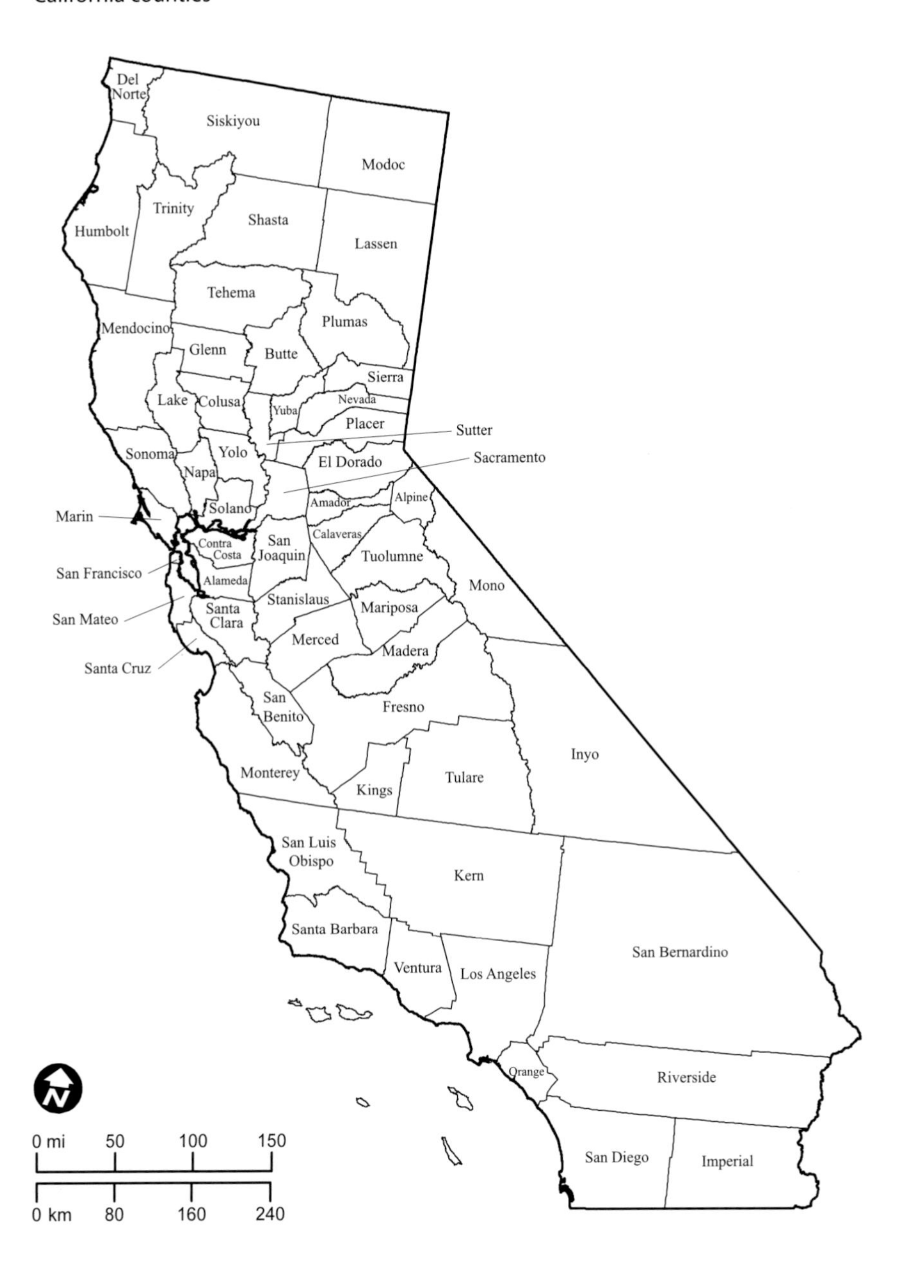

Introduction

CARSON JEFFRES

Confusion now hath made his masterpiece!

William Shakespeare, *Macbeth*

For more than 30 years, California has struggled to manage its water effectively. Numerous factors have contributed to this struggle, including changes in the value that society places on ecosystems, growing urbanization, declining state and federal financial and technical support, a shifting climate, and outdated water management systems. All of these factors make water scarcity and increasing flood risk a part of life in California, now and for the indefinite future.

Current policies have proved inadequate to meet diverse and growing demands for water supply reliability and water quality, flood protection, and ecosystem health:

- Competition for water has become intense. The state has run out of cheap "new" water sources, and agricultural and urban water users now compete both among themselves and with emerging environmental demands.
- Water quality concerns are growing, despite progress in cleaning up wastewater and industrial discharges. "Nonpoint" sources of pollution—the runoff from agricultural fields, timber harvesting, mining, and urban streets, gardens, and construction sites—are still not well managed, and California lacks adequate policies to prevent harmful new chemicals from entering the environment. The consequences are increased costs of drinking water treatment, risks to public health, lower crop yields, and harm to aquatic ecosystems.

Mount Shasta from the Shasta River.

- Flood risks are high and growing. Investments in flood protection have not been adequate to maintain existing infrastructure, and many local governments have promoted development behind weak levees, placing more lives and property at risk.
- Ecosystems and native species are in decline. Decades of harmful water and land management practices have degraded aquatic habitat, worsening conditions for native fish and other species that depend on California's wetlands, streams, lakes, and estuaries. The growing number of species listed under the Endangered Species Act reflects this decline, and ESA regulations to protect these species have, in turn, become a flashpoint in the increasing conflicts over water management.

In short, today's system of water management, developed in previous times for past conditions, is leading the state down a path of environmental and economic deterioration. Crises are brewing, waiting for the next drought, flood, or lawsuit to bring widespread or local catastrophe. In some ways, California is already in a crisis, but the crisis is moving so slowly that the state's leaders and residents often fail to recognize it. Given anticipated changes in demographic, economic, climatic, and ecosystem conditions, today's conflicts are likely to worsen unless California can quickly develop significant, forward-looking changes in water policy.

California's Failing Water Policy

Current conflicts over California's water are wide-ranging and reflect the diverse landscape, climate, economies, ecosystems, and cultures of the state. The struggles to remove four dams on the Klamath River, improve flood protection for Sacramento, find a solution to the decline of the Salton Sea, resolve aquifer overdraft in Central Coast basins, dispose of salt in the Santa Ana Basin, and manage the Sacramento–San Joaquin Delta for both water supply and ecosystem health all seem to be unique local problems. Yet they and myriad other water conflicts in California have important common, interrelated elements.

Infrastructure Limits

The elaborate 20th century water supply and flood control systems that are symbolic of what Norris Hundley, Jr., has called "the hydraulic society" made it possible for one of the world's most diverse and dynamic economies to prosper in a semiarid region highly susceptible to floods and droughts (Hundley 2001). A network of hundreds of groundwater basins, 1,400 dams, and thousands of miles of canals, aqueducts, and levees delivers water and manages floods for more than 38 million people. This development reflects the state's dry and variable climate and the geographic distance between California's major water sources and its population and farming centers—75 percent of California's precipitation occurs north of Sacramento, and 75 percent of its water demand lies to the south (Figure A).

But California has outstripped the capacity of traditional water infrastructure to satisfy its current economic, environmental, and social demands for water. Expanding traditional water infrastructure is increasingly costly and less effective. The most accessible and productive streams have already been tapped, and there is little room left to support aquatic ecosystems.

Funding Limits

The great expansion in water supply and flood control infrastructure in the 20th century relied on financial and technical support from federal and state governments. Over the past 30 years, diminishing institutional support (particularly federal funding for large water projects) has failed to keep pace with expanding needs. The state's financial contributions to water management have largely been funded by general obligation bonds that must be paid back with state tax revenues. Given the current and prospective fiscal climates in Washington and Sacramento, increased federal and state largesse is unlikely in the near future. At some point, reliance on state borrowing will no longer be viable, as the public begins to realize that dedicating tax revenues to pay off water bonds means reduced funding for other public services supported by the state's general fund. The legislature's 2010 decision to postpone an $11.1 billion water bond initiative for at least two years may be a tacit admission of this financial limit.

A Changing Climate

Most of California's water management infrastructure was designed during the first half of the 20th century. Yet the climate in California (and in much of the American West) has changed in the past 60 years—and will continue to change. A more volatile climate now appears to be the norm, with an increasing frequency and intensity of droughts, floods, extreme high tides, and heat waves. An overwhelming body of science suggests that this current trend will continue and intensify in the future, further testing the resiliency of water management systems designed for the past (Hanak and Lund 2008).

Figure A

Most of California's precipitation falls far from cities and farms

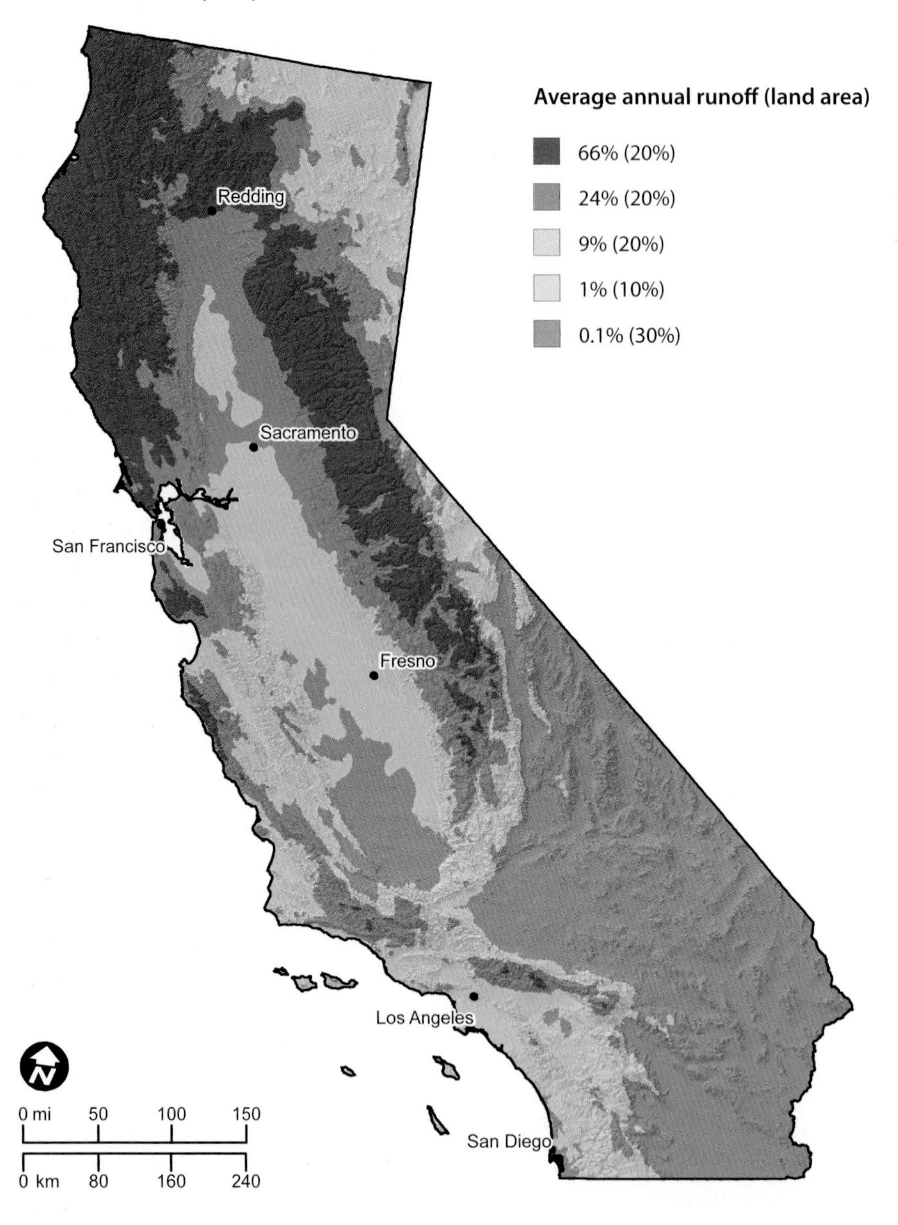

SOURCE: Calculations by J. Viers using data from PRISM, CIMIS, and the U.C. Davis Soil Resource Laboratory (see the notes).

NOTES: The map shows the distribution of runoff—the amount of local precipitation that flows into streams and recharges groundwater. Relative runoff is depicted as a percentage of annual runoff, calculated by adjusting average monthly precipitation (PRISM 1970–2000) by losses to soil storage capacity (U.C. Davis Soil Resource Laboratory, Beaudette, and O'Geen) and average monthly reference evapotranspiration (CIMIS 2000–2005, Hart).

Environmental Failures

Perhaps the most important factor affecting California's efforts to meet current demands for water management is the historical failure to adequately protect the environment. Ever since the Gold Rush, the environment has borne the brunt of the tremendous changes in land, water, and infrastructure development that have shaped California. The hydraulic mining industry—the state's first large-scale use of water—discharged vast quantities of mine tailings and mercury-laden wastes into Northern California's rivers. The hard rock mining industry proved equally destructive, leaving behind a legacy of more than 47,000 abandoned mines, many discharging the most toxic fluids known to mankind into the state's rivers and streams. The rapacious logging practices of this era laid waste to salmon habitat in California's North Coast rivers, which, coupled with overharvesting at sea, led to precipitous declines in salmon and steelhead populations. Rapid expansion of hydropower—damming and redirecting the flow of many Sierra Nevada and Coast Range rivers—damaged the ecosystems of native fish and amphibians. Sprawling urbanization in the South Coast and the San Francisco Bay Area converted rivers and streams into flood control channels carrying tainted storm runoff. The tremendous growth in grazing and agriculture in the late 1800s through the mid-1900s transformed California's native landscape, eliminating roughly 95 percent of the state's wetlands that were both vital components of the natural flood control systems and home to a diverse range of fish, birds, and other species (Mount 1995; Isenberg 2005).

Large water and flood control projects also created widespread and lasting changes in the environment. The Central Valley Project, the State Water Project, the Sacramento–San Joaquin Flood Control Project, San Francisco's Hetch Hetchy Project, Los Angeles's Owens Valley Project, and hundreds of other local and regional projects imposed extensive costs on the environment. When these projects were designed and constructed, they reflected the general thinking of the time. Environmental costs were either ignored or viewed as a necessary tradeoff. The only significant attempt at mitigation was the widespread introduction of hatcheries to offset the effects of dams that prevented the access of salmon and steelhead trout to spawning grounds. Ironically, even fish hatcheries have become an additional burden on the environment.

By the late 1960s, the aggregate degradation of the nation's air, water, lands, and natural resources gave rise to the modern environmental movement. This shift in societal values is reflected in a welter of statutes passed from the late 1960s through the 1970s that dominate water management in California today, including the National Environmental Policy Act, the Clean Water Act, and the Endangered Species Act, as well as their state counterparts. In the decades that followed, the environment would become a central consideration in debates over water.

Although environmental considerations have become integral to all water management and planning, progress in improving environmental conditions has been mixed. As noted above, the Clean Water Act has led to substantial improvements in water quality from "point" sources, including wastewater and industrial plants, but it has been less effective in managing polluted runoff from various agricultural and urban areas. And, although the Endangered Species Act appears to have reduced the overall rate of species extinction in the United States (Scott et al. 2006), it has not protected all species whose populations or habitats are in peril. In California, many native fish species ("fishes") continue to decline (Figure B). As scientists and regulators learn more about the needs and sensitivities of these species, the share of water that must be allocated to the environment usually increases. This trend seems unlikely to change soon.

Figure B
California's native fishes are in sharp decline

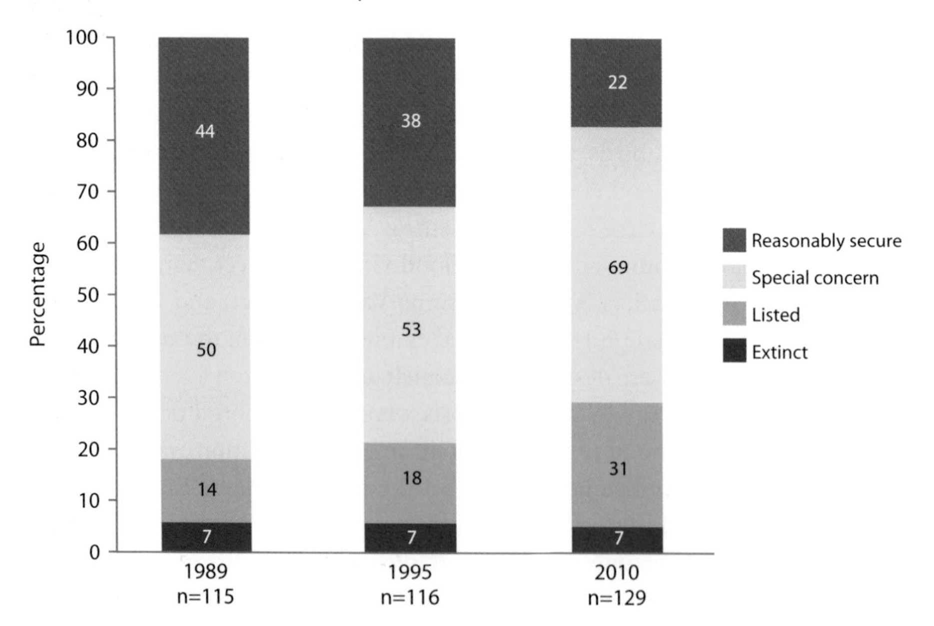

SOURCE: Moyle, Katz, and Quiñones (2010).

NOTES: Extinct = extirpated from California; listed = listed as threatened or endangered under state or federal Endangered Species Acts; special concern = species in decline that could qualify for listing in the future; reasonably secure = widespread, abundant species according to current knowledge.

Absence of Consensus

Growing recognition of environmental failures and disagreements about solutions (and how to pay for them) are central to the conflicts that characterize California water management today. The state also faces profound conflicts on other difficult issues, including how to regulate development in flood-prone areas, whether to regulate groundwater use, and how to allocate the costs of new infrastructure between direct beneficiaries and the general public. The decentralized, and often fragmented, nature of water management and decisionmaking in California has contributed to the current policy deadlock.

Although state and federal agencies built and operate some of the largest water projects in California, the state's water management system is highly decentralized, involving many hundreds of local and regional agencies responsible for water supply, wastewater treatment, drainage management, flood control, and land use decisions. This decentralization across scales and functions of government has created many responsive but narrowly focused stakeholders who drive most water policy today. Having many self-interested stakeholders in a system of decentralized governance encourages each party to hold out for a better deal. The result is often a game of "chicken," where the management of a declining resource becomes deadlocked. Each faction, while acknowledging the growing problems of decline, fears policy change and seeks only those changes that serve its own interests, thus collectively preventing anything but small changes in management despite growing prospects for catastrophe.

This deadlock is particularly prominent in the management of the Sacramento–San Joaquin Delta—the fragile hub of the state's water supply network—which is experiencing an ecological collapse and faces the prospect of a major physical collapse as well. Consensus processes over almost 15 years have been unable to develop effective long-term policies for reversing environmental decline and improving water supply reliability (Lund et al. 2010; Hanak et al. 2010; Madani and Lund 2011). Searching for consensus seems only to have continued the deteriorating status quo.

Scientific and technical work has become embroiled in the advocacy of stakeholders engaged in what can be called "combat science," where scientific work is sponsored or employed primarily to advocate or attack particular interests, rather than to gain better insights into problems and solutions. The lack of independent scientific and technical assessments of California's water problems and solutions has given rise to many popular and politically useful myths that hinder serious discussions and negotiations of water policy (Hanak et al. 2010).

Consequences of Inaction

These five factors—increasingly obsolete design of its water management system, reductions in federal and state funding, changing climate, the challenge of incorporating environmental protection and sustainable management of the state's aquatic ecosystems, and lack of consensus on the options for future reform—have led California water management into a dysfunctional impasse. As we describe in later chapters, continuing the current policies will lead to many environmentally and economically costly outcomes. These include:

- Continuing deterioration in the ecosystem of the Sacramento–San Joaquin Delta, with a corresponding deterioration in the region's ability to supply water to farms within the Delta and in the southern Central Valley and to cities from the Bay Area to San Diego;
- Growing conflicts over groundwater use in overdrafted aquifers;
- Declining crop yields and soil quality as a result of salinity in the southern Central Valley;
- Continuing damage to habitat for native fish and other aquatic and riparian species statewide, as a result of invasive species, deteriorating water quality, and unfavorable land and water management, leading to additional listings under the Endangered Species Act and disrupting water delivery and flood management systems;
- More frequent suspensions of recreational and commercial salmon fishing;
- Growing numbers of poorly understood and inadequately regulated chemicals entering the state's waterways, posing risks to public health and the environment;
- Higher drinking water treatment costs for urban dwellers and declining water quality for rural water users who depend on wells;
- Increasing flood risks for existing and new urban development in the Central Valley and coastal regions of the state;
- Inadequate funding for environmental regulation and protection; and
- Increasing fragmentation and dissipation of scientific effort and growing use of science in debilitating adversarial processes.

Many of these problems are likely to grow worse in light of continuing changes in the physical environment, including climate warming and sea level

Without new policies, flood risks will increase in many parts of the state. Photo by Monica M. Davey/epa/Corbis.

rise, which will bring increasing stress to aquatic ecosystems and the state's current systems for managing water supply and floods.

In the past, California water policy has changed to meet the needs of the times, albeit often by responding fitfully and imperfectly to controversies and crises. Today, California has arrived at a point once again where, given the circumstances, it *must* adapt its water management to changing conditions—perhaps through controversy and crises but perhaps with forethought and careful consideration as well.

From Conflict to Reconciliation

This book outlines an ambitious reform agenda to help put California water management on a more constructive and hopeful path. In this vision, California moves beyond the current Era of Conflict and continuing deterioration toward an Era of Reconciliation, in which water is managed more comprehensively and more flexibly for the benefit of the economy *and* the environment, meeting broad social goals of balance, efficiency, and fairness (see Box A). Water management in this new era seeks to promote reliability, at a reasonable cost, while being capable of adapting to changing conditions. The system is more integrated, more transparent, and better able to support decisionmaking and enforce compliance with the law. Conflicts will remain, but they will be less debilitating.

A

Goals for a modern California water policy

In developing a new water policy, California should seek to attain five broad societal goals:

Public health, safety, and welfare. Water management should support the well-being of the state's residents.

Ecosystem health. Ecosystems are not just a source of water for direct human uses; they are also a source of broader social and economic well-being and must be protected.

Balance. In recognition of environmental values, new policies must explicitly consider and balance tradeoffs between ecosystem benefits and traditional management of water supply and flood protection.

Efficient allocation and use. California water policy and law, embodied in Article X, § 2, of the state constitution, reflect the importance of efficient allocation and use of water and the need to adapt water uses to changing economic conditions. Policies supporting this goal need to be strengthened in response to unmet environmental demands and changing climatic conditions.

Fairness. New policies must be perceived as fair, not selectively supporting one interest at the expense of others. Efforts should be made to ease the costs of policies that harm disadvantaged groups.

Although conflicts among these goals are inevitable, all elements of society have a long-term interest in achieving a balance among them rather than adopting extreme solutions that are unsustainable in environmental, economic, or social terms.

These societal goals translate into five objectives for water system management:

Reliability and sustainability. Some degree of stability and predictability in water policy is essential to support continuing economic well-being.

Reasonable cost. Where possible, water management must reduce the costs of delivering services to the state's residents, without neglecting social and environmental costs.

Adaptability to changing conditions. Effective water policy must incorporate mechanisms for anticipating change and incorporating scientific projections and uncertainties into management.

Integration. Modern policy must continue current trends toward integrating water management for diverse purposes, linking policies that govern water supply and quality, flood management, and ecosystem health.

Transparency, clarity, and enforceability. New policies need better legal mechanisms to enforce compliance and better information systems to support decisionmaking and enforcement. Transparency is essential to support the societal goal of fairness.

In this new era, California will need to reconcile human and environmental uses of water in the face of chronic water scarcity, growing flood risk, and changing social, economic, and environmental conditions. Key elements of the reform agenda include the following:

- **Ecosystem reconciliation.** To reconcile human and ecosystem uses of water, the historical approach of desperate actions to preserve single species must give way to approaches that more broadly and systematically aim to restore ecosystem functions.
- **Integrated management portfolios.** To promote adaptive capacity, managers should use diversified and integrated water management portfolios, rather than traditional single-investment approaches, and should strive to better integrate California's fragmented networks of infrastructure and operations for managing surface and groundwater supplies, flood risk, water quality, and aquatic habitat.
- **Water as a public commodity.** To more efficiently manage water for the economy and the environment, the state should build on current efforts to manage water as a public commodity, promoting reasonable use and flexibility in the face of changing conditions. This will require developing more robust fee-based funding to support public aspects of the water system, including environmental management.
- **Decision-capable and adaptive governance.** To lead reconciliation under changing conditions, California needs more adaptive, responsive, and technically capable water governance institutions. This includes better integration of local, regional, and state efforts and state agencies with more streamlined authority and better mechanisms for protecting the public trust in water. California also needs to rebuild the capacity of state institutions to collect, analyze, and disseminate scientific and technical information necessary to the development of a forward-looking, balanced water policy.

Many of the changes we propose build on existing efforts and can be implemented within existing legal authority; some will require changes in laws and institutions. Most will require strategic shifts, including new forms of collaboration among California's myriad local and regional water and land use agencies, as well as new forms of leadership by both the state and federal governments.

This ambitious agenda can put California on a sustainable path for water management that serves the state's residents well for decades to come and that protects its environmental riches for generations. Changes to the status quo are never easy, and many of the reforms we propose will meet resistance from stakeholders who fear the loss of autonomy or the potential costs of change. We suggest ways to lessen this resistance and lower the costs of reform, by employing cooperative federalism approaches that allow local agencies and water users to develop detailed solutions under general direction from the state, phasing in some reforms and using other strategies to lessen the costs to affected parties. But even with these cooperative approaches, reforms will require bold leadership at all levels. The alternative—continuing deterioration of a system increasingly ill-suited to changing conditions—is bleak and unacceptable.

Overview of This Book

In this book, we take a broad, future-oriented look at water.[1] Today, all forms and uses of water in California are linked statewide—whether directly by rivers and canals or indirectly through markets, the economy, management institutions, and law. To address the complexity of California water and the need for integrated approaches, we bring together perspectives from biology, economics, engineering, geology, and the law. We draw information from many sources, including our own research and new modeling and data analysis. We also benefitted from the wisdom and insights of an advisory board of prominent policymakers and from interviews with more than 100 individuals with expertise in many facets of California water.[2]

The book consists of three parts. Part I reviews past, present, and future conditions of water management in California. It highlights the historical origins of many aspects of today's water system, the complexity and fragility of the current system, and key drivers of change that will exert increasing pressure on this system in the future. Part II focuses on major challenges and promising approaches for managing water in the future. We presume, perhaps

1. Many excellent books have been written on water management in California. Most focus on some specific aspect, such as water supply (Pisani 1984; Bain, Caves, and Margolis 1966), flood control (Kelley 1989), or particular regions (Arax and Wartzman 2005; Kahrl 1982), generally from a historical perspective and occasionally from a public policy perspective (Bain, Caves, and Margolis 1966). In his excellent overall history, Hundley (2001) examines a wide range of water management perspectives.

2. For a summary of the results of these interviews, see Null et al. (2011), available as an online technical appendix to this book at www.ppic.org/content/pubs/other/211EHR_appendix.pdf.

optimistically, that California can emerge from today's era of debilitating conflict into one of more adaptive, if imperfect, reconciliation. We summarize the major water management challenges facing the state and examine promising approaches for (1) reconciling human and environmental uses of water, (2) integrating a portfolio of water management tools to more effectively manage water supplies, water quality, and floods, and (3) managing water more flexibly and responsively as a public commodity. Part III explores strategies for implementing policy reforms. We suggest ways to reorganize and reform state and regional water institutions to meet current and future challenges, offer strategies for reducing the costs and raising the acceptability of reform to stakeholders, and propose the key elements of a water reform agenda.

Part I

California Water: Turbulent Past, Chaotic Present, Changing Future

You cannot step twice into the same river, for other waters are continually flowing on.

Heraclitus, ca. 500 B.C.E.

California's networks of dams, canals, levees, and water treatment plants, along with the laws, regulations, and institutions that govern them, were not developed in concert as part of a grand vision or plan. Rather, they evolved over the course of more than 160 years, responding to a rapidly growing population, changing demographics and demands, and the occasional drought, flood, and lawsuit. In Chapter 1, we examine the historical foundations of today's water system. The laws, policies, and infrastructure of today derive from the laissez-faire approaches to water during and immediately after the Gold Rush in the mid-1800s, the drive to develop local water supplies in the late 1800s, and the local, state, and federal efforts in the 20th century to redistribute water throughout California, creating one of the most complex and ambitious water supply and flood control systems in the world. The 1970s brought a new concern, as society acted to protect the ecological health of the state's waters. Ever since, California has struggled with the apparent conflict between ecosystem and water management.

California's Mediterranean climate is highly variable across seasons and across years, with a drought every summer, frequent multiyear droughts, and occasional deluges. Most precipitation falls in the northern part of the state, often far from the large population and farming centers served by the state's major water projects. Growing attention to the environment has placed new strains on this complex system. In Chapter 2, we examine how California water is currently managed to meet demand and the threat of flooding. Although the state has made extraordinary strides in meeting both urban and agricultural water demand with scarce and variable supplies, its water supply and flood management infrastructure is decaying, its water quality is impaired, and its highly fragmented and decentralized institutions are poorly suited to meet many future challenges.

The great reorganization of California's water system in the 20th century occurred under social, economic, and climatic conditions unlike those of today, and future conditions will be different still. In Chapter 3, we review changes that are likely to occur in the 21st century, including changes in climate, ecosystems, technology, water infrastructure and quality, and economic and demographic conditions. To meet the demands of this uncertain future, California water policy must promote the development of adaptive capacity in all forms of water management. If it does not, the state will be forced to manage by crisis instead.

1
Floods, Droughts, and Lawsuits: A Brief History of California Water Policy

MPI/GETTY IMAGES

> The history of California in the twentieth century is the story of a state inventing itself with water.
>
> William L. Kahrl, *Water and Power*, 1982

> California's water system might have been invented by a Soviet bureaucrat on an LSD trip.
>
> Peter Passell, "Economic Scene: Greening California," *New York Times*, 1991

California has always faced water management challenges and always will. The state's arid and semiarid climate, its ambitious and evolving economy, and its continually growing population have combined to make shortages and conflicting demands the norm. Over the past two centuries, California has tried to adapt to these challenges through major changes in water management. Institutions, laws, and technologies are now radically different from those brought by early settlers coming to California from more humid parts of the United States. These adaptations, and the political, economic, technologic, and social changes that spurred them on, have both alleviated and exacerbated the current conflicts in water management.

This chapter summarizes the forces and events that shaped water management in California, leading to today's complex array of policies, laws, and infrastructure. These legacies form the foundation of California's contemporary water system and will both guide and constrain the state's future water choices.[1]

1. Much of the description in this chapter is derived from Norris Hundley Jr.'s outstanding book, *The Great Thirst: Californians and Water: A History* (Hundley 2001), Robert Kelley's seminal history of floods in the Central Valley, *Battling the Inland Sea* (Kelley 1989), and Donald Pisani's influential study of the rise of irrigated agriculture in California, *From the Family Farm to Agribusiness: The Irrigation Crusade in California* (Pisani 1984).

Riverboats at the port of Sacramento, 1850.

California's Native Waterscape

California's rivers, streams, and estuaries reflect its dynamic landscape and climate. Straddling the divide between the temperate rainforests of the Pacific Northwest and the arid deserts of the Southwest, California hosts the most complex and diverse range of climates anywhere in the United States. This geographic diversity in climate is matched by its variability. Every year, California has a drought of six to seven months, with precipitation ending in April or May and largely absent again until November. Significant precipitation occurs only during the winter, with more than half of the state's annual precipitation delivered in a handful of large storms from December through March. Year-to-year variations in streamflow are also large, with annual totals ranging from less than 25 percent of average to more than 200 percent of average over the past century.

This variable climate is superimposed on a landscape that is equally diverse. California's rugged terrain, with large mountain ranges and adjacent alluvial valleys, coastal plains, and the Great Central Valley, processes and partitions its precipitation into snowpack, surface runoff, groundwater, and water returned to the atmosphere by evaporation and plant transpiration (together known as evapotranspiration).

The hallmark of California's *native* waterscape was its remarkable physical diversity, which supported extraordinary biological diversity and abundance. California's rivers were ideal for colonization by anadromous salmon and steelhead (fish species that live in ocean water but that swim inland to spawn). Each year, millions of adult salmon and steelhead spawned in California's rivers and streams, carrying with them enormous volumes of ocean nutrients that enriched the state's inland ecosystems. The Great Central Valley, with its extensive lowland floodplains and forests, was home to vast herds of elk and antelope, as well as beavers, otters, cougars, grizzly bears, and other species. Seasonal wetlands supported massive bird migrations along the Pacific Flyway. San Francisco Bay, at twice its current size, was one of the most productive estuaries in the lower 48 states. Upstream, the Sacramento–San Joaquin Delta was a 700,000-acre mosaic of tidal freshwater marsh, tidal channels, floodplains, and natural levees. The lower estuary was rimmed with salt and brackish marshes, which provided spawning and rearing habitat for dozens of fish species. California also had several freshwater lakes greater in surface area than Lake Tahoe. Located principally in the upper Klamath River watershed and the Tulare Basin, these vast lakes were surrounded by thousands of acres of wetlands and supported large populations of fish, amphibians, turtles, and birds.

The biological productivity of the inland waters of California, when linked to the productivity of the Pacific Ocean, supported a large population of Native Californians with diverse and complex cultures. Before the arrival of Europeans, California had more than 300,000 inhabitants who spoke between 80 and 100 languages, making it among the most densely populated regions of North America (Anderson 2005; Lightfoot and Parrish 2009). This diverse human landscape, as well as the natural waterscape of California itself, would change irrevocably—first with Spanish and Mexican settlements and later (more dramatically) with the discovery of gold and the economic transformation that ensued.

Spanish and Mexican Influences

The Spanish settled Alta California in 1769, conscripting thousands of Native Californians into labor, dividing the lands into missions, pueblos, and ranchos and establishing California's first system of water rights. The missions and pueblos were located along rivers or smaller coastal streams, and their inhabitants usually dug wells or diverted water, using small dams for domestic use and irrigation. Spanish law granted the missions and pueblos a preferential right to an adequate water supply for their residents, including water for irrigation. Following the U.S.-Mexico War in 1848, the Treaty of Guadalupe Hidalgo recognized all property rights established under Spanish and Mexican law. In a series of cases decided during the late 19th and early 20th centuries, the California Supreme Court ruled that California water rights law incorporated the Spanish law of pueblo rights. The largest beneficiary of these decisions was the City of Los Angeles; its pueblo rights gave it first call on all of the native waters of the Los Angeles River, as well as all hydrologically connected groundwater in the upper Los Angeles River Basin.

In contrast, Spanish law generally did not confer water rights on the more than 800 ranchos created before the U.S. acquisition of California. Spanish and Mexican land grants, therefore, were usually large enough to support cattle grazing on arid land, with small ranchos in the range of 15,000 to 20,000 acres and the largest exceeding 300,000 acres (Hundley 2001). California's pattern of large agricultural landholdings partly derives from these land grants. Although some of the ranchos subsequently obtained water rights for irrigation (either by purchase or by judicial confirmation of prescriptive use), neither the ranchos nor the pueblos significantly changed California's native waterscape. Most diversions were small and for use on lands adjacent to the river or stream from which the water was diverted. Substantial alteration of California's hydrologic systems would await the American takeover.

The Laissez-Faire Era of Water Development

Early water management was largely undertaken by uncoordinated individual, corporate, and local actions, with little federal or state intervention. John Marshall's discovery of gold at Sutter's Mill in 1848 and the ensuing Gold Rush brought irreversible changes to California. California's population was then about 160,000, of which 10,000 were nonnative (the native populations had already been decimated by disease). In 1849, the nonnative population grew to 100,000, and the immigrants soon eclipsed their Native Californian and *Californio* predecessors. By 1900, the state's population would swell to more than 1.5 million, supporting a rapidly growing and diversifying economy.

What began as simple panning for gold carried downstream by California's rivers quickly evolved into industrial-scale extraction. As the easy gold was sluiced, sifted, and panned out, the gold miners found that they had to move water from the rivers to the gold itself. These "hydraulic miners" diverted water from streams high in the gold country, carrying it (sometimes for many miles) through wooden flumes, dropping it through penstocks to generate hydraulic pressure, and then using the pressurized water to blast away hillsides containing valuable ore. The miners then washed the debris through sluices to separate the gold from its surrounding sediment. By 1880, the gold country had 20,000 miners and more than 6,000 miles of ditches, flumes, and canals. The industry generated more than $5.5 billion in wealth (in current dollars), roughly one-quarter of one year of California's agricultural production today (Hundley 2001). The hydraulic mining of the Sierra Nevada was the first large-scale effort to industrialize California's water resources, with profound consequences for the economy, the environment, and the laws that govern water use (Isenberg 2005).

From the Gold Rush came a new rule of law for allocating water among competing users. The miners had developed the practice of resolving disputes—over both water and conflicting claims to the gold itself—on the principle of "first-in-time, first-in-right." In *Irwin v. Phillips* (1855), the California Supreme

Court was asked to decide whether the miners' rule of prior appropriation or the common law doctrine of riparian rights should apply. The court recognized that the custom of the miners worked well in practice and was commonly accepted as the most fair and efficient means of apportioning water in times of shortage and therefore adopted the rule of prior appropriation as the law of the state. Although the rule of prior appropriation did not displace common-law riparian rights, prior appropriation would become, over time, the dominant form of water rights in California as more nonriparian lands were irrigated and cities created municipal water systems based on appropriative rights. Conflicts between riparian and appropriative rights would escalate throughout the 19th and early 20th centuries as large components of California's economy developed through reliance on the miners' rule of prior appropriation (Box 1.1).

1.1

Riparian versus appropriative rights

English and American common law gives owners of riparian land the right to use water from rivers and streams that flow within or along the boundaries of their property. This right to water is shared with all other riparian landowners along the river. Water may be used only on riparian land and within the watershed of the river from which it is diverted. In times of shortage, water is apportioned among riparians on the basis of reasonable use.

The riparian system is ill-suited to the hydrology of the American West, where rivers are few and far between and arable land may not be adjacent to an adequate water source. As a consequence, most western states rejected the doctrine of riparian rights entirely and recognized prior appropriation as the exclusive means of establishing water rights. Under the appropriation system, the right to water is based on actual use, not ownership of land, and there are no place-of-use restrictions. Moreover, in times of shortage, water is apportioned on the basis of first-in-time, first-in-right.

California recognizes both forms of water rights. Riparians as a class generally have first claim to the native waters of the state's rivers and streams. If there is water remaining after riparian demands are fulfilled, the appropriators may take the remaining water in order of their priority of appropriation. Originally, appropriators could not challenge a riparian's use as wasteful or unreasonable. However, after several decades of lawsuits, voters amended the California constitution in 1928 to make all water rights subject to the requirement of reasonable use—including the rights of riparians in competition with appropriative rights.

Mining led to the first large-scale uses of water in California and the creation of appropriative water rights. Photo by Bettmann/Corbis.

The Gold Rush also produced California's first significant experiments with local and collective flood management. Hydraulic mining generated more than a million acre-feet of debris that washed downriver during winter and spring torrents, entering the Sacramento Valley and eventually moving as a wave through the Delta and into San Francisco Bay (Gilbert 1917). The debris choked the river channels, reducing their capacity to carry flows and forcing water and sediment onto the lowland floodplains. These floodplains, which included the newly established state capitol in Sacramento, were prone to seasonal inundation even under normal conditions. Hydraulic mining amplified these inundations until even modest flows caused flooding. In 1862, for example, successive storms flooded both Northern and Southern California, causing widespread death and destruction and turning the Central Valley into an "inland sea" more than 200 miles long and 60 miles wide (Kelley 1989). When the floodwaters subsided, mining debris covered the orchards and fields of the Sacramento Valley and provided vivid evidence that flooding would be a major problem for water management.

In response, landowners along the Sacramento River and its tributaries built small embankments between themselves and the river. These small levees failed regularly and flooded both fields and homes. Recognizing the need to form local governments to address flood problems, the California legislature, in 1868, authorized the creation of local reclamation districts, which allowed landowners to join together and levy property assessments to fund construction of land reclamation and flood control projects. This legislation spurred the formation of hundreds of reclamation districts throughout the state, forming a key element in the growth of agriculture on the state's floodplains.

Unfortunately, the taller and stronger levees made possible by this collective action reduced natural attenuation of flood waves and channeled floodwaters, which would overflow or breach smaller, weaker levees. Flooded landowners responded in kind, forcing the floodwaters onto *their* neighbors. In times of major floods, each district essentially relied on adjacent districts having levees weaker than their own. The resulting escalation of levees proved to be ineffective for the Sacramento Valley, with some landowners finding demolition of a neighbor's levees during a flood to be more economical than raising the height of their own levees (Kelley 1989).

The flood problems of this early era plague California to this day (Chapters 2, 6). Development in the rivers' natural floodplains, combined with the construction of riverbank levees, denied the winter and spring floodwaters their natural outlets. The same development placed thousands of lives and millions of dollars of investment at annual risk of catastrophic loss. In addition, the channelization of rivers for flood control and mining debris removal destroyed seasonal and riparian wetlands and shallows that provided habitat for native fish and wildlife dependent on these wetlands.

By the 1880s, farmers, cities, and their state legislative representatives recognized that local solutions were inadequate (and perhaps even dangerous) to address regional flooding problems. The Laissez-Faire Era of California water development and flood control policy was poised to give way to a new era of management, characterized by efforts to organize at the local level (Figure 1.1).

Figure 1.1
Water management in California has undergone several eras of change

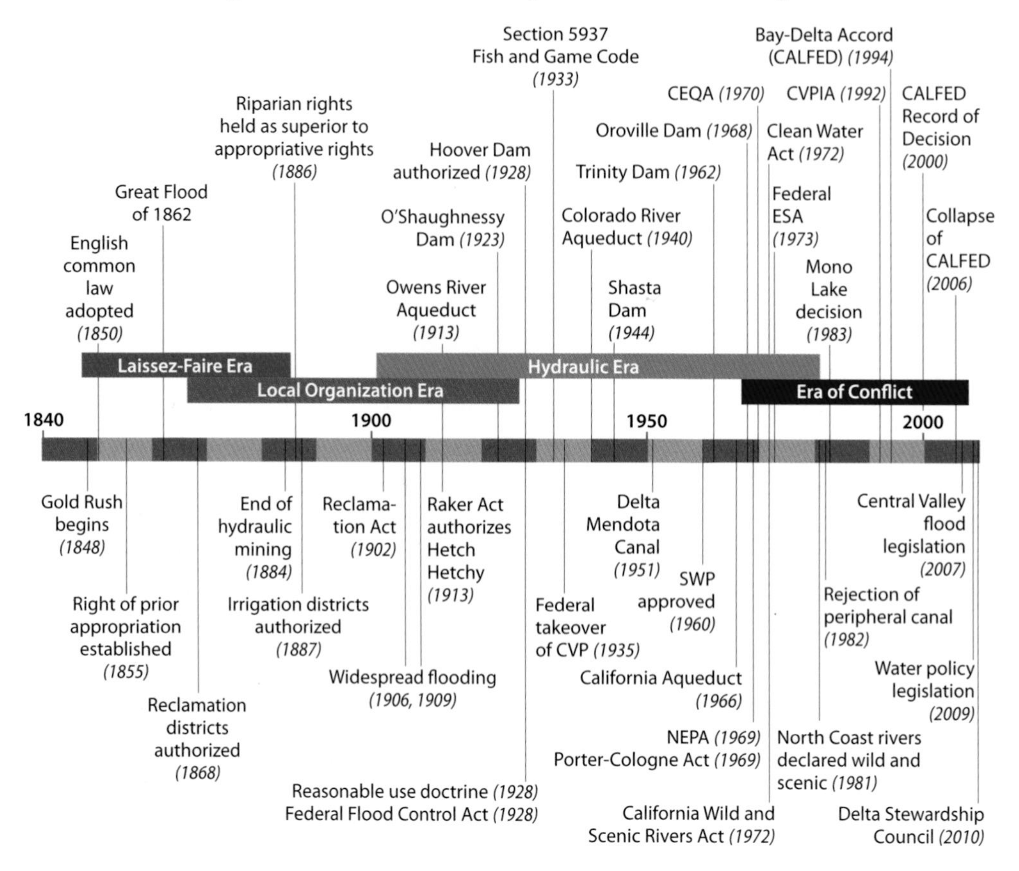

The Era of Local Organization

The end of the Laissez-Faire Era in California water management coincided with rapid population growth and a shift in the economy toward agricultural production, new demands for water supply and flood control, and a series of related court cases.

Two legal issues prevented significant legislative reform of California's water management policies. The first was the status of gold mining—the industry that created California's early economy but whose mine tailings and pollution had come to threaten growing economic sectors of agriculture, commerce, and shipping. The second issue was how to reconcile the two systems of water rights recognized by the California Supreme Court in the early years of statehood: the miners' custom of prior appropriation—based on actual use prioritized by date of first use—and the common law doctrine of riparian rights—based on ownership of land on a river (Box 1.1).

By the early 1880s, the environmental and economic problems caused by gold mining were widely recognized, and two lawsuits were filed to declare continued hydraulic mining a public nuisance. In *Woodruff v. North Bloomfield Mining Co.* (1884), a group of farmers along the Yuba and Feather Rivers whose lands were flooded and spoiled by mining tailings sued in federal court to prohibit the discharge of mining debris. In *People v. Gold Run Ditch & Mining Co.* (1884), the California attorney general brought suit in state court to prevent hydraulic mining in the watershed of the North Fork of the American River. Both courts prohibited continued mining, declaring it a public nuisance and holding that it must give way to the paramount public interest in navigation and commerce and to the burgeoning commercial and agricultural development in the Sacramento Valley.

Two years after the gold mining decisions, the California Supreme Court confronted the second water rights issue that had come to dominate the state's water policies—the relationship between the riparian and appropriative systems (Box 1.1).

In a series of early cases, the court concluded that the doctrine of riparian rights had been incorporated into California's water rights system in 1850, when the legislature enacted a statute that recognized the common law of England as the law of the new state. This meant that landowners along California's rivers and streams could claim the right to use water on their riparian lands simply by virtue of their ownership of such lands, whereas nonriparians could claim water only through its diversion and use under the law of prior appropriation.

As California agriculture expanded from lands adjacent to the principal rivers to upland areas, tensions grew between riparians and appropriators. Upstream appropriators diverted water for their own uses—sometimes transporting water to irrigate lands outside the watershed—and downstream riparians claimed the right to the full, unimpeded flow of the river.

This conflict was especially pronounced in the Tulare Basin, where two of California's largest water users (and three of its wealthiest individuals) squared off in a titanic battle over water rights. *Lux v. Haggin* (1886) was one of the great legal cases in California history, pitting powerful riparian landowners against an equally powerful appropriator who urged the California Supreme Court to abolish riparian rights. By a vote of 4 to 3, the court ruled in favor of the riparians. Appropriative rights would continue to exist alongside the riparian system, but in almost all cases, they would be inferior in priority to the rights of the riparians. In cases of conflict, riparians would be entitled to "the natural flow of the watercourse undiminished except by its reasonable consumption by upper [riparian] proprietors."

The hydraulic mining cases and *Lux v. Haggin* have many legacies—some constructive, others (at least in retrospect) a hindrance to California's evolving water policies. In *People v. Gold Run Ditch & Mining Co.*, for example, the court responded to new developments on the ground, both economic and environmental, and shaped the law to ensure that it kept pace with changing conditions and societal needs. The case also marked the court's first significant application of the public trust doctrine to resolve a conflict over use of the state's water resources (Box 1.2). These aspects of *People v. Gold Run Ditch & Mining Co.* would become essential features of the state's efforts to promote efficient and sustainable use of water resources.

In contrast, *Lux v. Haggin* was more of a mixed bag. Millions of acres of arable land throughout the Central Valley could not qualify for riparian rights because they were not adjacent to reliable sources of surface water, and their water rights were now effectively subordinate to those of riparians. This meant that downstream riparians—including those farming the lower reaches of the Sacramento and San Joaquin Rivers and in the Delta itself—could claim the full, unencumbered flow of the rivers despite the burdens such claims would place on upstream appropriators. Moreover, riparian rights would become an obstacle to developing water supplies for California's growing cities, which sought to acquire supplemental water sources. These conflicts would play out over the next four decades.

On the other hand, *Lux v. Haggin* also held that disputes *between* riparians would thereafter be decided on the basis of reasonable use. As developed by the court in a series of cases following *Lux v. Haggin*, the reasonable use doctrine would come to require that all riparians exercise their rights in a manner that did not result in waste, that was reasonably efficient under existing conditions, and that took into account the reasonable demands of competing riparian water users. The principle of reasonable use would later become a cornerstone of California water law.

Organizing Local Governments

As demands for irrigation grew beyond the scale of individual farmers, more governmental authority was sought to establish irrigation systems serving many

1.2

The public trust doctrine

Under the common law of England, the Crown held particular resources in trust for use by all of the people. These resources included navigable waters, as well as submerged lands beneath such waters up to the mean high tide or high-water mark. Although the King or Queen could grant these submerged lands as part of larger land grants, the private rights to both the navigable waters and the submerged lands were impressed with a "public trust." The private landowners could not exclude members of the public from using navigable waters and submerged lands for navigation, commerce, and fishing, nor could the landowners develop or alter the lands to obstruct or diminish these public trust uses.

When the United States gained its independence from England, it carried the public trust doctrine into its own laws. California incorporated the public trust into state law in 1850, when the legislature enacted a statute that adopted the common law of England. Over the course of the late 19th and 20th centuries, the California Supreme Court applied the public trust doctrine to preserve public rights of navigation, fishing, and recreation along the state's beaches, the San Francisco Bay waterfront, and inland waters including the American and Sacramento Rivers and Lake Tahoe. In *Marks v. Whitney* (1971), the court declared that the public trust protects not only the traditional uses recognized under English and American common law but also "the preservation of those lands [covered by the trust] in their natural state, so that they may serve as ecological units for scientific study, as open space, and as environments which provide food and habitat for birds and marine life, and which favorably affect the scenery and climate of the area."

In 1983, in the famous case of *National Audubon Society v. Superior Court*, the Supreme Court held that the "public trust doctrine and the appropriative water rights system are parts of an integrated system of water law. The public trust doctrine serves the function in that integrated system of preserving the continuing sovereign power of the state to protect public trust uses, a power which precludes anyone from acquiring a vested right to harm the public trust, and imposes a continuing duty on the state to take such uses into account in allocating water resources."

farmers in a local area. The decline of gold mining and the (temporary) legal resolution of the conflict between riparians and appropriators set the stage for California's first period of organized water development. During this era, irrigated acreage increased exponentially around the state, cities expanded their local water supplies, and groups of water users organized themselves locally into irrigation districts and mutual water companies (Figure 1.1).

Of course, farming in early California was hampered by the lack of summer rainfall. Farmers along the Sacramento River and its tributaries grew a variety of crops—including orchard fruit, wine grapes, peanuts, wheat, and barley—irrigated with water diverted from the rivers. In contrast, farmers in the San Joaquin Valley grew mostly wheat, alfalfa, and pasture, relying on scarce rain and spring flooding to water their crops. As the state's population grew and local and global demands for food increased, California's farmers sought to bring additional land into production. Expanding agriculture required irrigation methods able to bring water to arable land above the natural floodplains.

Expanding irrigation beyond a few riparian farms also required larger units of organization and finance. In a few areas, farmers pooled their resources to acquire water rights and to construct dams, canals, and irrigation ditches. But private water development lacked the investment capital needed to move water from Sierra Nevada streams to the lands that farmers hoped to irrigate. To address this problem, the legislature enacted the Wright Act in 1887, which (combined with earlier legislation to establish local reclamation districts) launched an era of local governmental development and control of water resources. This period established today's highly decentralized system of local water management. The Wright Act authorized the formation of irrigation districts with the power to acquire water rights, to construct water projects, and to sell bonds and impose property assessments to support water development and distribution (Pisani 1984).

Farmers throughout the Central Valley joined together to form local irrigation districts. The most successful districts were created in the lower San Joaquin Valley and Tulare Basin—the Turlock, Modesto, and Tulare Irrigation Districts—which financed and built the first significant-scale dams and canal systems to store and distribute water on a regional basis. These districts, along with several important private companies, such as the Fresno Canal and Land Company, sparked a dramatic increase in agricultural production.

Many of the first irrigation districts failed (including six of the seven established in the Sacramento Valley), but by the early 20th century, irrigation districts were successfully established around the state, including the Glenn-Colusa and Anderson-Cottonwood Irrigation Districts in the Sacramento Valley, the El Dorado and Nevada Irrigation Districts in the Sierra Nevada foothills, the Merced and Fresno Irrigation Districts in the San Joaquin Valley, and the Imperial Irrigation District along the Mexican border (Pisani 1984). And businesses and real estate developers in Southern California and the Bay

Area used water companies to develop and distribute domestic water supplies. The legislature subsequently authorized the creation of a panoply of new types of local water agencies to develop and distribute water for irrigation and domestic purposes.

Local development and control of California's water resources would be limited, however, by two factors. In some areas, local water availability was simply insufficient to support long-term growth. And local capital was inadequate to construct new projects on the scale needed to move water from where it was available to where growth (and ambition to grow) demanded it.

The Rise and Fall of Groundwater

As Central Valley agriculture continued to expand, farmers without access to surface irrigation turned to the aquifers beneath their lands as a more available source. Farmers and cities in Southern California also began to rely heavily on groundwater, initially tapping artesian springs and later pumping water from the dozens of basins that underlie the region. Conflicts between surface and groundwater users, and among groundwater users, inevitably followed. In the 1880s, Los Angeles sued neighboring cities and private groundwater users and persuaded the California Supreme Court that its pueblo rights in the upper Los Angeles River also gave it superior rights to all groundwater in the basin hydrologically connected to the river. This was the first case to recognize surface and groundwater as an integrated resource. Litigation was also common in water management in the San Gabriel and Santa Ana River Basins (Blomquist 1992).

For most of the 19th century, access to groundwater was limited by technology—with windmills and steam engines providing power for irrigation pumps. Toward the end of the century, however, drilling technology and gasoline- and diesel-powered pumps became more widely available, allowing farmers to pump more water from greater depths. By the early 20th century, wells in some cases exceeded 300 feet. As with the levee wars in the Sacramento Valley, the new technology led to conflict. The new pumps lowered groundwater levels below the depth of neighboring pumps. Thus, neighbors were forced to drill deeper wells, which lowered the groundwater table below the depth of recent wells, and the race to the bottom was on.

Conflicts over well-lowering and groundwater depletion eventually made their way into the courts, and in 1903, the California Supreme Court handed down its opinion in *Katz v. Walkinshaw.* The court held that the common law rule of "absolute ownership" of groundwater, under which all landowners overlying an aquifer could pump as much water as they needed, was no longer compatible with California's hydrologic and economic conditions. The rule of absolute ownership, the court noted, afforded groundwater users no protection against stronger pumps or deeper wells. Nor did it protect surface water users, whose rights were impaired when excessive groundwater extractions lowered the level of aquifers that fed and supported the state's rivers.

In place of the old common law rule, the court borrowed from the surface water law of riparian rights and held that all overlying landowners had correlative rights to the "safe yield" of the aquifer—the quantity of water that could be extracted without sustained lowering of the groundwater table. Disputes among overlying owners would be resolved on the basis of reasonable use. As a group, overlying landowners would have first claim to the available groundwater. If additional groundwater could be extracted within the safe yield of the aquifer, other users could pump it in order of priority of appropriation.

Although it was an improvement on the rule of absolute ownership, the court's decision in *Katz v. Walkinshaw* did not address two fundamental problems with groundwater use in early 20th century California. First, as with surface water rights, no state regulatory system existed to supervise groundwater extraction and use. Although several districts were formed under the Wright Act in Southern California to manage ground and surface water supplies in the San Gabriel and Santa Ana River Basins, all had failed by the early years of the 20th century (Blomquist 1992), and the irrigation districts in the San Joaquin Valley focused only on surface water development. As a result, no local or regional entities existed to fill the void of state regulation.

Second, the two regions with the greatest use of groundwater—Southern California and the Tulare and western San Joaquin Basins—simply lacked enough surface water to replenish their aquifers under existing and projected future levels of extraction. Consistent with the times, water users and political leaders in both regions addressed groundwater overdraft by seeking ever-greater supplies of imported surface water, rather than by limiting groundwater use—a harbinger of the next era of water management.

Local Flood Management

As with their irrigation district counterparts, local flood control and reclamation districts found themselves at the mercy of forces beyond their local jurisdictional boundaries. The "levee wars" had failed to provide effective flood protection in the Sacramento Valley, and the rapid urban growth in Sacramento,

Southern California, and the Bay Area increased demand for flood management improvements on a larger geographic scale. This political pressure, coupled with the intractable problems of hydraulic mining sediment, brought the first federal foray into state water management.

The U.S. Army Corps of Engineers, with its mandate to protect and to facilitate navigation on the nation's waterways, became involved in managing floods in California as early as the 1880s. The corps advocated two strategies for managing hydraulic mining sediment. The first was to construct brush dams upstream to trap sediments. Several dams were erected on the Yuba and Bear Rivers in 1880, but all failed within the first year. The second approach stemmed from the corps' 30 years of experience in maintaining navigation channels on the Mississippi River. It urged reclamation districts to place levees as close as practicable to river channels to scour sediment. This strategy was pursued in a loosely coordinated fashion through the latter years of the 19th century, but these close riverbank levees also failed to provide sufficient flood protection.

Although flood management during the Era of Local Organization was not as sophisticated or successful as the local development of water supplies, it did produce three important legacies. First, placing levees close to the river created the footprint of flood control that remains in place today. Second, the repeated failures to address flood issues, both in Sacramento and in urban areas throughout the state, led to new efforts to cooperate. These efforts are reflected in the ambitious Manson-Grunsky Plan developed in the late 1890s to address flooding in the greater Sacramento Valley. Finally, this new flood plan was the first large-scale engagement of the federal government in water management—a role that would expand dramatically in the next century.

The Hydraulic Era

The Hydraulic Era is defined by large regional, interregional, and statewide water management schemes, driven by continued growth in agricultural and urban water demands. These large projects called for the involvement of state and federal agencies, as well as existing and new local authorities.

At the turn of the 20th century, California had the nation's fastest-growing economy and population. This growth required a shift in water and flood policy from local to interregional projects that could manage water over much larger distances. Four intertwined forces would initiate California's transition into what Norris Hundley, Jr., has called the "hydraulic society": the decision of Los

Angeles and San Francisco to secure water supplies that would enable them to grow and to prosper for the next 100 years; Congress's creation and lavish support of a federal reclamation program; the state legislature's decision to build a California water project; and the engagement of the federal government—with dollars, expertise, and land use controls—in the management of floods (Figure 1.1).

Los Angeles and the Conquest of Owens Valley

By 1900, Los Angeles had largely exhausted its local sources of water from the Los Angeles River and its tributary groundwater basin, and city leaders began the quest for supplemental supplies.[2] They eschewed smaller local water sources in favor of a grander ambition—to secure a larger source of clean water that would meet the city's needs for a century or more. For this, they looked 240 miles north to the Owens Valley, on the east side of the Sierra Nevada.

Mayor Fred Eaton appointed William Mulholland, superintendent of the Los Angeles Water Company, to be the chief engineer of the new Los Angeles Department of Water and Power. Eaton and Mulholland traveled numerous times to the Owens Valley, with Mulholland designing the water project and Eaton acquiring land and water rights under his own name. They teamed with J. B. Lippincott, the United States Reclamation Service's supervising engineer for the Pacific Coast states, who was evaluating Owens Valley for inclusion in the new federal reclamation program, described below. Eaton and Mulholland persuaded Lippincott to give them access to the Reclamation Service's land records, which enabled the men to secure options on land and water rights. By 1905, Eaton and Mulholland had acquired almost all riparian land and water rights in the valley, including the Reclamation Service's planned reservoir site, and transferred them to the city. The following year, the United States granted the city a right-of-way across federal lands for the Owens Valley Aqueduct. Construction began in 1908, and five years later, on November 5, 1913, the first Owens River water poured into the San Fernando Valley, where it would be stored in the local aquifer for distribution to residents of Los Angeles.

By 1920, the city's population had grown to 500,000. A decade later, it reached 1.2 million. As the city grew, so did its demand for water, and Los Angeles built new diversion works higher up in the Owens River Valley. As the valley dried out, its residents became increasingly hostile. Although protesters

2. Kahrl (1982) is an excellent reference on the history of Los Angeles's water supplies.

San Francisco's water system relied on building a reservoir in Yosemite's Hetch Hetchy Valley. Photo by Sarah Null.

dynamited sections of the aqueduct several times during the 1920s, Los Angeles was undeterred in its search for additional water. By 1933, the city had acquired most of the remaining private land in the Owens Valley and began pumping groundwater. With few overlying landowners still possessing groundwater rights, valley residents could do little to limit exports.

In 1930, Los Angeles voters approved a bond to extend the aqueduct north into the Mono Basin. Diversion dams on four of the five tributaries that fed Mono Lake were completed in 1940. Over the next four decades, the city's diversions would diminish the lake, imperil its wildlife, and ultimately set the stage for the California Supreme Court's recognition of the public trust as a fundamental limit on the exercise of water rights.

San Francisco and the Battle for Hetch Hetchy Valley

San Francisco, Oakland, and other Bay Area cities also trained *their* sights on Sierra Nevada streams to support their growing populations and economies. James Phelan, San Francisco's mayor from 1897 to 1902, wanted to ensure that his city remained the dominant commercial and industrial center of California and the West. He wanted to break the monopolistic grip of the privately owned Spring Valley Water Company, and he recognized that the meager local water sources of San Francisco would be inadequate for the city's growth into the coming century.

San Francisco's quest was led by the city's chief engineer, Michael Maurice O'Shaughnessy, who settled on the Tuolumne River as the ideal source of water for the city. O'Shaughnessy proposed to construct a dam and divert water high in the watershed at the mouth of Hetch Hetchy Valley. This would protect the city's water quality at its source, generate hydroelectric power, and deliver water to the city and other East Bay and peninsula locales by gravity. The main problem with O'Shaughnessy's plan was that Congress had included Hetch Hetchy Valley in the Yosemite National Park in 1890.

The opposition, led by John Muir and the newly formed Sierra Club, delayed the project for more than a decade. In the end, however, the city's arguments prevailed, and in 1913, Congress passed the Raker Act, authorizing San Francisco's use of Hetch Hetchy Valley as a reservoir. Plagued by construction and financial problems, Tuolumne River water finally arrived in San Francisco in 1934.[3]

The Owens Valley and Hetch Hetchy Projects began a long period in which both Congress and the California legislature authorized large interbasin water projects that would promote statewide urban and agricultural development, spurring the growth of California's population and economy. Yet both projects would also spawn a deep and enduring suspicion of interbasin water development.

In response to the Owens Valley Project, the legislature included in the Central Valley Project (CVP) Act of 1933 a law recognizing the superior rights of the areas of the state that are the sources of California's developed water supplies. The County-of-Origin Act would influence the planning and administration of the CVP and later the State Water Project (SWP). In addition, Los Angeles's destruction of Owens Lake and the Owens River, and its plans to divert from streams feeding Mono Lake, would move the legislature to place in the new Fish and Game Code of 1933 an obscure requirement of the Penal Code that the owners of all dams release or bypass water to protect downstream fisheries. Five decades later, this statute would be applied to restrict Los Angeles's water rights in both Owens Valley and the Mono Basin and would become one of the state's strongest fisheries protection laws (Box 1.3; Chapter 5). Perhaps most significantly, San Francisco's damming of Hetch Hetchy planted the seeds of the environmental movement that would play a major role in California (and national) water policy during the latter decades of the 20th century.

3. Oakland and the East Bay area engaged in a similar period of water system acquisition and development, culminating in the East Bay Municipal Utility District bringing water from the Mokelumne River in 1929 (Elkind 1998).

1.3

Fish and Game Code, § 5937

"The owner of any dam shall allow sufficient water at all times to pass over, around, or through the dam, to keep in good condition any fish that may be planted or exist below the dam."

California's statutory protection of its fisheries dates back to 1872 when the legislature enacted § 637 of the California Penal Code, which required that dam owners build a fishway over or around the dam if requested to do so by the State Board of Fish Commissioners. In 1903, the legislature expanded the duties of the fish commissioners, requiring that they determine if dams throughout the state were hindering passage of migratory fish, especially salmon and shad. In 1915, it revised § 637 again to apply to all fish, not just migratory species.

In 1933, the legislature created the Fish and Game Code and transferred the Penal Code language to it with only minor modifications. Although § 5937 was rarely applied until modern times, it is nonetheless a powerful fisheries protection law. The lawsuits that ultimately led to the restoration of both Mono Lake and the San Joaquin River were both based in part on § 5937.

Modernization of California Water Laws

California's transition to the Hydraulic Era was facilitated by the modernization of its water laws. In 1913, the legislature created the first regulatory system to administer new surface water rights. Fifteen years later, the electorate amended California's Constitution to repair the breach between the riparian and appropriative rights systems that the Supreme Court left open in *Lux v. Haggin* and to establish the doctrine of reasonable use as the foundation of California water resources law.

The modern water code

Although the legislature had addressed water rights in the Civil Code in 1872, that statute did little more than codify (with minor changes) the common law rules of prior appropriation developed by the gold miners and the courts. In the Water Commission Act of 1913, however, it endeavored to devise a comprehensive system for regulating water rights. The act created a State Water Commission with the power to issue permits and licenses to govern the exercise of water rights.

Unfortunately, because of political pressure from various vested interests, the legislature exempted more uses of water than it included in the new regulatory scheme. Pueblo rights, riparian rights, and groundwater rights were completely exempt. Only water appropriations beginning after the effective date of the statute were included. Because the Water Commission Act was put to referendum, it did not pass the vote of the electorate until December 19, 1914. To this day, surface water appropriations initiated after this date must be authorized by a water rights permit or license; appropriations existing before this date do not require a permit or license and are commonly known as "pre-1914 rights." As a result of these statutory exemptions, the State Water Resources Control Board (SWRCB) or "the board"—the successor to the Water Commission—regulates through the permit and license system less than half of the water used by agricultural and urban interests in California today.

Despite these shortcomings, the Water Commission Act was an important development in California water policy because it laid the foundation for the modern regulation of water rights and use. Over time, the legislature would add to the authority of the commission (and its successors), granting the power not only to monitor a permittee's or licensee's uses but also to protect the rights of other legal water users, water quality, fish and wildlife, recreational uses, and the public interest generally. Today, the SWRCB also has the power to enforce the mandates of reasonable use and the public trust, and this authority applies to *all* water users regardless of the type or source of their water rights (Littleworth and Garner 2007).

The reasonable use doctrine

A more significant advance in state power over the water resources system, however, would come from the constitutional resolution of the long-standing conflict between the riparian and appropriative water rights systems. Following *Lux v. Haggin*, the California Supreme Court employed the doctrine of reasonable use as a fundamental limitation on the exercise of water rights. In disputes among riparians, the court applied the standard of reasonable use as the principal means of allocating water in times of shortage. In disputes between appropriators, the court held that water could be allocated to a junior appropriator out of priority if the senior appropriator was using water unreasonably under the circumstances. For example, in the important case of *Town of Antioch v. Williams Irrigation District* (1922), the court refused to protect the city's senior downstream water right because it required that upstream junior appropriators forgo too much water to repel salinity intrusion at Antioch's point of diversion in the western Delta.

In disputes between a riparian and an appropriator, however, the court held that the doctrine of reasonable use was inapplicable because riparian rights were categorically superior to appropriative rights (Gray 1989). Thus, in *Herminghaus v. Southern California Edison* (1926), the court held that downstream riparians were entitled to the unimpaired flow of the San Joaquin River, even though that would require that the upstream public utility forgo its uses. The gross inefficiency mandated by the court would lead voters to amend the California Constitution to close the divide between the riparian and appropriative systems.

The resulting 1928 amendment, which now appears as Article X, § 2, of the constitution (Box 1.4), changed California water law in three fundamental ways.

1.4

The reasonable use doctrine of California water law

CALIFORNIA CONSTITUTION, ARTICLE X, § 2 (1928)

"It is hereby declared that because of the conditions prevailing in this State the general welfare requires that the water resources of the State be put to beneficial use to the fullest extent of which they are capable, and that the waste or unreasonable use or unreasonable method of use of water be prevented, and that the conservation of such waters is to be exercised with a view to the reasonable and beneficial use thereof in the interest of the people and for the public welfare. The right to water or to the use or flow of water in or from any natural stream or water course in this State is and shall be limited to such water as shall be reasonably required for the beneficial use to be served, and such right does not and shall not extend to the waste or unreasonable use or unreasonable method of use or unreasonable method of diversion of water. Riparian rights in a stream or water course attach to, but to no more than so much of the flow thereof as may be required or used consistently with this section, for the purposes for which such lands are, or may be made adaptable, in view of such reasonable and beneficial uses; provided, however, that nothing herein contained shall be construed as depriving any riparian owner of the reasonable use of water of the stream to which the owner's land is riparian under reasonable methods of diversion and use, or as depriving any appropriator of water to which the appropriator is lawfully entitled.

"This section shall be self-executing, and the Legislature may also enact laws in the furtherance of the policy in this section contained."

First, it declared the doctrines of reasonable and beneficial use to be the foundation of all water rights in California. Second, it stipulated that the requirement of reasonable use could be asserted in all water rights disputes, including those where an appropriator challenges a riparian use. Third, it invested all branches of government with significant authority to implement the mandates of reasonable and beneficial use.

The enactment of the 1928 constitutional amendment would facilitate the dramatic expansion of the hydraulic society that would take place during the middle of the 20th century. By removing the obstacle of riparian claims to the full flow of the state's rivers—and by declaring a state policy to prevent waste and to promote the reasonably efficient use and allocation of California's water resources—the constitutional amendment laid the legal foundation for the statewide water projects that were on the drawing boards. Later, as the era of the great projects was nearing its end, Article X, § 2, would be employed to require that California's water resources also be used so as not to cause unreasonable harm to water quality, fish, and the aquatic ecosystems that are the sources of the states developed water supplies.

Large Federal Water Projects

The next phase of the Hydraulic Era was led by the federal government; it resulted in the development of two of the state's major water sources: the Boulder Canyon Project, which delivers Colorado River water to farms and cities in Southern California, and the Central Valley Project, which carries water from the state's northern and eastern mountain watersheds to farms and cities in the Central Valley and the Bay Area.

Although these projects did not get under way until the 1920s and 1930s, the federal government had established its involvement earlier in the 20th century. Congress enacted the Reclamation Act of 1902 under pressure from western farmers who had suffered through two decades of almost constant drought and by western politicians who had witnessed the failure of local and regional water projects because of insufficient capital. The legislation gained the support of the Progressives, who sought to promote public ownership of utilities and who insisted on statutory terms to guard against land speculation and to focus benefits on small family farms. The Reclamation Act authorized the construction of dams and irrigation projects throughout the West, created a new Reclamation Service (later the Bureau of Reclamation) within the Department of the Interior to administer the program, and made water available at subsidized rates to farms no larger than 160 acres.

The first reclamation projects to develop California's rivers were relatively small and designed to supplement water supplies for farmers in several areas that had experienced only limited success in developing local sources. Construction of the Newlands Project (named after the author of the act, Representative Francis Newlands) began in 1903. The project included dams on the Truckee and Carson Rivers and a six-foot-high addition to Lake Tahoe's outlet to the Truckee River. These dams impounded the Truckee and Carson Rivers for distribution to farmers in the Lahontan Valley in Nevada. Another effort, the Klamath Project, which began in 1906, included the construction of dams on the Klamath River and its tributaries in southern Oregon and northeastern California, supplying irrigation water to farmers throughout the upper Klamath Basin in both states.

Meanwhile, Imperial Valley farmers continued to struggle with unpredictable water supplies from the Colorado River. With no significant dams upstream, river flows ranged from languid to violent. During a large flood in 1905, the Colorado River destroyed the Imperial diversion structures and flowed unimpeded onto the farm lands, converting the long-dry Salton Sink into the Salton Sea. It took years to rebuild the diversion structures and to restore flows in the Alamo Canal that irrigators shared with Mexico. The unreliability of flows affected agricultural development on both sides of the border.

The Imperial Valley irrigators sought to build an "All-American Canal" that would end their forced sharing of water with Mexico. But diverting Colorado River waters north of the international border would require larger dams—so large, in fact, that funding was well beyond the financial ability of either the Imperial farmers or the state. Federal involvement, on a scale unprecedented for the Reclamation Service, would be imperative.

The Boulder Canyon Project

Led by its new director and chief engineer, Arthur Russell Davis, the Reclamation Service proposed a massive concrete gravity-arch dam across the Colorado River at the mouth of Boulder Canyon, Nevada, 342 river miles upstream from the Mexican border. The dam would impound the river for flood control, hydroelectric power, and water supply for users in Arizona, Nevada, and California. The California users would include the Imperial farmers, who would receive water by diversion from a new Imperial Dam (49 miles north of the Mexican border) through their long-desired All-American Canal.

Davis's plan was met initially with opposition from almost all quarters, including the U.S. Army Corps of Engineers, which planned to control lower

Colorado River flooding through levee construction; the upper-basin states of the Colorado River Basin and Arizona, which feared a California water grab; and Mexico, which (correctly) anticipated that a large dam on the Colorado River would enable the United States to dominate the river.[4]

The upper-basin states' opposition was relieved by the Colorado River Compact of 1922, which divided the waters of the Colorado River equally between the upper and lower basins. Each basin would be entitled to 7.5 million acre-feet (maf) annually, although the upper basin could not deprive the lower basin of water that the upper-basin states did not need. Without dams comparable to that proposed for Boulder Canyon, however, this caveat would allow the lower-basin states, especially California, to claim the lion's share of Colorado River water for most of the 20th century without violating the compact.

Congress's authorization of the Boulder Canyon Project in 1928 resolved some of the remaining opposition. It sided with the Reclamation Service and funded construction of a 726-foot-high dam at Boulder Canyon (subsequently named Hoover Dam after then–Secretary of Commerce Herbert Hoover), creating a 28 million acre-foot reservoir (later named Lake Mead in honor of the new Bureau of Reclamation director, Elwood Mead). The statute garnered additional political support in California by also authorizing construction of the Imperial Dam and All-American Canal, as well as Parker Dam (143 river miles upstream of Imperial) and the Colorado River Aqueduct, which would deliver water to the newly formed Metropolitan Water District of Southern California. In addition, Congress allowed the Secretary of the Interior to determine whether the hydroelectric power would be sold by the United States directly or through long-term leases to public and private utilities that would then profit from their resale of the electricity. This compromise secured support from both the Los Angeles Department of Water and Power and Southern California Edison, which would sign 50-year contracts with the Department of the Interior for power produced at Hoover Dam.

Although Congress attempted to accommodate Arizona by giving its advance approval to an interstate compact that would apportion the waters of the lower basin among Arizona, California, and Nevada, Arizona maintained its opposition. Indeed, in 1933, its governor sent National Guard troops to the river to block construction of the Arizona footings for Parker Dam. Arizona's

4. The "upper-basin states" commonly refers to Colorado, New Mexico, Utah, and Wyoming. In addition to California and Arizona, Nevada is a "lower-basin" state. Technically, the upper basin also includes the northern part of Arizona and the lower basin includes portions of Utah and New Mexico.

opposition to the project would last another 50 years and require a decision by the U.S. Supreme Court in *Arizona v. California* (1963), congressional enactment of the Colorado River Basin Project Act of 1968, and completion of the Central Arizona Project in 1982 (to pump Colorado River water into Arizona's central plateau) to bring the state into the fold.

The water provided by the Boulder Canyon Project's All-American Canal sustained farms in the Imperial Valley, enabling the development of agriculture as well as cities and resorts in the Coachella Valley north of the Salton Sea. In addition, the Colorado River Aqueduct fueled the rapid growth of cities within the Metropolitan Water District during and after World War II. The population of the Los Angeles–Orange County–San Diego metropolitan area grew from 4 million in 1940, the year before the first Colorado River water arrived, to more than 10 million in 1970. Southern California established itself as the West's preeminent economic center, surpassing Chicago, with defense, aerospace, manufacturing, shipping, housing, and commercial services quickly crowding out dairies and agriculture as its principal industries.

This development did not come without costs. As Lake Mead filled, water supplies diminished for Mexicali farmers (although flooding was largely eliminated), and the combined U.S. and Mexican diversions dried up the lush Colorado River Delta, eliminating its abundant fish and wildlife and causing the tamed river to end in a puddle, miles upstream of its natural terminus at the Gulf of California. Excessive water use and lack of regulating reservoirs within the Imperial Irrigation District would cause the Salton Sea to rise and flood shoreline landowners. The Colorado River supplies to the Metropolitan Water District would soon prove insufficient for Southern California's ever-growing demands. By the mid-1960s, California would exceed its 4.4 million acre-feet annual allocation under the Boulder Canyon Act. As the population and corresponding demands of Arizona and Nevada grew, California would face renewed conflicts over the fair apportionment of lower-basin Colorado River flows.

The Central Valley Project

Farmers in California's Central Valley also sought a large water project to harness water from the North Coast and the Sierra Nevada. Irrigated acreage had increased from less than one million acres in 1900 to more than three million by 1930. With less surface water than arable land in the San Joaquin Valley and Tulare Basin, much of this new irrigation relied heavily on groundwater, leading to extensive overdraft of regional aquifers. The larger landowners were wary of federal development, however, because the acreage limits of the Reclamation Act would require that they break up their existing farms (some of which covered tens of thousands of acres). In contrast to their Imperial brethren, these farmers supported U.S. Army Corps of Engineers' dams on nearby streams (nominally for flood control) and lobbied the California legislature for a state-funded, state-operated project to import additional water from the Sacramento River Basin (Maass 1951).

For decades, state, federal, and local governments had engaged in sporadic efforts to conceptualize and plan a comprehensive interregional water project, taking water from wetter northern and mountainous regions to areas of growing agricultural and urban demands. A federally sponsored plan for the Central Valley released in 1873 envisioned a vast series of canals that would move water across the valley. The 1919 Marshall Plan (developed by Robert Marshall, a retired U.S. Geological Survey hydrologist working at the University of California) gained widespread support for a statewide scheme of reservoirs and aqueducts to bring water from the Sacramento River to the San Joaquin Valley and divert water from the Kern River to Southern California. The Marshall Plan became the basis for California's preliminary comprehensive plan for water in 1924 and the first State Water Plan of 1930 under the direction of State Engineer Edward Hyatt.

Hyatt's "Central Valley Project" had as its capstone a large dam on the Sacramento River (at the location of today's Shasta Dam) to control the flow of the river and distribute the water to users in the Sacramento Valley, the Delta, and the northern San Joaquin Valley. A smaller dam on the San Joaquin River northeast of Fresno would divert most of that river to irrigate lands in Madera, Kings, Fresno, Tulare, and Kern Counties. Riparian water users on the San Joaquin River below the dam, as well as lands on the west side of the San Joaquin Valley that relied heavily on groundwater, would be supplied by water pumped from the Delta via a series of check dams on the San Joaquin River. The plan essentially required that the lower San Joaquin River run backward during the irrigation season (Division of Water Resources 1930). Releases from the Sacramento River Dam would not only supply water but also provide a freshwater barrier against salt water intruding into the Delta from San Francisco Bay. This would enhance summer water quality for Delta farmers using water pumped from the southern Delta. Water users on the Sacramento River would receive water to fulfill their pre-project water rights, as well as additional water made available by releases from the project. Because the dam on the San Joaquin River would dry up the river during most hydrologic conditions, the state would either "condemn" (or invalidate) existing downstream water rights impaired by the project or, in some cases, offer pre-project San Joaquin water rights holders Sacramento River water pumped from the Delta (Lund et al. 2010).

It was an audacious proposal. The legislature authorized the Central Valley Project in 1933, but opposition by Pacific Gas & Electric, Southern California Edison, Sacramento River Basin area-of-origin advocates, and some senior water rights holders forced a referendum on the act. Voters narrowly approved the CVP legislation in December 1933.

Although California was in the midst of a sustained drought, it was also in the midst of the Great Depression, and economic conditions prevented the state from selling the bonds needed to finance the project's construction. The Roosevelt administration offered to take over the CVP as part of the federal reclamation program. Congress authorized the federal Central Valley Project in 1935 and again in 1937. The purposes of the CVP were navigation, flood control, water supply, and hydroelectric power. Construction of Shasta Dam began in 1937, with water and power deliveries beginning in 1944. Pumping from the Delta through the Delta Mendota Canal and diversions from the San Joaquin River began in 1951.

Over time, Congress added other units and facilities to the CVP. These included dams on the Trinity River (which divert water from the North Coast to the Sacramento River), the American River, and the Stanislaus River; San Luis Reservoir, an off-stream storage facility near the Pacheco Pass, which allows storage of Sacramento River water pumped south from the Delta; and canals that supply water to users in the Sacramento Valley, the Bay Area, and additional areas on the western side of the San Joaquin Valley. Today, the CVP manages roughly 7 million acre-feet of water annually, about 90 percent of which is for irrigation.

The Central Valley Project is by far the largest water purveyor in California and is probably the most controversial. The dams and reservoirs, in conjunction with those constructed for the State Water Project (described below), blocked access for salmon and steelhead to their native spawning grounds. Attempts to use fish hatcheries to offset these losses ultimately failed (Chapter 5). The impoundment and diversion of water and the conversion of new land for farming made possible by the new supplies of project water resulted in the loss of more than half of the Central Valley's remaining freshwater wetlands (Figure 1.2). In

Figure 1.2
California's Central Valley has lost most of its native wetlands

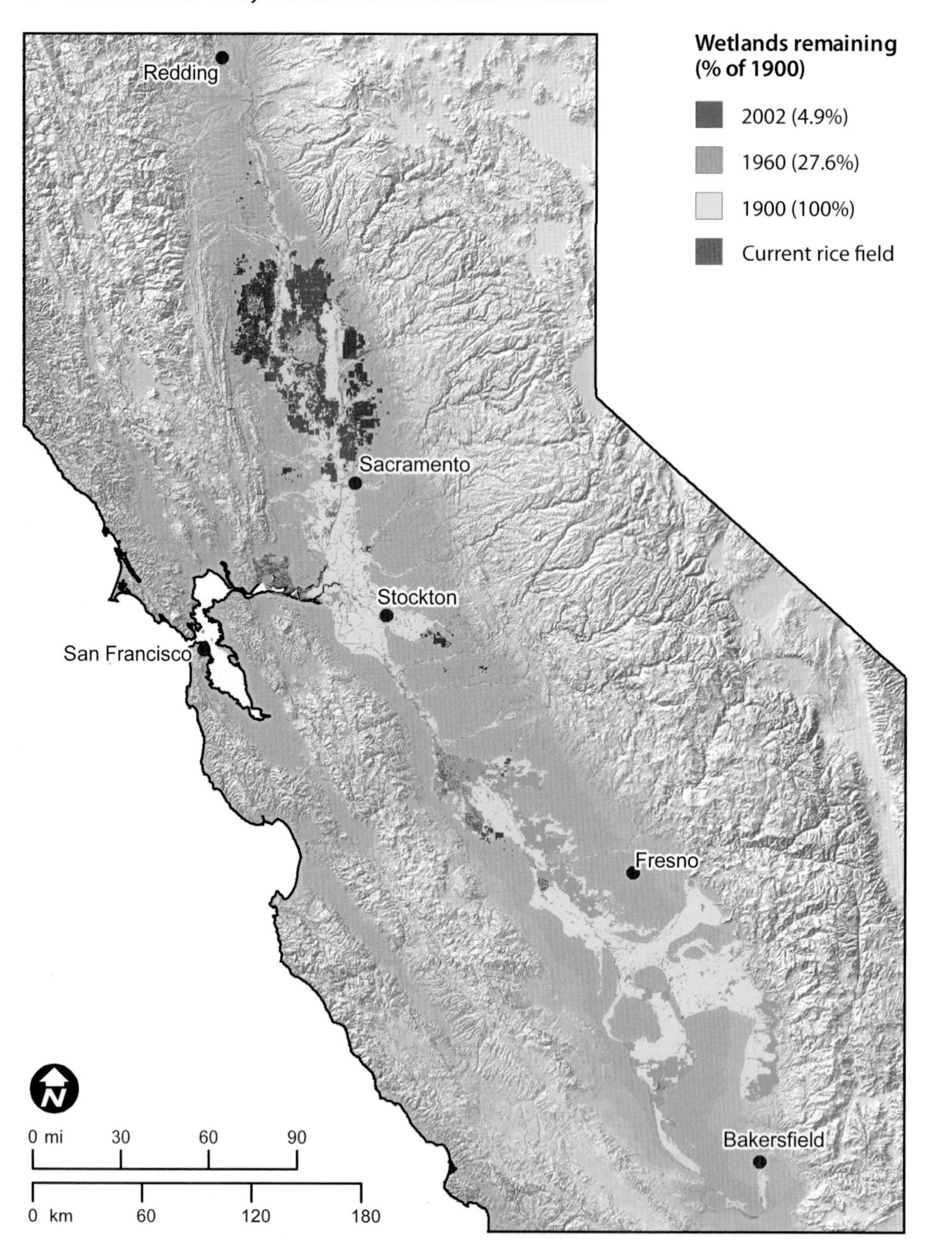

SOURCES: California State University, Chico (2003); Dahl and Allord (1997); California Department of Forestry and Fire Protection (2002); California Department of Fish and Game (1997); U.S. Fish and Wildlife Service (undated).

NOTES: 1900 wetlands include the yellow, orange, and red areas, and 1960 wetlands include the orange and red areas. Sacramento Valley rice fields provide some seasonal wetlands functions for migrating birds and terrestrial and riparian species such as the giant garter snake.

the Tulare Basin, dams constructed on the Kings, Kaweah, Tule, and Kern Rivers by the U.S. Army Corps of Engineers captured most of the water that historically flooded the low-lying lands, allowing these lands to be cultivated (Arax and Wartzman 2005). Tulare Lake, once with a surface area far larger than Lake Tahoe, has vanished in all but the wettest of years. The loss of the Central Valley's natural wetlands—while necessary to expand farming—had the unintended consequence of reducing habitat for migratory birds, fish, and terrestrial species and eliminating most of the system's natural flood control capability.

In the San Joaquin Valley, the availability of Sacramento River water pumped from the southern Delta enabled many thousands of acres of new land to be irrigated. The completion of San Luis Reservoir in 1963 allowed Sacramento River water to be stored south of the Delta, so more water could be exported through the Delta pumps. Extension of the CVP south of San Luis in the late 1960s brought more lands into production. These lands sit on an impermeable formation of Corcoran clay, which prevents surface water from percolating into the confined aquifer below. Without adequate drainage, irrigation water applied to the land would flood the crops' root zone, and salts from the irrigation water would accumulate. The Bureau of Reclamation therefore agreed to construct an elaborate system of subterranean tile drains to collect and convey the drainage water to a larger San Luis Drain, which in turn would discharge the agricultural drainage into the Delta. However, when Congress failed to appropriate funds to complete the drain, the bureau decided simply to allow the drainage water to pool and evaporate at the Kesterson National Wildlife Refuge, the drain's de facto terminus. The drainage water carried salts, selenium, and heavy metals that are natural components of the soil on the west side of the San Joaquin Valley. As the water evaporated from the ponds, the selenium and other solids were left in increasing concentrations at Kesterson. In the late 1970s, biologists noticed high rates of birth defects in birds hatched in the area. Increasing levels of selenium had turned the refuge into a killing field.

In addition, Shasta and Friant Dams and the other large "rim" dams subsequently added to the system did not include fish ladders, thus eliminating all of the salmon and steelhead runs on the upper Sacramento and San Joaquin Rivers and their major tributaries. Friant Dam was especially harmful to anadromous fish because it diverted almost the entire river flow, leaving an intermittently dry riverbed for about 150 miles downstream. Salmon and steelhead runs of up to 100,000 adults migrating upriver to spawn—already representing only perhaps 5 to 10 percent of historical runs—dwindled rapidly during the 1940s and became extinct except in sparse habitat below the main stem and tributary dams (in such places as the Merced, Tuolumne, and Stanislaus Rivers). Indeed, for most of its 60-year history, the riverbed below Friant Dam has functioned primarily as a regional drain and flood channel.

The impoundment and diversion of water at northern installations of the CVP also exacerbated the decline of the salmon runs. Trinity Dam, completed in 1964, diverted 75–90 percent of the Trinity River to support Sacramento River diversions to the San Joaquin Valley. These diversions reduced Trinity River salmon and steelhead runs by more than 80 percent and created intense conflict between the United States and the Yurok and Hoopa Tribes, which have aboriginal and treaty-based fishing rights on the river. Moreover, as described below, the alteration of the quantity and timing of flows in California's major river systems—combined with the pumping of the water from the southern Delta—has had disastrous consequences for anadromous fish that migrate through the Delta as well as for its other native fish species.

When Congress authorized the federal takeover of the Central Valley Project in the depths of the Great Depression, it foresaw some of these environmental consequences but chose to sacrifice facets of the environment for the greater economic good of creating a secure and abundant water supply for the people and farms in the Central Valley. Yet, in the end, the 7 million acre-feet of water produced annually by the project would not be enough for the farmers—especially those south of the Delta. Nor was it enough for municipal and industrial users who had largely been excluded from the congressional largesse and whose rapidly growing demands for water eclipsed (in economic value) those of their agricultural neighbors.

The State Water Project

The idea of a State Water Project to complement (and perhaps to complete) the CVP formally began as early as 1945, when the legislature passed the State Water Resources Act. The statute created a Water Resources Board to investigate California's water resources and formulate plans to address water issues throughout the state. In 1951, the board reported that 40 percent of the harvestable water in California's rivers was allowed to flow unused to the Pacific Ocean. California's greatest challenge, the board concluded, would be to redistribute water from areas of surplus—the North Coast rivers and the tributaries of the Sacramento River—to the areas of deficiency in Central and Southern

California. Later that year, State Engineer Arthur Edmonston published his own report, which called for constructing a large dam on the Feather River to help control Sacramento Valley floods and provide water for the Bay Area, the western San Joaquin Valley, and Southern California.

The State Water Project that emerged combined the central features of both reports to create an integrated system of dams and canals that would parallel (and rival) the CVP. The capstone of the SWP would be the 3.5 million acre-feet Oroville Reservoir on the Feather River. The project would release this stored water into the lower Feather River, where it would be joined by water from the Yuba and Bear and then flow into the Sacramento River and the Delta. Communities in the Sacramento Valley and North Bay Area would take some of the water, but most would be pumped from the southern Delta into the California Aqueduct. From there, the water would supply farms along the west side of the San Joaquin Valley and the Tulare Basin, as well as cities in the eastern and southern parts of the San Francisco Bay Area. The balance would be pumped 3,000 feet up and over the Tehachapi Mountains for distribution to the customers of the Metropolitan Water District of Southern California and other communities. Over time, additional installations could be added to the project, including dams on the North Coast rivers and a canal that would allow the waters of the Sacramento Basin to bypass the Delta and flow directly to the southern Delta pumps.

In 1956, the legislature took the first step to make the State Water Project a reality, creating a Department of Water Resources that consolidated the water planning and development responsibilities of 52 state agencies. The law establishing the new department passed shortly after the Christmas floods of 1955, which inundated large parts of California, took 64 lives, and caused more than $200 million in property damage. Three years later, the legislature approved the Water Resources Development Bond Act (commonly known as the Burns-Porter Act), which authorized the sale of $1.75 billion in general obligation bonds, plus the use of additional revenue from California's offshore oil drilling revenues, to pay for the project. The bond measure was the largest in the nation's history, almost equal to California's entire state budget for 1959 (Hundley 2001). As required by the state constitution, the legislature submitted the Water Resources Development Bond Act to voters for their approval.

Governor Edmund G. (Pat) Brown believed that the SWP was essential for California's future growth and economic prosperity and campaigned throughout the state for the Burns-Porter Act. The bond measure had strong support in the San Joaquin Valley. Sacramento Valley voters, fearing that their water would be contracted away to users in the south, generally opposed the measure. In the November 1960 election that sent John F. Kennedy to the White House, California voters approved the State Water Project by a margin of less than three-tenths of one percent of the 5.8 million ballots cast, the narrowest election in the state's history. All northern counties except for the recently flooded Yuba and Butte Counties (the future site of the Oroville Dam) voted no, with strong Southern California support providing the margin of victory. The SWP vote highlighted the north-south divide that would dominate California water politics for the next quarter century.

Construction began on the project in 1961, and the initial facilities at Oroville Dam were completed by 1965. In 1966, the great pumps at Clifton Court in the southern Delta were installed and water began flowing south through the California Aqueduct to San Joaquin Valley farmers. Five years later, the Edmonston Pumping Plant began lifting SWP water over the Tehachapi Mountains to Southern California. The Department of Water Resources signed contracts with 30 agencies throughout the state for permanent water service. The contracts pledged deliveries of 4.2 million acre-feet annually, although the SWP facilities built during the first phase of development could provide, on average, only about half that amount.

Flood Management During the Hydraulic Era

Although the Hydraulic Era is best known for its extensive water supply developments and interbasin transfers, a parallel expansion occurred in flood management. The Central Valley's unique geographic and hydrologic conditions and its legacy of failed attempts to manage hydraulic mining sediment, spurred the nation's most comprehensive, and in some ways most innovative, flood management. At the same time, the explosive growth in urban areas, particularly in the South Coast region, was occurring in flood-prone areas, requiring major structural investments against future flooding.

The dramatic expansion of flood management shared a common characteristic with the expansion of water supply during the Hydraulic Era: By the 1930s, it turned to massive flood control projects dependent on federal largesse and expertise, principally through the U.S. Army Corps of Engineers. This commonality between water supply and flood control created a complex, co-dependent relationship between the two that led to conflicts for both management objectives to this day. When managing floods using levees and river diversions proved ineffectual for controlling large floods, flood management strategists joined with water supply strategists in focusing their attention on big, multipurpose reservoirs. This led to further conflicts. Although multiple objectives made these structures more economically viable, the objectives often diverge (Chapters 3, 6): Flood managers have an interest in keeping reservoirs empty, to capture large winter and spring flood flows, whereas water supply managers have an interest in keeping reservoirs full, to have more water available for the dry summer months.

Central Valley flood control

At the end of the 19th century and the beginning of the 20th century, the legacy of hydraulic mining continued to plague efforts to manage floods in the Central Valley. Urban growth in the Sacramento and Marysville–Yuba City areas, along with rapid expansion of farms throughout the Central Valley created great pressures to resolve flood issues. Between 1902 and 1909, a series of devastating floods wracked the Central Valley, building pressure for, and focusing public attention on, more effective flood management.

The solutions put forward by the corps in the 19th century and carried out principally by local reclamation districts had failed to reduce large floods in Central Valley rivers. In 1911, the legislature chose a new direction by following the advice of the first state engineer, William Hammond Hall, who, in the 1880s, proposed storing and conveying floodwaters on leveed portions of floodplains to bypass major floods outside the regular stream channels. Known as the Major Project, or the Jackson Plan, this effort involved establishing major bypass areas on the Sacramento River floodplain to receive floodwaters over weirs. The largest of these, the Yolo Bypass west of Sacramento, became an international model for flood management. The legislature also broke with the traditions of the Laissez-Faire and Local Organization Eras and took state control over reclamation policy by forming the State Reclamation Board.

Such an ambitious effort could not succeed without extensive federal involvement, given the exceptionally high costs of this project and its need for extensive technical expertise. Moreover, the federal government had authority over the navigable streams that would be affected by the project. Federal involvement began in the late 19th century and included the federally authorized California Debris Commission in 1893 to improve navigation in river channels and to reduce flooding. Congress dramatically expanded the federal role with two statutes enacted in the early 20th century. The Major Project

Act of 1917 funded about half the costs of California's flood control project and welded together the state and federal government in managing floods in California. Following a series of great floods on the Mississippi River, Congress authorized the Flood Control Act of 1928. This statute put the U.S. Army Corps of Engineers firmly in charge of flood control projects in California and throughout the nation.

The California flood control project was later expanded to include flood control works for the San Joaquin Valley and portions of the Sacramento–San Joaquin Delta. Today, the federal and state governments jointly manage flood control in the Central Valley.

The flood control projects of the Central Valley became integrated with water supply during the Hydraulic Era in two ways. The first was early recognition that the initial designs for the project were insufficient to protect portions of the floodplain undergoing rapid urban expansion. The second involved the role of flood management in maintaining the ability of the CVP and the SWP to export water from the Delta. Together, these factors created additional demand and economic justification for the era's primary tool in water management: the multipurpose dam. All major dams along the west slope of the Sierra Nevada and at the head of the Sacramento Valley allocate some of their winter and spring storage capacity to managing floods, which creates an inherent conflict between water supply and flood management. Water supply operations prefer full reservoirs; flood operations prefer empty reservoirs. This tangled relationship between water supply and flood control remains a thorny problem for water management (Lund et al. 2007, 2010).

Despite investments in more than 1,600 miles of levees for flood control, the levees have failed to live up to expectations. Water administrators and flood control managers have consistently underestimated the potential magnitude of floods and overestimated the reliability of levees in the system (Chapter 6). Moreover, floods are regional events that require federal, state, and local cooperation for management; yet land use decisions, which ultimately dictate risks from flooding, remain at the local level. Thus, urban development has frequently occurred behind inadequate levees.

Urban flood control in Southern California

Equally ambitious and costly exercises in flood management occurred simultaneously in Southern California and the Bay Area. Dramatic increases in population during the Hydraulic Era created the urban footprint that defines much of California's landscape.[5] Flood problems were most pronounced in the Los Angeles region where a combination of factors led to chronic flood problems. First, intense winter rainfall occurs in the rugged mountains surrounding the Los Angeles Basin, causing the rapid rise and fall of local rivers. Second, the culture of indiscriminate sprawl that took root in Southern California early in the 20th century led to the development and paving over of lands in the floodplains of the region's principal streams. Better land use planning might have prevented many of Southern California's flood problems.

After multiple failed attempts by Los Angeles County to develop and fund a comprehensive flood control project for the Los Angeles River, the U.S. Army Corps of Engineers, with newfound powers from the Flood Control Act of 1928, took over the project's design and construction. The unplanned urban sprawl left them few choices: They channelized the river, seeking to move floodwater from the urban area as fast as possible without encumbering floodplain development. This effort set the California standard for urban streams during the latter half of the Hydraulic Era. Throughout the Bay Area and Southern California, urban streams became concrete-lined canals, often underground, that channelized flows and minimized the footprint of the watercourse. Thousands of miles of rivers and streams underwent this type of "improvement" with profound implications for water supply and river ecosystems. In the end, most of these projects supported development but failed to eliminate flooding.

The End of the Hydraulic Era

The state, federal, and local projects of the Hydraulic Era—the heyday of California water development and flood control from the early 1900s through the 1970s—transformed the state. In less than a century, the state's economy evolved from its early domination by mining, to a period of dramatic expansion of agriculture, followed by a sustained, explosive growth in manufacturing and service industries to become the world's sixth or seventh largest economy (Figure 1.3). California's water infrastructure had harnessed the rivers of the Coast Range, the Sierra Nevada, and the Rocky Mountains, making it possible for farms in Kern County to irrigate their crops with water from the Pit River in Modoc County, for businesses in the Silicon Valley to produce computer chips using runoff from Mount Lyell in the Yosemite back country, for Budweiser

5. The history of Southern California's battles with floods and the tendency to ignore them is well captured by John McPhee in his book *Control of Nature* (1989) and in Blake Gumprecht's extensive review entitled *The Los Angeles River: Its Life, Death, and Possible Rebirth* (1999).

Figure 1.3
Since statehood, California's economy has undergone major structural changes

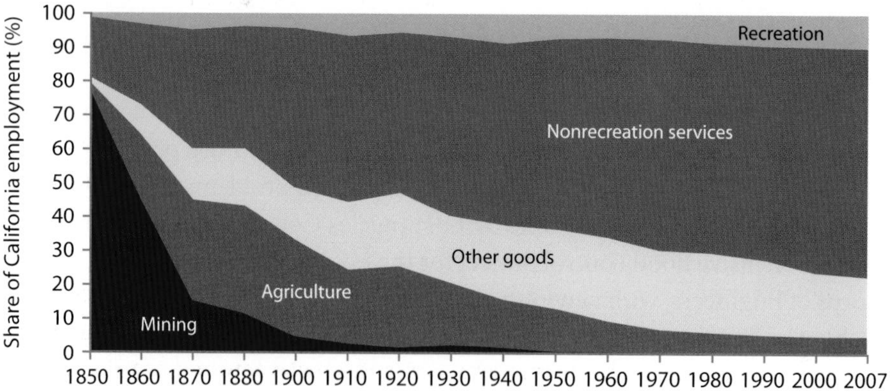

SOURCE: Hanak et al. (2010) using data from the U.S. Census (Integrated Public Use Microdata Series) (1950 industry basis).

NOTES: Agriculture includes farm-related wholesale trade and manufacturing as well as forestry (which never exceeded 0.2 percent of employment and now accounts for less than 0.1 percent). Other goods includes nonfood manufacturing and construction. Recreation includes fisheries (which never exceeded 0.5 percent of employment and now accounts for less than 0.1 percent).

to brew beer in the San Fernando Valley with groundwater from the eastern Sierra Nevada, and for the residents of San Diego to drink water that fell as snow outside Pinedale, Wyoming. The economic glories of California, its social and cultural achievements—indeed, much of what the state's residents take for granted as quintessentially *Californian*—are attributable to its water projects.

The Hydraulic Era also left in its wake a set of less beneficent legacies. The economy of Owens Valley had been reduced to scattered agriculture, ranching, and tourism. Owens Lake was a dry lakebed, subject to toxic dust storms, and most of the Owens River and valley groundwater flowed into the Los Angeles Aqueduct. To the north, the ecosystem of Mono Lake was collapsing from the diminished freshwater inflows. To the west, Hetch Hetchy Valley in Yosemite National Park, was buried under 300 feet of water. The San Joaquin River below Friant Dam was dry for most of the year, and the lower river had become a drain for irrigation and wastewater rather than a natural waterway. Salmon and steelhead runs in the Sacramento River continued to decline as Oroville Reservoir filled and SWP exports from the Delta approached capacity. Delta farmers complained of increasing salinity in their water supplies as upstream diversions and combined CVP/SWP operations depleted more of the natural flow. Biological surveys revealed precipitous declines in native fish species dependent on the channels, shallows, and quality of water within the Delta. As California's population increased—from 20 million in 1970 to 24 million in 1980 to 30 million in 1990—it became clear that there still was not enough water to satisfy all water demands. And, despite large investments in flood management, the risk of catastrophic flooding remained unacceptably high.

After many decades of interregional and statewide development, California would enter the difficult modern period of water policy. The extensive development of water supply and flood control projects could not provide completely reliable water supplies or end flood risk for a growing economy and population. Furthermore, developing these water management systems had greatly harmed the native species and the natural environment. Changing societal values and a long history of degrading the state's ecosystems created a new, unsettling reality for water management: Environmental demands held a new and prominent seat at the water management negotiating table. The water world was deviating from the 1930 and 1957 water plans in fundamental ways. But no new fundamental state plan existed for moving forward. With little consensus on how California should proceed, almost all water users (urban, agricultural, and environmental) had reason to fear for the future.

The Hydraulic Era ended for many reasons, accumulating over several decades (Figure 1.1). As the environmental movement took hold in the late 1960s, public interest in outdoor recreation and environmental protection increased and popular support for new dams and flood control projects waned. The best reservoir sites had already been taken, which meant that additional dams—which would have provided increasingly meager contributions to water supplies and flood control—would be increasingly expensive. The inflation of the late 1960s and 1970s exacerbated this problem. By the 1980s, the rising federal deficit reduced the willingness of the United States to pay for major new reclamation projects. Indeed, the federal government, which had been California's essential partner throughout the Hydraulic Era, was transformed from principal funder and promoter of water development into its new, opposite role as chief regulator. The symbolic end of the Hydraulic Era though came in 1982 when California's electorate rejected the peripheral canal, a large water project that would have routed Sacramento and Trinity River Basin water around the Delta to the CVP and SWP pumps (see below).

More positively, the Hydraulic Era left California with a broadly capable physical infrastructure, as well as a state economy in which prosperity was no longer closely tied to the availability of water as a direct input into production.

The most water-dependent sectors of the economy, including agriculture and some manufacturing industries, had largely ceased to increase their water use and had become a small share of California's employment and economic output, replaced by a service economy with much greater flexibility to reduce water use without reducing wealth (Figure 1.3; Chapter 2). The growth in recreational services, moreover, suggests a shift over time toward water demands more compatible with environmental protection.

The Era of Conflict

The Hydraulic Era gave way to the current Era of Conflict, in which the dominant water policies have struggled to achieve contemporary management needs for water supply reliability and quality, environmental restoration and protection, conservation and efficiency of use, and adaptation to new laws, new science, and ever-changing hydrologic, economic, and demographic conditions. These new conflicts and changes have challenged current institutions, users, managers, and scientists to adapt more quickly, and with greater uncertainty, than existed before. Many incremental changes, largely led by local agencies, have occurred during this Era of Conflict, but strategic changes needed to adapt to changing conditions have largely eluded California.

The Environment as a Stakeholder

During the late 1960s and early 1970s, Congress and the state legislature enacted a series of landmark environmental statutes. These laws transformed the environment into a major factor in water planning and administration.

New environmental statutes transform the water management landscape

The National Environmental Policy Act of 1969 and the California Environmental Quality Act of 1970 required that new water management and flood control projects be preceded by an analysis of their potential environmental effects and include a range of project alternatives and consideration of actions to mitigate or offset any unavoidable environmental damage. California's Porter-Cologne Act of 1969 and the Federal Water Pollution Control Act Amendments of 1972, which constitute the modern Clean Water Act (CWA), gave power and impetus to the State Water Resources Control Board to set standards for water quality and other beneficial uses of California's waters. The National Wild and Scenic Rivers Act of 1968 and the California Wild and Scenic Rivers Act of 1972 protected numerous rivers that had been identified for dam projects to support the CVP and SWP. And the federal Endangered Species Act of 1973, together with the California Endangered Species Act of 1984, profoundly influenced the administration of California's water resources systems as a variety of native fish species from suckerfish to salmon were listed for protection.

These environmental laws played out in diverse forums. In 1973, Governor Ronald Reagan signed a bill that included the Eel River in the California Wild and Scenic Rivers System. The legislation prevented construction of the Dos Rios Reservoir, which would have flooded ranch lands and the town of Covelo in Round Valley to augment water supplies for the SWP. In 1978, the State Water Resources Control Board acted to protect whitewater recreation and fisheries in the Stanislaus River by denying the U.S. Bureau of Reclamation permission to fill the newly constructed New Melones Reservoir. Although the board's decision was only a temporary reprieve and the reservoir ultimately was filled, the intense public controversy would make New Melones the last unit added to the CVP. After New Melones, it could no longer be assumed that development of California's rivers to supply agricultural and urban demands was necessarily the highest and best use of water. These same arguments later constrained several large water supply and flood control projects, including attempts to build a large dam on the American River near the city of Auburn (a project also beset with seismic problems) and East Bay Municipal Utility District's proposal to divert water from Folsom Reservoir on the American River to augment its Mokelumne River supplies.

By the early 1980s, the long period of water development was reaching its end. On January 20, 1981, in one of the last acts of the Carter administration, Secretary of the Interior Cecil Andrus added the North Coast rivers and the lower American River to the National Wild and Scenic Rivers System, which meant that these rivers could not be dammed without an act of Congress. The prohibition of new water projects on these rivers was especially significant because the North Coast rivers carry an average of 26 million acre-feet of water annually, an amount exceeding the average flow of the Sacramento River (Chapter 2). Proponents of expanding the CVP and SWP had seen these rivers as the principal source of additional project water supplies.

Then, in the fall of 1982, the California electorate decisively rejected another key feature of the projects—a 43-mile, concrete-lined peripheral canal—which would have more efficiently linked the northern and southern units of the CVP and SWP.

The conveyance of water from the Sacramento River through the channels of the Delta to the southern Delta pumping plants had emerged as a major inefficiency for both projects (Lund et al. 2007, 2010). From a water supply perspective, the transport of water through the Delta meant that additional "carriage water" had to be released to prevent salt water from San Francisco Bay from contaminating the fresh water that would be exported at the pumps. From a water quality and environmental perspective, the operation of the projects reduced outflow and altered flows of water through the Delta, which both impaired agricultural uses within the Delta region and harmed the native fish that inhabited or migrated through the Delta. Peripheral canal proponents argued that the new infrastructure would reduce these conflicts and improve the reliability, quality, and quantity of Delta exports.

Legislation authorizing the construction of a canal was passed and signed into law in 1980. But opponents of the canal succeeded in putting an initiative on the ballot in June 1982. The voters sided with the canal opponents, rejecting the peripheral canal by a margin of 54 percent to 46 percent. All counties north of Ventura on the coast and Kern inland voted no—many with more than 90 percent of voters opposing the measure.[6] The yes votes in Southern California were insufficient to overcome monolithic northern opposition.

The Hydraulic Era was over. In the wake of the peripheral canal defeat, the continuing debate over California water resource policy moved to the courts, which were struggling with two landmark cases that would begin to define how the state would redress the accumulated problems that massive water development had created—one concerning Los Angeles's diversions from Mono Lake and the other involving CVP and SWP exports from the Delta.

The Mono Lake decision

The first decision came in litigation to limit Los Angeles's export of water from the Mono Lake watershed and to restore the lake's collapsing ecosystem. The plaintiffs, led by the National Audubon Society and the Committee to Save Mono Lake, asserted that Los Angeles's diversions violated the public trust, the legal doctrine on which the California Supreme Court relied in enjoining mining in 1884 (Box 1.2). The traditional public trust doctrine protected navigation, fishing, and recreational uses. But in 1971, the court significantly expanded

6. For a map of votes by county, see Lund et al. 2010 or www.ppic.org/main/mapdetail.asp?i=855.

the doctrine's scope to include protection of ecological services, habitat, and preservation (*Marks v. Whitney* 1971).

In its historic *National Audubon Society v. Superior Court* (1983) decision, the California Supreme Court held that, although the public trust does not trump other uses of water, the state has an obligation to protect public trust uses "whenever feasible" in planning and allocating water. Most significantly, it ruled that the state has a continuing responsibility to protect the public trust uses of Mono Lake and is not bound by past water allocation decisions that "may be incorrect in light of current knowledge or inconsistent with current needs."

This ruling and subsequent litigation brought under Fish and Game Code § 5937 (Box 1.3) forced Los Angeles to release water from its dams on tributaries to Mono Lake to protect trout in the river. The cases ultimately were referred to the SWRCB, which amended Los Angeles's water rights in 1991 requiring that the city bypass sufficient water to protect the public trust in Mono Lake and again in 1998 to establish minimum stream flows in the tributaries.

The Supreme Court's incorporation of the public trust doctrine into the water rights system would have profound effects on California water policy. Following *National Audubon Society v. Superior Court*, neither water administrators nor water users could continue to ignore the needs of the ecosystems that are the sources of the state's developed water supplies. Moreover, the court's recognition that protection of the public trust requires regulatory flexibility to respond to ecological changes significantly strengthened the legal authority of the SWRCB, the courts, and the legislature to continue their efforts to rebalance economic and environmental uses of the state's rivers and estuaries, which had been overexploited and damaged during the Hydraulic Era.

The Bay-Delta controversy

California's most complex and intractable water dispute is the four-decade-long struggle to manage the decline of the Bay-Delta ecosystem (Lund et al. 2007, 2010). Indeed, the Bay-Delta controversy is emblematic of the Era of Conflict.

After the SWP began operations in the late 1960s, the combined effects of CVP and SWP impoundments and diversions—along with those of hundreds of other water users—became clearly apparent. River flows and water quality declined, threatening both economic and environmental uses; and the ecological balance of the Delta became disastrous to native fish species (Moyle and Bennett 2008; Lund et al. 2007, 2010). The conversion of the 700,000-acre tidal freshwater marsh to a network of rock-lined channels had severely limited available habitat for fish, and dramatic reductions in the quantity and quality of Delta inflows further degraded that habitat. As the SWP increased its exports in the 1980s—almost doubling direct extractions from the Delta—conditions reached a crisis point (Figure 1.4).

Throughout this period, the SWRCB undertook a series of unsuccessful proceedings to regulate CVP and SWP operations to protect Delta water quality for fish, in-Delta water users, and exporters. In 1978 the board promulgated water quality standards for the Delta and amended water rights permits of the CVP and SWP to regulate project operations. Both projects and an array of water users and environmentalists filed suit, and the litigation quickly became the largest water resources dispute in California's history.

In 1986, at the beginning of what would be one of the worst droughts of the 20th century, the California Court of Appeal ruled that the water quality standards adopted by the board were unlawful and ordered it to conduct new

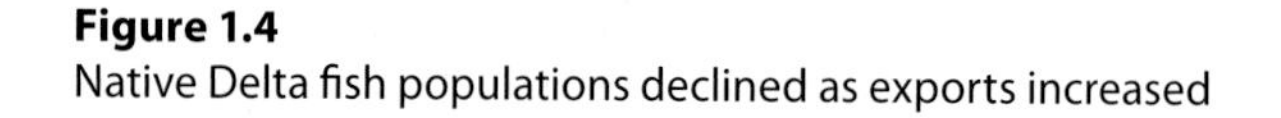

Figure 1.4
Native Delta fish populations declined as exports increased

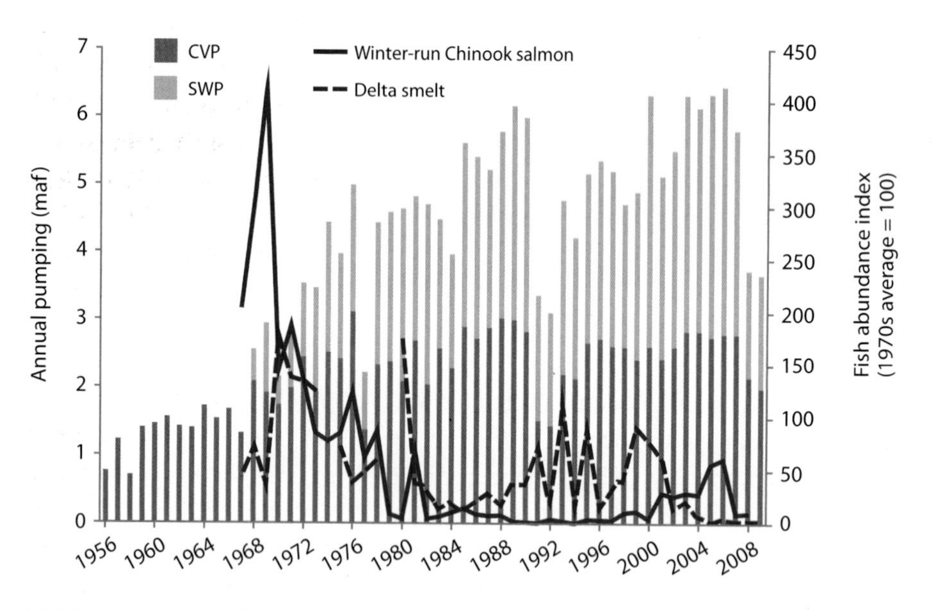

SOURCES: For Delta exports, California Department of Water Resources Dayflow data; for fish populations, California Department of Fish and Game survey data.

NOTES: Both the CVP and the SWP pump water from the southwestern Delta. CVP exports include pumping from the Contra Costa Water District, which draws from the Contra Costa Canal in the western Delta (roughly 120,000 acre-feet [af] in the 2000s), and SWP exports include pumping from the North Bay Aqueduct, which draws from the northern Delta to supply Solano and Napa Counties (roughly 50,000 af in the 2000s). Series for salmon and adult delta smelt are not available before the years shown.

hearings. The court emphasized that the SWRCB had broad authority to amend the water rights of the CVP and SWP to ensure that project operations did not threaten water quality, aquatic species, and other beneficial uses, and it authorized the board to apply the new water quality standards to other water rights holders whose uses contribute to flow depletion and water quality degradation (*United States v. State Water Resources Control Board* 1986).

The SWRCB's Bay-Delta water quality proceedings convened after the court's decision included more than 100 water agencies, representing a variety of water users from all parts of the state. The board's first draft water quality plan, announced in 1989, proposed to cap Delta exports at 1986 levels. It also contained a "California Conservation Ethic" that assigned most of the burden of conserving water on users in Southern California. The draft plan provoked a firestorm of political protest. The water quality plan that replaced it in 1991 deleted all references to the water ethic and imposed no limits on exports. It set water quality standards for salinity that were almost identical to the 1978 standards and failed to address one of the most important issues before the board—the quantity and timing of flows needed to protect endangered and threatened fish species.

Because of these failings, the U.S. Environmental Protection Agency (EPA) disapproved the water quality plan. EPA's veto returned the matter to the board, which conducted new hearings. In March 1993, the SWRCB announced revised standards and a proposed water rights order. The board established water quality and flow standards for salmon and steelhead and imposed water release requirements and water use fees on more than 100 appropriators in the Central Valley and Trinity River Basins. This proposal set off another political firestorm, and Governor Pete Wilson directed the board to rescind it. EPA responded by promulgating federal water quality and flow standards for the Bay-Delta Estuary in January 1994.

Meanwhile, additional federal regulatory agencies stepped to the forefront of California's water policy debates. In 1989, the National Marine Fisheries Service listed the Sacramento River winter-run Chinook salmon as a threatened species (upgrading the listing to endangered status in 1994), and in 1993, the U.S. Fish and Wildlife Service listed the delta smelt as threatened. Returning winter-run Chinook salmon had declined from more than 100,000 in 1940 to fewer than 500 in 1989, and the delta smelt population had diminished by more than 90 percent. Federal biological opinions arising from these listings regulating the CVP and SWP called for significant changes in project operations—including reservoir releases to increase outflows and restrictions on exports through the southern

Delta pumps—to protect the species from extinction. These actions cemented the central role of the federal fish protection agencies in California's Era of Conflict.

In October 1992, Congress also interceded by enacting the Central Valley Project Improvement Act (CVPIA). Congress acknowledged in the statute that the CVP had been dedicated almost exclusively to providing water for agricultural and municipal uses and that project operations had diminished water quality, degraded the ecology of the Central Valley and the Delta, and threatened the extinction of native fish species. The CVPIA thus added fish and wildlife protection to the operational directives of the project, and ordered the Bureau of Reclamation to dedicate 800,000 acre-feet annually (about 20 percent of the face value of water delivery contracts) to a variety of environmental purposes.[7] These included restoration of wetlands, protection of water quality in the Delta, provision of flows for fish, and assistance with state and federal efforts to protect these resources in other regulatory forums such as in the Bay-Delta proceedings and threatened and endangered species biological opinions. Although this new environmental water would be initially released and dedicated to environmental purposes, most of it would be reused for economic purposes, including significant expanded SWP exports from the Delta during the late 1990s and early 2000s (Figure 1.4).

The CVPIA also included provisions that brought the project into greater conformity with state law. Congress ordered the bureau to comply with all aspects of California law, ending the long-standing uncertainty whether the decisions of the SWRCB—as well as other vital state laws such as the reasonable use and public trust doctrines—could be applied to the CVP. The act also borrowed from California's expanding policy of promoting water markets by authorizing the transfer of project water, both within the CVP and to users outside the project service area (see below).

CALFED and the failure of consensus politics

The EPA veto of California's Bay-Delta water quality standards and the listings of winter-run salmon and delta smelt presented state water managers and their constituents with the threat of a federal regulatory takeover of California's largest water projects and most important sources of water supply. In the spring of 1994, negotiations to resolve the crisis began. They included not just

7. The CVP delivers roughly 7 million acre-feet, but roughly 2.6 million acre-feet is "settlement" or "exchange" water to parties already diverting water before the project's arrival, and another 0.4 million for wildlife refuges. The "project" deliveries are on the order of 4 million acre-feet, and only these were affected by the CVPIA.

representatives of agricultural, urban, and environmental interests but also California's business community and political leaders from Sacramento and Washington, D.C. The December 1994 Bay-Delta Accord incorporated the restrictions of the biological opinions, took advantage of the 800,000 acre-feet per year provided by the CVPIA, and laid the groundwork for revising SWRCB water quality standards, which were adopted the next year.

The Bay-Delta Accord and new water quality plan were followed by an even more ambitious proposal—to convene all state and federal agencies charged with administering or regulating the waters of the Delta system to devise a long-term management plan. This convening, which came to be known as "CALFED," was "to develop a long-term comprehensive program that will restore ecological health and improve water management for beneficial uses of the Bay-Delta system." To achieve these twin goals, the CALFED agencies stated that they would "concurrently and comprehensively address problems of the Bay-Delta system within four critical resource categories: ecosystem quality, water quality, water supply reliability, and levee system integrity." The program examined a range of approaches to resolving the issues of the Delta, albeit with only modest technical analysis (CALFED 1996). In 2000, the agencies with authority over the Delta published the CALFED Record of Decision (ROD), which set forth a seven-year plan to achieve the goals defined by the Bay-Delta Accord. The CALFED ROD promoted continuing the current system of pulling water exports through the Delta to the southern Delta pumps until 2007, effectively putting off the difficult, strategic decisions.

The CALFED program was a well-funded (at least initially), grand experiment in consensus politics (Kallis, Kiparsky, and Norgaard 2009). The goal was to keep the warring parties at the table under the notion that "everyone would get better together." In this regard, the program was successful. The amount of litigation declined significantly after the Bay-Delta Accord and through the early years of implementing the CALFED ROD. By the mid-2000s, however, consensus politics (which often serves to avoid difficult decisions) had run its course and the program began to fall apart. Under aggressive pressure from disaffected water users, federal and state support for the program disappeared.

The collapse of CALFED had many causes (Little Hoover Commission 2005; Hanneman and Dyckman 2009; Lund et al. 2007; Hanak et al. 2010; Madani and Lund 2011). These included the sharp increase in SWP exports from 2000 through 2007; a precipitous decline in open-water (or pelagic) species such as the delta smelt, followed by similar declines in salmon and steelhead at the end of the decade; and a failure to arrange funding from two of the three anticipated sources—the federal government and local agencies. (State general obligation bonds were the major initial source of funds.) CALFED also was not structured to achieve its goals. It lacked mechanisms to craft decisions that might be unpopular with some stakeholders, it never implemented a "beneficiary pays" financing plan that could wean it from state bonds as a primary source of funding, and it ultimately failed to develop a coherent vision for the future of the Delta where, by necessity, not everyone would necessarily get better together.

With the demise of CALFED, the Delta returned to its tradition of litigation and confrontation. In response to lawsuits filed by environmental groups, in May 2007 and April 2008 federal district Judge Oliver Wanger invalidated the biological opinions that governed CVP and SWP operations to protect delta smelt and salmon. Citing the insufficiency of federal efforts to protect declining species, Judge Wanger ordered severe restrictions on exports and a redrafting of the biological opinions. The new biological opinions, issued in 2008 and 2009, were adopted by the project operators. Then, in response to lawsuits filed by CVP and SWP contractors, the same judge invalidated the new biological opinions, concluding that the fish protection agencies did not adequately explain the linkage between project operations and the decline of the species and failed to consider effects of export restrictions on employment and production. At the time of this writing (late 2010), the judge has ordered a temporary increase in exports while all parties attempt to negotiate a solution. Clearly, California's water management institutions have been unable to cope.

With CALFED moribund and the litigation wars back in full swing, the state embarked on a yet another new approach to the problems of the Delta ecosystem. Governor Arnold Schwarzenegger convened a Delta Vision Blue Ribbon Task Force in February 2007 to study the situation and to recommend institutional changes to enable California to better manage the array of competing interests. In its *Strategic Plan for the Delta* published in October 2008, the task force called on the legislature to create a new governance structure that would manage the waters of the ecosystem to achieve two "co-equal" goals: "Restore the Delta ecosystem and create a more reliable water supply for California." The task force emphasized that these "are co-equal goals because one objective can't be achieved without the other" (Delta Vision Blue Ribbon Task Force 2008).

The legislature responded the following year with a broad package of reforms, as well as an $11.1 billion bond measure to fund new water projects around the state. The Delta Reform Act adopted the task force's recommendation to create a Delta Stewardship Council to manage the Delta to achieve the goals of "restoring the Delta and providing for a clean, reliable, and sustainable water supply for all of the uses that depend on the waters of the ecosystem" (Water Code § 85001(c)). The legislature also declared that the "longstanding constitutional principle of reasonable use and the public trust doctrine shall be the foundation of state water management policy and are particularly important and applicable to the Delta" (Water Code § 85023). The package of reforms also included statewide measures to increase urban water conservation, better account for groundwater use, and increase water rights enforcement.

The Delta Reform Act is a promising beginning for the contemporary era of California water policy. So is the Bay Delta Conservation Plan, currently being negotiated by federal and state water managers, government regulators, water users, and environmental interests. These negotiations seek to create a comprehensive habitat conservation and management plan to protect the endangered and threatened species of the Delta ecosystem while also permitting continued export of water by the SWP and CVP.

Flood Management in an Era of Conflict

During the Era of Conflict, traditional approaches to flood management also began to change. The massive flood control projects of the Hydraulic Era largely ended in the 1970s. Although environmental constraints restricted new flood control projects, a more significant factor was the general decline in federal support for water (and other infrastructure) projects, starting in the 1970s. Most large flood control projects in California depended on the federal government paying the bulk of the costs—occasionally reaching 80 percent—and providing much of the technical expertise. This decline in support is the cause of both the long backlog of repairs and maintenance on existing flood control projects (Chapter 2) and the relative dearth of proposals for additional projects.[8]

Ironically, the decline in federal investment coincided with dramatic increases in demand for flood management as urban development encroached into floodplains. This encroachment was particularly acute in the Central Valley, where cash-strapped communities increasingly depended on taxes from new development. Arguments that growth should be located in less hazardous areas fell on deaf ears.

8. In real terms, annual federal flood control spending in California fell to an average of only $70 million per year in the mid-1980s (2009 dollars); it has hovered in the range of $140 million per year over the past decade (Figure 2.16). The most sustained reduction occurred during the Reagan administration.

A series of large floods highlighted the system's weaknesses. In February 1986, floodwaters overwhelmed Folsom Dam on the American River and came perilously close to flooding Sacramento. In January 1997, floodwaters from levee failures throughout the Central Valley necessitated the largest flood evacuation in California's history. These floods highlighted an unpleasant truth about the Central Valley flood control system: It can fail catastrophically.

Neither flood was enough to spur the federal and state governments back into the business of flood control, leaving local areas to prepare for floods largely on their own (Chapter 6). The state's lethargy changed with the California Court of Appeal's decision in *Paterno v. State of California* (2003), which held the state liable for failure of a levee along the Yuba River during the 1986 flood. This levee was within the federally authorized Sacramento Flood Control Project and maintained by a local reclamation district. The $500 million damages award paid by the state highlighted how a levee failure in a more populated area could, in the words of more than one legislator, "bankrupt the state."

In 2004, on a warm day in June, a levee protecting Jones Tract in the Delta gave way, flooding the island whose lands were well below sea level. Repair costs for this levee failure reached almost $90 million, with the state paying the bulk of the cost. The levee failure also shut down the CVP and SWP pumps, signaling the close connection between flood control and water supply.

Then came Hurricane Katrina in August 2005. The images of the destruction and loss of life from failure of New Orleans's levees galvanized the legislature and Governor Schwarzenegger to begin flood reform in the Central Valley. This urgency to act increased when the Department of Water Resources announced that failure to maintain Central Valley levees had led to more than 300 critical erosion sites, with many threatening large cities.

In the two years following Hurricane Katrina, the state legislature took several actions. It passed emergency legislation to address levee erosion, allocating almost $500 million from the general fund, and placed a $4 billion general obligation bond on the November 2006 ballot for floods as part of a set of infrastructure measures. Voter approval for this bond and another placed on the ballot by initiative made almost $5 billion available for flood control works. The legislature also developed a package of flood policy bills. This legislation, signed by the governor in 2007, raised the required level of protection for urban areas above federal standards (200-year flood), reorganized the Reclamation Board, required shared liability on the part of communities building on the floodplain, and required that the Department of Water Resources develop a new State Plan of Flood Control.

The federal government, California's flood control partner for over a century, was almost entirely absent during these developments. In a precedent that has rankled flood managers nationwide, California was forced to address flood management largely on its own, at a very high cost. Following the change of federal administrations in January 2009, federal flood control activity has increased in California. However, compared to federal involvement during the Hydraulic Era, it remains modest and focused principally on regulation rather than infrastructure.

Conflict as Impetus for Innovation

During the Era of Conflict, water managers were forced to adapt to reduced quantities of water and funding, increasing legal complexity, growing demands due to population growth, and diminished certainty about the future. As described in later chapters, these changes spawned a range of innovations in water management that could lay a foundation for the next era.

Several innovations, born out of necessity over the past 30 years, will be particularly crucial to creating adaptive capacity in the future. These include (1) agricultural and urban water conservation, driven by new metering and monitoring requirements, new plumbing codes, technological innovation, pricing incentives, and regulatory cutbacks; (2) more flexible operations and water allocations, reflecting more use of water markets; (3) conjunctive use of surface and groundwater, including better groundwater management; and reuse and recycling of wastewater and stormwater discharges. Of these, water marketing is perhaps the most promising means of creating incentives to change how California's water management institutions function in the future (Hanak 2003; Israel and Lund 1995; Vaux and Howitt 1984).

The drought of 1976–1977 was one of the most severe in state history. Luckily, it was relatively short-lived. This drought spurred widespread urban water conservation programs, with unexpected success and acceptance. In the wake of this drought, both the governor and the legislature commissioned studies that suggested that water marketing—involving the voluntary transfer of water from those holding historical rights to others willing to pay for it—had great potential to reduce scarcity during times of drought and support longer-term shifts in demand (Governor's Commission 1978; Phelps et al. 1978; Phelps, Moore, and Graubard 1978). Although there was considerable initial political resistance to water marketing, it became much more accepted in the early 1990s during yet another drought. The state created an emergency drought water bank in 1991 and acquired about 800,000 acre-feet of water for transfer. A year later, when Congress passed the CVPIA, it included provisions that facilitated water marketing and purchase of water for environmental purposes. The state followed suit in 1994, making it easier for SWP contractors to exchange water.

In 2000, the state created an Environmental Water Account (EWA) as part of the CALFED Record of Decision. The program was intended to provide water to protect listed fish species in the Delta while providing assurances to water users against additional water supply losses. Its goal was to reduce conflicts between ecosystem and water supply demands. Under the EWA, fish agency managers could store surplus water in reservoirs or aquifers and purchase water from willing sellers and then use the water to protect endangered species. The EWA also could be used to purchase water to replace water lost to agricultural and urban users from curtailment of export pumping. The federal and state governments funded the EWA, with the state shouldering most of the burden (Hollinshead and Lund 2006).

The benefits of the EWA remain unclear. Most state and federal officials tout it as a success principally because it reduced conflicts between water users and fish agencies. However, a comprehensive review of the EWA's effects on fish from 2000 to 2006 found that the initial benefits were small: Survival of winter-run Chinook salmon increased by 0–6 percent, adult delta smelt by 0–1 percent, and juvenile delta smelt by 2–4 percent (Brown, Kimmerer, and Brown 2009). Despite these low returns on investment, the authors concluded that, with adequate financial and scientific support, the EWA had considerable potential. Although water is still available for the EWA under a new long-term transfer agreement with the Yuba County Water Agency, the ability to use it has virtually disappeared with the new biological opinions governing Delta operations.

An Era of Reconciliation?

Water management in California has evolved substantially over the past two centuries. This evolution is captured in a series of overlapping eras, defined by activities meant to meet growing and changing demands for water and flood control with a rapidly expanding economy and population. Natural and human events, involving floods, droughts, lawsuits, an evolving economy, and changing societal values, have shaped California's water history. Each era has also left indelible marks on California's landscape and ecosystems, both influencing and constraining future management.

Today's Era of Conflict is characterized by the rise of environmental values that must now be integrated into all facets of water management and the hard realities of a water management system that may be extracting more than California's climate and ecosystems can support. This era is also characterized by financial constraints. The federal government—an essential source of financing, expertise, and leadership for more than a century—has become less able to support projects. Today, the federal government is focusing more on regulating solutions developed by others than on developing solutions to current and foreseen problems. Federal regulations are particularly important for achieving many public health and environmental objectives, but the lack of traditional federal funding, expertise, and initiative has made it more difficult for state and local water managers to adapt to change. At the same time, a state weary of borrowing money to patch over structural budget deficits may soon join the federal government in reducing its commitments to water projects.

The Era of Conflict has framed conditions for the next era in water management in California. New environmental concerns and other changes will constrain and influence the shape of the next era, in which water management must balance and reconcile environmental and human water uses. Recent policy efforts, including the new Delta governance framework and the attempt to craft a comprehensive habitat conservation plan for the Delta, suggest paths for achieving this balance. And continued innovations and adaptations in water management, born of necessity during previous eras, could facilitate this shift by allowing agricultural and urban water users to live with less. Of course, current efforts may fail, and battles among water users may continue, prolonging the Era of Conflict. The remainder of this book explores the more hopeful path—and the challenges likely to be faced—in an Era of Reconciliation that may be emerging today.

2 California Water Today

RICHARD A. COOKE/CORBIS

> We are confronted by insurmountable opportunities.
>
> Walt Kelly, *Pogo*

California's water system is large, complex, and interconnected. Most precipitation falls in the sparsely populated northern and mountainous regions of the state during the winter, whereas most human water demands occur during the late spring, summer, and early fall in the population and farming centers farther south and along the coast. Precipitation also varies greatly across years, making the state susceptible to large floods and prolonged droughts. These conditions have led to the development of vast infrastructure systems that store and convey water to demand centers and that protect residents from flooding. The successive eras of water management over California's history, in turn, have spawned a wide array of management institutions involving local, regional, state, and federal entities.

This chapter reviews major aspects of California's current water system. We start with some basics on water availability: precipitation patterns, movement and storage of water in surface reservoirs and groundwater basins, and water quality characteristics. We then examine water uses, including an assessment of the volumes and values of flows for economic and environmental activities. We also review flood vulnerability and flood management infrastructure. Finally, we look at water management institutions responsible for supply, quality, and flood operations; funding arrangements; and scientific and technical activities that make the system work. At each stage, we highlight strengths and vulnerabilities of the current system and point to changes needed as California enters a new era of water management.

Electrical line over the Los Angeles Aqueduct in the Owens Valley.

Water Availability

California's water supplies are variable and diverse, with most water originating as precipitation. This is then supplemented with imported water, artificial and natural water reuse, and overdraft of groundwater.

Geographic, Seasonal, and Interannual Disparities

On average, roughly 200 million acre-feet (maf) of precipitation fall annually on California. Most of this water evaporates, particularly in the hottest and driest areas of the state. The remainder, known as "unimpaired runoff" (averaging about 75 maf/year) flows downhill into streams and groundwater basins, and becomes available for management and use (Table 2.1).

The geographic disparities in natural water availability are particularly stark: About two-thirds of annual runoff comes from about one-fifth of California's land area, primarily mountainous areas in the northern half of the state (Figure A). In contrast, the driest one-third of the state contributes only about 0.1 percent of total water availability. These driest areas include not only the sparsely

Table 2.1
Regional average annual water availability, storage, and use, 1998–2005 (maf)

Hydrologic region	Precipitation	Unimpaired water availability	Storage capacity		Water use	
			Surface	Ground	Gross	Net
North Coast	53.0	26.0	3.8	11.0	22.0	22.0
San Francisco Bay	6.9	2.3	1.0	3.6	1.9	1.7
Central Coast	13.0	3.7	1.2	45.0	1.5	1.0
South Coast	11.0	2.2	3.1	140.0	5.0	4.2
Sacramento River	57.0	22.0	16.0	91.0	23.0	15.0
San Joaquin River	23.0	8.0	11.0	270.0	11.0	7.3
Tulare Lake	14.0	3.6	2.0	510.0	13.0	8.0
North Lahontan	6.9	2.2	1.2	8.0	0.9	0.5
South Lahontan	11.0	0.8	1.0	210.0	0.7	0.5
Colorado River	5.7	0.2	1.0	170.0	4.6	4.1
California	**200.0**	**71.0**	**41.0**	**1,458.6**	**83.0**	**64.0**

SOURCES: Authors' calculations using regional portfolio data from the California Department of Water Resources (DWR) (2009); data on unimpaired water availability were calculated by J. Viers.

NOTES: The table shows average annual values in millions of acre-feet. See Table 2.2 for more details on water use, Figure 2.1 for a map of hydrologic regions, and Box 2.1 on the distinction between gross and net use. Overall hydrologic region water availability estimates vary across sources and calculation methods. Unimpaired water availability includes surface runoff and groundwater infiltration; total volumes estimated by DWR were distributed across regions by Geographic Information System modeling.

populated deserts of Southern California but also the immense irrigated agricultural areas in the Tulare Basin and the Imperial Valley and rapidly growing urban communities in the Palm Springs area. Most of urban Southern California also has little natural runoff. The large infrastructure projects of the mid-20th century, designed to import water from other regions, have allowed water use patterns to diverge starkly from the distribution of runoff. Net water use (Box 2.1) is twice as high as locally available supplies in the South Coast

2.1

Gross and net water use: some water is reused

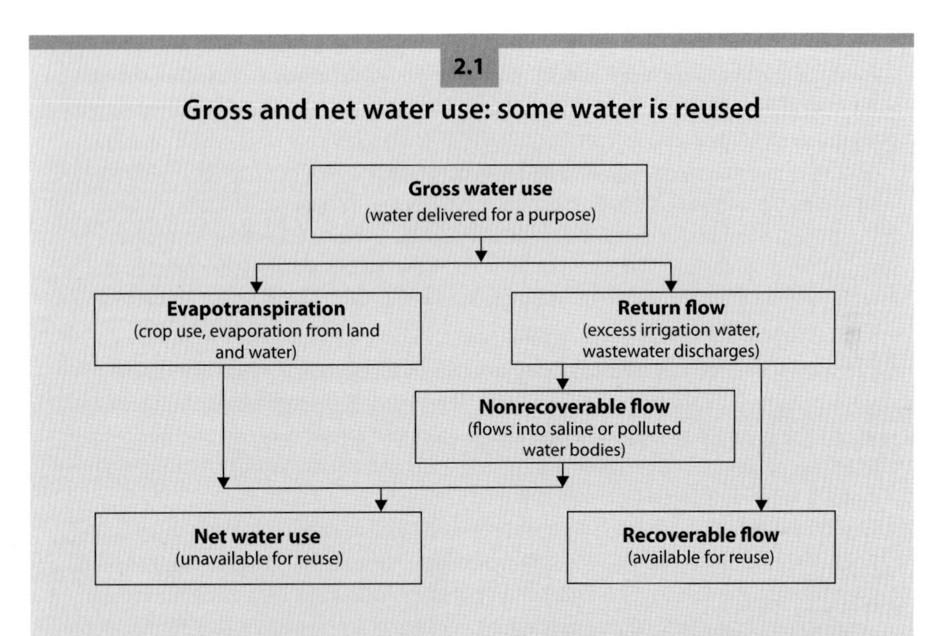

Gross (or "applied") water use is the water delivered to a home, business, or farm—not all of which is consumed. Some water—such as excess irrigation water and discharges from wastewater treatment plants—flows to streams, lakes, aquifers, or the sea ("return flow"). Some of this return flow ("recoverable flow") is available for reuse, because it returns to freshwater streams, lakes, or canals or recharges groundwater basins. Net (or "consumptive") water use is that part of gross water that is unavailable for reuse. Net use consists of (1) water consumed by people or plants, embodied in manufactured goods, or evaporated into the air (evapotranspiration) and (2) water return flows discharged into saline or contaminated waters or groundwater basins ("nonrecoverable flow"). Once this water is used, it is generally not available for reuse within the watershed without prohibitive treatment cost.

(continued)

Very little indoor water use is net use, unless the resulting wastewater is discharged to the sea. Most (but not all) landscape and agricultural irrigation becomes net water use, as it evapotranspires to the atmosphere.

Net use can never exceed gross use. But because recoverable flow is often reused, total gross water use usually exceeds total flow into a region. This can be seen by comparing average statewide gross water use (about 83 maf/year) with the total available supplies over the same period (71 maf/year) (Table 2.1).

Conservation actions often target reductions in gross water use. But only net water savings provide more water (Ward and Pulido-Velazquez 2008; Clemmens, Allen, and Burt 2008; Huffaker 2008; Hanak et al. 2010; CALFED 2006; Scheierling, Young, and Cardon 2006). In agriculture, achieving significant net water savings generally requires switching to crops that consume less water or reducing irrigated land area. By contrast, irrigation efficiency investments may reduce gross water use per acre but increase net water use on farms by making it easier for farmers to stretch their gross supplies across additional acres of cropland. Reductions in net water use by agriculture usually imply reductions in agricultural production (Perry et al. 2009).

Even when they do not result in lower net use, reductions in water withdrawals from streams and groundwater basins can have environmental benefits, including improved stream flow; reduced pollution runoff into rivers, streams, and beaches (Noble et al. 2003); and reduced energy use and costs for acquiring and treating water (California Energy Commission 2005). For example, a major means of managing soil and aquifer salinization in the southern Central Valley has been to improve irrigation efficiencies, so that less salt-laden water from the Delta is applied to fields. Even though these irrigation improvements make little net water available for use, the resulting runoff is of better quality.

and Tulare Basin, and 20 times as high as local runoff in the arid Colorado River region (Figure 2.1).

Water availability also varies by season and between years. California's Mediterranean climate has wet winters and very dry summers, reflected in the monthly variations in the Sacramento River's natural stream flow (Figure 2.2), the state's largest river. The historical record also shows both very wet years, often with substantial floods, and long multiyear droughts (Figure 2.3). The geologic record of the past 2,000 years shows even larger and longer droughts (Stine 1994).

Figure 2.1
Net water use far exceeds local supplies in the southern half of the state

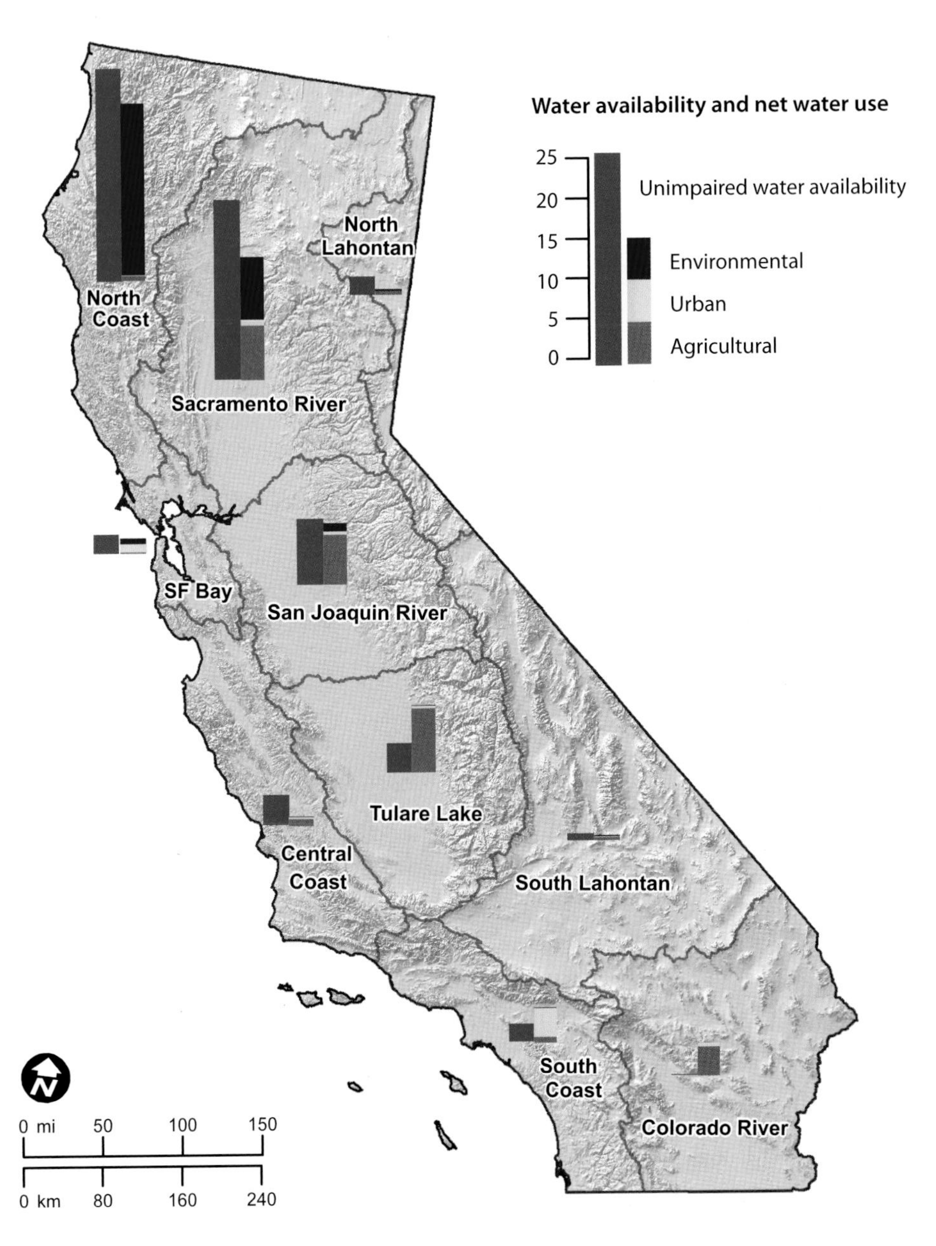

SOURCE: California Department of Water Resources (2009).

NOTES: The map shows annual average values for 1998–2005 in millions of acre-feet. For regional data on water availability and net use, see Tables 2.1 and 2.2.

Figure 2.2
Natural stream flow is highest in the winter and spring

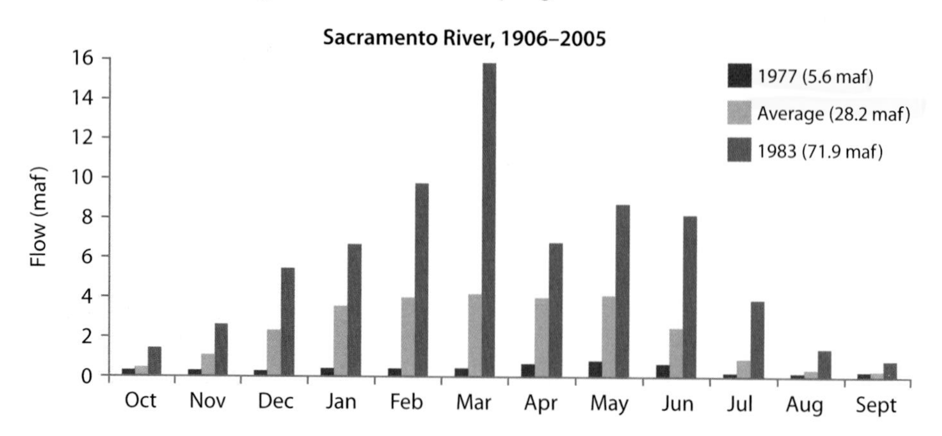

SOURCE: California Department of Water Resources.

NOTES: Unimpaired flows (without dams or diversions) on the Sacramento River, 1906–2005. Water year 1977 (October 1976–September 1977) is the driest year on record, and water year 1983 is the wettest year on record.

Figure 2.3
Natural stream flow varies greatly across years

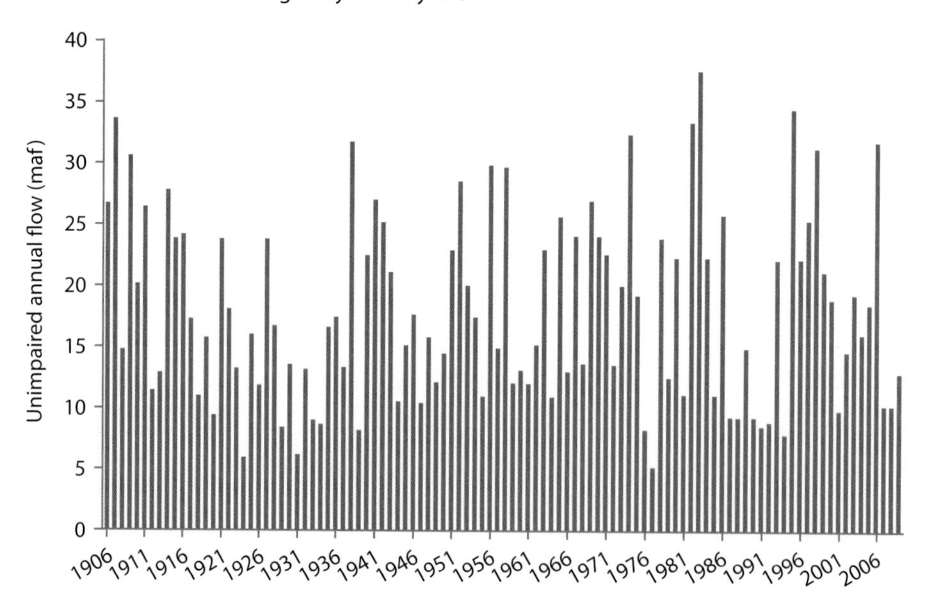

SOURCE: California Department of Water Resources, California Data Exchange Center data.

NOTE: The figure shows unimpaired flows (the natural flows that would have occurred without dams or diversions) on the Sacramento River, 1906–2009.

Water Sources: Local, Imported, Mined, and Reused

California supplements water supplies available from in-state precipitation with imports from other states, groundwater mining, and some recovery of wastewater and brackish water following intensive treatment. In addition, available water supplies exceed the amounts flowing into the state because of natural reuse, as excess irrigation water (the amount not consumed by crops) and treated urban wastewater become available for use by others after being returned to streams (Box 2.1).

Figure 2.4 shows the relative importance of these sources in total usable supplies for agricultural, environmental, and urban uses. Overall, more than 80 percent of the initial total (before reuse) is derived from local and out-of-state streams: Three-quarters of these surface flows are from local projects and diversions and roughly one-quarter are from the state and federal projects. About 18 percent of the initial total is supplied by groundwater. Natural reuse constitutes roughly one-quarter of gross supplies (almost half of all groundwater pumping

Figure 2.4
California employs a diverse portfolio of water sources for agricultural, environmental, and urban water uses

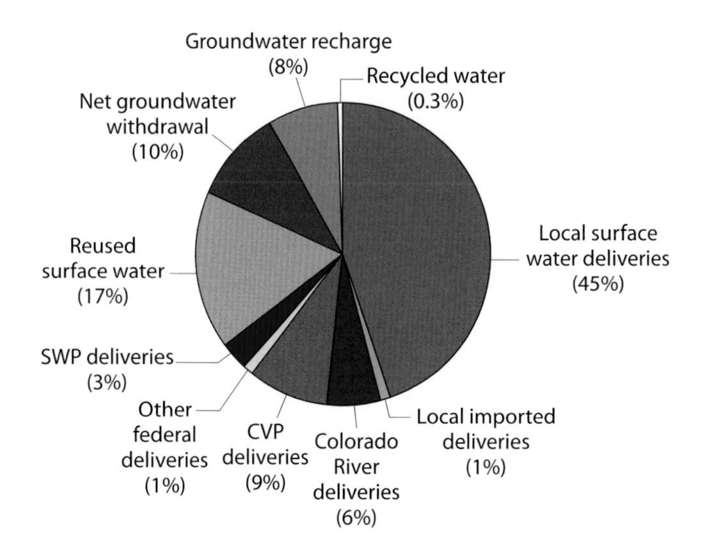

SOURCE: California Department of Water Resources (2009).

NOTES: The figure shows sources of gross water supplies, 1998–2005 average. Total water supply is 83 maf per year. Total does not sum to 100 percent because of rounding. SWP = State Water Project. CVP = Central Valley Project.

nd one-fifth of surface water).[1] Small, but locally important, amounts of water are derived from other sources, including recycled wastewater and brackish water desalination.

The state's primary imported water source is the Colorado River, which now provides 4.4 maf/year, California's allotment under the federal law that apportions Colorado River water among Arizona, California, and Nevada. These supplies have diminished from a high of 5.1 maf/year in the late 1990s and early 2000s as other states' demands have grown, limiting California's ability to draw on their allotments.[2] Although supplies on the Colorado are also variable (and expected to diminish over time),[3] California's Colorado River entitlement is stable. Other interstate flows are relatively small and affect only local basins in the eastern Sierra Nevada and upper Klamath Basin.

Much of California's runoff flows into the groundwater basins that underlie most of California's land area, where it often becomes a major source of water supply. Over the eight-year period shown in Table 2.1, groundwater pumps withdrew an average of 15 maf/year and accounted for 28 to 42 percent of gross agricultural and urban water use. Groundwater is more important in dry years and is particularly important for agricultural and urban uses in several regions (Figure 2.5). Most of this water is regularly replenished with irrigation water, artificial recharge (from managed recharge basins), seepage from stream flow, and precipitation.

However, in some regions more water is pumped out of basins than is replenished over many years; this is known as overdraft. Chronic overdraft—essentially groundwater mining—could be as high as 2 maf/year on average statewide (California Department of Water Resources 2009). As much as 1.4 maf/year of overdraft occurs from agricultural uses in the Tulare Basin (Kern, Tulare, and Kings Counties) (U.S. Geological Survey 2009). In the Central Coast, the Salinas Basin also suffers from chronic groundwater overdraft (about 19 taf/year [thousand acre-feet per year]), largely from agricultural pumping (Monterey County Water Resources Agency 2001; California Department of Water Resources 1995a). Although groundwater mining can help meet demands during droughts, it is an ultimately unsustainable water source (Harou and Lund 2008).

1. Over the 1998 to 2005 period, surface water reuse ranged from 8 to 15 maf/year and aquifer recharge ranged from 5 to 7 maf/year.

2. As discussed in Chapters 4 and 6, a variety of conservation and water transfer arrangements, known collectively as the Quantification Settlement Agreement of 2003, were developed to help wean California off these surplus water supplies from the Colorado River.

3. On projected declines in Colorado River supplies, see Barnett et al. (2008) and Rajagopalan et al. (2009). Although there is general agreement that supplies are likely to diminish with climate change, there is debate about the likely timing and the extent to which improved water management can forestall extreme shortages of supplies.

Figure 2.5
Groundwater dependence varies widely across California

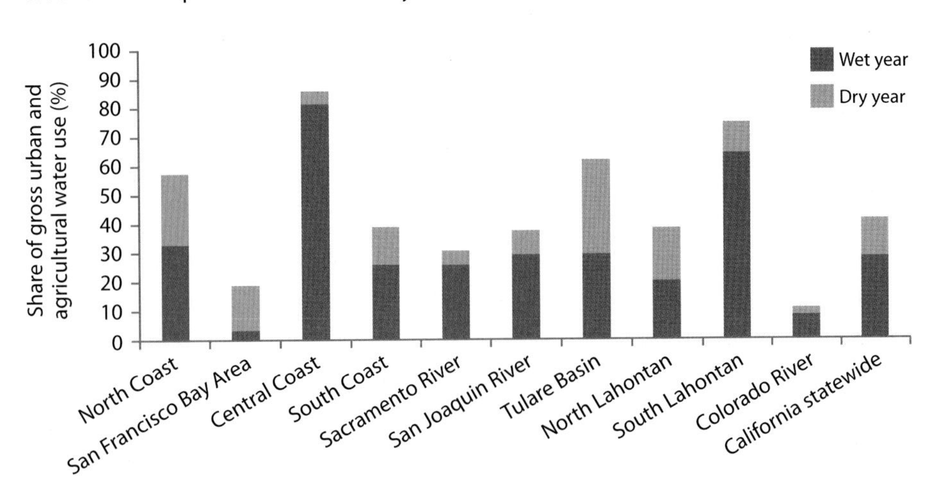

SOURCE: California Department of Water Resources (2009).

NOTES: The figure shows total groundwater withdrawals as a share of total gross water use in the urban and agricultural sectors in the period 1998–2005. The dry and wet year shares refer to 2001 and 1998, respectively.

Groundwater overdraft and unregulated pumping is a source of growing conflict among water users in many parts of the state, with repercussions including higher costs of pumping, aquifer damage from saltwater intrusion, reduced groundwater availability during droughts, above-ground infrastructure damage from sinking lands, and environmental damage to wildlife in adjacent streams (Chapters 3, 5, 6).

Apart from natural reuse, water reuse also can involve more engineered (and more expensive) treatment and recycling of urban wastewater. The volumes are still quite small: 0.2–0.5 maf/year by the mid-2000s—or about 0.5 percent to 1 percent of California's agricultural and urban use.[4] The amount might rise considerably—to 2 million acre-feet—in the next few decades (Recycled Water Task Force 2003; California Department of Water Resources 2009). To date, recycled water has primarily been used for crop or landscape irrigation, because the stigma of treated wastewater has prevented potable reuse. However, several Southern California agencies are now looking to follow the lead of Orange

4. According to the state's Recycled Water Task Force (2003), over 200 treatment plants produced between 450 to 580 taf/year by 2002. The most recent California Water Plan update estimates that recycled municipal water provided between 0.2 and 0.5 maf/year between 1998 and 2005 (California Department of Water Resources 2009).

County's Groundwater Replenishment System, a partnership between the Orange County Water District and the Orange County Sanitation District, which recharges the groundwater basin with highly treated, potable wastewater (Groundwater Replenishment System, undated). Some parts of inland Southern California have also reclaimed groundwater that was too saline or otherwise contaminated for untreated use (California Department of Water Resources 2009).[5]

Storage and Movement to Population and Farming Centers

Water is moved from wetter to drier areas through a network of rivers, canals, aqueducts, and pipelines (Figure 2.6). This network of federal, state, and local projects connects local water users with local and statewide water sources and reflects the history of water management (Chapter 1). Although the State Water Project, the Central Valley Project, and other federal projects are the most extensive storage and conveyance projects supporting agricultural and urban water use, major local and regional projects also store and deliver distant supplies to urban centers in the San Francisco Bay Area and Southern California. The hub of both the SWP and CVP systems, and the link between Northern and Southern California, is the network of channels within the Sacramento–San Joaquin Delta. This conveyance hub is at significant risk of failure from flood and earthquake risks to the fragile levees that surround the Delta's man-made islands, most of which now lie well below sea level (Chapter 3) (Lund et al. 2010; Suddeth, Mount, and Lund 2010).

The state's elaborate conveyance network is coupled with an extensive surface water storage system, capable of storing about half the average annual statewide runoff (Figure 2.6, Table 2.1). Most surface storage is located near the source, far from major farming and urban centers. The state's capacity for storing water in aquifers is far greater and much of this capacity is nearer to water users.

Surface and groundwater reservoirs have different advantages and drawbacks. Surface reservoirs can fill quickly and release water fairly quickly, making them flexible for water supply and flood management. But expanding surface storage capacity is costly and ecologically damaging. Groundwater storage

5. As discussed further in Chapter 6, many local agencies are looking to recycled water as a costly, but relatively stable, alternative to supplies imported from distant locations. Ocean water desalination, which relies on similar treatment technologies, also is being considered in some coastal areas. In contrast to coastal areas, where wastewater reuse results in a net expansion of water supplies for the region, expanding reuse of upstream wastewater to support new development is likely to increase upstream net water use and reduce return flows to downstream users (Box 2.1).

Figure 2.6
California has an elaborate network of conveyance and storage infrastructure, controlled by different agencies

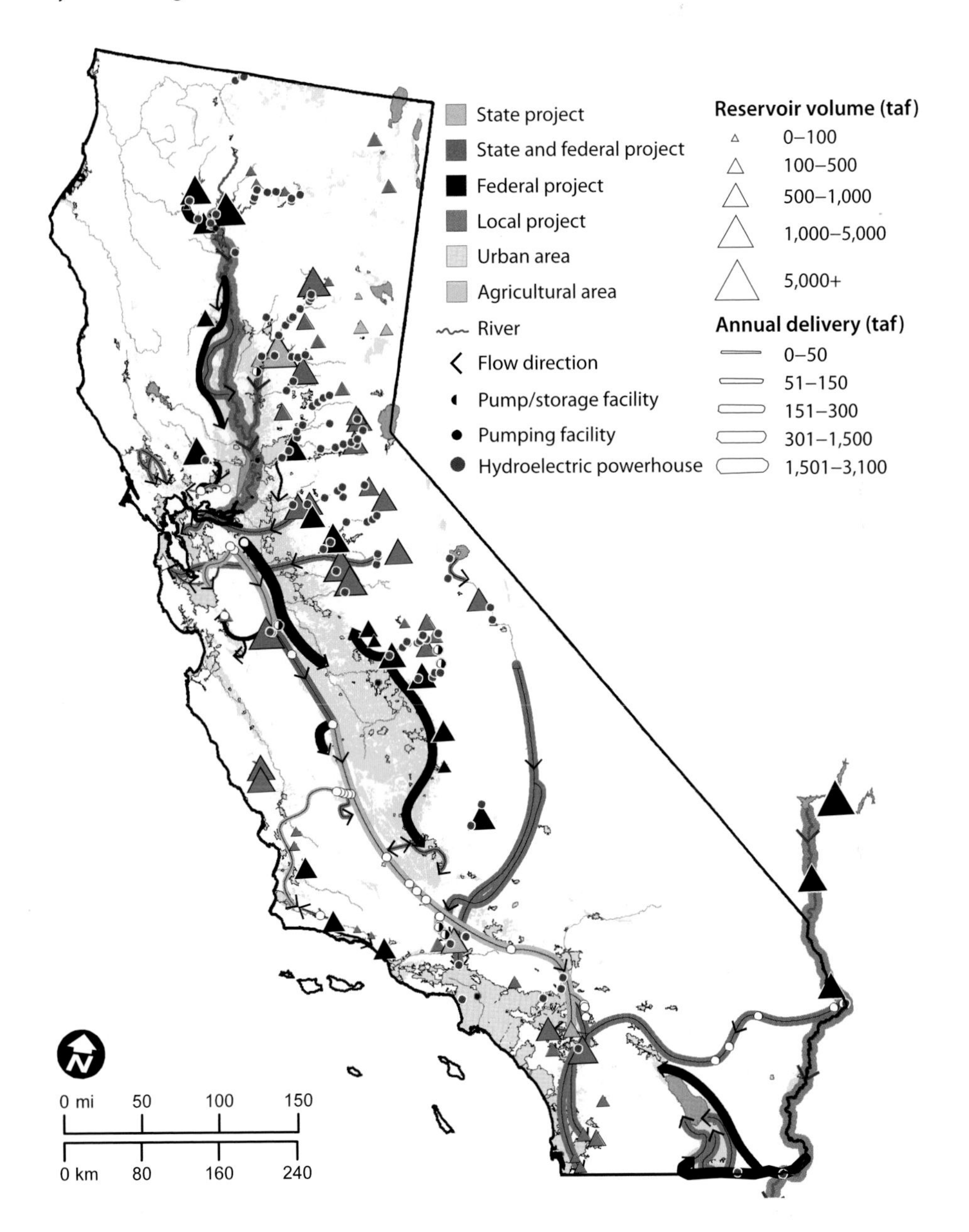

capacity is already abundant, but aquifers recharge and empty far more slowly than surface reservoirs, making them more suitable for long-term or dry-year storage. Withdrawal from aquifers typically requires pumping. In California, much recharge is a by-product of crop irrigation, although natural streams and precipitation also contribute. Increasingly, artificial recharge programs are employed. These programs spread surface water over dedicated recharge fields or inject it into wells. Conjunctive use programs, which manage surface water and aquifers jointly, make it possible to expand the system's overall capacity, by storing more water in aquifers during wet years for use in dry years. Although such programs are expanding, the ability to fully exploit the system's potential is limited by the lack of comprehensive aquifer management in many regions, cumbersome institutional rules regarding surface reservoir operations, and limited synthesis of technical information regarding the capacity and condition of groundwater basins (Chapter 6).

As an illustration of this last point, DWR's occasional bulletin on the state's groundwater basins, Bulletin 118, has been issued only twice since 1980. These reports include little analysis or strategic overview of the condition of California's aquifers, how they are employed, or how their management could improve. For instance, although DWR gathers data on over 400 aquifers in the state, these data are not maintained in a way that allows statewide or regional assessments of aquifer conditions, such as overdraft or contamination.

Water Quality Concerns

It is not enough to have "enough" water. Water must also be of adequate quality for each use, either in its natural state or with affordable treatment.

Different qualities for different purposes

Different uses often require different types of water quality. Urban water users require the highest water purity, and costs of treatment increase when the quality of water sources is lower. Drinking water quality standards are being tightened and treatment facilities upgraded as additional contaminants are identified and studied (Calder and Schmitt 2010). This trend is likely to continue and perhaps accelerate, as understanding of public health and water chemistry improves (Chapter 3).

Agricultural water users face significant, but less constraining, water quality concerns, mostly involving excesses of salinity and minerals such as boron that reduce crop productivity and limit crop choices.

The quality of water for environmental uses varies with the species or ecosystem of concern, and water management for human uses has often disturbed the natural conditions in which native species thrive. Artificially high water temperatures in many California streams—resulting from dams, diversions, streamside development, and irrigation—limit spawning and rearing habitat for salmon and other fishes (Chapter 5). Agricultural and urban runoff often adds diverse contaminants to streams, harming aquatic species.[6] In the Sacramento–San Joaquin Delta, native species thrive in murky, muddy water, with more variable salinity, and the system's use as a conveyance hub has made it artificially more stable and clearer, favoring invasive species (Moyle and Bennett 2008; Moyle et al. 2010). A general problem in California is that as streams become more altered in flows and water quality, alien fishes, invertebrates, and plants tend to become predominant (Brown and Moyle 2004; Brown and Bauer 2009). On the other hand, treated wastewater provides much of the flow in some sections of the Santa Ana River, and it is of high enough quality to support a diverse fish fauna, including the endangered Santa Ana sucker (*Catostomus santaanae)* (Brown, Burton, and Belitz 2005).

Salinity and other contaminants

Local runoff and stream flow accumulate dissolved solids, salts, and nutrients as they flow downstream from pristine upper mountain watersheds. Likewise, aquifer quality varies widely. In some areas, groundwater is so pure that it requires no treatment for direct potable use, whereas in others, salinity and other contaminants necessitate blending or costly wellhead treatment.

Statewide, salinity is the most widespread quality concern, both for aquifers and surface flows. Salts come from several sources: They occur naturally in minerals in some soils (where they are released by precipitation or excess irrigation), and they are also present in mineral-based fertilizers and urban wastewater. The salinity of many streams and aquifers has increased as a result of irrigation and urban water uses. When the rate of salt input exceeds the rate of discharge, salts accumulate in soils, water bodies, and aquifers. Salt accumulation can change conditions for ecosystems, reduce the productivity of soils for agriculture, and increase costs for urban water users (Box 2.2).

Salinity problems are greatest in the southern Central Valley and the Salton Sea. High salinity in the lower San Joaquin River from agricultural drainage

6. See Brown (2000) for an illustration relating to the San Joaquin River.

2.2

How salty is it?

Sierra runoff contains roughly 50 milligrams per liter (mg/l) of dissolved solids (0.005 percent salt by weight), the Sacramento River roughly 150 mg/l, the Colorado River (at the Nevada border) about 700 mg/l, and the middle reaches of the San Joaquin River about 775 mg/l (0.0775 percent salt by weight). Yields for many crops begin to steeply decline when irrigation water salinity exceeds about 950 mg/l, and urban water treatment and use become much more expensive with salt concentrations above 500 mg/l. Seawater has 33,000 mg/l of salts (3.3 percent salt by weight). Salton Sea and Mono Lake—two "terminal" inland lakes in California that do not flow out to the sea—have salinity levels of roughly 44,000 mg/l and 81,000 mg/l, respectively. (Dead Sea salinity is about 220,000 mg/l (22 percent salt by weight); Utah's Great Salt Lake salinity varies between 50,000 and 270,000 mg/l depending on lake levels.)

has reduced agricultural production, deprived local cities such as Stockton and Lathrop of a water source, and compromised habitat for native fish species. In western areas of the San Joaquin and Tulare Basins, salt accumulations in soils and groundwater have reduced output and removed some land from production, with more land threatened as salts continue to accumulate (Chapter 3). Increasing salinity is diminishing the recreational and environmental uses of the Salton Sea—a man-made inland sea fed by drainage water with no outflow to the ocean and little natural inflow, which is already almost 50 percent more saline than seawater (Box 5.4).

Many other, more localized, water quality problems exist as well (Figure 2.7). The accumulation of excess nutrients including nitrogen and phosphorus often leads to a proliferation of plant life, especially algal blooms, in lakes and sections of streams. Sediment as well as algae growth from nutrients can reduce the clarity of lakes, as with Lake Tahoe. And by-products of fertilizers and pesticides can accumulate in aquifers and streams. In many rural areas, the accumulation of nitrates in groundwater has become a serious concern and a problem for local drinking water users. As a result of groundwater overdraft, some coastal aquifers (e.g., the Salinas and Pajaro Basins in the Central Coast) suffer from seawater intrusion. California must also contend with the legacies of toxic chemicals introduced by mining activities long ago, such as mercury (Chapter 3).

Figure 2.7
California faces numerous water quality problems

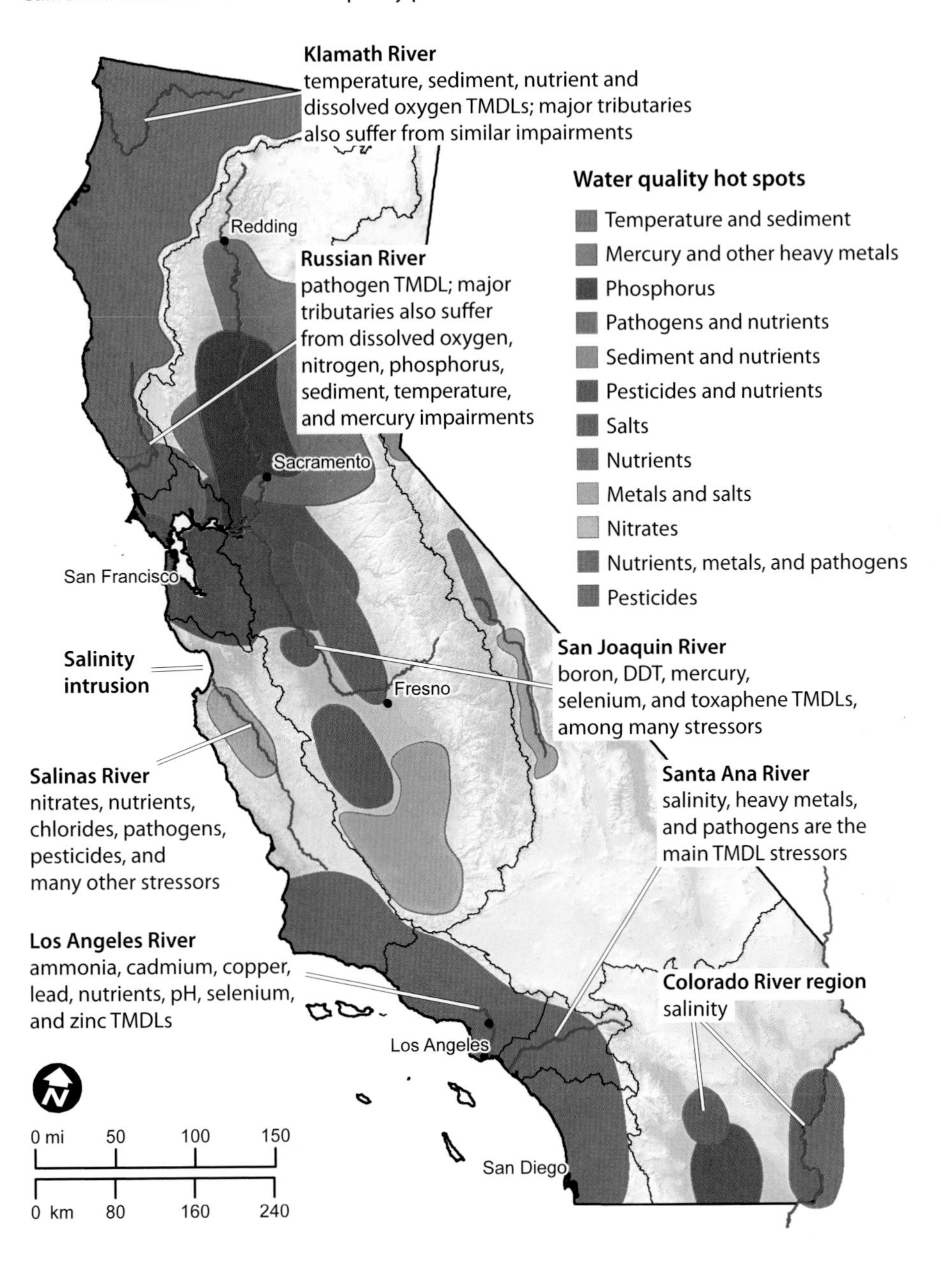

SOURCE: Authors' calculations using data from the State Water Resources Control Board.

NOTE: The map highlights only major regional problems, including those for which total maximum daily loads (TMDLs) have been set by water quality regulators.

Pharmaceuticals and a host of other chemicals—often referred to as emerging contaminants—also are causing increasing concern in California (Chapters 3, 6). Establishing a better system for protecting water sources from contamination is a major unresolved water policy challenge for California.

Uses and Value of Water

Water has many uses in California. Households, businesses, industries, and institutions use water in urban areas. Farms use water for crop irrigation and livestock. Water is used to generate power, both directly (hydroelectric generation from falling water) and indirectly (to cool thermal power plants). And, of course, water is essential for healthy aquatic and riparian environments, as well as human recreation.

Estimating water use is problematic in California because of a lack of monitoring and reporting requirements. Table 2.2 summarizes DWR's estimates of the major water supply uses in the agricultural, urban, and environmental sectors for the same eight-year period as Table 2.1.

Table 2.2
Average annual water use by sector, 1998–2005

		Agriculture			Urban			Environmental		
Hydrologic region	Irrigated Land[a] (1,000s of acres)	Gross (maf)	Net (maf)	Net/gross (%)	Gross (maf)	Net (maf)	Net/gross (%)	Gross (maf)	Net (maf)	Net/gross (%)
North Coast	330	0.8	0.6	77	0.2	0.1	74	21.0	21.0	100
San Francisco Bay	81	0.1	0.1	96	1.2	1.0	84	0.6	0.6	100
Central Coast	430	1.0	0.8	74	0.3	0.2	67	0.1	0.1	100
South Coast	250	0.8	0.7	87	4.1	3.5	85	0.2	0.1	50
Sacramento River	2,000	8.3	6.6	79	0.9	0.7	79	14.0	7.6	54
San Joaquin River	1,900	7.0	6.0	85	0.6	0.4	59	3.7	1.0	27
Tulare Lake	3,000	10.0	7.7	74	0.7	0.3	36	1.6	0.1	6
North Lahontan	130	0.5	0.4	80	0.0	0.0	50	0.4	0.2	50
South Lahontan	64	0.4	0.3	81	0.3	0.1	52	0.1	0.1	100
Colorado River	610	3.9	3.7	93	0.7	0.5	70	0.0	0.0	–
California	**8,800**	**33.0**	**27.0**	**82**	**8.7**	**6.6**	**76**	**41.0**	**31.0**	**76**

SOURCE: Authors' calculations using regional portfolio data from California Department of Water Resources (2009).

NOTE: Urban uses include 0.1 maf/year of gross water use (and no net water use) for cooling thermoelectric power generation.

[a] Some land is cropped more than once during the year, so irrigated crop acreage exceeds irrigated land area. Statewide irrigated crop acreage is about 9.2 million acres.

Although DWR has made greater efforts in recent years to quantify and document gross and net water use by sector in different parts of California, these efforts are hampered by a lack of local reporting of water use. Estimating gross use is less difficult where water deliveries are quantified for billing purposes—e.g., surface water deliveries to contractors of the CVP and SWP and metered household water deliveries. But measurement is problematic for self-supplied surface water and groundwater, which have few if any reporting requirements. As a result, DWR must essentially back out estimates of agricultural groundwater use from crop production estimates, themselves imprecise. Net water use is even more approximately estimated.[7] Water use reporting is a highly charged issue, and water users—particularly agricultural users—have successfully resisted legislative efforts to strengthen reporting requirements for groundwater withdrawals and stream diversions. Yet without better reporting, California's water accounting and water rights enforcement will remain approximate at best—an increasingly difficult handicap for policy discussions and water management in a water-scarce state.

How Much Water for the Environment?

Environmental water use and demand estimation is particularly difficult and controversial (Null 2008; Fleenor et al. 2010). Since the late 1990s, the state's Department of Water Resources has published water use estimates that explicitly show dedicated environmental flows as a share of total water use.[8] Environmental water use estimates include flows in designated Wild and Scenic Rivers, required Delta outflows, and managed wetlands. Based on data such as those presented in Table 2.2, it has become common for some observers to argue that the environment receives the lion's share of water supplies (implying that it should not receive more).[9] Indeed, statewide, environmental flows accounted for nearly 50 percent of both gross and net water use in the 1998–2005 period and about 40 percent for agriculture and 10 percent for the urban sector.

---

7. For example, net urban use should be significantly higher in the coastal areas because treated wastewater generally flows to the sea. In inland areas, return flows from water users go to rivers and are available for reuse downstream. Oddly, the ratios of net to gross use from DWR water use estimates do not reflect the expected pattern—inland regions such as the Sacramento and Colorado Rivers have higher ratios of net to gross water use than the Central Coast.

8. This practice began with the publication of Bulletin 132-98, the first to consider the environmental share of water as a portion of the total (California Department of Water Resources 1998).

9. As an example, this comment by Tom Birmingham, General Manager of Westlands Water District, in the October 24, 2009, edition of *The Economist*: "Westlands' Mr Birmingham says that, in practice, water usage has already become equal. Whereas agriculture used to consume 80% of the state's water supply, today 46% of captured and stored water goes to environmental purposes, such as rebuilding wetlands. Meanwhile 43% goes to farming and 11% to municipal use."

But statewide totals are misleading, because the share of environmental water varies considerably across California. The wet, North Coast region is distinct in two respects: It is largely isolated hydraulically from the rest of California (the major exception being diversions from the Trinity River to the Sacramento River for CVP water supply) and its water is dedicated overwhelmingly to environmental flows. Excluding the North Coast and North Lahontan—another hydraulically isolated region—to look at California's main interconnected water system, average gross water use is 61 maf/year, with about 52 percent agricultural, 14 percent urban, and 33 percent environmental. The environmental share of net use is even lower—23 percent—because much of the environmental water in these regions is available for reuse downstream as Delta exports. In net terms, agriculture accounts for more than three-fifths of the total (62%), urban uses 16 percent, and environmental uses 22 percent.

Looking across hydrologic regions, California has essentially specialized many of its river systems. North Coast rivers are more specialized in environmental flows, whereas many other regions are more specialized for agricultural and urban uses (Figure 2.1). The one other region with a large volume and share of net environmental water use is the Sacramento River Basin, which sends significant net outflows through the Delta and the San Francisco Estuary. In contrast, environmental water use in the Tulare Basin is almost entirely in upstream areas, with almost all of that water subsequently consumed by agriculture downstream. The effectiveness of dedicated environmental flows has been hampered by a range of water and land management practices, including legacies from past land uses, dams, contaminants, and other problems. Chapter 5 examines approaches for improving the effectiveness of environmental water management. Where watersheds and streams can provide more environmental benefits with only limited economic losses (or vice versa), more deliberate specialization may be a key to better performance.

Farms' and Cities' Adaptation to Water Scarcity

California's agricultural and urban water users have been adapting to increasing water scarcity. Over time, the urban sector's share of total human water use has increased with population growth. In 1960, agriculture accounted for 90 percent of gross human water use, but by 2005 this share had fallen to 77 percent (Figure 2.8). Gross urban and agricultural water use appears to have leveled off or declined in recent years, following decades of expansion. (Note that Figure 2.8 shows long-term trends calculated to reflect "normal" water years, so the declines are not the result

Figure 2.8
Total gross agricultural and urban water use has been decreasing

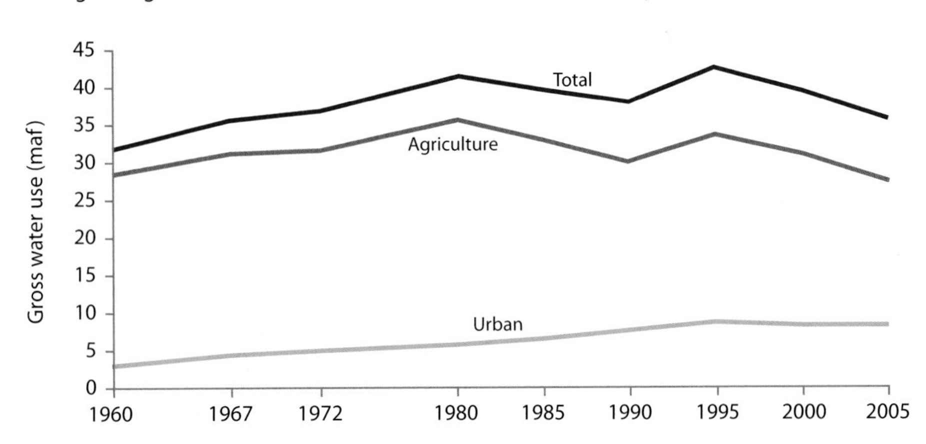

SOURCE: Authors' calculations using data from *California Water Plan Update* (California Department of Water Resources, various years).

NOTES: The figure shows gross water use. Urban includes residential and nonagricultural business uses. Pre-2000 estimates are adjusted to levels that would have been used in a year of normal rainfall. Estimates for 2000 and 2005 are for actual use; both years had near-normal precipitation. Estimates omit conveyance losses, which account for 6 percent to 9 percent of the total.

of drought.) Although California's population has continued to grow rapidly, water conservation activities and changes in economic structure (notably, less water-consuming manufacturing) have reduced per capita urban water use enough since the mid-1990s to keep total gross urban water use roughly constant (Figure 2.9).

Gross agricultural water use appears to have been falling since the early 1980s, due to irrigation efficiency improvements and retirement of some farmland with urbanization and accumulating soil salinity.[10] Despite these declines in farm water use, crop production and the value of farm output continue to rise owing to productivity improvements and shifts to higher-value crops. Over the last four decades, yields have risen at an average rate of 1.42 percent per year as both crop varieties and farming practices have improved (Brunke, Howitt, and Sumner 2005). As farmers have shifted to higher-value horticultural and orchard crops, they have adopted more efficient drip and sprinkler irrigation technologies and management practices.[11] Together, rising yields and a shift to

10. Irrigated crop acreage (which counts acreage more than once if it is farmed more than once during the year) fell from a high of nearly 10 million acres in 1980 to roughly 9.2 million acres in the mid-2000s. Irrigated land area (which counts acreage only once) fell from 9.6 to 8.8 million acres (authors' calculations using data from the California Department of Water Resources).

11. Orang, Matyac, and Snyder (2008) report that surface irrigation decreased by about 30 percent from 1972 to 2001 and drip/microsystem increased by about 31 percent, mostly from reduced field crop and increased orchard and vineyard planting. Most of the switch occurred from the early 1990s onward.

Figure 2.9
Gross per capita urban water use is now declining

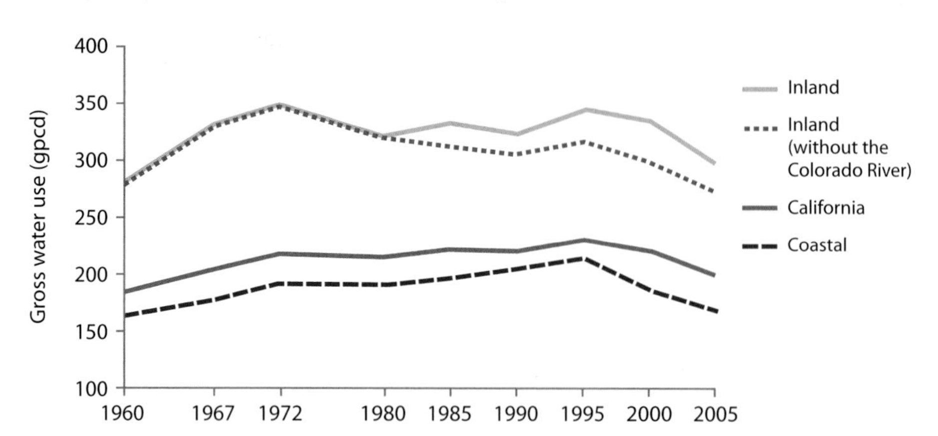

SOURCE: Authors' calculations using data from *California Water Plan Update* (California Department of Water Resources, various years).

NOTES: Water use is shown in gallons per capita per day (gpcd). Outdoor water use is much higher in inland areas because of hotter temperatures and larger lot sizes (Hanak and Davis 2006). The low-desert Colorado River region, including areas such as Palm Springs, has especially high per capita use from golf-based tourism.

higher-value crops have considerably increased the real dollar value per acre-foot of irrigation water.[12]

Although comparable trends in environmental water allocations are not available, it is likely that new environmental water dedications play some role in the tightening of overall supplies available for agricultural and urban use in recent decades.[13] During this time, California's population and economy have both increased, reflecting a substantial decoupling of economic prosperity from the availability of abundant water supplies. Having more water is no longer as fundamentally important as when California's economy was based largely on irrigated agriculture or mining.

The declining trends in gross agricultural and urban water use may have accelerated in the late 2000s, as a multiyear drought and new restrictions on

12. From 1972 to 1995, the real economic value of output per acre-foot of applied irrigation water increased by 19.3 percent when using the Gross Domestic Product deflator to measure inflation, and by 92.6 percent when deflated using U.S. Department of Agriculture index of prices received by farmers (Brunke, Howitt, and Sumner 2005).

13. For example, since 1993, the federal Central Valley Project Improvement Act has restricted supplies to some agricultural contractors south of the Delta (Chapter 2). Overall pumping through the Delta continued to increase during the late 1990s and early 2000 as State Water Project contractors increased their draw (Figure 2.4), but much of the additional water went to storage for dry years in groundwater banks and Metropolitan Water District of Southern California's new surface reservoir, Diamond Valley Lake. Since the 1990s, Los Angeles has cut its diversions from the Mono Lake and Owens Valley region in response to environmental rulings.

Delta pumping led many urban water agencies to pursue more aggressive conservation measures and as many farmers south of the Delta faced severe water shortages. California water users are likely to face increasing scarcity and the need to continue adapting, as a result of a changing climate and deteriorating conditions of the state's aquatic ecosystems (Chapter 3).

The Economic Value of Water

The debates on how to allocate water across sectors reflect perceptions of the underlying value of water in different activities. Some of these values are easier to measure than others.

Wide disparities in the value of agricultural water use

The economic value of water in agriculture—the largest human use of water—is relatively easy to determine because almost all agricultural production is sold on the market. California has the highest grossing agricultural sector in the nation, but its value is small relative to the state's overall economy. In 2007, the value-added of crop and animal production in the state totaled $22.4 billion, or 1.2 percent of the state's $1.85 trillion gross domestic product.[14] This share nearly doubles (to $40 billion) when food processing is included and would be somewhat higher if the value of farm services and agriculture-related transport were also included. In that same year, agriculture and all related industries accounted for about 5 percent of the state's employment (Figure 1.3). Within some regions, agriculture is far more important as a source of revenue and jobs; it accounts for as much as 15 percent of employment in the San Joaquin Valley.

The value of water use in agriculture varies from a few tens of dollars to thousands of dollars per acre-foot. Table 2.3 shows the estimated water use and revenue generated by major crop types for 2005, along with average revenues per acre-foot of gross and net water used. Irrigated pasture generated less than $50 per acre-foot of net water use—less than 1 percent of the average value of an acre-foot of water used to grow fresh vegetables, flowers, and other horticultural crops. The value of most "field crops" (alfalfa, rice, corn, and various grains and legumes) is also relatively low on average—ranging from $200 to $600/acre-foot

14. Value added, used to calculate gross state product, includes farm revenues from crop and livestock production and forestry and net government transfers *less* the cost of purchased inputs. Data are from the U.S. Bureau of Economic Analysis, gross domestic product by state: www.bea.gov/regional/gsp/. This total is lower than the gross value of farm production (such as that used to calculate crop water values in Table 2.3), which does not subtract the cost of purchased inputs.

Table 2.3
Water use, revenues, and value of water by major crop categories, 2005

Crops	Gross water (%)	Net water (%)	Gross revenues (%)	Irrigated acres (%)	Gross revenues/ gross water ($/af)	Gross revenues/ net water ($/af)
Irrigated pasture	12	11	0.4	9	31	47
Rice	10	9	2	6	127	223
Corn	7	7	1	7	176	258
Alfalfa	18	18	4	12	200	287
Cotton	7	8	3	7	416	551
Other field crops	8	8	3	13	375	573
Fruits and nuts	27	29	44	30	1,401	1,875
Truck farming and horticulture	10	10	42	16	3,724	5,363

SOURCES: Authors' calculations using data provided by DWR staff. Revenue information draws on California Agricultural Statistics and county agricultural commissioner reports.

NOTES: Gross water use = 27.3 maf, net water use = 18.9 maf; crop revenues from irrigated agriculture = $23.9 billion (2005 $); irrigated crop acres (including multiple cropping) = 9.2 million acres. In addition to field corn, corn acreage and water use includes some sweet corn, which is included in the value estimates for truck farming. "Truck farming and horticulture" includes assorted vegetables, some fruits (e.g., melons), flowers, and nursery products. "Fruits and nuts" includes all fruit and nut tree crops plus berries.

of net water used, whereas fruits and nuts (mostly tree crops) average close to $2,000/acre-foot. Within these aggregate categories, the values of some crops are much higher (e.g., high-quality wine grapes sell for much more than table grapes or nuts), and these values also vary with world market conditions (e.g., rice and wheat prices have been higher in recent years because of drought in Australia and Russia, respectively). Also, some of the lowest-value crops (notably pasture and alfalfa) are inputs into the state's meat and dairy production activities, which generate about a quarter of total agricultural revenues. But the general picture is one of striking contrasts, especially if one considers the volumes of water allocated to different commodities; irrigated pasture and all field crops combined accounted for 61 percent of net water use and only 14 percent of gross crop revenues.

Although such simple comparisons do not reflect the complexities of needs for crop rotations and the use of low-value crops for high-value livestock, there still appears to be a considerable volume of low-value agricultural water use in an increasingly parched California. As discussed below, these low-value activities potentially provide the state with some flexibility to cope with droughts and longer-term shifts in demand through the continued development of the water market.

The large differences in crop revenues per acre-foot are reflected in considerable differences in the value of agricultural water use across regions. Coastal areas specializing in fresh vegetables, other horticultural crops, citrus, avocados, and vineyards generate much higher revenues per acre of irrigated cropland than many farms in the agricultural heartland of the Central Valley (Figure 2.10). To some extent, these discrepancies reflect the costs farmers incur to apply water to their fields, a function of seniority of water rights, water subsidies to some CVP contractors,[15] and the financial and energy costs of moving water to users. In coastal Southern California, for instance, farmers pay up to $600 to $800 per acre-foot for State Water Project water that must travel over the Tehachapi Mountains, whereas in Imperial County, parts of the northern Sacramento Valley, and the east side of the San Joaquin Valley, farmers receive water deliveries from local and federal projects for as little as $8 to $40 per acre-foot.[16] Irrigated pasture and low-value field crops are viable only when the water is relatively inexpensive.

Federal crop subsidies artificially boost the value of many low-value crops. Direct subsidies are now provided for roughly half of the state's cotton crop, as well as for corn, rice, and some other field crops.[17] Subsidies to the dairy industry indirectly boost demand for alfalfa.[18] In contrast, prices for the higher-value fruits, nuts, and horticultural crops are entirely driven by local and world markets.

Another way to view the value of water is by examining the costs of shortages. Figure 2.11 shows the incremental revenue loss (or "marginal costs") from reducing irrigation water deliveries by 5 and 25 percent. Much higher losses occur in areas growing higher-value crops, and losses increase substantially with larger cuts. These disparities in agricultural water values provide incentives for farm-to-farm water sales. Many farmers with more senior and secure water rights grow relatively low-value crops, whereas some junior rights holders, such

---

15. The estimated yearly subsidy to farmers receiving CVP water, relative to the full-cost rate, is roughly $60 million (Environmental Working Group 2004). In addition to its subsidized contractors, the CVP also delivers about 2.6 maf of water to "settlement" and "exchange" contractors who were already receiving the water before the CVP began operations at low (but not subsidized) prices (Hanak et al. 2010).

16. Comprehensive information on agricultural water prices is not available, but most large irrigation districts publish their rate structures.

17. In 2005, for instance, direct subsidies to cotton, rice, corn, wheat, and barley amounted to $534 million (current dollars), roughly 16 percent of the gross revenue of all field crops (Environmental Working Group undated).

18. Dairy subsidies vary considerably by year. In 2009, they were as much as $125 million in California (Environmental Working Group undated).

Figure 2.10
Agricultural revenues per acre vary widely

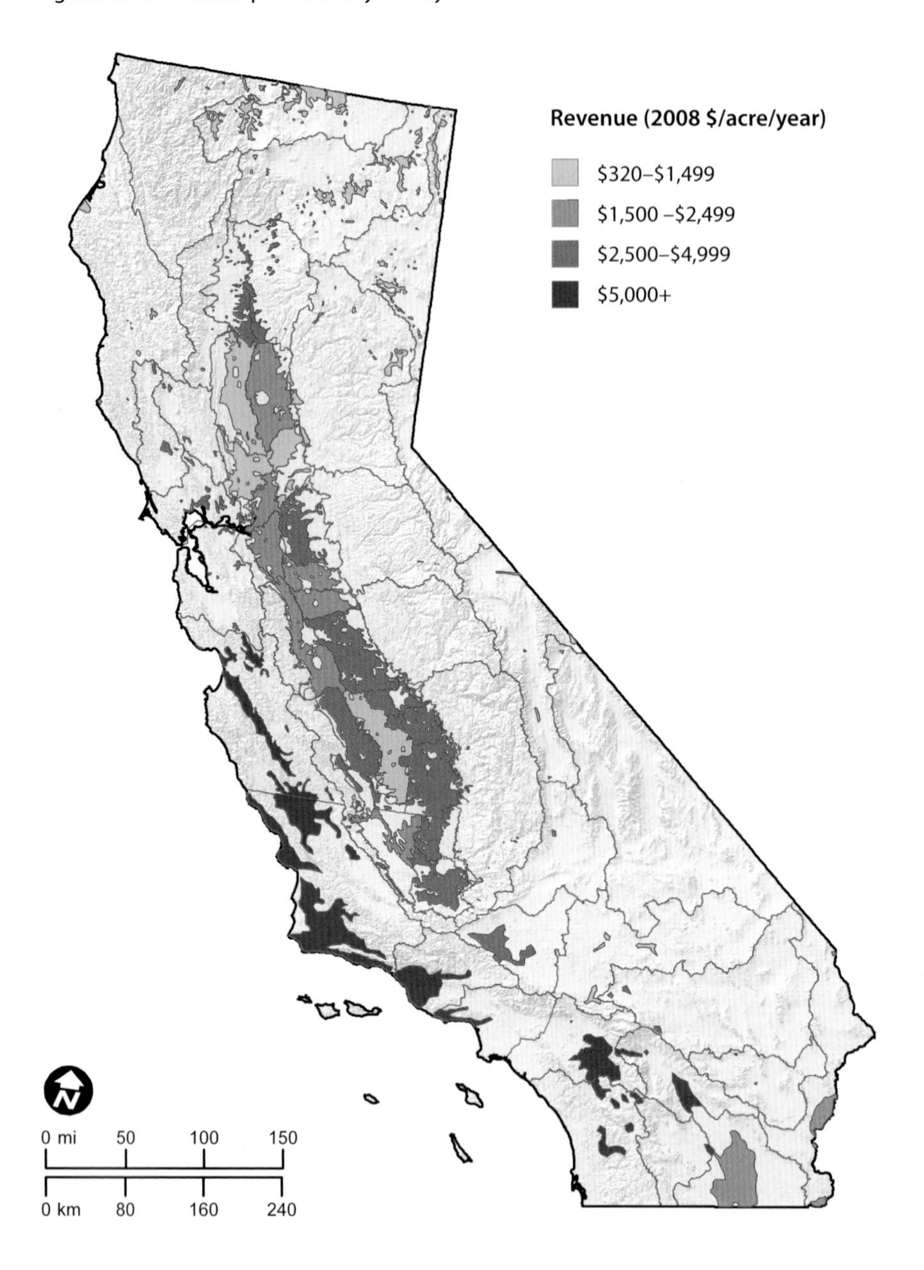

SOURCES: County Agricultural Commissioner Reports and Statewide Agricultural Production model.

NOTE: Values are calculated for DWR planning areas; the borders of these areas are shown on the map.

Figure 2.11
Costs escalate quickly with higher agricultural water cutbacks

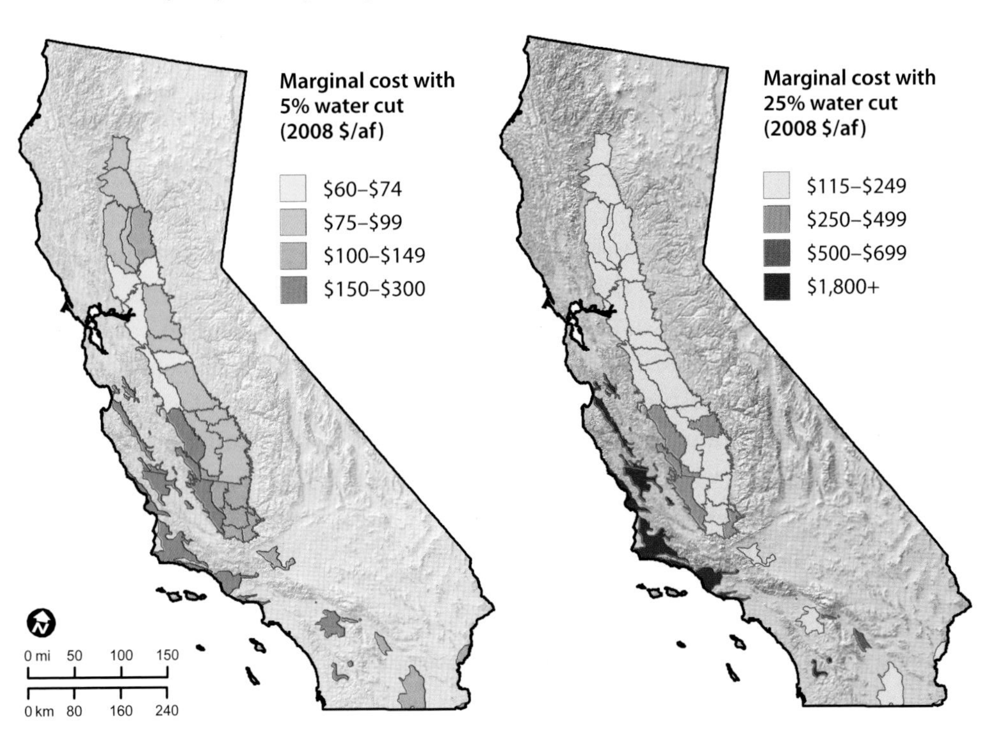

SOURCE: Statewide Agricultural Production model.

NOTES: The maps show the loss of farm revenue incurred by the last acre-foot of water lost when supplies are reduced by 5 and 25 percent. This is the value that farmers would be willing to pay to purchase an additional acre-foot of water to apply to their fields.

as those in the west side of the San Joaquin Valley, have more productive farms but less secure water supply contracts. Water transfers are particularly valuable when farmers with less secure rights grow tree crops, which will die without water.

Water subsidies are not necessarily a hindrance to water marketing, because farmers still have incentives to sell water as long as they can earn more by selling water than by producing crops. In contrast, crop subsidies can create a disincentive if the subsidy payment is tied to the volume of production. Crop subsidies are now less closely tied to crop acreage and production than in the past, with payments based on past volumes and acreage. However, it is likely that farmers still consider the potential for the loss of subsidies with program adjustments when they make their planting decisions (Bhaskar and Beghin

2009; Blandford and Josling 2007).[19] Changes in federal farm policy are needed to break this link and facilitate more efficient use of water.

When water to some CVP contractors became less reliable as a result of the listing of several species for protection under the Endangered Species Act and the environmental water allocations mandated by the Central Valley Project Improvement Act of 1992, farm-to-farm water transfers became an important tool for supplementing farm water supplies on the western side of the San Joaquin Valley, including the Westlands Water District (Hanak 2003). The still large discrepancies in crop values and water use suggest the potential for much more use of water markets in response to further regulatory cutbacks and drought-related scarcity. For instance, during the recent drought, irrigated pasture still accounted for a sizable share of gross water use within the San Joaquin Valley.[20] In Chapter 6, we discuss obstacles to continued development of water markets, including institutional and legal barriers, infrastructure limits (e.g., the difficulty of moving water from the east to the west side of the San Joaquin Valley), and concerns within source regions about local economic harm from transfers. Getting past these obstacles is an important priority for California water policy.

Little growth in urban water use despite economic growth

Urban water use is less directly linked to economic prosperity than in the case of agriculture, suggesting considerable flexibility to reduce use, if done carefully, without reducing regional or statewide economic activity. As a rough illustration, the state's economy was 2.4 times larger in real terms in 2005 than in 1980, despite a 14 percent drop in total gross water use and a 30 percent increase in urban gross use (Figure 2.8). The economy grew another 14 percent from 2000 to 2005 with no increase in gross urban water use and an 11 percent decline in gross agricultural water use.[21]

Urban water use has a large, but less direct, effect on economic prosperity (Figure 2.12). Industrial water use tends to have an extremely high marginal

19. As an example, cotton subsidies are tied to past cotton acreage, but farmers are not allowed to grow fruits and nuts on that acreage and continue to qualify for the subsidy.

20. According to DWR statistics, in 2005, irrigated pasture accounted for 12 percent of gross water use in the San Joaquin River hydrologic region. In 2008, County Agricultural Commissioner Reports estimate that acreage of irrigated pasture within the eight-county San Joaquin Valley had fallen by 20 percent, suggesting some adaptation but considerable remaining water use for this low-value crop.

21. Within agriculture, the real value of farm output was 1.12 times higher in 2005 than in 1980, despite a 23 percent decline in applied water on farms and a 7 percent decline in irrigated crop acreage (authors' calculations using gross state product data from the U.S. Bureau of Economic Analysis and water use data from the California Department of Water Resources).

Figure 2.12
Landscaping accounts for at least half of gross urban water use

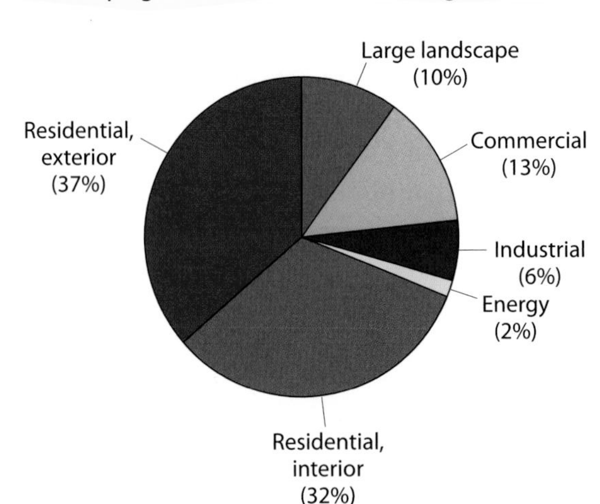

SOURCE: California Department of Water Resources (2009).

NOTES: The total (8.3 million acre-feet) excludes conveyance losses and active groundwater recharge. Water for landscaping uses include residential exterior, large landscapes (e.g., parks, golf courses, cemeteries), and a portion of commercial and industrial water use.

value, because of high potential for revenue and job losses with cutbacks, but it accounts for only about 6 percent of total urban use. Preventing shutdowns of chip manufacturing and other water-intensive industries was an important impetus of the emergency drought water bank that the state established during the prolonged drought of the late 1980s and early 1990s (California Urban Water Agencies 1991).

The value of water and the costs of cutbacks, while substantial, is harder to measure in most other urban uses. Water is important for businesses involved with large landscape water uses, e.g., golf courses, as well as for businesses relying on household water use, such as landscaping firms and swimming pool vendors. These businesses often can use less water without losing revenues, although this often requires some changes in the business (e.g., switching from lawn maintenance to installing low-water-using gardens). Water shortages primarily generate costs to end users, in terms of either new equipment (e.g., more water-efficient plumbing, which provides similar service while using less water), or inconvenience (e.g., taking shorter showers, letting lawns go brown, or leaving pools empty). Economists measure these noncommercial values of urban water in terms of how much people would be willing to pay not to have their supplies reduced.[22] This willingness to pay increases as water becomes scarcer, and it is likely higher in the short term than in the longer term—when time allows adaptation with new technology, such as more efficient shower heads or low-water-using plants.[23]

As shown in Chapter 6, continued urban conservation will be important for managing scarce water resources, and this shift will be most effective if technologies, tastes, and habits can adapt to minimize the costs of adjustment. An especially important frontier will be outdoor water use, which now accounts for most net urban use (residential exterior, large landscape, plus some proportion of commercial and industrial uses—Figure 2.12). Shifting landscapes from thirsty lawns to low-water-using plants can greatly reduce net urban water use (Hanak and Davis 2006).

Do urban water users pay too little?

In water management circles, it is often said that California's urban water users pay too little for water. A comparison is made with monthly cell phone bills, and the implication is that consumers are getting a bargain on their water bill relative to the value of the water to them—or the amount they would (or should) be willing to pay. The comparison with cell phone bills is apt. As of 2006, the average price of treated water delivered to households was roughly $960 per acre-foot (in 2008 $), and the average monthly water bill for single-family households was $42, less than a typical cell phone subscription (Table 2.4).

The important question, however, is not whether users pay too little relative to the value of water to them—this is true, on average, for most goods and services.[24] Rather, what matters from a water policy perspective is whether they pay enough to cover the full costs of providing water, including the capital and maintenance costs to the water utility and the costs of protecting environmental values affected by water diversions. As discussed below in our review of water system finances, the first part of this answer is a qualified "yes," but the second part is a definite "no." Not only can adapting water prices to reflect the full cost of water generate an appropriate stream of funding for public benefits of the water system, it can also send the right signal to consumers to use the resource more efficiently (Chapter 6).

---

22. See Renwick and Green (2000), Barakat & Chamberlin, Inc. (1994), Genius et al. (2008), Jenkins, Lund, and Howitt (2003), Rosenberg, Howitt, and Lund (2008), Rosenberg et al. (2008), and California Department of Water Resources (2009).

23. Economists also measure the consumer benefits from using water under different water price structures by comparing the additional benefits from additional amounts of water consumed to the marginal cost (price) of that amount (Hewitt and Hanemann 1995; Olmsted, Hanemann, and Stavins 2007; Hall 1996). As discussed in Chapter 6, the social goal is to design an economically efficient, revenue sufficient, and politically acceptable water rate (Hall 2000, 2009).

24. Economists refer to the excess in willingness to pay over price as the "consumer surplus."

Table 2.4
Household water and wastewater costs in the mid-2000s (2008 $)

Region	Average yearly gross water use (af)	Average water price ($/af)	Average monthly water bill ($)	Average monthly wastewater bill ($)	Water and wastewater bills as a share of median income (%)
San Francisco Bay Area	0.37	1,190	36	31	1.07
Central Coast	0.38	1,857	59	28	1.68
South Coast	0.58	985	48	23	1.46
Inland Empire	0.59	748	36	18	1.28
Sacramento Metro Area	0.49	789	32	26	1.23
San Joaquin Valley	0.63	545	29	19	1.26
Rest of state	0.47	886	35	25	1.78
California	**0.52**	**959**	**42**	**24**	**1.36**

SOURCES: Authors' calculations using data from Black and Veatch (2004, 2006) for water and wastewater rates and the U.S. Census for household incomes.

NOTES: The table reports charges for single-family households. Water rates are for 2006; wastewater rates are for 2004; both are converted to 2008 dollars using the consumer price index. The sample includes 443 water service areas and 560 wastewater service areas. The considerable regional variation in water prices reflects differences in local infrastructure and water supply costs. The regional breakdowns here are based on counties and differ slightly from the hydrologic regions in Tables 2.1 and 2.2. Communities in the Inland Empire (Riverside and San Bernardino) are located in the South Coast, the South Lahontan, and the Colorado River regions. San Joaquin Valley includes the San Joaquin River and Tulare Basin regions. "Rest of state" includes rural counties in the Sacramento River region, the North Coast, and the North Lahontan regions.

Environmental water: an undervalued resource

Environmental flows, healthy watersheds, and the services they provide—often known as *ecosystem services*—add economic value to California (Box 2.3). However, these benefits are often not readily apparent because the market does not generally put a price on them (National Research Council 2005; Brauman et al. 2007; Daily et al. 2009). As a result, the value of ecosystem benefits is overlooked in many cost-benefit analyses used to evaluate water investments. The failure to consider environmental values has contributed significantly to the degradation of aquatic ecosystems (Introduction, Chapter 5).

Although new tools are emerging to estimate the economic values of ecosystem services, such valuation is not without challenges (Boyd and Banzhaf 2006). The difficulties stem, in part, from the different methods of valuation that must be used to compare services (Freeman 2003). Some commodities produced by freshwater ecosystems, such as produce and fish, have easily identified market values. For instance, in 2007, fisheries and

2.3

Freshwater ecosystem services in California

Ecosystems provide many economic services. A major global study done for the United Nations considered four overlapping categories: provisioning, regulating, cultural, and supporting services (Millennium Ecosystem Assessment 2005). Some services are easier to measure than others.

Provisioning services. Provisioning involves the production of (1) food, both from irrigated agriculture and fisheries; (2) materials, including timber and cotton; (3) fresh water, for household, industrial, and service uses; and (4) hydropower. Provisioning services have the longest tradition of economic valuation and are regularly calculated for water management projects.

Regulating services. Freshwater ecosystems also regulate a range of environmental conditions that affect human well-being. Some prominent examples in California include (1) flow regulation, including use of watersheds and floodplains to recharge groundwater basins and reduce downstream harm from floods; (2) water quality regulation, including the use of wetlands and rivers to remove nutrients and pesticides from waterways; and (3) climate regulation, including regional air quality (e.g., reducing airborne particulates and summer temperatures) and carbon sequestration in floodplain wetlands and riparian forests. Economic benefits from these services are rarely measured.

Cultural services. Some cultural services have direct, measurable market value: recreation, ecotourism, and the aesthetic values of scenic views and parks. Cultural services with nonmonetized value are more difficult to measure: spiritual renewal, religious and cultural values, and the use of freshwater ecosystems for formal and informal education.

Supporting services. Many of California's freshwater ecosystems provide support for other economic activities that are only realized over very long periods of time or through indirect connections to other ecosystem services. Supporting services include soil formation and fertility, particularly in floodplain and wetland settings subject to seasonal flooding; removal of carbon dioxide through photosynthesis; nutrient cycling (the natural cycling of nutrients necessary to sustain life in freshwater ecosystems); and water cycling (regulating the rates of movement and pathways of water through the hydrologic cycle). Supporting services are rarely measured.

forestry accounted for $7.6 billion of gross state product (2008 $).[25] Other services are essentially public, free for use, such as recreation, and must be valued using nonmarket methods, which can generate wide ranges of estimates. Some services, particularly support services, have no easy method for measurement.

25. Bureau of Economic Analysis gross state product data (current values, converted to 2008 values using the ratio of nominal to real U.S. gross domestic product).

For this reason, many ecosystem service valuation efforts focus on a few services that can be most easily quantified and tend to ignore or qualitatively discuss the rest.[26]

These difficulties notwithstanding, California has much to gain by adopting a more comprehensive approach to assessing the value of ecosystem services. Even where full economic valuation is not practical, an approach that considers nonmarket functions of aquatic ecosystems can inform and guide decisions for water supply and flood management to maximize overall benefits (Chapters 5, 6). Considering the value of ecosystem services comports well with recent state legislation and policies seeking to establish "co-equal" goals for ecosystem health and water supply (Chapter 1). This approach also can help to dispel the myth that healthy aquatic ecosystems conflict with a healthy economy (Hanak et al. 2010).

Water and Energy

Water is heavy; average urban use (about 200 gallons per capita per day) comes to over 1,500 pounds a day. So the energy needed to move water can be considerable. This is particularly true for Southern California's urban water supplies, which often involve lifting large amounts of water over mountains. These pumping costs alone offer considerable incentive for water conservation (Wilkinson 2000). In addition to long-standing management concerns about the high cost of energy involved in water production and use (Palmer and Lund 1986), there have been growing policy concerns about greenhouse gas emissions from both the production and use of water. In the latter context, it is frequently reported that water use accounts for roughly 20 percent of the state's electricity use, making it a target for state policy efforts to reduce emissions (California Air Resources Board 2008). However, public discussions of this issue do not usually recognize that almost three-quarters of water-related energy use occurs in the homes, businesses, offices, and farms of end users (Table 2.5). Less than one-quarter is devoted to operating local, regional, and statewide water infrastructure.

Most water-related energy use is in the urban sector. The most energy-intensive urban uses involve water heating, electricity for washing machines, chilling water and ice, and in-building pumps for spas, hot water circulation, evaporative coolers, etc., as well as industrial and commercial processes. Agricultural end

26. A recent study by the Science Advisory Board for the U.S. Environmental Protection Agency (2009) discusses a variety of methods for valuing ecosystem services: (1) measures of public attitudes—surveys and focus groups that elicit public preferences for ecosystem services, (2) economic methods—methods to estimate how much people are willing to spend to avoid losing a service, and (3) civil valuation methods—public referenda or initiatives, which provide information about how much the voting population values particular services.

Table 2.5
Water-related energy use in California, 2001

	Electricity		Natural gas	
	Gigawatt hours	Share of state total (%)	Million therms	Share of state total (%)
End uses		14.1		31.2
Urban	27,887	11.1	4,220	31.1
Residential	13,526	5.4	2,055	15.1
Commercial	8,341	3.3	250	1.8
Industrial	6,017	2.4	1,914	14.1
Agricultural	7,372	2.9	18	0.1
Water supply and treatment		4.3		0.1
Urban	7,554	3.0	19	0.1
Agricultural	3,188	1.3	0	0
Wastewater treatment	2,012	0.8	27	0.2
Total water-related energy use	48,012	19.2	4,284	31.6
Total California energy use	250,494	100.0	13,571	100.0

SOURCE: California Energy Commission (2005).

NOTE: Statistics on natural gas use refer to the portion of natural gas that is not used as an input in electricity production.

uses mainly include operating pumps for groundwater and irrigation systems. Infrastructure-related energy ("supply and treatment" in Table 2.5) is primarily for pumping supplies through conveyance channels and (in the urban sector) to move water in and out of treatment plants and distribution networks. The high energy content of some end uses means that energy costs drive the economics of some water conservation activities (especially for hot water). As with some energy efficiency measures, water use efficiency investments that reduce hot water use can save customers money within a short time.[27] Energy costs also affect the economics of design and operating decisions by water utilities. The high energy requirements of seawater desalination makes this technology particularly vulnerable to rising energy prices (Semiat 2008).

Water also is a major source of energy. California relies on hydropower for between 15 and 30 percent of its annual electricity generation, depending on annual runoff and droughts (Madani and Lund 2010).[28] The flexibility of hydro-

27. On water, see Gleick et al. (2003). On energy, see McKinsey & Company (2007).

28. Statewide hydropower revenues exceed $2 billion per year (authors' calculations, assuming 34,000 gigawatt hours × $0.05 per kilowatt hour = $1.7 billion per year at average wholesale prices, plus the ancillary services of hydropower, such as maintaining reserve capacity and regulating voltage on the grid).

power makes it particularly valuable for meeting peak summertime demands. This resource will diminish if California's climate becomes drier, as less stream flow means less fuel for hydroelectric power plants.[29] Hydropower management also has major implications for ecosystem health, because of the disruptions caused by dams and flow alterations to the aquatic environment (Chapter 5).

Flood Vulnerability and Flood Management Infrastructure

Protecting people and businesses from flooding has been a long-standing concern of California water management (Chapter 1). The current system of flood management infrastructure includes surface reservoirs (many of which also provide water supply storage), levees, and flood bypasses (Figure 2.13). This infrastructure is used in conjunction with land use regulations, insurance, and warning systems (Chapter 6).

Levees, the most common tool, attempt to limit the area of flooding by containing flows with embankments. Because levees are managed by many diverse public agencies and private individuals, no comprehensive statewide levee inventory exists. The Central Valley alone has as many as 6,000 miles of levees. The Sacramento–San Joaquin Delta and the federally authorized Sacramento–San Joaquin Flood Control projects together have about 2,700 miles of levees. In the Sacramento Valley, levees are supplemented by a system of flood bypasses established in the early 20th century. The bypasses are large areas of seasonal farmland and habitat, bounded by levees, which essentially create a second Sacramento River to accommodate large floods. Upstream reservoirs also help manage floods by storing water to reduce flood peaks that must be accommodated downstream by levees and bypasses.

In 2000, almost 5 percent of California's households were living in what is known as the "100-year" floodplain—an area susceptible to more frequent floods, where land use is regulated by federal flood policy and where federal flood insurance is required (Chapter 6).[30] Another 12.5 percent of households lived in the "500-year" floodplain, an area susceptible to larger, less frequent floods that have a 0.2 percent or more chance of occurring in any given year.

---

29. The adaptability of hydropower to changes in climate and water management purposes has been widely examined (Jacobs et al. 1995; Madani and Lund 2009, 2010; Tanaka et al. 2006; Vicuna et al. 2008).

30. Authors' calculations, using Census 2000 block data for household population and floodplain designations from the Federal Emergency Management Association.

Figure 2.13
California relies mostly on levees, flood bypasses, and reservoirs for flood protection

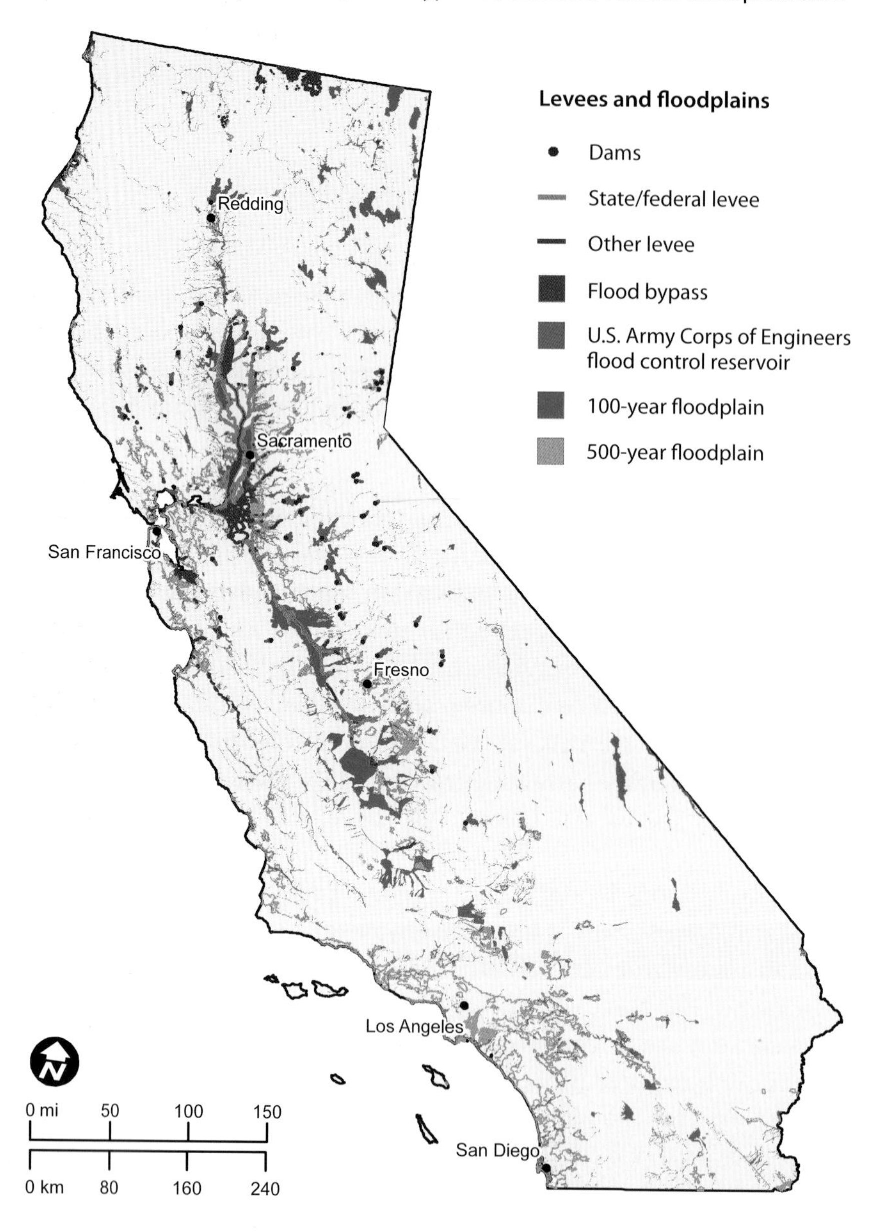

SOURCES: For levees, reservoirs, and bypasses, California Department of Water Resources; for floodplains, Federal Emergency Management Agency.

NOTES: The map does not show all locally managed levees; it shows only flood reservoirs overseen by the U.S. Army Corps of Engineers. It shows two of the largest flood bypasses—Yolo Bypass and Sutter Bypass. Urban areas are outlined in gray.

Under federal law, homes in these areas are not required to have flood insurance, and land use is not regulated. Levees protect many homes that would otherwise be located in the 100-year floodplain. Flood insurance subscription in California is low. In 2006, just over 30 percent of the households in the 100-year floodplain had flood insurance and just 7 percent of those within the 101 to 500-year floodplain had insurance.[31]

Overall, this system protects most of California's Central Valley from the most frequent floods, with the exception of parts of the Delta. Parts of Southern California, the California coast, and local streams in Northern California have recurrent localized flooding problems, as evidenced by the number of federally declared flood disaster events since the late 1970s (Figure 2.14). For large floods, which occur only a few times per century on average, many parts of the state face much greater challenges. The Sacramento area, in particular, has been singled out as having some of the weakest flood defenses of any major metropolitan area in the country, well below New Orleans—a fact not missed by California's media and policy community following Hurricane Katrina's devastation of New Orleans.[32] A large flood in the Sacramento area would put thousands of lives at risk and lay waste to tens of billions of dollars in property damage.[33]

Hurricane Katrina brought renewed attention to flood risks and flood infrastructure in California, the poor state of many levees, the growing numbers of residents living in areas with high flood risk, and the potential for increasing flood risk with climate change (Chapter 1).[34] In 2005, federal authorities began requiring testing and recertification of all levees in communities that wish to maintain access to federal flood insurance, resulting in the downgrading of

---

31. Authors' calculations using estimates of households in floodplains (see the preceding footnote) and data on insurance by zone for California's communities from the Federal Emergency Management Agency. In contrast, over 80 percent of U.S. homes have fire insurance, a hazard that strikes about 0.3 percent of homes per year (a 1-in-330 chance per year) (authors' calculations using data from the National Fire Protection Association (www.nfpa.org), the National Association of Insurance Commissioners (www.naic.org), and the U.S. Census). California fire insurance coverage and fire frequency rates appear roughly similar to these national averages.

32. On August 31, 2005, a *Sacramento Bee* article titled "New Orleans flooding 'wake-up call' for capital" gave an early diagnosis: "Levee failures . . . [are] a chilling reminder that the two cities have a lot in common" (Weiser 2005). The website of the Sacramento Area Flood Control Agency (SAFCA) depicts a graphic comparing the flood risk of Sacramento with that of a number of other major cities, including New Orleans (www.safca.org/floodRisk/floodThreat.html).

33. In the area managed by SAFCA (the City of Sacramento and part of Sacramento County), property losses from flooding are projected to be close to $20 billion in 2019 (Sacramento Area Flood Control Agency 2008), and many other communities are at high risk of flooding at the same time, including West Sacramento, Yuba City, Marysville, and surrounding areas. Ongoing efforts to upgrade SAFCA levees are likely to reduce the likelihood of flooding from about 1.5 percent per year to about 0.5 percent per year (www.safca.org). But Sacramento will still face large residual risks (defined as damage times likelihood) of more than $90 million per year. Moreover, in some low-lying areas such as Natomas, levee failures could still put many lives at risk.

34. The California Department of Water Resources (2005a) issued a white paper on the coming flood crisis in January 2005, months before Katrina, and the Federal Emergency Management Agency issued its order for levee recertification a week before Katrina. But both state and federal policy attention was clearly galvanized by the devastation caused by the hurricane.

Figure 2.14
Flooding affects many parts of California

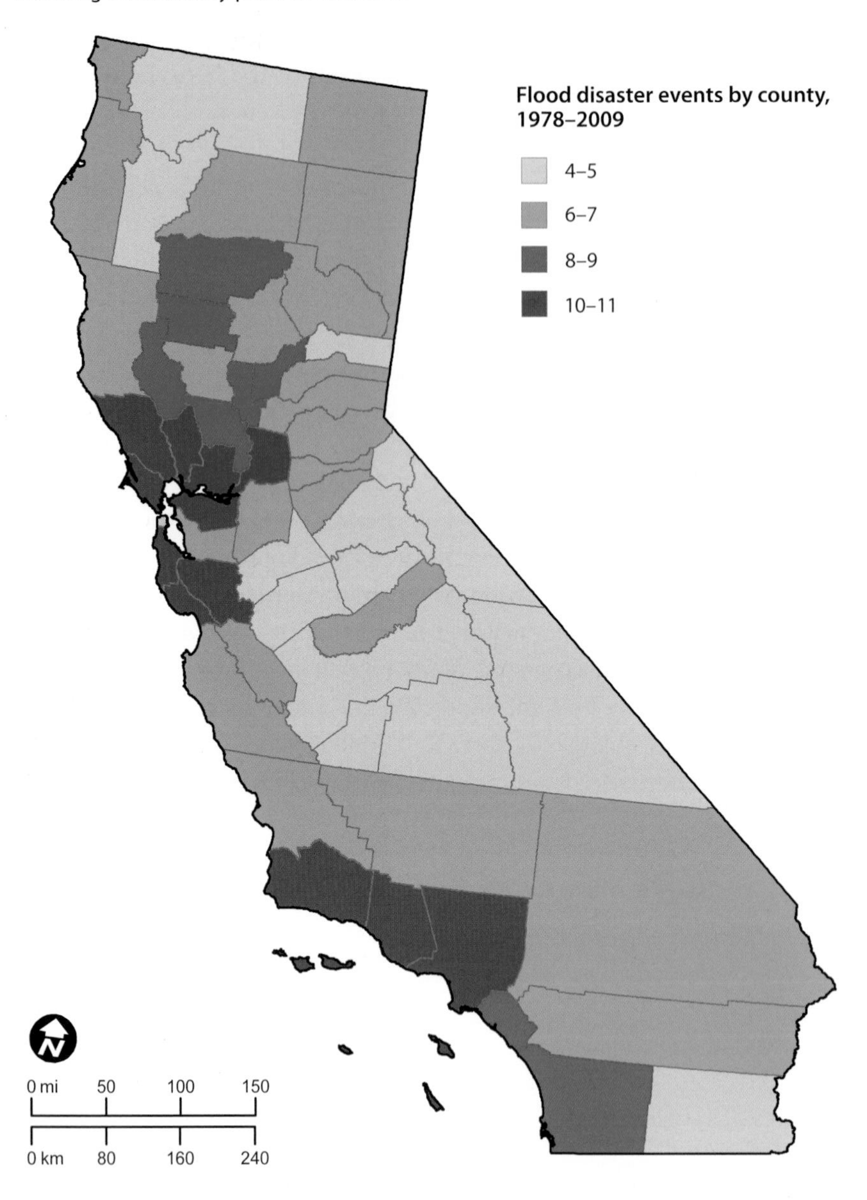

SOURCE: Authors' calculations using data from the Federal Emergency Management Agency.

some levees and reclassification of some areas as within the 100-year floodplain. In 2006, state voters approved nearly $5 billion in bonds to fund flood system upgrades, and in 2007, the state legislature passed, and the governor signed, a set of flood policy bills to raise the level of flood protection in urban areas and reduce new development in high-risk areas. Although this renewed attention to flood protection is valuable, more fundamental policy shifts are needed to protect California's residents from harm and to improve the environmental performance of flood infrastructure (Chapters 5, 6).

Water System Management and Finance

In the United States, most water management is local, and California is no exception. Although state and federal legislatures, agencies, and courts have roles in all aspects of water management, thousands of local entities have the frontline responsibility for serving customers, complying with water quality regulations, and raising revenues to cover the operations, maintenance, and capital investments needed to support these tasks. The governance of water in California also involves many nongovernmental interest-based organizations and many large and small private groups, including business interests and ultimately the general public, which make water-related decisions in homes, in businesses and farms, and at the ballot box. In this section, we review the primary roles of different players in managing water, including their opportunities to improve their management and their principal constraints—financial and otherwise. We begin with local decisionmakers (the most numerous and important group) and proceed to state, federal, and other groups involved in managing California's water.

An "Adhocracy" of Decentralized Decisionmakers

Although the federal and state governments played a major role in large-scale water infrastructure development, California's water system remains highly decentralized, with roots dating back to the Era of Local Organization in the late 19th century (Chapter 1).[35] Well over a thousand specialized and general purpose local governments, water companies, and other organizations manage water locally (Table 2.6). Several dozen wholesale utilities sell water to other water agencies, and roughly 400 large retail utilities (those serving at least 3,000

35. This reality contrasts with traditional views of water management in the western United States, which emphasize the role of the state and especially federal governments (e.g., Worster 1985).

Table 2.6
Principal types of local water management agencies

Agency	Responsibility
Urban water and wastewater utilities (city departments, special districts, and private utilities)	Urban water supply, wastewater treatment
Agricultural water agencies (irrigation districts, other special districts, mutual water companies)	Agricultural surface water supply (sometimes also management of groundwater recharge and conjunctive use)
County flood control agencies and reclamation districts	Local flood management, including maintenance of federally authorized levees
Groundwater management entities (water masters, special districts)	Local groundwater basin management for adjudicated basins and special groundwater management areas
City and county governments	Land use permitting and stormwater management
Resource conservation districts	Land and water use management for habitat improvements
Power utilities (private utilities, urban and agricultural water agencies)	Hydroelectric projects

NOTES: For details on special districts, see Special Districts Annual Report Fiscal Year 2007–08, Appendix B: Number of Special Districts by Type and Governing Body (www.sco.ca.gov/Files-ARD-Local/LocRep/0708specialdistrictosp.pdf). For a list of California water districts, see www.lib.berkeley.edu/WRCA/district.html. And for a digital repository of California water district documents, see http://webarchives.cdlib.org/a/CAWaterDistricts.

customers) deliver water to most California homes and businesses.[36] Several thousands more serve smaller, more rural communities. Several dozen public entities oversee adjudicated and other specially managed groundwater basins (primarily in Southern California) (Chapters 4, 6). Hundreds of agricultural water districts supply surface water to California's farmers. Nearly 600 local wastewater utilities are responsible for meeting Clean Water Act standards in discharging municipal waste. Many of California's county governments and numerous special districts oversee local flood management programs. Over the past decade, many city and county governments have become responsible for the quality of stormwater runoff under the CWA. These local governments—538 in all—also have principal responsibility for local water-related land use decisions and local codes, which affect water demands, flood vulnerability, and stormwater flows.[37] Along with the state and federal water projects, various

36. These are the utilities required to comply with the Urban Water Management Planning Act. See Hanak (2005b, 2010).

37. Local decisions on the location of development are especially important for flood risk management and source-water protection. Local ordinances and codes on outdoor landscaping and stormwater capture are important for water conservation and water quality.

local and regional public and private entities manage over 150 hydroelectric facilities. In some areas, local resource conservation districts are charged with overseeing ecosystem-related land and water management.

This institutional diversity creates the potential for innovation and flexible responses to management challenges, but it can also limit the scope for effective coordination (Bish 1982). Coordination can be particularly important—indeed necessary—when water management involves multiple functions, or when the scope of management is geographically defined. For instance, water and wastewater utilities need to collaborate to effectively manage recycled wastewater programs, and significant problems can occur if land use authorities do not coordinate with water suppliers, wastewater utilities, and flood management agencies when making zoning and land-use-permitting decisions. Coordination at the level of groundwater basins is required to limit problems of groundwater overdraft, and broader watershed coordination can create benefits that cut across institutional lines (e.g., recharging aquifers with stormwater to augment water supply and limit polluted runoff from entering local streams). Coordination also can enable local entities to realize scale economies in some activities.

Some of California's local water management entities already benefit from structures that facilitate coordination. For instance, a few agencies manage both water supply and floods, and about 40 percent of water utilities also treat wastewater.[38] About 70 percent of large urban water utilities belong to wholesale networks, the largest of which—the Metropolitan Water District of Southern California—indirectly serves roughly 18 million of the state's residents.[39] Utilities that jointly manage water and wastewater and members of wholesale networks produced significantly better urban water management plans than utilities not benefitting from this integration (Hanak 2009a). The physical linkages and institutional arrangements within wholesale networks also can significantly improve the capacity to respond to supply shortfalls. Many Southern California utilities are also linked through their membership in adjudicated basins, supervised by court-appointed water masters who oversee water supply and use; such adjudications facilitate the trading of supplies.[40]

38. Estimates on the share of joint water and wastewater utilities are from Hanak (2005b). Examples of agencies that provide both water supply and flood control functions include the Yuba County Water Agency and the Santa Clara Valley Water District.

39. Estimate on the share of retail utilities within wholesale networks is from Hanak (2005b).

40. For instance, sales of water between members of the Mojave Basin and several other Southern California adjudicated basins are common (*Water Strategist*, various issues).

The value of coordination is spurring the expansion of new forms of formal and informal cooperation. Joint powers authorities are becoming a popular mechanism to allow agencies to conduct joint investments and operations in areas such as watershed and groundwater basin management.[41] The past 15 years also have seen the rise of groups engaged in groundwater management planning and regional water planning, encouraged in part by the availability of state bond funds for these activities (Chapter 6).[42] In addition, state laws (Senate Bill [SB] 610 and SB 221, passed in 2001) now require local land use authorities to coordinate with water utilities before approving large urban development projects (more than 500 units) to ensure that long-term supplies will be available (Hanak 2005b, 2010). As part of the 2007 flood legislation, local governments in the Central Valley will soon be required to incorporate flood risk considerations in their general plans and establish community protection goals (AB 162). This progress notwithstanding, more systematic efforts will be needed to coordinate and integrate water management activities at the basin and watershed scale to effectively address growing water supply, flood, water quality, and ecosystem management challenges (Chapters 5, 6, 8).

State and Federal Roles in a Decentralized System

Although day-to-day management of California water is highly decentralized, federal and state authorities from all three branches of government set the overall policy framework and regulatory context for local entities. Congress and the state legislature are the ultimate policymakers, but a range of federal and state agencies have considerable regulatory authority over water policy, planning, and operations. The judicial branch's role in resolving legal disputes makes it a critical arbiter of many controversial issues.

Legislatures

Congress and the California legislature have been responsible for numerous large and small water policy decisions and directives. As described in Chapter 1, the federal Flood Control Act of 1928 brought major changes to flood management policy, and state legislative and congressional approval of the Central Valley Project in the 1930s and the State Water Project in 1959 set the stage for the

41. Examples include the Santa Ana Watershed Project Authority (watershed management, including the operation of a brine line) (Chapter 6), the Sacramento Regional Water Authority (groundwater management within the Sacramento area) (www.rwah2o.org/rwa/), and the Orange County's Groundwater Replenishment System, noted above.

42. Hanak (2003) provides information on multiagency groundwater management planning entities formed under Assembly Bill (AB) 3030, adopted in 1992.

development of the large interregional water projects that form the backbone of California's water infrastructure. State and federal environmental laws enacted beginning in the late 1960s have fundamentally reshaped the context of almost all water management decisions. The absence of legislative action has also left its mark. Notably, the failure of California's legislature to include groundwater in the modern Water Code in 1913 and its subsequent failure to regulate groundwater have resulted in the fragmented and often ineffective management of this resource.

Over time, state legislation also has shaped the institutional framework of California's decentralized water management system by establishing the authority of cities, counties, and the various forms of special districts that operate in California (Chapter 1; Hundley 2001). Over the past three decades, most state water legislation has sought to require or facilitate action by these decentralized entities (Table 2.7). A variety of laws aim to improve local planning and coordination, and some impose conservation efforts on local entities. In the 1980s, a suite of laws was enacted to facilitate the transfer of water between local agencies and water users through water markets. Beginning in the early 1990s, a series of laws mandating the use of low-flow plumbing devices and appliances have also targeted water conservation by end users. Although local districts often object to such measures, state-imposed requirements can make it easier for them to withstand local opposition. For instance, 2004 legislation requiring that all utilities install water meters and begin billing by the amount of water used targeted many unmetered Central Valley communities, where local opposition to metering had prevented reform.

These laws have facilitated incremental improvements in water management at the local level. In recent decades, however, the legislature has had less success instituting broader changes that will be necessary to meet future management challenges. For instance, two laws enacted as part of the 2009 water policy package—on groundwater monitoring and on water rights enforcement—addressed crucial areas of reform but were significantly watered down in response to opposition from local stakeholders.

Administrative agencies

Over time, state and federal legislation has also established state and federal agencies concerned with different aspects of California's water system (Table 2.8). These agencies regulate and support the actions of local entities, and many also manage large water supply, flood, and environmental management projects. Some state and federal agencies also collect and analyze data to improve the technical and scientific basis for decisionmaking.

Table 2.7
Major state water legislation since 1980

Year	Legislation
1980	Water transfer legislation Conservation for water transfers is a beneficial use of water Third-party protections against harm from water transfers extended to fish and wildlife
1983	Urban Water Management Planning Act, requiring large urban suppliers to develop long-term water plans (amended numerous times since to incorporate additional elements and require coordination)
1986	Agricultural Water Management Planning Act, requiring agricultural districts to develop water conservation plans Water transfer legislation: DWR directed to encourage and facilitate water transfers "Wheeling" statute, providing for the conveyance of water through unused aqueduct capacity
1991	Water Recycling Act, establishing a statewide goal for reclaiming wastewater Water transfers authorized for environmental uses
1992	Formation of groundwater management districts and the adoption of local groundwater management plans authorized (AB 3030) Low-flow plumbing fixtures required in new construction (toilets, showers) (updated in 2007)
1999	Water transfer legislation: Expedition of short-term transfers and increased protection of water rights (Model Water Transfer Act)
2001	"Show me the water" laws (SB 210 and 610), requiring that local governments verify long-term water availability for new development with local water suppliers
2004	Urban utilities required to meter water and bill by volume used
2006	Urban outdoor water use conservation: Outdoor sprinklers required to meet water efficiency standards Cities and counties required to prepare local landscape ordinances
2007	Central Valley flood control package: 200-year flood frequency protection required for new urban development General plans and zoning ordinances required to comply with state plan of flood control Local governments responsible for some flood liability for new urban development (shared with state) Annual notification of landowners protected by levees
2009	Water policy package: New governance structure for the Sacramento–San Joaquin Delta and the development of a Delta Plan based on the co-equal goals of ecosystem protection and reliable water supplies; recognizing reasonable use and the public trust as the foundation of California water resources management (SB X7-1) Submission of $11.1 billion water bond to voters (SB X7-2) Local agencies required to monitor the elevation of groundwater basins (SB X7-6) Urban water agencies required to reduce per capita water use by 20 percent by 2020 and agricultural water agencies required to develop new water management plans and impose water charges based at least partly on quantity delivered (SB X7-7) More resources for water rights enforcement (SB X7-8)

Table 2.8
Primary state and federal water management agencies

Agency	Responsibility
State	
State Water Resources Control Board	Permits and administers state surface water rights; regulates water quality (along with nine regional boards)
California Department of Water Resources (California Natural Resources Agency)	Administers the State Water Project; oversees state flood control operations and overall state water planning
California Department of Fish and Game (California Natural Resources Agency) and Fish and Game Commission	Implements California fish protection laws and the state Endangered Species Act
California Department of Public Health	Regulates drinking water quality (utilities, devices)
Central Valley Flood Protection Board	Permits construction and modification of levees within the Central Valley
California Public Utilities Commission	Regulates water rate structures for private water utilities (~20 percent of urban customers)
Federal	
U.S. Department of the Interior	Acts as watermaster for the Colorado River
U.S. Bureau of Reclamation (USBR) (U.S. Department of the Interior)	Administers the Central Valley, Klamath River, Colorado River, and other projects
U.S. Fish and Wildlife Service (U.S. Department of the Interior)	Administers the federal Endangered Species Act for inland fish species
National Marine Fisheries Service National Oceanic and Atmospheric Administration (U.S. Department of Commerce)	Administers federal Endangered Species Act for salmon, steelhead trout, and other species that spend at least part of their lives in the ocean
U.S. Environmental Protection Agency (EPA)	Regulates water quality through the Clean Water Act, Safe Drinking Water Act, Resource Conservation and Recovery Act, and other federal laws
U.S. Army Corps of Engineers (U.S. Department of Defense)	Builds and oversees flood control systems and flood operations of most reservoirs
Federal Emergency Management Agency (U.S. Department of Homeland Security)	Operates the National Flood Insurance Program (including levee certification and regulation of land use in floodplains) and provides flood disaster assistance
Federal Energy Regulatory Commission (FERC)	Licenses and regulates dams that produce hydropower

Some of the same coordination challenges found at the local level occur at the state and federal levels as well. For example, through an accident of history, two different federal agencies, housed in separate cabinet departments, administer the Endangered Species Act for different fish that live within the same inland water systems. Through another accident of history, the federal government owns and operates the Central Valley Project, which shares the Delta as a conveyance hub and runs parallel to the state-run State Water Project for much of its length (Chapter 1). Although USBR and DWR work together on operations under a Coordinated Operating Agreement, differences in CVP and SWP rules and distinct water rights have complicated water transfers between users on either side of this administrative line. Coordination is also necessary, and often difficult, between the state and federal agencies that operate water supply infrastructure and the U.S. Army Corps of Engineers, in charge of flood control operations in most reservoirs. Coordination gaps among these and other agencies operating in complex systems, such as the Delta, were one of the impetuses behind the CALFED process in the mid-1990s, which formed numerous interagency working groups (Chapter 1; Little Hoover Commission 2005). The Delta Stewardship Council, created under the 2009 legislative package, is another attempt to resolve coordination problems, this time by centralizing some planning functions at the level of a seven-member appointed council. As discussed below, lack of coordination poses particular problems in the conduct of science to support policymaking.

Agencies are often constrained in exercising their authority by staff and funding limitations, which frequently reflect political opposition to action. This has been a particular challenge for state agencies. For instance, water rights administration by the State Water Resources Control Board has been hamstrung by low levels of staffing, resulting in multidecade backlogs in processing water rights applications in such areas as the Russian River (Little Hoover Commission 2010). In the past, the board also has been criticized for failing to exercise its wide latitude to place restrictions on the exercise of water rights for the benefit of the public interest.[43] The Department of Fish and Game, which has broad authority to regulate dams and water diversions to protect aquatic species under the Fish and Game Code, faces even greater challenges related to staffing, resources, and lack

---

43. In 1986, for example, the California Court of Appeal criticized the State Water Resources Control Board's failure to more aggressively address water quality issues in the Delta. According to the court, the board overlooked its "statutory commitment to establish objectives assuring the 'reasonable protection of beneficial uses,'" which "grants the Board broad discretion to establish reasonable standards consistent with overall statewide standards" (*United States v. State Water Resources Control Board [Racanelli]* 1986). More generally, see Hundley (2001).

of political clout. Critics of the Department of Water Resources express concern that the agency's broader public mission of statewide water resource planning conflicts with (and is compromised by) its operation of the State Water Project (Little Hoover Commission 2010). In Chapter 8, we suggest some institutional reforms to improve the performance of these state agencies.

Federal agencies also face resource constraints, exacerbating the effects of diminished federal involvement in California water in recent decades (Chapter 1). In particular, the ability of the U.S. Army Corps of Engineers to play a major role in California has been severely taxed by American involvement in wars and reconstruction in Iraq and Afghanistan, as well as the need to focus domestic efforts on the Gulf of Mexico in the aftermath of Hurricane Katrina and the British Petroleum oil spill.

The courts

California's judicial system also plays an important role in water governance, with the courts serving as arbiters of disputes over particular water management and use issues that often affect or reflect broader policies. State courts, rather than the legislature, established the initial contours of California's hybrid system of water rights, and courts continue to define and redefine those contours (such as the meaning of "reasonable use") (Gray 2004). In the absence of state groundwater permitting, courts have been the locus of adjudication proceedings for groundwater basins. Federal and state courts also have had a central role in environmental policy. In recent years, court actions have been particularly important in protecting environmental flows and other environmental amenities of water, both through the judicially enforced public trust doctrine (*National Audubon Society v. Superior Court* 1983) and through their interpretation and enforcement of the federal and state Endangered Species Acts (Moore, Mulville, and Weinberg 1996; Doremus and Tarlock 2003). For instance, current controversies over water supply and endangered species management in the Delta are largely being played out in a federal court in Fresno (Chapter 1). The threat of a court decision can also lead parties to come to a settlement—the case with the recent agreement to restore flows to the San Joaquin River to bring back salmon and other fish species (Box 9.1).

A Diverse Mix of Other Actors

Many other groups, both formal and informal, are involved in making and implementing water policies and managing water resources.

Indian tribes and water stewardship

California is home to more than 100 federally recognized Indian tribes and over 200 distinct Indian water allotments, both on reservations and in the federal public domain (Parr and Parr 2009). Under U.S. Supreme Court rulings, these Indian holdings potentially include federal water rights (*Winters v. United States* 1908; Sax et al. 2006).[44] Indian tribes are entitled to as much water as necessary to fulfill the purpose of the Indian reservation, usually enough to irrigate the "practicably irrigable acreage" on the reservation (*Arizona v. California* 1963, 2006). Although the law is not clear, once Indian water rights are quantified, tribes may be entitled to use the water for purposes other than those used to measure the rights—e.g., for environmental flows (Sax et al. 2006).

In contrast to some other western states, Indian water rights have not had a major role in California to date.[45] However, California Indian tribes are interested in the quantification and use of their federal water rights. As Indian tribes seek to quantify and use their water rights, tribal claims could affect existing allocations of water in California. This would be especially true for intrastate allocations of water from the Colorado River, where the U.S. Supreme Court has held that tribal claims may exceed 900,000 acre-feet per year (*Arizona v. California* 1963). Even without greater quantification of their water rights, California tribes sometimes have important roles in California water policy. Northern California tribes, for example, used their fishing rights to help drive the 2009 agreement to remove four dams from the Klamath River (Box 2.4). As holders of Colorado River rights, the San Luis Rey Indians of Southern California helped enable the transfer of water from the Imperial Irrigation District to the San Diego County Water Authority.[46] Indian tribes also have expressed concern about siting infrastructure that may interfere with sacred sites, loss of access to native-resource plants as a result of water activities, the effect of abandoned mines on water quality, illegal diversions, flood planning

---

44. Federal water rights enjoy priorities that date to the year the tribal land was reserved from the public domain by executive order or statute, and Indian water rights are not lost by nonuse (*Cappaert v. United States* 1976). The priority date for Indian water rights actually dates to the year in which an Indian reservation was created by treaty, executive order, or statute. No Indian tribes in California, however, are subject to treaties.

45. This is mostly because the water rights of only a few tribes have been quantified (Parr and Parr 2009). In addition, the priority dates for most Indian water rights in California might be late enough to be junior to most existing state water rights. Various legal theories might entitle tribes to earlier priority dates (California Tribal Water Summit Regional Tribal Water Plenary 2009). For experiences in some other southwestern states, see Colby, Thorson and Britton (2005).

46. The tribe and the San Diego County Water Authority are sharing the water savings from the lining of the All-American Canal, one of the components of the Quantification Settlement Agreement noted above. For the time being, the Metropolitan Water District of Southern California is buying the tribe's share until it can put the water to use.

2.4

Indian tribes and the Klamath River

A recent agreement to remove four dams from the Klamath River illustrates the importance of lawsuits and Indian tribes in reforming western water use. The Klamath River once supported the third largest salmon run in the West. The Klamath tribes of the upper basin, as well as the Karuk, Yurok, and Hoopa tribes of the lower basin, relied on salmon and other fish from the Klamath for food, and the salmon runs formed an integral part of their culture. However, six dams built between 1908 and 1962 blocked salmon runs and caused salmon populations to plummet. Despite 19th century treaties guaranteeing them fishing and water rights, the lower basin tribes had to drastically reduce catches, and the upper basin tribes were unable to fish at all. The dams stored water under the federal reclamation program for farmers in south-central Oregon and in Northern California (National Research Council 2004).

When fishermen filed lawsuits against the dam operations under the ESA, the Klamath Tribes filed a brief as amicus curiae. In 2001, a federal court held that these dam operations violated the ESA and enjoined the supply of irrigation water to the farmers (*Pacific Coast Federation of Fishermen's Associations v. National Marine Fisheries Service* 2001). Some farmers resisted the court order by illegally opening headgates, and some men even drove through the Klamath tribes' hometown shooting shotguns. After the bureau resumed irrigation deliveries in 2002, over 30,000 salmon and other fish died from infection, likely brought on by overcrowding in warm, low-flow water (Doremus and Tarlock 2008).

The tribes took advantage of the impending 2006 expiration of several of the dam licenses to push for their removal. They sent representatives to the dam operators and owners and held rallies asking each state's governor to support dam removal. They joined environmental groups in filing a new lawsuit in 2007 against the dam operators and submitted comments during the FERC relicensing process. FERC concluded that license renewal would require the installation of fish ladders and other modifications to allow fish to freely swim upstream past the dams.

By 2005, more than 20 organizations representing the farmers, tribes, salmon fishermen, government agencies, and environmental groups were seeking a negotiated solution. By 2008, the dam operator was also at the bargaining table, having determined that the cost of removing the dams was less than the cost of modifying the dams for fish passage. At a February 18, 2010, ceremony, the major interests signed conditional agreements to study and prepare for the removal of four of the dams—and Governor Schwarzenegger declared "I can see already the salmon are screaming, 'I'll be back.'" The process, however, may take decades before any concrete is moved.

and management that affect tribal lands, and groundwater overdraft. Some tribes have significantly affected FERC relicensing proceedings for hydroelectric projects by identifying traditional cultural properties and Indian trust asset lands within the project vicinity.[47] Tribes also have called for a more active role in regional water planning processes, adjudications, and agreements (California Tribal Water Summit Regional Tribal Water Plenary 2009).

Stakeholder associations

Stakeholder associations representing various interests significantly influence California's water policies. Historically, farm groups, urban water agencies, associations of water agencies and contractors, and environmental organizations have played a leading role, but business, recreation, and community organizations have also often demonstrated their interest.[48] Interest group organizations influence policies and management in various ways, most notably by providing data and information to decisionmakers, lobbying, placing initiatives on the ballot, and initiating lawsuits. Since the introduction of term limits in the California legislature in the early 1990s, stakeholder associations have gained more direct influence on the legislative process, both as a source of expertise and as crafters of legislation (Cain and Kousser 2004).

California residents: water users and ballot box policymakers

As water and land users, the state's residents clearly have an important, direct influence on a range of water policy outcomes. For example, the effectiveness of water conservation incentives, the volume of contaminants that enter storm drains, and the extent of uninsured flood risk exposure all depend on individual actions. The views of the general public also can sway the decisions of legislatures, administrative agencies, and local governments. California residents are also frequently asked to make policy directly at the ballot box, by voting on policy initiatives and approving spending proposals.

---

47. Agencies and licensees must take into account the effect of their project on these properties (Federal Energy Regulatory Commission 2004).

48. For instance, in the early 1990s, the Bay Area Economic Forum promoted the development of water marketing. In the mid-1990s, business leaders were also active in negotiations leading up to the Bay-Delta Accord (Chapter 1). In 2001, the California Building Industry Association played an important role in negotiations surrounding the passage of the "show me the water" laws (SB 610 and SB 221) (Association of California Water Agencies 2002). Environmental preservation, recreational fishing, bird-watching, rafting, and other nongovernmental organizations representing specific interests are prominent in California water policy discussions at local, state, and national levels.

Relative to other states, California has an active initiative process, whereby interest groups can put both policy and spending measures on the ballot.[49] In addition, the California legislature must place general obligation (GO) bonds up for public vote, and it has the option to seek voter approval for policy measures. Policy and fiscal initiatives are also common at the local level (Gordon 2004).

Although relatively few policy initiatives have addressed water issues at the state level,[50] the electorate has weighed in on fundamental water policy decisions at several key times in the past: The first modern water code (1914), the Central Valley Project (1933), the "reasonable use" provisions of the California constitution (1928), and the State Water Project (1960) all went before voters for their approval (Chapter 1). Voters were also responsible for two important pieces of recent policy: the 1982 defeat of the peripheral canal, which had been approved by the governor and the legislature two years earlier, and the 1986 passage of Proposition 65, the Safe Drinking Water and Toxics Enforcement Act, which aimed to protect drinking water from several types of hazardous chemicals.

In recent decades, voters have been solicited numerous times to approve GO bonds to support water-related activities. Between 1970 and 2006, voters approved more than 20 water bonds—covering water supply, water quality, and flood control—authorizing a total of over $32 billion (2008 $) in spending (Table 2.9). The size of these bonds has increased dramatically over the past decade, and GO bonds have become a major mechanism for funding state water-related activity. The largest water bond to date ($11.1 billion), part of the 2009 legislative package, was initially scheduled to go before voters in November 2010 and has now been rescheduled for November 2012 over concerns that the economic recession and state budget woes would dissuade voters from approving it.

In parallel to their largesse on state general obligation bonds for water, California voters have directly restricted the financial options of state and local governments, including local water agencies. Proposition 13, passed in 1978, limited property assessments and mandated supermajority voter approval for the passage of local special taxes. California is also one of only eight states with supermajority requirements on the passage of local GO bonds.[51] (State GO bonds require only a simple majority to pass.) For water-related activities, two

49. Out of 24 states that have an initiative process, California was second only to Oregon in the cumulative frequency of initiatives on statewide ballots as of August 31, 2010 (353 vs. 342) (National Conference of State Legislatures 2010).

50. Only 6 percent have addressed environmental issues more broadly (Center for Governmental Studies 2008).

51. This restriction dates back to the early 1900s. Other states with supermajority requirements include Missouri and North Dakota (two-thirds majority to pass local debt) and Idaho, Iowa, Oklahoma, Washington, and West Virginia (three-fifths majority).

Table 2.9
State general obligation bonds for water, 1970–2010

Year	Bond title	Amount authorized (million)		Pass rate
		Current $	2008 $	(%)
1970	Clean Water Bond Law of 1970 (Prop. 1)	250	1,504	75.4
1974	Clean Water Bond Law of 1974 (Prop. 2)	250	1,028	70.5
1976	California Safe Drinking Water Bond Law of 1976 (Prop. 3)	175	606	62.6
1978	Clean Water and Water Conservation Bond Law of 1978 (Prop. 2)	375	1,123	53.5
1982	Lake Tahoe Acquisitions Bond Act (Prop. 4)	85	185	52.9
1984	California Safe Drinking Water Bond Law of 1984 (Prop. 25)	75	150	72.9
1984	Clean Water Bond Law of 1984 (Prop. 28)	325	651	73.5
1984	Fish and Wildlife Habitat Enhancement Act of 1984 (Prop. 19)	85	170	64.0
1986	Water Conservation and Water Quality Bond Law of 1986 (Prop. 44)	150	290	74.1
1986	California Safe Drinking Water Bond Law of 1986 (Prop. 55)	100	193	78.7
1988	California Safe Drinking Water Bond Law of 1988 (Prop. 81)	75	138	71.7
1988	California Wildlife, Coastal, and Park Land Conservation Act (Prop. 70)	776	1,427	65.2
1988	Water Conservation Bond Law of 1988 (Prop. 82)	60	110	62.4
1988	Clean Water and Water Reclamation Bond Law of 1988 (Prop. 83)	65	120	64.4
1996	Safe, Clean, Reliable Water Supply Act (Prop. 204)	995	1,471	62.9
2000	Safe Drinking Water, Clean Water, Watershed Protection, and Flood Protection Act (Prop. 13)	1,970	2,632	64.8
2000	Safe Neighborhood Parks, Clean Water, Clean Air, and Coastal Protection Bond Act of 2000 (Prop. 12)	2,100	2,805	63.2
2002	California Clean Water, Clean Air, Safe Neighborhood Parks, and Coastal Protection Act of 2002 (Prop. 40)	2,600	3,305	56.9
2002	Water Security, Clean Drinking Water, Coastal and Beach Protection Act of 2002 (Prop. 50)	3,440	4,372	55.4
2006	Disaster Preparedness and Flood Protection Bond Act of 2006 (Prop. 1E)	4,090	4,385	64.0
2006	Safe Drinking Water, Water Quality and Supply, Flood Control, River and Coastal Protection Bond Act of 2006 (Prop. 84)	5,388	5,777	53.8
Total		**$23,429**	**$32,442**	

SOURCES: Legislative Analyst's Office (2008); de Alth and Rueben (2005); California Secretary of State.

NOTES: Nominal values were converted to 2008 dollars using the Engineering News Record Construction Cost Index. During this period, one water supply–oriented bond for $380 million ($667 million in 2008 $) was rejected by voters in November 1990 (de Alth and Rueben 2005).

measures are particularly important: Proposition 218, a constitutional amendment passed in 1996, mandated majority or supermajority votes for local general taxes, assessments, and "property-related" fees. Proposition 26, a constitutional amendment enacted in November 2010, raises voting requirements for most state and local regulatory fees—including fees designed to mitigate or remediate environmental harm—from a simple majority to a two-thirds majority.

Proposition 218 has substantially complicated funding for flood control and stormwater programs, which now require direct voter approval to raise funds: a simple majority of property owners, or at least two-thirds of the general public.[52] Although some Sacramento area agencies were able to win high voter approval for new assessments in the wake of Hurricane Katrina, some flood-prone Bay Area communities came up short.[53] Water and wastewater utilities can still raise rates through a vote of their governing boards, although ratepayers can overturn them if a majority protests the increases. However, court interpretations of Proposition 218 are restricting the flexibility of water and wastewater utilities to raise funds to support new development, which can complicate capital project funding (Hanak 2009b). And the courts are also calling into question the ability of groundwater management districts to charge pumping fees without a majority vote of the affected property owners or a two-thirds vote of the electorate (*Pajaro Valley Water Management Agency v. Amrhein* 2007; *Great Oaks Water Company v. Santa Clara Valley Water District* 2010). These decisions are problematic, as groundwater pumping charges are an important tool for managing overdraft.

Proposition 26 affects regulatory fees, which are a natural way to fund environmental mitigation associated with the use of water resources or other activities that impair water bodies. Regulatory fees are typically surcharges on the activity in question, for instance a surcharge on a chemical that causes harm to the environment or public health. Regulatory fees are already used in California to fund programs related to the disposal of hazardous materials and the recycling of oil, among others.[54] Under Proposition 26, regulatory fees with

52. For assessments, the requirement is a weighted majority of property owners. For property-related fees (such as payments for local stormwater control), an alternative to a majority of property owners is a two-thirds majority of the general electorate (Legislative Analyst's Office 1996; Rueben and Cerdán 2003).

53. In 2007, the Sacramento Area Flood Control Agency and the West Sacramento Area Flood Control Agency passed new assessments with 82 percent and 70 percent affirmative vote of property owners, respectively. But in November 2008, the cities of Orinda and Burlingame lost with 62 percent and 64 percent of the popular vote, respectively.

54. See "Official Title and Summary" in the California Voter Guide for the November 2010 election: www.voterguide.sos.ca.gov/pdf/english/26-title-summ-analysis.pdf.

a broad public purpose may now be considered taxes, subject to a two-thirds vote of the state legislature (up from a simple majority). Local governing bodies, which could approve these fees without a vote of the general public, would also be required to seek a two-thirds vote of the general public for such fees. Although the text of the new amendment is uncertain in some respects and will certainly be tested in litigation, Proposition 26 is likely to substantially restrict California's ability to address the current gaps in resources for broad public purposes, including environmental stewardship and water resources planning.

Is There Enough Money to Pay for California's Water System?

Restrictions on state and local funding, along with the budget woes of federal and state governments, naturally raise the question of whether California can maintain, let alone enhance, its current water operations and infrastructure. Water managers in all sectors tend to answer with a resounding "no." But the answer is more nuanced than is commonly believed, reflecting the roles and responsibilities of different levels of government in water system management and differences in funding rules.

Utilities

Urban water and wastewater utilities, which are responsible for the vast majority of spending on water supply and wastewater infrastructure and operations, appear to be in relatively good financial shape. Every four years, these utilities are required to submit estimates of their long-term capital needs to the EPA, which tracks investment needs nationwide. The most recent assessments, from 2007 for water and from 2008 for wastewater, indicate that California's 20-year spending needs for publicly owned utilities are on the order of $40.7 billion and $24.4 billion (2008 $), respectively, or roughly $2 billion and $1.2 billion per year.[55] An additional estimated $3.9 billion over 20 years ($194 million per year) is needed for managing stormwater and nonpoint source pollution, some of which is also handled by wastewater utilities.

In 2007, capital spending by these utilities was substantially higher. According to estimates from the State Controller's Office, publicly owned water utilities invested roughly $3.6 billion and wastewater utilities roughly $2.2 billion (2008 $). (U.S. Census of Governments estimates put total capital outlays for water in

55. U.S. Environmental Protection Agency (2008, 2009). Estimates of both needs and capital outlays reported in the text exclude interest payments.

California even higher, at $5 billion.) For water, these levels of spending reflect increases in real per capita spending since the early 1980s, and for wastewater, a relatively stable rate of spending since the mid-1970s (Figure 2.15).

Although utilities have benefited from state bond funding as well as some property tax receipts, utility revenue comes predominately from ratepayers.[56] Compared with their own estimates of needs, water and wastewater utilities generally appear to have sufficient flexibility to raise rates to fund capital improvements in their systems, although they now face greater procedural requirements arising from Propositions 218. Moreover, water and wastewater rates in California generally fall well within the range considered "affordable" by federal guidelines (less than 4 percent of household income) (Table 2.4).[57] Although raising rates is never easy politically, the ability to raise rates, while

Figure 2.15
Real per capita investments have been rising for water and holding steady for wastewater

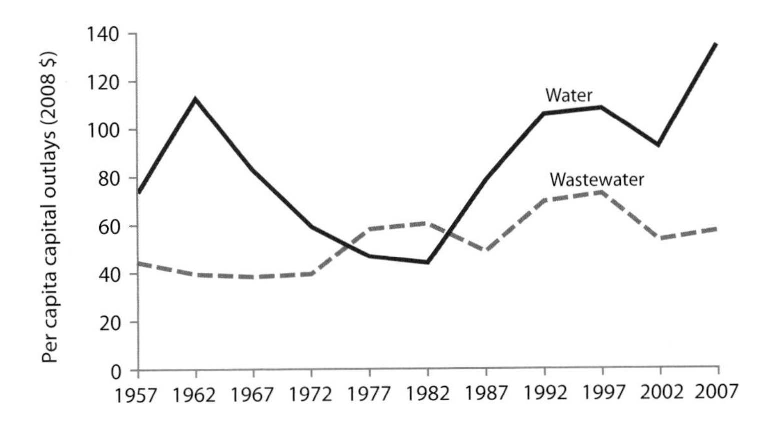

SOURCES: Census of Governments; de Alth and Rueben (2005).

NOTE: Nominal values were converted to 2008 dollars using the Engineering News Record Construction Cost Index.

56. In 2007, grants and equity contributions from federal and state sources accounted for less than 2 percent of revenues and contributed capital for all publicly owned local and regional urban and agricultural water agencies and wastewater utilities. Property taxes accounted for 5 percent of urban and agricultural water district revenues and 8 percent of wastewater district revenues; and voter-approved assessments accounted for 6 percent and 2 percent of revenues, respectively (comparable information on the share of tax revenues is not available for city-owned utilities) (authors' calculations using data from the State Controller's Office files).

57. See Hanak and Barbour (2005) for a discussion of affordability guidelines.

maintaining affordability, positions these utilities relatively well for the challenges of upgrading aging infrastructure, a perennial challenge for utilities (Chapter 3).

Flood management

Flood management faces greater financial difficulties. This sector traditionally has relied on federal cost-sharing (typically 65 percent, sometimes higher), and local entities are now subject to public votes for raising local assessments under Proposition 218. Although no comparable exercise exists to estimate statewide flood control spending needs, the Department of Water Resources estimates that the minimum cost of restoring the Sacramento–San Joaquin Flood Control Projects is more than $20 billion (M. Inamine, DWR, personal communication).[58] This estimate does not include upgrading the system to a higher level of protection, as mandated by the new flood legislation passed in 2007, nor does it include flood-related investment needs in other parts of California, many of which are also vulnerable.

In recent decades, federal investments in California flood protection have been modest, leaving Californians to shoulder most of this financial burden. State flood protection funds have come from general obligation bonds ($5 billion from Propositions 1E and 84—see Table 2.9) and other general fund resources (such as emergency levee repair legislation). State bond funding has put California well ahead of the U.S. Army Corps of Engineers, although bond sales were limited by the onset of the recession (Figure 2.16). Over the longer term, the bigger problem will be raising new sources when the bonds are exhausted, given the vast unfunded capital needs. As discussed in Chapter 6, new forms of regional or statewide risk-based assessments or fees will be needed.

Environmental mitigation

Although the estimated funding requirements for environmental mitigation are smaller than those in the flood management sector, the management of polluted stormwater and other types of runoff face similar challenges because of Propositions 218 and 26. City and county governments are required by law to meet Clean Water Act standards regarding these nonpoint sources of pollutants, yet they are required to go to voters to raise the necessary funding—a difficult task when the problems caused by pollution occur downstream rather than close to home (Hanak and Barbour 2005).

---

58. For comparison purposes, the *New York Times* reports the cost of levee system reconstruction in New Orleans at $15 billion (Schwartz 2010).

Figure 2.16
The state has surpassed the federal government in flood protection spending in California

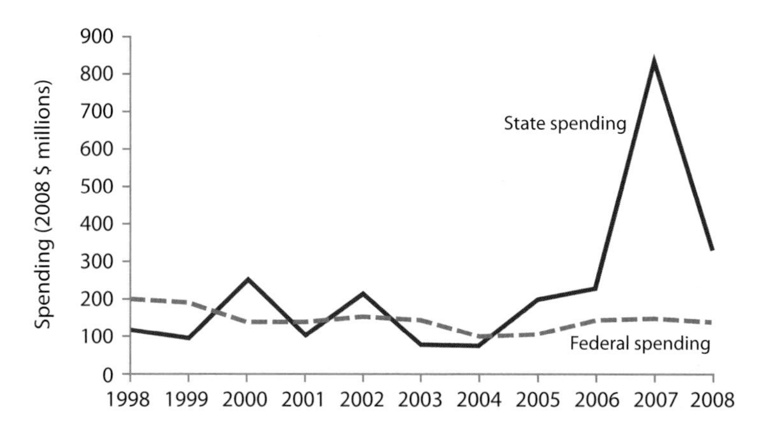

SOURCES: U.S. Army Corps of Engineers; governor's budgets.

NOTE: Nominal values were converted to 2008 dollars using the Engineering News Record Construction Cost Index.

Another area of systematic mismatch between funding mechanisms and funding needs is environmental management. California water users pay only for the infrastructure-related costs of water delivery, not the environmental costs of diversions. Although, in principle, new water supply and flood control projects are required to mitigate environmental harm, the cumulative effects of decades of water system development have contributed to the widespread degradation of aquatic ecosystems described in the Introduction. Recent bonds have provided some support to scientific research and habitat investments, but bonds are an unreliable source of funds for these purposes. This is where the new constraints imposed by Proposition 26 will be felt the most. Surcharges on water use and other water-related activities, such as flood infrastructure investments and the discharge of contaminants, are an appropriate way to fund environmental mitigation and the related science needed to redress the decline of California's aquatic ecosystems.

Budget woes

Finally, state budget problems over the past decade have reduced funding for the basic state operations of monitoring, analysis, and enforcement of water policy. Bond funds have provided stopgap funding for activities once supported by the general fund.[59]

California needs more reliable, user-fee based funding to support publicly related water expenses, including the basic science, monitoring and planning functions of government as well as investments to improve aquatic habitat. As discussed in Chapter 7, the state's energy and transportation sectors provide useful user-fee models.

Whether the public can be convinced to shift to more fee-based funding of such public functions is an important question. Voter support for numerous water bonds suggests a willingness to support these activities with taxpayer dollars, but it is not clear that voters recognize the costs of state general obligation bonds in terms of new taxes or reduced spending in other areas. (Indeed, state general obligation bonds are often promoted by their sponsors as *not* requiring new taxes; in contrast, local bonds are generally proposed along with a revenue source to cover the obligation [Hanak 2009b]).

In contrast to such issues as the economy, education, and crime, water is generally not the foremost policy issue on the minds of the state's residents.[60] However, public opinion surveys suggest that the public is concerned with water conditions in the state. Over the past decade, water issues (supply and quality) have generally ranked second after air quality as the state's top environmental issue (Figure 2.17). (Water surpassed air quality in 2009, when many residents faced voluntary or mandatory rationing because of drought conditions and cutbacks in Delta pumping.) In recent surveys, more than two-thirds of respondents said that water supply is at least somewhat of a problem in their region (Baldassare et al. 2009a, 2010). Looking ahead, most said that they are very or somewhat concerned about the potential for more severe floods (55–60 percent) and droughts (78–85 percent) as a result of climate change (Baldassare et al. 2005, 2007, 2009). Although raising new fees to support the water sector is not likely to be popular with California voters, better public information about water system conditions might help foster public discussion for reform of the inadequate funding mechanisms currently available.

---

59. Since the onset of chronic state budget problems in 2001, bonds have funded at least one-quarter —and sometimes more than half—of DWR's operational expenses in every year except 2005 (authors' calculations using information from the governor's budgets).

60. In 38 surveys conducted by the Public Policy Institute of California between August 1999 and June 2010, water (supply or quality) never accounted for more than 2 percent to 3 percent of responses to the open-ended question: "Thinking about the state as a whole, what do you think is the most important issue facing people in California today?" Jobs and the economy were almost always the highest, occasionally surpassed by immigration (in 2007), crime (in 2003), energy prices (in 2001), and schools (1999) (all surveys are available at www.ppic.org).

Figure 2.17
Water is one of residents' top environmental concerns

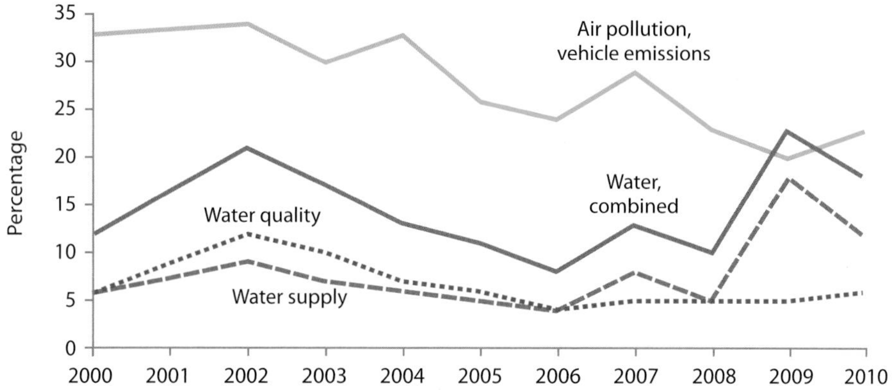

SOURCE: Baldassare et al. (2000–2010).

NOTE: The figure reports the share of residents identifying these issues in open-ended responses to the question: "What do you think is the most important environmental issue facing California today?"

Scientific and Technical Support for Decisionmaking

Effective water management requires sound information, and water management systems as complex and extensive as California's require commensurately broad and well-organized scientific and technical support. The development of the Central Valley Project, the State Water Project, and the Central Valley flood control system all involved focused and systematic development of scientific and technical knowledge and expertise over decades (Chapter 1). The Hydraulic Era in California's water development required tremendous growth in technical expertise in all branches of government and the private sector. From this emerged one of the most complex and effective water supply and flood control systems in the world.

The Era of Conflict stimulated dramatic growth in demand for scientific support for environmental regulations. Setting Clean Water Act standards for flow and pollutant discharge, evaluating mitigation alternatives, constructing wastewater treatment plants, determining the causes of decline of native species subject to the Endangered Species Act, and evaluating the effects of water operations on ecosystems each required advances and organized application of science. Today, California's scientific infrastructure is extensive and diverse. Hundreds of scientists are involved in water management in California at government agencies, at universities, and as private consultants. Yet few would argue that this infrastructure meets current needs, and even fewer would suggest that California is prepared for the next era.

The dramatic changes in conditions that California will face through the rest of the century will require greater synthesis and emphasis on developing solutions, beyond regulatory problems and details (Chapter 3). Science will have a major role in an Era of Reconciliation. Along with its traditional roles of facilitating design and operation of water management, science and technological innovations must facilitate the adaptation of management. Science will be essential for effective strategic and incremental reconciliation of environmental and human water uses, locally, regionally, and statewide, just as engineering science was required for the Hydraulic Era to effectively achieve that era's goals.

A Fragmented, Underfunded System

A recent review by the National Research Council (2010) of the biological opinions that govern operations of the Central Valley Project and the State Water Project pointed out that scientific support for water management in the Delta is weak, poorly organized, and lacking integration. The Little Hoover Commission (2005, 2010) offered similar observations, as has the Delta Vision Blue Ribbon Task Force (2008). Yet the Delta has perhaps the state's *most* organized and best-funded science programs to support decisionmaking. National Research Council reviews of science for Klamath Basin management have had similar findings (National Research Council, 2004, 2008).

It is not enough to simply state that insufficient resources have been invested in science for improving water management. Beyond an almost entirely nontechnical California Water Plan Update developed by the Department of Water Resources every five years or so, there is little to no statewide organization, prioritization, and synthesis of technical and scientific activity applied to water problems. This gap stems partly from the highly decentralized management of water. The tensions between water districts—stemming from perceived competition for resources—and institutional barriers between federal, state, and local agencies have balkanized water science and engineering in California. To illustrate the complexity of this problem, Table 2.10 lists federal, state, and local entities that fund scientific and engineering studies in ecosystem management, water supply/quality, flood management, and water-based tourism/recreation. This list neglects many other agencies with jurisdiction and funding control. A recent summary of agencies with responsibilities in these four areas conducted

Table 2.10
Agencies funding or overseeing scientific research on water

Agency	Ecosystem/ environment	Water supply/ quality	Flood management	Recreation/ tourism
Federal				
Bureau of Land Management	●	●		●
Bureau of Reclamation	●	●	●	●
Coast Guard	●	●		●
Department of Agriculture	●	●	●	
Department of the Interior	●	●	●	●
Environmental Protection Agency	●	●		●
Federal Emergency Management Agency		●	●	
Federal Energy Regulatory Commission	●	●	●	●
Fish and Wildlife Service	●	●		
Forest Service	●	●	●	●
Geological Survey	●	●	●	
National Marine Fisheries Service	●	●		
Natural Resources Conservation Service	●	●	●	
U.S. Army Corps of Engineers	●	●	●	●
State				
Department of Boating and Waterways	●			●
Department of Conservation	●	●		
Department of Fish and Game	●	●		●
Department of Food and Agriculture	●	●		
Department of Health Services		●		
Department of Parks and Recreation	●	●		●
Department of Public Health		●		
Department of Transportation	●	●	●	
Department of Water Resources	●	●	●	
Energy Commission	●	●		
Environmental Protection Agency	●	●		
Flood Management Board	●		●	
Natural Resources Agency	●	●	●	●
State Lands Commission	●	●	●	●
Water Resources Control Board	●	●		
Local				
Cities	●	●	●	●
Counties	●	●	●	●
Flood control districts			●	
Irrigation districts	●	●		
Port authorities	●	●	●	●
Reclamation districts	●	●	●	
Resource conservation districts	●	●	●	
Sanitation districts	●	●		
Water districts	●	●		

SOURCE: Authors' survey of agencies with responsibilities for managing or regulating water.

for the Delta Vision Blue Ribbon Task Force identified more than 100 within the Delta alone, and this was considered an incomplete list. Excessive decentralization has greatly reduced the ability of fragmented scientific and technical activity to provide coherent and consistent advice to policymakers.

In addition, investments in science have not kept up with demands for increasing information and analysis. Federal investments in science for California water through the Bureau of Reclamation, U.S. Army Corps of Engineers, Fish and Wildlife Service, National Marine Fisheries Service, and U.S. Geological Survey have been modest and centered mostly on narrow agency missions and mandates, with little broader synthesis or exploration of strategic solutions to long-term problems. Major construction projects, which provided an overall focus, ended decades ago, and, since then, technical management in these agencies has deteriorated badly. The three state agencies responsible for statewide water management and regulation—Department of Water Resources, State Water Resources Control Board, and Department of Fish and Game—have seen a steady erosion of their technical capacity. California has many universities famous for their extensive and high-quality scholarly water research. But this work is often ad hoc, with little coordination or integration beyond a few efforts at a handful of campuses.

One of the largest concerns regarding California's scientific infrastructure comes from changes in how agencies are staffed. For the last 30 years, a strong political drive has shrunk agency staffing and funding while increasing the scope and complexity of their responsibilities. The result has been a long-term shift from in-house agency expertise to reliance on external, for-profit consulting firms to complete both major and minor initiatives. Many major ongoing studies of water management in California—Bay Delta Conservation Plan, Delta Stewardship Council, State Plan of Flood Control, Delta Risk Management Study, and more—are run by consultants directed by agencies. Although this shift reflects fiscal necessities, the loss of in-house expertise—particularly more senior and experienced technical and scientific managers with deep knowledge of operations or ecosystems—reduces the ability of agencies to be nimble and authoritative in their responses or the management of consultants.

Finally, there is a growing information gap regarding water in the state. Dramatic advances have occurred in technology for monitoring water as it moves through the hydrologic cycle. Monitoring the flow and quality of water is essential for water management today and will become increasingly important for an Era of Reconciliation. Yet cash-strapped federal and state agencies, forced to deal with daily crises, have no program for coordinated development of networks that better account for and analyze water movement and management.[61] Without this information, successful adaptation to changing conditions will be hindered or foreclosed.

Costs of "Combat" Science

The failure to organize, integrate, and fund robust science and technical programs to support decisionmaking imposes a high cost on California. The lack of strong, coherent governmental scientific and technical programs has provoked efforts to attack or augment (depending on one's perspective) existing governmental and academic scientific and technical conclusions. Weak government scientific programs contribute to the proliferation of "combat" science—the selective development and presentation of facts and analysis primarily for the political or regulatory advantage (or disadvantage) of one stakeholder group or agency. When the National Research Council (2004) was asked to review the biological opinions governing the operations of the Klamath Project, the authors of the report were struck by the amount of combat science on the basin and how little trust existed in the science being used to make decisions (Doremus and Tarlock 2008).

The recent dust-up over the role of ammonium in the decline of delta smelt is another example. For several years, concern existed in the scientific community over ammonium in the Delta and its potential to disrupt food webs on which native fish depend. Consultants were hired to help the Sacramento Regional County Sanitation District with press releases and studies claiming that although they are the primary source of ammonium in the Delta, the ammonium poses no problem and the Delta's problems are from downstream water exports (www.srcsd.com). To counter this combat science, a coalition of water contractors, led by the Metropolitan Water District of Southern California, funded a researcher from the University of Maryland with no experience in the Delta who drew a sharply different conclusion, suggesting that the ammonium was *the* cause of the decline of delta smelt and that the exporters were blameless

61. Data-collection efforts are typically fragmented and incomplete. For example, the SWRCB collects annual water use reports from surface water right-holders, but these often bear little relation to actual volumes used, and the exercise neglects groundwater users and many riparian and pre-1914 surface water rights holders. Regional water quality control boards collect a substantial volume of water quality data, but there is little synthesis that would enable the use of these data in basin management. Similarly, DWR had a wide range of data-collection and assessment activities but lacks a coherent technical organization that would allow such data to inform or guide integrated water management at regional or statewide scales.

(Glibert 2010). Such combat science has been noted in other basins outside California (White 1995).

Combat science is an inevitable and occasionally useful aspect of California water management. Yet, the recent increase in political manipulation of science, which is highly effective from political and legal standpoints, is a sign of weak, ineffective governmental science programs. It inevitably leads to a loss of transparency and further loss of trust in the science needed to support effective decisionmaking. Weak governmental technical programs and strong combat science are major reasons why so many water management decisions are decided in the courts rather than at the negotiating table.

A New Approach to Water System Science

Improving the science to support decisionmaking, while reducing the influence of combat science in California water management, will require a sustained, integrated effort by the state and federal governments. This must begin with finding new ways to fund scientific infrastructure so that it is less vulnerable to economic and political cycles. In addition, the programs and agencies conducting the research must increase, retain, and better employ in-house expertise and talent. The state must modernize how it tracks water quality and its ecosystem and human uses. Finally, the state needs more independent means to conduct scientific and technical synthesis, less subject to political influence.

A model for a successful program might be the California Energy Commission's Public Interest Energy Research (PIER) program (www.energy.ca.gov/research/index.html). Funded by ratepayers and overseen by a committee chaired by a commissioner, this program has become the focus of energy-related research and monitoring to support policy throughout California. PIER projects focus on energy research projects unlikely to be funded by utilities or consultants because of the general nature of their results or the innovative technical questions addressed. It is structured as a research, development, and demonstration program, largely shielded from political influence, and has become the center of the state's research regarding climate change adaptation. The PIER program is too new to allow a comprehensive assessment of its overall effectiveness, but its climate change efforts have generated a critical mass of research to support climate change policy discussions. The California Air Resources Board also has an extensive scientific and technical program that may provide a model for the water sector (Little Hoover Commission 2009).

Strengths and Weaknesses in Today's Water System

California's water system today has both impressive assets and significant vulnerabilities. A major asset is the sophisticated physical infrastructure that enables water to be delivered to urban and agricultural demand centers and successfully protects residents from frequent floods. Vulnerabilities in this infrastructure—which threaten water supplies and increase flood risk—include a fragile water supply conveyance hub in the Sacramento–San Joaquin Delta, deteriorating flood control structures, chronic overdraft in some major groundwater basins, and increasing problems of water salinity and other contaminants.

Another major asset is the resilience of California's economy, which has shown an ability to adapt and continue to grow, despite increasing water scarcity. Continued adaptation seems possible, with suitable management and policy changes, given the economy's decreasing reliance on water as a direct input into production, the sizable proportion of agricultural water still allocated to low-value crops, and the large share of urban water now used for landscape irrigation. However, economic adaptation potential is limited by regional economic concerns (which can make agricultural communities reluctant to sell or divert water from lower-value crops) and difficulties of reducing outdoor water use by millions of California households and businesses.

For all their complexity, California's diverse water management institutions also have some strong positive features that can serve the state well in confronting the challenges it faces. The state has many dedicated, highly trained staff working on all aspects of its water system, and their decentralized governance means that water managers are quite responsive to local water user needs. However, this system will fail to satisfy the broader needs of the economy and the environment without better coordination that aligns management oversight with the appropriate geographical scale (e.g., basins and watersheds) and that connects activities across different functional areas to benefit water supply, flood protection, water quality, and ecosystems. Similar challenges of coordination exist among state and federal agencies, which also face resource constraints and limits on their authority. Inadequate technical information and scientific capacity is a particular weakness in California's current institutional landscape. Decentralization, fragmentation, and limited resources to collect and analyze information on water use and to support solution-oriented science by major state and federal agencies have hobbled the state's ability to address the major environmental management challenges of the current era. Such redirection of science will be essential in an Era of Reconciliation.

Finally, although money alone is not sufficient for successful water management, it is necessary. Those parts of the water system that rely primarily on ratepayer contributions—water supply and wastewater utilities—seem relatively well-positioned to meet their investment needs. In contrast, flood management, ecosystem management, and the state's overall strategic planning, monitoring, and technical functions have become dependent on unreliable state general obligation bond funding, often well below the levels needed to sustain adequate efforts. California residents have supported these bonds, while also voting to restrict local funding and state funding through fees on water users. Fiscal reforms are needed to provide the state with the financial capacity to adapt and strengthen water supply reliability and flood protection and to redress its failing aquatic ecosystems.

Despite a history of hard-won successes in managing water, California's water system, designed in the 1930s for a very different economy and society, is showing signs of decay and potential disaster. The state is standing on the edge of a very real crisis as it faces the collapse of native ecosystems, the effects of droughts, threats of widespread flooding, and a conspicuous absence of governmental technical and political leadership and funding.

Today's challenges are likely to become even more acute in the coming decades. As described in the next chapter, a range of natural, physical, economic, and demographic forces will increasingly threaten scarce water supplies and heighten the risk of continuing the ecological and economic deterioration of the state's water system.

3 Drivers of Change

GERD LUDWIG/CORBIS

He who foretells the future lies, even if he tells the truth.

Arabian proverb

California's water management systems have always had to accommodate changing conditions, such as population growth and major shifts in the state's economic structure, from mining in the 1800s to agriculture in the 1900s to today's predominantly urban economy. The most urgent and overarching challenge for water management in the modern era is to reconcile the demands of the environment with the large and evolving demands for water for human activities. Policymakers at all levels will need to address this task in the midst of shifting conditions. In the coming decades, California is likely to experience wide-ranging and simultaneous changes that will further complicate water management but that will also present new opportunities (Table 3.1).

- **Climate.** Sea level rise, warming land and water temperatures, and shifting precipitation will affect water supply, flood risk, and the environment.
- **Deterioration.** The physical conditions of the water system—including both infrastructure and water quality—will deteriorate as a result of wear and tear, earthquakes, accumulating contaminants, and other complications.
- **Economy and demography.** California will experience a growing urban population, ongoing shifts in its economic structure, and further state and federal financial constraints.
- **Ecosystems.** Natural systems and species will face additional pressures as a result of growing human populations, new invasive species, more variable climate, and other sources of stress.

Farmland and housing developments in the Coachella Valley.

- **Science and technology.** Innovation and advances in knowledge may create new problems (such as new chemicals in the environment) as well as new technical and management solutions that benefit ecosystems and the economy.

This chapter discusses these drivers of change and how they will affect water management in California. Although there is uncertainty regarding the magnitudes and rates of change to expect, the presence and importance of such changes are rather certain. Responding to competing demands for water is difficult enough with the natural vagaries of California's Mediterranean climate. Planning for these new conditions will tax the adaptive capacity of existing water management systems and institutions and require that institutions themselves change to keep pace.

Table 3.1
Drivers of change in California water management

Category	Driver	Major changes
Climate	Sea level rise	Submergence of western and central Delta and Suisun Marsh Movement of coastal estuaries inland Seawater intrusion into coastal aquifers Problems for coastal infrastructure and housing
	Warming	Decline in total runoff Decline in snowpack, more winter/less spring and summer runoff Higher stream temperatures Increased demand for cold water for fish
	Precipitation changes	More floods or droughts, or both
Deterioration	Aging infrastructure	Increasing expense for maintenance and upkeep Higher risk of dam, levee, and aqueduct failures
	Accumulating contaminants	Accumulating salts in western San Joaquin and Tulare Basin soils, with some agricultural land retirements Accumulating nitrates in groundwater basins (statewide) Accumulating emerging contaminants in surface and groundwater Tighter drinking water and wastewater discharge standards More polluted environmental water
	Mining legacies	Continued but diminishing mercury and other mine contaminants Episodic failures of mine drainage containment
	Accumulating groundwater overdraft	Long-term reduction in water supply from groundwater, in Tulare Basin especially

Table 3.1 *(continued)*

Category	Driver	Major changes
	Earthquakes	Episodic interruptions of water supply (statewide) Permanent flooding in western and central Delta and interrupted Delta water exports
	Sacramento–San Joaquin Delta	Permanent flooding of western and central Delta and Suisun Marsh Reductions or end of through-Delta water exports
Economy and demography	State and federal financial constraints	Less state and federal funding for water management More local financing of water management More state use of regulation instead of financial incentives
	Globalization	Continued reduction in agricultural share of economy Continued growth of service economy Shifts to higher-value and permanent crops
	Population growth and urbanization	Residential growth, especially in floodplains and hotter inland areas Higher housing densities with lower per-capita urban water use Urbanization of agricultural land, reducing agricultural water use
Ecosystems	New invasive species	Additional pressure on native species and infrastructure
	Accumulating degradation	Continued loss of desirable aquatic and riparian habitat Decline of native species and ecological regime shifts Extinctions plus more Endangered Species Act listings More and bigger wildfires, reducing water quality
Science and technology	New chemicals	New pesticides and chemicals in the environment
	Water use improvements	Improved agricultural yields Improved water conservation technologies
	Improved infrastructure and operations	New water treatment technologies (conventional, reuse, and desalination) Improved flood and climate forecasts Remote sensing of net water use
	Improved ecological science and technology	Better understanding of what is not working Improved emergency measures, such as hatcheries Potential to better integrate ecosystem and water system management

Climate Change

All major water projects in California were designed assuming that hydrologic conditions in the recent past represent future conditions. This approach has two limitations. First, hydrologic data are available only for about the last century, which severely limits the ability to gauge the size and frequencies of the largest droughts and floods. Second, this approach does not account for long-term observed and expected changes in climate (Milly et al. 2008; Palmer et al. 2008).

Many field and modeling studies of the western United States demonstrate long-term climate warming, increasingly early spring runoff, and potential variability and changes in precipitation patterns (Ellis, Goodrich, and Garfin 2010; Barnett et al. 2008). Many independent modeling efforts have examined global warming as a driver of these changes in California. Observed warming and changes in runoff during the late 20th century are due to both natural climate variability in California and global warming (Maurer et al. 2007; Hidalgo et al. 2009; Das et al. 2009; Cayan et al. 2001).

Changes in climate will drive water management in California through three primary channels: sea level rise, warming temperatures, and changes in precipitation. Some of these events are more certain than others, and uncertainty also exists in their timing and magnitude. But it is certain that climate change will affect water management, and it would be imprudent to ignore such threats in preparing infrastructure and institutions for managing California water over the long term.

Rising Sea Level

Sea level rise is the most certain long-term environmental change. Sea levels throughout the world have been rising since the end of the last ice age. This rise stems from both an increased mass of water in the oceans from melting ice and snowpacks and an increase in water volume in the oceans as warmer water becomes less dense and takes up more space (Jevrejeva, Moore, and Grinsted 2008).

Mean sea level along California's coast has risen an average of 2.2 cm (0.87 inches) per decade over the past century and a half, roughly consistent with global sea level rise (Figure 3.1). Short-term rates of rise have fluctuated considerably in response to astronomical conditions and circulation changes in the Pacific Ocean (Bromirski, Flick, and Cayan 2003; Ryan and Noble 2007).

Projections of sea level rise vary widely. The Intergovernmental Panel on Climate Change (IPCC) (2007) projections are lower than recently observed sea level rise but do not account for melting of ice sheets. CALFED's Independent Science Board recommended using semi-empirical models—which take into account recent observed changes—for projecting future sea level rise for planning purposes (Mount 2007). For the range of greenhouse gas emission scenarios used by the IPCC, this approach projects from 1 to 1.4 meters (39 to 55 inches) above present levels by the end of this century (Figure 3.2).

Figure 3.1
Sea level along the California coast has risen nearly 12 inches since the mid-1800s

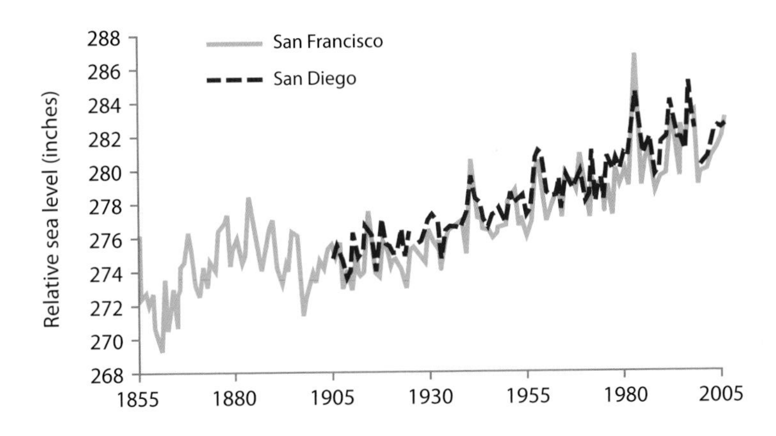

SOURCE: California Energy Commission (2009).

Figure 3.2
Sea level could rise another 39 to 55 inches by 2100

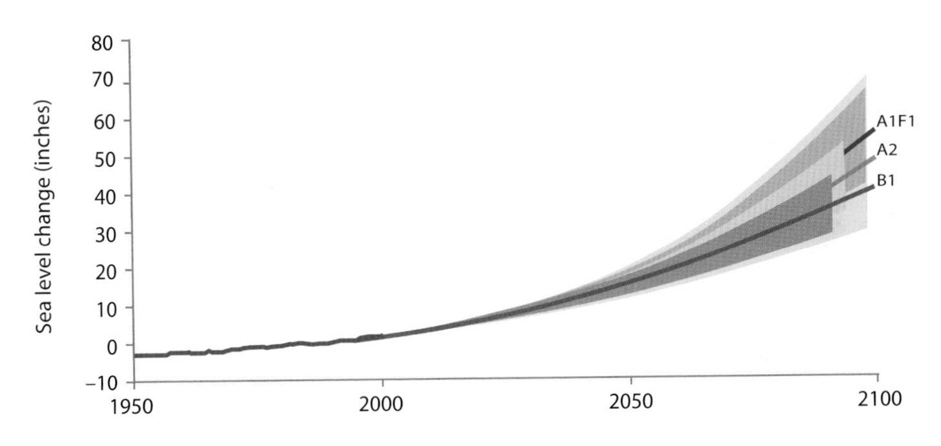

SOURCE: Based on Vermeer and Rahmstorf (2009), using emission scenarios from the IPCC.

NOTES: High emissions scenario is A1F1; low emissions scenario is B1. The red line shows historical data.

Table 3.2
Climate change: physical responses and management challenges

Climate event	Physical responses	Management challenges
Sea level rise	Higher average sea level Higher extreme high tides Higher estuarine salinities Greater seawater intrusion into aquifers	Lower Delta water export reliability and quality Larger estuarine and coastal floods Reduced coastal aquifer quality and yield
Warming climate	Reduced total runoff Changes in watershed vegetation Greater proportion of precipitation as rainfall Reduced snowpack Reduced spring and summer stream flow Higher stream temperatures; reduced cold-water habitat	Less water supply stored in snowpack Increased likelihood of flooding More demand for cold water releases for fish Reservoir operation changes needed Greater peak electricity and hydropower demands
Precipitation changes	Either a drier or wetter climate overall Potentially more variable and extreme weather	More floods and droughts Higher or lower demands for storage in reservoirs and aquifers

Rising sea level will have major effects on water management in California (Table 3.2). Coastal regions and estuarine areas such as the Delta will have to make the greatest adjustments, responding to increases in estuarine salinity, extreme high tides, and seawater intrusion into coastal aquifers.

Increasing difficulties in keeping Delta waters fresh

The Sacramento–San Joaquin Delta and San Francisco Bay (San Francisco Estuary) lie between the Pacific Ocean and Central Valley rivers. Water flows and quality in this region are driven largely by tides and sea level. Upstream reservoirs and export pumping are currently managed to keep the Delta fresh for Delta farming and for exports of fresh water to cities and farms in areas south and west of the Delta. Even modest rises in sea level will shift salinity landward enough to interfere with Delta water exports and agriculture in the western Delta (Fleenor et al. 2008; Chen et al. 2010). Failure of subsided islands in the western Delta—resulting from sea level rise and other factors (discussed below)—will further increase Delta salinity. Increased salinity is likely to be common in other California estuaries, such as Humboldt Bay, particularly during periods of low freshwater flow.

Increasing coastal flood risks

Beyond its effects on average sea level, sea level rise also increases the frequency of extreme sea level heights. Such sea level height "anomalies" occur when high astronomical tides, storm surges, low pressure systems, and warm ocean conditions coincide. Typically, they occur when El Niño events and major Pacific storms affect the coast simultaneously (Cayan et al. 2008). Extreme sea level anomalies have increased since 1915. For San Francisco during 1915–1969, extreme sea level anomalies occurred on average once in every four years. During 1969–2004 anomalies occurred roughly twice per year. In addition, the maximum anomaly recorded during the 1969–2004 interval was almost 40 cm (16 inches) higher than the pre-1969 period. Sea level anomalies could increase dramatically over the next century, perhaps going from a current average of one to two per year to roughly 17 per year by the end of the century in San Francisco Bay (Cayan et al. 2008).

Large increases in coastal and estuarine high-water levels, will contribute to failures in the Delta's fragile levees (Mount and Twiss 2005; Lund et al. 2007, 2010). The combination of rise in sea level and increases in salinity could eventually render current Delta water export facilities obsolete (Lund et al. 2010).

Increasing magnitude and frequency of sea level anomalies are also likely to overwhelm some unprepared coastal flood defenses. Assuming year 2000 coastal population levels, as many as 480,000 California residents would be placed at risk by a 55 inch rise in sea level (Heberger et al. 2009). In addition, coastal lagoons and marshes, important habitats for rare species, from steelhead trout to marsh birds such as the California clapper rail, are likely to flood more frequently with seawater. In most watersheds, there is little room for these habitats to shift upstream or inland, either because of natural geologic restrictions or urbanization and the hardening of streambanks with levees.

Sea level rise also will affect wastewater treatment plants and stormwater systems in coastal California, which rely on gravity to collect water to wastewater treatment plants at low seashore locations. Twenty-eight existing wastewater treatment plants in California would be placed at high risk by a 55 inch sea level rise (Heberger et al. 2009). Mitigation would require extensive reengineering of these facilities.

Saltwater intrusion in coastal aquifers

Many large and heavily utilized aquifers are situated along California's coast. The seaward margin of these freshwater aquifers usually rests on top of denser salt water. One challenge to groundwater managers is preventing salt water from migrating landward as sea levels rise, reducing the ability to store and distribute fresh water (California Department of Water Resources 2009). Saltwater intrusion is already a common problem for coastal aquifers in the South Coast and the Central Coast regions, particularly in the aquifers that underlie coastal Orange County, Los Angeles, the Oxnard Plain (Ventura County), and the lower Salinas and Pajaro Valleys (Monterey and Santa Cruz Counties). Accelerating sea level rise will augment basin management challenges. Responses can include reducing aquifer pumping coupled with increased artificial recharge, both translating to lower yield (Nishikawa et al. 2009).

Warming Temperatures

Average annual temperatures in California have risen in the last century by roughly 0.1°C (0.18°F) per decade (Anderson et al. 2008). This warming has accelerated spring snowmelt, resulting in a larger share of stream flow occurring in winter than in spring in recent decades. Global Circulation Models (GCMs) used to simulate future climate changes for various greenhouse gas emission scenarios all point to continuing or accelerating warming for California and the western United States. (Intergovernmental Panel on Climate Change 2007).

Recent summaries of results from downscaled GCMs (which translate global results to the regional level) show a range of average annual temperature increases for California depending on model differences and policies adopted to slow greenhouse gas emissions (Cayan et al. 2007; Moser et al. 2009; Chung et al. 2009). Under optimistic assumptions, projected increases range from 3°F to 5.5°F by 2100. A more pessimistic view leads to projected increases between 8°F and 10.5°F. The current trend of warming seems likely to accelerate; uncertainty lies only in how much and how fast. Prudent water managers will want to prepare for such changes.

Increasing temperatures have broad implications for water management in California (Table 3.2). Primary changes include (1) direct reductions in the total amount of water available from precipitation (total runoff), as a result of increased consumption of water by natural vegetation; (2) reduced snowfall and a shift of stream flow timing from spring to winter; and (3) increases in stream temperatures.

Reductions in total available water

Under current climatic conditions, between one-half and two-thirds of the precipitation in California never becomes stream flow or groundwater (Table 2.1). Even if the average volume of precipitation remains unchanged, warming is likely to reduce overall water available to streams and aquifers, by increasing

Warming temperatures are diminishing the share of precipitation stored as snow in the Sierra Nevada and Cascade Mountains. Photo by Sarah Null.

the evapotranspiration rate and by lengthening the growing season (Hidalgo, Cayan, and Dettinger 2005).

Modeling studies of average annual increased temperatures in the western Sierra Nevada watersheds suggest that low- to mid-elevation locations (up to about 6,000 feet) will experience declines of 4 percent to 10 percent in annual runoff with temperature increases of 7.2°F (Null, Viers, and Mount 2010). Watersheds at higher elevations show comparable reductions with higher temperature gains (10.8°F), which may occur by the end of the century.

Warming also dries soils for longer periods, changing natural vegetative cover within watersheds. Streams, riparian lands, and soils at high altitudes may dry earlier in summer in semiarid regions where precipitation occurs only in narrow windows of time and where less snowmelt is available to fill streams and keep the ground moist. Irrigation water demand may also increase as soils dry, leading farmers to alter cropping patterns.

Less snow, earlier runoff

Climate warming also reduces the proportion of winter precipitation that falls as snow and accelerates the melting of snow in winter and early spring, with consequences for water storage, flooding potential, and the ability to maintain stored cold water needed for some native fish species.

Having less precipitation falling as snow reduces the accumulation of the mountain snowpack, an important form of seasonal water storage in California (Knowles, Dettinger, and Cayan 2006; Pierce et al. 2008; Das et al. 2009). In the northern Sierra Nevada, late season snowpack water storage has declined since the 1950s. However, snowpack water storage is not declining in the southern Sierra Nevada and may even be increasing slightly (Mote et al. 2005; Pierce et al. 2008). This difference may be due to higher elevations in the southern Sierra Nevada, where temperatures, although warmer, still remain cool enough for snow to form and accumulate.

Increases in temperature also accelerate the melting of snowpack. In most mountains of California, the historical peak in snow water storage occurred around April 1st. The timing of this peak is related to meteorological conditions, driven mostly by temperature, and the increasing intensity of solar radiation in the spring. Over the last century, declining snow water storage and warmer air temperatures have shifted spring snowmelt to earlier in the year (Barnett et al. 2008) (Figure 3.3).

Models that project future warming also project significant and, in some cases, dramatic decreases in snow water storage and shifts from spring to winter stream flows (Barnett et al. 2008; Knowles and Cayan 2004; Knowles, Dettinger,

Figure 3.3
Spring and summer runoff has been declining as a share of annual runoff on California's major rivers

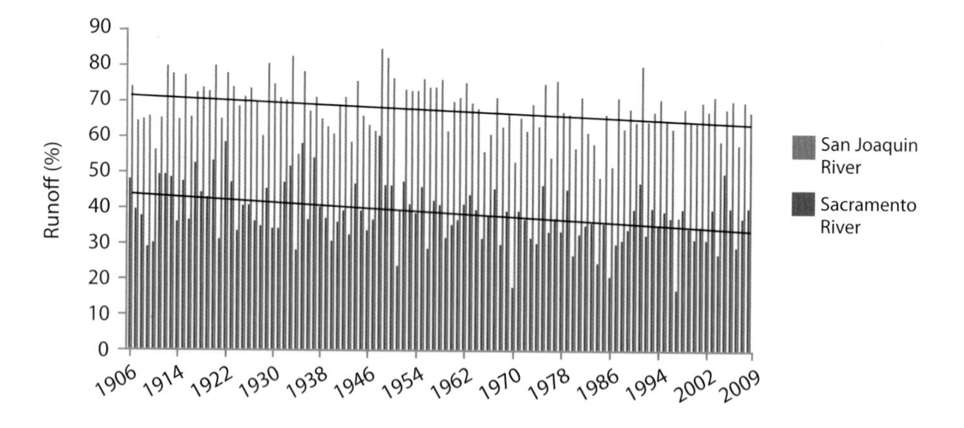

SOURCE: Authors' calculations using data from the California Department of Water Resources.

NOTES: The figure shows unimpaired spring and summer runoff (April 1–September 30) as a share of total annual runoff (October 1–September 30). The lines show trends over the period 1906–2009. Runoff shift from spring to winter has been 1 percent per decade ($R^2 = 0.12$) for the Sacramento River and 0.7 percent per decade ($R^2 = 0.07$) for the San Joaquin River.

and Cayan 2006). The magnitude of these changes differs with watershed elevation and latitude. Moderate warming could decrease April snow water content by more than one-third in the Sierra Nevada (Knowles, Dettinger, and Cayan 2006). The shifts in runoff from spring to winter begin with mid-altitude watersheds, moving to higher watersheds as warming progresses, with spring ultimately arriving more than a month earlier than today (Null, Viers, and Mount 2010). Figure 3.4 illustrates the declines in snowpack projected over this century with a relatively modest increase in temperatures; at higher temperatures, reductions could exceed 80 percent by the end of the century (Maurer et al. 2007).

This change will complicate water supply management, because the snowpack now provides a "free" source of seasonal storage. In a typical year, about one-third of annual supplies are conveniently stored as snowpack. Water managers can make up for much of this lost storage by using downstream reservoirs and, at some additional cost, by storing more water in aquifers, thereby freeing up space in surface reservoirs for more seasonal storage (Tanaka et al. 2006;

Figure 3.4
Rising temperatures will reduce the role of snowpack for water storage

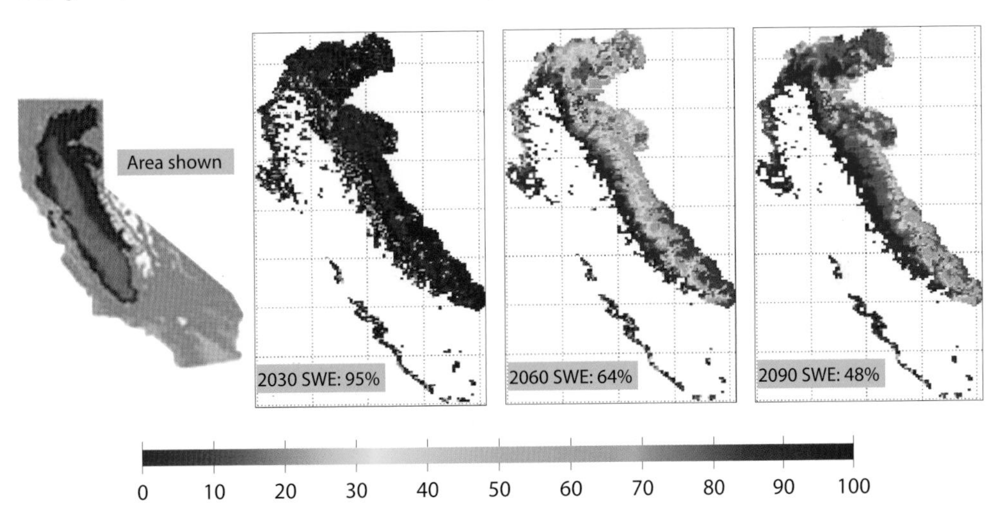

SOURCE: Knowles and Cayan (2002).

NOTES: SWE is snow water equivalent. The scenarios are based on projected temperature increases: 0.6°C (1.1°F) (2020–2039), 1.6°C (2.9°F) (2050–2069), and 2.1°C (3.8°F) (2080–2099), expressed as an increase over present conditions (1995–2005). These are modest increases in temperature relative to some model projections (see the text). With higher temperature increases, the snowpack would be commensurately smaller.

Connell 2009; Madani and Lund 2010). Expanding this type of "conjunctive use" of groundwater and surface water will require changes in reservoir operations and strong groundwater basin management systems, often lacking today. New surface storage facilities are likely to be a more costly way to make up for the lost snowpack, particularly if climate change also reduces average precipitation and runoff, as discussed below.

Declining snowpacks and more precipitation falling as rain will also affect future flooding potential. During large winter storms, the proportion of precipitation that falls as snow is retained in mountains, reducing potential flood peaks. The greater proportion of precipitation falling as rain as a consequence of warming increases storm runoff. The loss of snowpack accentuates this effect because snowpack itself can dampen flood peaks (Dettinger et al. 2009). The extent to which these changes will increase flood damage depends on California's ability to respond effectively. Fissekis (2008) finds, for instance, that flood-operating policies that consider real-time watershed snow, precipitation, and soil moisture conditions would generally be adequate to handle anticipated increases in runoff volumes and peak flows for the largest winter storms experienced in California over the last 50 years. In addition to operational changes (for instance, making more reservoir storage available for flood flows in winter), there is likely to be an increased demand for larger flood defenses such as levees to protect homes and businesses in vulnerable areas (Zhu et al. 2007). This demand will be influenced, in part, by the requirement under current federal policy that urban areas have flood defenses adequate to pass a flow having a 1 percent probability of occurring in any year (Chapter 2). With changing conditions and new flow information, that 1 percent probability flow will increase (Mount 1995; Das et al. submitted).

Increasing water temperatures

Higher water temperatures are likely to affect a wide range of aquatic organisms. In the Delta, higher overall temperatures are likely to threaten some native species, such as delta smelt, which traditionally spawn in a fairly narrow range of water temperatures (Moyle and Bennett 2008).

Warming also is likely to significantly complicate the management of water to maintain adequate habitat for such fish as salmon and steelhead, now confined to the lower-elevation portions of rivers and streams because of dams. Releases of cold water from deeper parts of reservoirs are currently needed in summer to maintain this habitat. Managers of large reservoirs often rely on the stratification of water layers to preserve denser cold water at the bottom of the reservoir, with warmer, lower-density water resting on top. Where reservoirs can tap water from various levels, they often blend warm and cold water to keep downstream temperatures for fish within optimal ranges. Management of this cold water pool over the course of the summer can be complicated. The reservoir operator must retain sufficient cold water for the season while drawing down the reservoir to meet temperature and other requirements downstream, including irrigation demands.

Warming temperatures have several implications for cold water pool management. First, to offset higher air temperatures downstream, more of the cold water pool must be released for a longer period, increasing the likelihood of exhausting the cold water supply by late summer. Second, if water flowing into the reservoir during winter is warmer, then the temperature of the cold water pool will be higher the following summer, requiring more cold water to be blended with warmer waters to meet temperature standards. Third, when the difference in temperature between the bottom cold water and top warm water decreases, the reservoir is more likely to destratify and mix, losing the cold water pool entirely. Finally, with warmer air temperatures, the release of cold water from a reservoir preserves fish temperatures for a shorter distance downstream. These effects have occurred in the state's reservoirs historically during warm drought periods.

In sum, the frequency of releases of warm water from reservoirs is likely to increase as conditions warm, increasing the temperatures of rivers and worsening conditions for many species of fish. To mitigate these problems, reservoir operators are likely to be required to reserve more water for cold water releases for fish, raising the potential for competition and conflicts between water management for environmental and direct human uses. For areas further downstream, beyond the temperature influence of cold water from reservoirs, warmer temperatures will permanently and increasingly stress some fish and other organisms.

Changing Precipitation

Precipitation drives water availability. Three aspects of precipitation are most relevant for water management: (1) total precipitation, usually expressed as a long-term average; (2) interannual variability, reflecting the length and intensity of dry and wet years; and (3) precipitation intensity during individual storms, which drives floods. Compared with sea level rise and warming, there is generally less certainty about what will happen to precipitation with climate change.

Changes in total precipitation

About a century of detailed precipitation records are available for California. They reveal no statistically significant trend in precipitation statewide. The GCMs used to estimate future temperatures also predict future precipitation patterns, but there is less consensus on precipitation results for California (Cayan et al. 2007; Chung et al. 2009). Projections vary widely, and the average precipitation levels across all models differ little from the historical average (Cayan et al. 2007).

Thus, average precipitation in California could change little over this century, or the future could be significantly wetter or much drier. A drier climate would increase water supply and environmental problems, while decreasing flooding problems and the effectiveness of new surface storage. A wetter climate would decrease water supply and environmental water quantity problems but probably increase flooding. Modeling studies have examined management adaptation to a wide range of warmer and drier or wetter climate scenarios in California.[1] These studies tend to show that California's water supply and flood control system are more affected by precipitation changes than by temperature changes alone. In Chapter 6, we present the results of some management scenarios with a drier future, which has been the focus of much of the state's recent attention.[2]

Interannual variability

Although average precipitation appears not to have changed in California over the past century, interannual variability may be increasing, with longer, more intense wet and dry periods (Anderson et al. 2008). This phenomenon has been noted throughout the American West (Barnett et al. 2008). Overall, climate simulation models for California do not agree on significant shifts in the frequency of dry and wet periods. However, model results evaluated by Cayan et al. (2007) indicate increased intensity of dry years, particularly in the latter

1. See Tanaka et al. (2006); Medellin-Azuara et al. (2008b); Connell (2009); Fissekis (2008); Ragatz (2011); Lettenmaier and Sheer (1991); Vicuna et al. (2008); Madani and Lund (2009, 2010); and California Department of Water Resources (2006).

2. In particular, the second biennial assessment of California climate effects, organized by the California Energy Commission (2009), focused on a dry-warm form of climate change.

half of the 21st century. These simulation results deserve some caution, however. The GCMs are calibrated to the weather of the past 100 years. During this time, no droughts lasted more than six years without significant intervening periods of above-average precipitation. The water systems of California and much of the West are constructed around this range of variability. However, evidence from a wide range of studies demonstrates that the past century had exceptionally low climatic variability compared with the previous 3,000 years (Box 3.1).

3.1

The past may *yet* be a predictor of the future

Broad concern exists in the scientific community over using the past 100–150 years of climate record to design water resource and flood management infrastructure and to guide operations, particularly in the face of climate change (Milly et al. 2008; Intergovernmental Panel on Climate Change 2007).

Reconstructions of past climate conditions are based on many sources of information, including tree rings, fossil pollen, rodent middens, lake and marine sediments, cave speleothems (mineral deposits), and ice cores, leading to extensive information on California's and the western U.S. climate over the past 3,000 years, a period known as the Late Holocene.

All information available about the Late Holocene points to significant past changes in precipitation and runoff. Studies of the climate of the Sierra Nevada and adjacent areas of the Great Basin indicate that long-term droughts, vastly exceeding current six-year droughts, were quite common. Studies by Benson et al. (2002) of lakes that drain the Sierra Nevada show that Late Holocene droughts lasting from 20 to 100 years recurred in intervals of 80 to 230 years. Two droughts during the Medieval Warm Period (from AD 890–1110 and AD 1210–1350) may be the longest and most severe droughts of the entire 12,000-year Holocene epoch (Stine 1994). What is striking about these droughts is not the reduction in amount of runoff (25 percent reduction at the centennial scale, 40 percent at the decadal scale [Graham and Hughes 2007]) but their extreme duration without intervening wet periods. Modeling studies have examined how California's water system might respond to such extreme changes in climate (Harou et al. 2010; Brekke et al. 2009).

The Late Holocene was not particularly warm compared to the earlier Holocene, except for the Medieval Warm Period; temperatures were roughly equivalent to Northern Hemisphere temperatures during the 1980s (Mann et al. 2008). These are, in turn, lower than the temperatures of the 1990s. The current warming trend exceeds anything found in the past 3,000 years. The climate of the past 150 years may have been benign compared to earlier climates (MacDonald 2007) and future climates.

Precipitation intensity

Intense precipitation during winter storms causes the most damaging floods in California. In concept, warming should increase precipitation intensity, and this appears in some model results (Cayan et al. 2007). However, this is difficult to model with confidence because of the short timescale of most storms.

Much climate modeling of California for the next century does not show a great increase in the frequency of winter storms. However, a recent study indicates greater storm intensity and frequency with warming (Das et al. submitted). A particular concern is unusual meteorological phenomena known as *atmospheric rivers*. These storms occur when narrow bands of moisture in the upper atmosphere flow directly from the subtropics near Hawaii into California, producing warm, intense precipitation (the so-called "Pineapple Express"). These storms can produce high rainfall intensities for several days and are responsible for most of the major floods California has experienced over the past 100 years (Dettinger et al. 2004; Dettinger 2005).

Conditions necessary for winter storms to become atmospheric rivers may become more frequent over time (Dettinger et al. 2009). On average, models predict an increase of roughly 30 percent in the number of winter days in which atmospheric river conditions occur by the end of the century, and most predict that the largest events will have storm intensities exceeding anything recorded in the last century.[3] Greater frequency and intensity of large, flood-generating storms could further stress water management, if reservoirs must make room for additional flood storage capacity.

These various aspects of climate change will impose many changes on water management, from the Delta to reservoir operations to management for native species (Hanak and Lund 2008). The uncertainties of climate change for planning and design purposes are great, particularly for flood frequency estimation (Klemes 2000a, 2000b). The estimation of extreme floods, necessary for proper risk analysis, becomes still more approximate when the climate is changing. Although these changes are substantial and profound, many management options and directions are available to adapt, as we discuss in later chapters.

Deterioration of the Water System

California is now a well-settled state, with water and land having been employed intensely in the interest of its population for over a century. This intense use

3. Atmospheric river conditions do not always create atmospheric river-type storms.

of land and water, as well as various naturally occurring events such as earthquakes, are contributing to a continual deterioration of the state's water system, resulting in a dated and aging infrastructure, accumulating contaminants, groundwater overdraft, toxic drainage from old mines, earthquake damage, changes in estuaries, and the sinking and likely ultimate disappearance of many low-lying islands in the Sacramento–San Joaquin Delta. Although serious, this deterioration need not prove fatal to the operation of the state's water system. Indeed, given capable and timely management, it may provide opportunities for modernization and improvement.

Aging Infrastructure

California's extensive water and wastewater management infrastructure is largely established and is now aging. Aging infrastructure has three problems: obsolete design and operation, increasing maintenance costs, and increasing likelihood of some components failing.

First, existing infrastructure was often designed for conditions that have changed and will further change in the future. For example, increases in water quality standards often have required costly increases in water and wastewater treatment. Similarly, urban water conservation efforts reduce dry-season flows in sewers designed to support higher-volume toilets and summer flows. These older sewers required less slope and trenching to achieve required scouring, but with lower wastewater flows resulting from water conservation, more maintenance may be required, such as periodic sewer flushing.

Second, aging itself can increase maintenance costs. After construction, water and wastewater facilities commonly have several decades of low-cost operations. But with time, aging pipes, pumps, and other components need to be replaced. Replacement of aging or obsolete components is often more expensive than the original costs (after inflation), because replacement often lacks the economies of scale present in original construction; it also becomes necessary to accommodate transportation infrastructure, houses, and other activities that have grown around the original water infrastructure (notably, underground pipes). Failure to keep up with deteriorating infrastructure can increase the risks of failure and contamination and increase ultimate replacement costs.

Third, failure of major infrastructure components—including dams, levees, and aqueducts—becomes more likely with time. California's geologic and climatic setting makes the state prone to rare but significant natural disasters with a high potential to disrupt water supply and flood management. California has a long history of overconfidence in efforts to manage these forces (Kelley 1989; McPhee 1989). If they were to fail, roughly half of the 1,400 state-regulated dams pose a high potential hazard to downstream populations.[4] But annual funding for state dam safety programs averages only about $6,000 for each regulated dam (Association of State Dam Safety Officials 2005). The biggest threats to most dams involve insufficient spillway capacity for very large floods. But as discussed below, earthquake risks are a particular concern for some dams; similarly, the elaborate levee systems of the Delta, Central Valley, and Southern California are all at risk from large earthquakes and floods.

Replacement of aging infrastructure sometimes provides opportunities to modernize and update for both contemporary and anticipated conditions. For instance, new wastewater treatment plants can be designed to facilitate the delivery of highly treated recycled wastewater to end users, something more difficult for older facilities. For some dams, deterioration can facilitate removal. As discussed in Chapter 5, retirement of dams that no longer serve their original water supply and hydroelectric functions well can support important environmental improvements. Dam removal is likely to increase with time, as even some large dams become unsafe, fill with sediments, or are ill-suited to changing conditions.

The replacement and updating of local water and wastewater infrastructure are typically funded by local ratepayers, who directly benefit from these services. As shown in Chapter 2, California's utilities appear to be on track for making the capital investments needed to maintain their systems, thanks largely to local utilities' abilities to adjust charges to customers. These investments will cause significant rate increases, however. For instance, the major seismic repair and upgrade work under way for San Francisco's Hetch Hetchy 80-year-old system, which supplies roughly 2.5 million Bay Area residents, is costing over $4.5 billion and will more than double wholesale water rates by 2016.[5] Such rate increases will create additional incentives to conserve water.

Significant gaps in funding capacity exist for maintaining and upgrading flood management infrastructure, which is largely funded by federal and state agencies and which requires direct voter approval for local funding. Dam

---

4. The dams regulated by the state are either at least six feet high with more than 50 acre-feet of water storage capacity or over 25 feet high with more than 15 acre-feet of storage capacity.

5. Wholesale rates in early 2009 were approximately $600/af, and they are projected to increase to $1,400/af by 2016 (Palo Alto Utilities Department 2010).

removal is another area where the current funding system is inadequate. In later chapters, we discuss some options for funding system reform.

Accumulating Contaminants

Accumulating contaminants in both surface and groundwater—including salts and residues from fertilizers, pesticides, and other chemicals—are raising the costs of farming, spoiling some farmland entirely, raising the costs of drinking water and wastewater treatment, and posing as yet largely unknown risks to public health, fish, and other wildlife.

Salinization of farmland

The accumulation of salts in some large agricultural areas south of the Delta has long been noted (Orlob 1991). For decades, approximately half a million tons of salt annually have accumulated in the San Joaquin and Tulare Basins. For the San Joaquin Basin, more salt enters the basin through irrigation water than leaves via drainage into the San Joaquin River. The Tulare Basin drains to the San Joaquin River only in rare wet years and so retains almost all the salt entering the basin. This accumulation of salts has already led to the retirement of 70,000 acres of agricultural land and has diminished productivity on some remaining farmland (Medellin-Azuara et al. 2008a; Shoups et al. 2005). Further reductions in agricultural acreage can be expected as salts continue to accumulate. Roughly a million acres of irrigated farmland are susceptible to this problem (Letey 2000; U.S. Department of the Interior 1990).

The productive life of much of this area has already been extended by improvements in agricultural water use efficiency (which results in not only less water, but also less salt, being applied to the soils), set-asides of some local areas for salt disposal, improved leaching methods, and retirement of some lands with high natural soil salinity (Letey et al. in press). Maintaining a sustainable salt balance in remaining areas requires the development of drains from the basin, reductions in salt loads entering the basin, or further reductions in irrigated area (Orlob 1991). Drainage solutions can be particularly difficult where the salts themselves are highly toxic. This is the case with selenium on the west side of the San Joaquin Valley, which can accumulate and harm wildlife at even moderate concentrations. For instance, an attempt to establish drainage in the western San Joaquin Valley in the early 1980s, in which selenium-laced water was out in the open, led to bird mutations and die-offs (Chapter 1). One advantage of a new water conveyance system around or under the Delta would be to significantly reduce salt loads entering the basin, as Delta water is roughly three times saltier than water diverted upstream from the Sacramento River (Lund et al. 2010).

Even if these various efforts can help extend the productive life of salinity-affected farmland, it will also be necessary to have a better plan for retiring some of these lands before they become too toxic for alternative uses. Current economic incentives encourage farmers to farm the land to the point where it becomes unsuitable as native dryland habitat. From an ecosystem management standpoint, it might be better to stop farming such lands sooner, so that they could be converted to wildlife-friendly dryland habitat or at least be able to support enough natural vegetation to reduce dust clouds. Such a solution would require a regional land management plan with incentives to encourage farmers to manage the lands for conservation purposes instead of farming them intensively.

In addition to impairing local farmland, San Joaquin Basin salinity is a major source of surface water pollution on the lower San Joaquin River and the southern Delta. These salts contribute to an environment in the southern Delta that favors nonnative fish species and is a major impediment to ecological restoration in the Delta (Brown 2000).

Finally, salinity also raises the costs of drinking water and poses some still uncertain public health risks. The costs of treating water from the Sacramento/San Joaquin Delta for urban uses, for example, could increase by $400/af with increased salinity driven by sea level rise (Chen et al. 2010). Moreover, these treatment technologies may not fully remove potentially harmful by-products of the treatment process.

Contamination of groundwater basins

Salts and a range of other contaminants such as nitrates (largely from fertilizers and livestock wastes) and some pesticides are also accumulating in California's groundwater basins. Nitrate accumulations are especially widespread, affecting most groundwater basins underlying agricultural areas (e.g., the Chino Basin and the San Joaquin Basin: Harter et al. 2002; Dubrovsky et al. 1998). Nitrates can have adverse health effects, particularly on infants and young children. Because water can remain in aquifers for a very long time, it will often take centuries to decrease contamination. The slow percolation of contaminants from irrigation water laced with agro-chemicals also means that the full weight of contaminant loads often has yet to arrive in the main bodies of aquifers (Fogg and LaBolle 2006).

Groundwater basins also contain some naturally occurring contaminants. Arsenic, present in many groundwater basins in the southern Central Valley, is a highly carcinogenic contaminant for which regulatory standards have recently been tightened.[6] The primary solution for addressing groundwater contamination—wellhead treatment—is usually too costly for agricultural uses and small rural drinking water systems.[7]

Emerging contaminants

The number of chemicals and biological contaminants in drinking water subject to federal and state regulation has been rising. In 1977, the first set of maximum concentration levels (MCLs) for drinking water in California included 20 chemicals; as of 2010, this number had jumped more than fourfold, to 84.[8] Increases in the number of MCLs reflect increased understanding of the public health consequences of these constituents, improvements in detection capability, and increasing use of poorer quality water sources.

The current number of drinking water MCLs pales, however, compared to the immense and growing number of new chemicals entering the environment. According to the Environmental Protection Agency (EPA), more than 80,000 known chemicals are used for industrial and household applications, with more than 700 new chemicals registered each year.[9] In California, there are more than 12,500 registered pesticide products.[10] Only some of these are monitored, with guidelines limiting what constitutes safe exposure. The number, magnitudes, and uncertainties of these chemicals pose significant challenges for proper public health and environmental regulation.

Although chemical regulation issues go well beyond the water sector, they are important for both drinking water quality and the quality of water for the environment. Recent advances in detection technologies and environmental toxicology are making it possible to identify previously neglected chemicals from wastewater treatment plants and urban and agricultural runoff. These

---

6. See http://water.epa.gov/lawsregs/rulesregs/sdwa/arsenic/index.cfm. See also Welch et al. (2000).

7. A recent study of domestic wells in Tulare County found that 40 percent of 181 domestic wells tested for nitrates exceeded the public water supply standard of 10 mg/l (State Water Resources Control Board 2010a). There are 600,000 domestic wells in California serving over 1.6 million people not connected to regulated public water supply systems.

8. These 84 chemicals include inorganic elements (e.g., copper, lead, mercury, nitrate), radionucleids (e.g., uranium, radium), volatile organic compounds (paints, benzene, MTBE [methyl tertiary butyl ether]), synthetic organic compounds (mostly pesticides and fungicides), and disinfection by-products (e.g., trihalomethanes, bromate).

9. This figure refers to chemical substances as defined under the Toxic Substances Control Act. See www.epa.gov/oppt/newchems/pubs/invntory.htm.

10. See http://state.ceris.purdue.edu/htbin/stweb.com.

compounds, known as "emerging environmental contaminants" or "chemicals of emerging concern," include ingredients in pharmaceuticals, sunscreens, flame retardants, and artificial sweeteners, among others. The health and environmental effects of such seemingly innocuous products, found in surface water and groundwater throughout California, are just beginning to be understood (la Farré et al. 2008; Richardson 2009; U.S. Environmental Protection Agency undated (f)). They are often difficult to remove using conventional wastewater treatment methods.

In the future, drinking water regulators are likely to establish MCLs for some, perhaps many, additional contaminants. The EPA currently has 104 contaminants on its watch list, and more are likely to be added as toxicology improves.[11] This growing list will raise the costs of treating both drinking water and wastewater and increase the value of water sources with low contamination such as high mountain streams (e.g., San Francisco's Hetch Hetchy Reservoir) and spring systems in volcanic areas.

Emerging contaminants are likely to significantly affect water treatment and quality for wastewater recycling as well. At present, California recycles approximately 200–300 taf [thousand acre-feet] per year (Figure 2.4), and efforts are under way to expand this supply option considerably, to as much as 2 million acre-feet. Depending on the number of cycles of reuse and the treatments applied each time, recycled water can develop high concentrations of urban and agricultural chemicals (most notoriously, salt). A State Water Resources Control Board Science Advisory Panel report (Anderson et al. 2010; National Water Research Institute 2009) illustrates the complexity of this issue and highlights some challenges for expanding recycled water use.

Treatment to remove contaminants from drinking water is, at best, a partial solution to the problems posed by chemicals in California's waterways. It raises the costs of water for urban users and does nothing to address the negative effects of these contaminants on fish and other wildlife. A more comprehensive approach, focusing on source protection and pollution discharge control (to prevent harmful chemicals from entering water in the first place), is urgently needed. As described in Chapter 6, federal and state agencies have had difficulty regulating the use of chemicals under existing authority, and there are weaknesses in the control of polluted agricultural and urban runoff.

---

11. The current "contaminant candidate list" includes 11 microbiological and 93 chemical contaminants (www.epa.gov/ogwdw000/ccl/ccl3.html).

Mine Pollution

Water quality management in the future will also be affected by the legacies of pollution from California's early mining economy. California has more than 47,000 abandoned mines, and more than 5,200 of these have the potential to significantly degrade water quality for human use and wildlife (www.consrv.ca.gov). One hundred and fifty of these mines are currently considered dangerous and in need of immediate attention, mostly because they produce acidic solutions laced with a complex mix of toxic chemicals. These mines are most dangerous following intense storms, when runoff overwhelms discharge capture and treatment programs. The state's abandoned mines are a chronic problem that requires extensive investments to manage. Federal regulations in recent decades have greatly reduced the potential for new mine drainage problems, so new mines are unlikely to be a major driver of change in the future in California, although the U.S. General Mining Law of 1872 is still unchanged and thus new mines are always a possibility (Woody et al. 2010).

A larger legacy of California's gold mining era is large amounts of mercury in Central Valley and Delta sediments. The Gold Rush in the Sierra Nevada created a mercury rush in the nearby Coast Ranges. Mercury was used to separate gold from ore. More than 10 million pounds of mercury were released into the Sierras' streams (Churchill 2000). Mines of the Coast Ranges also discharged large quantities of mercury into Central Valley tributaries. Mercury is stored in and transported with the sediments that historically moved from the Coast Ranges and the Sierra Nevada. Hydraulic mining from 1852 to 1884 moved vast quantities of mercury-laden sediment into the Central Valley, the Delta, and San Francisco Bay (Bouse et al. 2010).

Mercury is a powerful neurotoxin at high concentrations. In many environmental settings rich in organic material, elemental mercury can undergo methylation, making it available for assimilation into food webs (Morel, Kraepiel, and Amyot 1998). As this mercury moves up the food web, it concentrates in higher-order predators such as predatory fish, fish-eating birds, and humans (Alpers et al. 2005), although effects on health and reproduction of organisms may nevertheless be less than expected (Suchanek et al. 2008). Mercury poisoning health warnings are common against consuming large numbers of resident wild fish from the Sierra Nevada, Clear Lake, the Coast Ranges, the Delta, and San Francisco Bay.

Many water and environmental management activities will have to address potential releases of additional mercury into the environment. Mercury is trapped in sediments behind dams, creating a concern for dam removal efforts

(James 2005). Riverfront levees in the Sacramento Valley now isolate floodplain sediments deposited during the Hydraulic Era, so levee setbacks could reintroduce this stored mercury into the environment. Restoration of riparian and tidal wetlands to support fish will also have to consider the potential that disturbing the existing landscapes will reintroduce mercury and increase its methylation (Marvin-DiPasquale 2000).

However, agencies and organizations often use mercury as an excuse to do nothing. Indeed, regulatory agencies commonly cite mercury as a reason *not* to restore habitat, to the detriment of the species they are charged with recovering. There are rational reasons for a conservative approach. Yet, decades of research in California show no indication that habitat restoration efforts create a significant problem regarding mercury, harming either aquatic organisms or humans. Regardless, mercury will remain a fundamental issue in future water management in California, particularly for restoring wetland and tidal marsh habitats.

Accumulating Groundwater Overdraft

As noted in Chapter 2, chronic overdraft—or groundwater mining—accounts for as much as 2 million acre-feet, or 5 percent of gross agricultural and urban water use. The two major basins affected by persistent overdraft are the Tulare and Salinas Basins (Faunt 2009). Long-term overdraft in the Tulare Basin is estimated to be about 1.4 million acre-feet (maf)/year. For the smaller Salinas Basin, overdraft is about 19 taf per year. More localized overdraft occurs in other smaller Central Coast basins (Pajaro Valley, Santa Paula, Nipomo).

In some historically overdrafted basins in Southern California and Silicon Valley, active aquifer recharge programs, supplied by imported surface water, have helped to stabilize groundwater levels (Walker and Williams 1982; Blomquist 1992). In some heavily used basins in wetter parts of the state, groundwater levels have been stabilized by local surface supplies. In these cases, pumping induces faster recharge from local rainfall and adjacent rivers and streams—reducing local surface water flows. The Cosumnes River is an example of this tradeoff (Fleckenstein et al. 2004). Even where groundwater levels are now stabilized, the water table remains low enough that stream flow and native vegetation are reduced (Howard and Merrifield 2010).

Groundwater overdraft often causes land subsidence, as has occurred particularly in the San Joaquin Valley (Galloway, Jones, and Ingebritsen 1999; Poland et al. 1975). This subsidence has implications for flood management (since lands are lower and more susceptible to flooding) as well as the functioning of roads and long canal systems (which can break down when the ground sinks too much).[12] The acceleration of pumping during the drought occurring in the late 2000s has created instabilities in the concrete lining of the California Aqueduct, for instance.

Like many mining operations, overdraft also provides economic benefits, at least for a period. However, ultimately, overdraft must end, and it will end either by diverting more surface water to current groundwater uses or by reducing net use of groundwater (Harou and Lund 2008).

Earthquakes

Given California's geologic setting, large earthquakes will episodically and abruptly affect all facets of life. The Uniform California Earthquake Rupture Forecast (Field et al. 2008) estimates a 99 percent probability of a major quake (magnitude 6.7 or greater) in California over the next 30 years, with Southern California at slightly higher risk than Northern California.

The design of most water supply structures in California is significantly driven by the expectation of earthquakes. This is especially pertinent to the roughly 1,400 state-regulated dams and to the complex system of canals and pumping stations that make up regional, state, and federal water projects. Although these structures must meet basic design criteria for earthquakes, almost no structure is entirely earthquake-proof. And because standards and methods of analysis for earthquakes are constantly changing, many older structures in California can be expected to need costly upgrades or else be retired.

Although most water supply structures in the state have reasonably high resistance to earthquakes, several large dams are considered at high risk of failure during an earthquake.[13] In addition, California's network of levees is at risk. Earthquake vulnerability is particularly acute in the levees of the Delta, whose design does not incorporate significant earthquake risk (Mount and Twiss 2005). Levee failure from earthquakes has a high potential for disrupting water supply operations in the Delta, with profound economic and social

12. The initial lowering of a groundwater table usually implies some irreversible subsidence from compaction of the aquifer. This implies some unavoidable mining of groundwater from the compacted aquifer material but also creates depletion in the groundwater basin which can later be used for water storage (Galloway, Jones, and Ingebritsen 1999).

13. Several large dams, including Success Dam on the Tule River, Lake Perris Dam in Riverside County (part of the State Water Project), Isabella Dam on the Kern River, and numerous smaller structures have been deemed by state and federal dam safety regulators to be insufficiently safe and in need of significant upgrades.

consequences statewide (Chapter 6).[14] Less appreciated, but no less significant, earthquakes also increase the risk of catastrophic flooding in existing and proposed urban areas protected by Delta levees. Advances in technical understanding and regulatory responses should drive change in the design and maintenance of levees and will likely increase costs.

Converging Pressures on the Sacramento–San Joaquin Delta

One persistent theme in this review of deteriorating water system assets concerns conditions in the Delta. This hub of California's water supply system, which supplies about 15 percent of California's urban and agricultural water use, is undergoing profound change (Lund et al. 2010). Change in the Delta is likely from earthquakes, as well as from other fundamental geological and climate processes. Subsidence of Delta islands from oxidation and erosion of their peat soils has long been recognized as an eventual cause for the demise of many western and central Delta islands (Figure 3.5).[15] Unavoidable sea level rise and permanent failure of the most subsided Delta islands will reduce the quality of water available for export. State policy for Delta levees and water supply management will need to change as earthquakes and floods make existing policies untenable or irrelevant.

The accumulating number of endangered fish species in the Delta, and resulting restrictions on Delta pumping operations, also will drive continued changes in Delta water exports. The immediate costs to water users of a catastrophic failure of Delta levees, which would draw seawater into the Delta and shut down the export pumps for many months, could amount to more than $15 billion (Lund et al. 2010). The costs of eliminating, reducing, or replumbing Delta water exports over the longer term will involve billions in up-front investments and up to several billion dollars per year of expenses statewide (Chapter 6). But these inevitable changes will also provide opportunities to improve water quality for agricultural and urban users, create better habitat for native species, and shift the Delta's economy to more sustainable foundations. The changes in the Delta's ecosystem and inevitable landscape changes in the central and western Delta are among the most fundamental changes that will drive water management in California in the coming decades.

---

14. See Lund et al. (2010) and recent technical reports (URS Corporation and J. R. Benjamin and Associates, 2009a, 2009b).

15. For a historical analysis, see Thompson (1957); for recent analyses of levee problems, see Suddeth, Mount, and Lund (2010) and Lund et al. (2010).

Figure 3.5
Many Delta islands are well below sea level, heightening vulnerability to floods and earthquakes

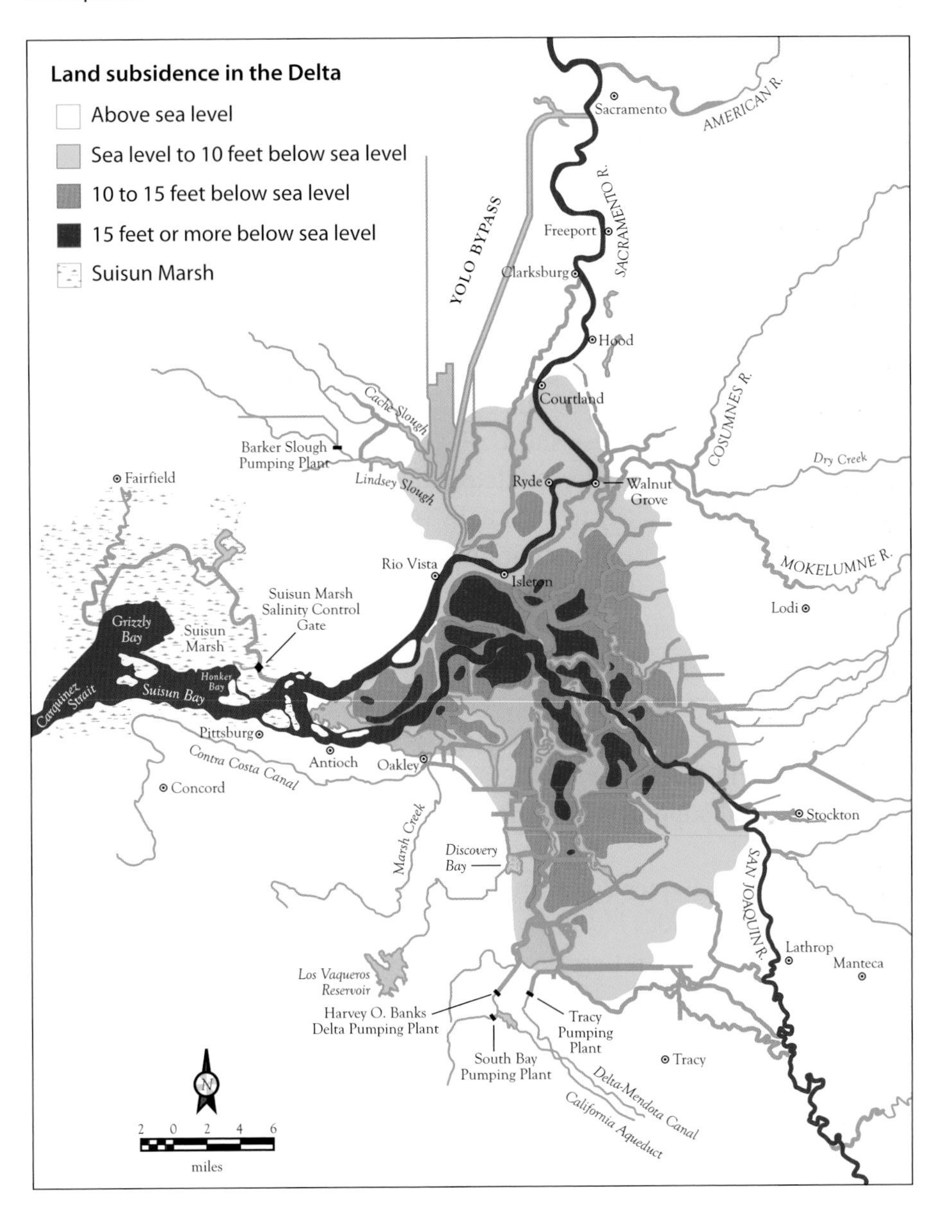

SOURCE: California Department of Water Resources (1995b).

Economic and Demographic Conditions

Economic and demographic factors have always driven water use and management in California, and several trends already under way will strongly influence the future of the state's water delivery system: the financial constraints on state and federal governments, continued strong population growth and urbanization, and the growing globalization of the California economy.

State and Federal Financial Distress

The 2010–2011 California budget year began with the prospect of a $20 billion shortfall for a total budget of about $120 billion (Gordon 2010). The federal budget, for its part, has a $1.4 trillion deficit of a roughly $3.6 trillion budget total. Although California's budget woes have been exacerbated by the economic recession, the state has suffered structural financial shortfalls throughout the past decade. Each year, these shortfalls require additional spending cuts or revenue increases, because adopted state budgets cannot legally include a deficit. Economic recovery is likely to eventually improve the state's revenue picture, but long-term liabilities, including undercapitalized pension funds, rapidly escalating costs for Medicaid, and underfunded retiree health benefits, will maintain pressure on state resources. At the federal level, where deficit finance is possible, similar cost uncertainties loom large, and there is widespread concern about the long-term economic effects of sustaining such large deficits. Large-scale increases in taxes—the alternative to reduced spending—are unpopular at both state and federal levels. These trends imply long-term reductions in state and federal support for California water investments, as well as other investments.

As shown in Chapter 2, a primary source of state funding for the water sector in recent decades has been general obligation (GO) bonds, which are funded by general state tax revenues.[16] These bonds have been used not only to finance infrastructure construction but also to support a wide range of operating expenses, from science to conservation to environmental mitigation. In a tight state budget without new tax revenues, repayment of GO bonds takes priority over other major state expenditures, making it likely that education

16. One exception was the initial general obligation bond supporting the construction of the State Water Project (SWP), passed by voters in 1960, which is being repaid by water users who receive SWP water, not taxpayers. Subsequent SWP extensions to the Central Coast have been funded through revenue bonds, directly backed by revenues from ratepayers, rather than the general fund.

and other sectors relying on state general funds will oppose continued reliance on GO bonds to fund water projects.[17]

In recent decades, federal contributions for California water have declined in real terms, following the winding down of large grant programs for wastewater treatment facilities in the late 1970s and 1980s and real reductions in flood control spending since the 1970s. Despite a recent, short-term boost from stimulus spending, the large and likely long-lived federal budget deficit can be expected to preclude major long-term increases in federal funds for California water.

These financial woes at the state and federal levels imply that local governments and water users will have no choice but to take more direct financial responsibility for California's water system. This shift also implies less ability for state and federal government to provide financial incentives to induce behavioral shifts by local and regional entities. The "carrot" approach has been a focus of much of the recent state bond funding, to encourage cooperation among local groundwater users and among regional water entities. As we discuss in Chapter 7, this constraint might be mitigated if California were to create a water trust fund by levying a surcharge on water use. Parallels include the federal highway trust fund, which is supported by a transportation fuel tax, and the public goods charge on energy use in California. These revenues fund local transportation and energy efficiency investments as well as research and development.

Population Growth

California's population today is nearly 39 million.[18] Mid-range projections put the state's population at nearly 60 million by 2050 and perhaps as high as 85 million by 2100.[19] This growth will bring large increases in housing, commerce, and employment and major changes in land use. Growth in the number of households will expand urban land areas, with much of this expansion replacing

17. For instance, the California Teachers' Association opposed the $11.14 billion general obligation bond that was part of the 2009 legislative water package, on the grounds that it would encumber general fund resources available for schools (Buchanan 2010).

18. As of July 2009, the California Department of Finance estimated the state's population at 38,477,000. The U.S. Census had a somewhat lower estimate, at 36,962,000.

19. The California Department of Finance (2007) projects the 2050 population at 59.5 million. Using projections developed by Hans Johnson, Sanstad et al. (2009) project a similar level for their mid-range estimates and 85.3 million by 2100. Earlier in the decade, Landis and Reilly (2002) projected even higher growth by the end of the century, to 92 million. Sanstad et al. (2009) also project low and high growth scenarios that place a wide band around these levels, with 44.2 to 69.4 million residents by 2050 and 43.8 to 147.7 million by 2100. This wide range highlights the difficulties inherent in long-run population projections. For the purposes of assessing the ranges of urban water demand in Figure 3.8 (see below), we use a more moderate, slower growth scenario of 51.7 million residents in 2050 and 64.6 million residents in 2100 (personal communication from Hans Johnson).

agricultural land on the urban fringe, reducing agricultural water use. Some of this growth will occur on floodplains and fire-prone hills.

Land use policies can significantly affect these factors, however. For instance, Figure 3.6 presents two alternative scenarios of urban growth by mid-century. In a compact vision of new development (shown in red), population increases to 65 million inhabitants, displacing roughly 1 million acres of farmland. In contrast, a more sprawling vision of new development (largely covering the red areas as well as the area shown in yellow) projects a loss of nearly 2 million acres of farmland, despite more modest population growth (59.2 million).[20]

Generally, new urban development can be expected to use less water per capita than existing homes within the same regions: It will generally contain newer, more efficient appliances and plumbing fixtures, and it will require less landscape irrigation because of smaller lots and higher residential densities. However, a larger proportion of growth will occur in hotter inland areas, where housing densities tend to be lower and landscape evaporation is higher than in the coastal metropolitan areas (Hanak and Davis 2006). Growth in these inland areas also increases peak electricity demands for summer air conditioning, much of which is provided by hydropower (Vine 2008). Urbanization also will increase discharges of urban runoff and treated wastewater, while decreasing agricultural runoff from urbanized agricultural lands.

It is commonly assumed that population growth and the accompanying shift from urban to agricultural land uses will increase overall water use. But this is not entirely certain. If land and water resources are well managed, new urbanization can have a smaller per capita water use rate and can replace relatively water-intensive agricultural water uses. Urban water use efficiency efforts, the urbanization of some agricultural lands, and the retirement of agricultural lands in saline areas could combine to decrease overall human water use and particularly net water use.

Although California's population will also change in other ways, such as its ethnic composition, age structure, and income, growth in population is likely to be the most important demographic change from a water management perspective. Other studies have found that the effects of growth in population and water demands are likely to be important for water management worldwide, with global effects on water use greater than those likely from climate change (Vörösmarty et al. 2000).

20. See Teitz, Dietzel, and Fulton (2005) for an examination of multiple scenarios for the San Joaquin Valley.

Figure 3.6
Urban growth will displace farmland

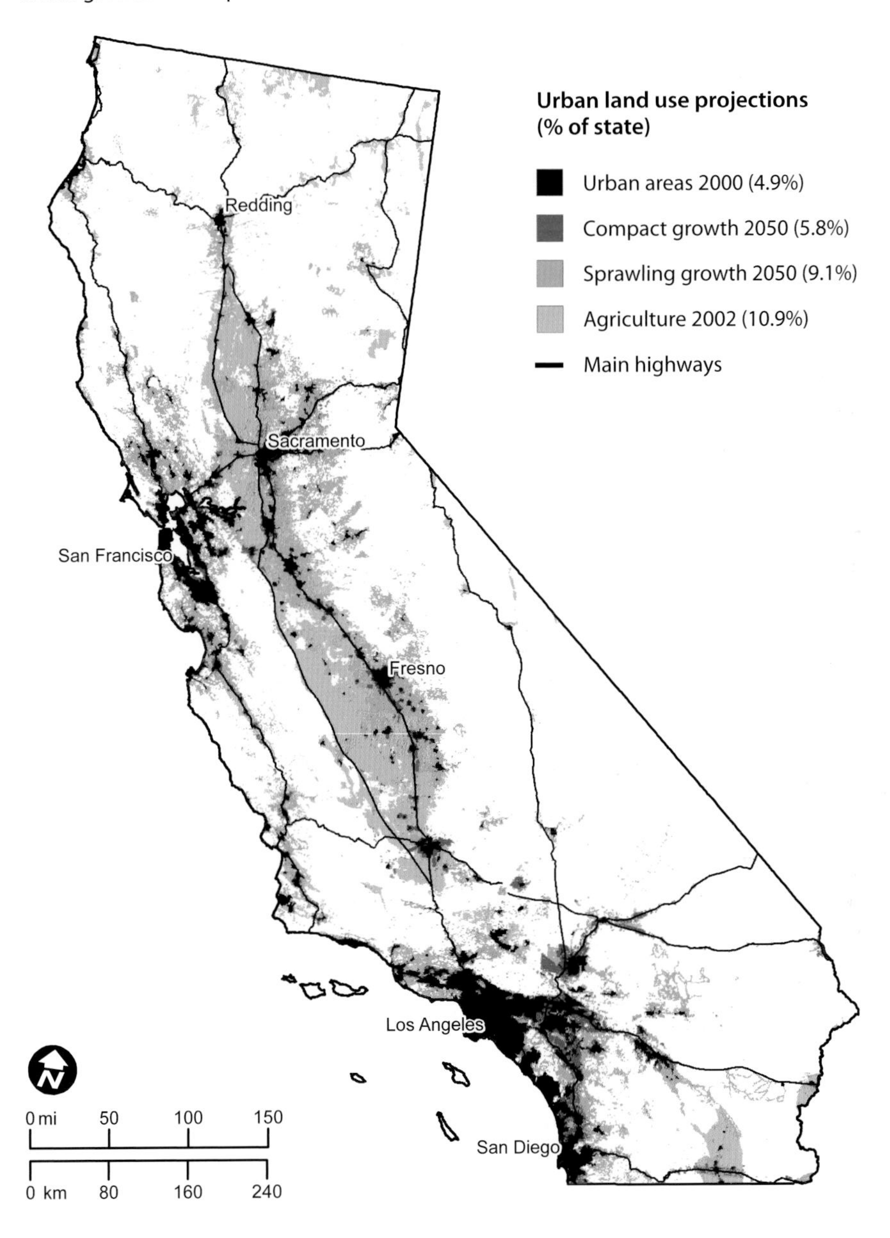

SOURCES: Authors' calculations using 2002 agricultural land use data from the California Department of Water Resources; 2000 urban land use and compact growth scenario data from Landis and Reilly (2002); and sprawling growth scenario data from Sanstad et al. (2009).

NOTE: Urban areas in 2000 would remain urban in the two growth scenarios, which largely overlap, with greater overall land use by urbanization in the sprawling growth scenario.

Globalization and Continuing Shifts in California's Economy

Along with population growth, globalization of the world's economy is likely to reinforce some trends already under way in California's economy (Figure 1.3), including the increasing share of service-sector employment and the declining shares of manufacturing and agricultural employment. Global market forces are also likely to continue the shift in California's agriculture toward more permanent and higher-value tree and vine crops. Since the early 1980s, these crops have already increased substantially as a share of total acreage (Figure 3.7). In the water-short San Joaquin Valley, perennials now constitute 32 percent of all cropland.[21]

California agriculture already serves a largely global market. The state's favorable climate and the increasing demand for higher-value agricultural products worldwide is likely to foster demand growth for fruits, nuts, and other high-value agricultural commodities (Howitt, Medellin-Azuara, and MacEwan 2009; Hanak et al. 2010). This shift toward perennial crops will increase agricultural revenues. But by reducing the flexibility of the agricultural sector to fallow crops during droughts, this shift will also increase the costs of farm water shortages.

Figure 3.7
Acreage shifts toward higher-value perennial crops have reduced flexibility to cope with droughts

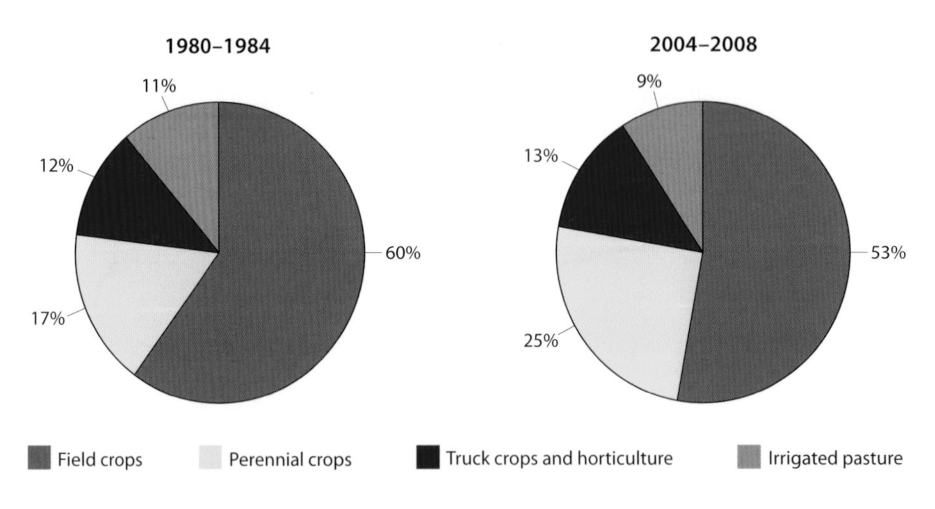

SOURCE: Authors' calculations using data from County Agricultural Commissioner Reports (various years).

NOTES: Acreage includes nonirrigated cropland. Average acreage totals: 10.6 million in 1980–1984 and 10.4 million in 2004–2008.

21. Authors' calculations using data from County Agricultural Commissioner Reports. These data include nonirrigated crop land; the share of perennials in irrigated acreage is likely somewhat higher.

Changing Ecosystems

Changes in the size, structure, and species-composition of California's aquatic ecosystems will also drive changes in water management. Major ecological drivers include the growing problem of new invasive species and the degradation of habitats for native species, both of which will lead to additional organisms becoming threatened or endangered, and thus increasing the conflicts over water uses.

Invasive Species

California's intensive commerce with the rest of the world brings many new species of plants, animals, and microorganisms to the state. At the same time, changing environments create conditions that increasingly favor established alien (nonnative) species over native species. Most rivers and estuaries in California already contain a mix of native and alien species. The San Francisco Estuary and Sacramento–San Joaquin Delta are dominated by alien species, from plants to invertebrates to fish (Cohen and Carlton 1998), making it one of the most invaded estuaries in the world. Large populations of alien species alter ecosystem function and community dynamics and complicate management efforts to maintain native species (Lund et al. 2010; Moyle and Marchetti 2006). Alien species at this stage are usually labeled as invasive species, or as alien invaders, because many alien species, if not most, do not cause significant harm.

The dominance of aliens in many of California's streams, lakes, estuaries, and riparian areas stems largely from human alterations of physical habitat, combined with introductions of new organisms into the system either by individuals and agencies or as by-products of water-based transportation systems. Examples of sources include dumping of ship ballast water, disposal of aquarium fish into water bodies, transport of organisms such as mussels on recreational boats, and the spread of fish and other organisms through aqueducts. In rivers, the "homogenization" of habitat through flow regulation, reservoir creation, and levee construction provides conditions favoring widespread aliens at the expense of natives (Moyle and Mount 2007).

Most reservoirs in California, for example, contain alien fish (e.g., bass, sunfish, shad, catfish, minnows, carp), crayfish, Asian clams, and aquatic weeds, with very few native species. These organisms are then transported elsewhere with the water. Other alien species, once introduced, spread well both on their own and with assistance from humans (e.g., anglers, aquarists, fish farmers) into more natural systems. As a result, brook trout (*Salvelinus fontinalis*) from the eastern United States have displaced native trout and amphibians in lakes and streams throughout the Sierra Nevada and Cascade Mountains, and redeye bass (*Micropterus coosae*) have eliminated most native fishes from the Cosumnes and Santa Margarita Rivers (Moyle 2002; Moyle et al. 2003). Lake Tahoe has been invaded by so many species of fish and invertebrates that the aquatic ecosystem today bares scant resemblance to the one that existed before European settlement, and new species continue to arrive (Moyle 2002).

Although the displacement of native species by alien invaders is perhaps the most studied problem in aquatic systems, the direct effects of these species on water management are of concern as well. For example, dense beds of aquatic plants known as macrophytes (e.g., *Egeria densa* or Brazilian waterweed) can impede navigation and therefore require application of herbicides to water supply systems. Likewise, dense growths of some macrophytes (e.g., *Hydrilla*) can clog irrigation canals, reducing delivery capacity. The dense growth of invasive clams (*Corbicula fluminea*) in aqueducts can reduce water-carrying capacity, a problem likely to worsen as zebra and quagga mussels (*Dreissena* spp.) invade the water supply system (Stokstad 2007). These mussel invasions are both predictable and preventable (Lund et al. 2007).

Current management efforts are unlikely to resolve the alien invader issue, particularly under changing climatic conditions, although plans are in place (California Department of Fish and Game 2008). At best, careful management can reduce the frequencies of new invasions, conduct eradication programs before invaders are well established, and provide conditions that allow native species to thrive, recognizing they will be coexisting with aliens already established in much of their habitat (Chapter 5).

Habitat Degradation

Alien species are just one of many factors contributing to the decline in California's native aquatic and riparian species. California's aquatic ecosystems have been fundamentally changed by 150 years of water and land management. Today's river, lake, riparian, and wetland ecosystems reflect an interweaving of pre-development natural systems and the accumulated effects of human uses and management of water and land. Indeed, no completely pristine ecosystems remain in California; all are affected by human uses, which have resulted in habitat loss and fragmentation, unfavorable changes in flow conditions and quality, and invasions of alien plants and animals. Climate change will exacerbate many already unfavorable trends.

For example, wildfires are increasing in frequency and severity in California as a consequence of increased human presence in wild areas and failure to recognize that wildfires of low to moderate severity are important for ecosystem functioning (Sugihara et al. 2006). Warming temperatures are likely to be contributing to this trend, which favors conditions for invasive insects that kill various tree species (Miller et al. 2009). By allowing fuels to accumulate, fire-suppression policies have contributed to more severe fires, with numerous negative effects on aquatic systems: direct kills of organisms, destruction of riparian systems, increased siltation from erosion, increased nutrients from burned materials, and altered stream flows as the burned landscapes are less able to retain water. These factors imperil more species, especially in Southern California (e.g., southern steelhead).

Likewise, the anticipated changes in stream flow timing and magnitude with warming, outlined above, will harm freshwater ecosystems, particularly in mountain rivers and in streams that depend on seasonal snowpacks. These shifts are likely to affect a wide range of fishes, amphibians, and riparian plants whose life-history strategies depend on the spring snowmelt pulse—previously the most predictable flow event of the year (Yarnell, Viers, and Mount 2010). This pulse provides an extended period of abundant, low-temperature flow that occurs around the same time almost every year, providing an ideal cue and habitat for the reproductive cycle of these species. Reproduction, both egg-laying and release of seeds, is highly sensitive to changes in the timing, magnitude, and rate of change in this critical flow. These conditions are likely to change significantly in mountain watersheds as a result of climate warming (Null, Deas, and Lund 2010), threatening the survival of native species such as the foothill yellow-legged frog and the hardhead minnow.

Changes in the timing and amount of flow also will harm native species in lowland river systems. As discussed in Chapter 5, conditions of large riverine and estuarine ecosystems in California are already increasingly unfavorable to native fishes. Systems such as the Klamath, Sacramento, San Joaquin, and Colorado Rivers have witnessed significant declines in native fish populations because of harmful flow regulation, flood management, invasive species, and discharge of agricultural and urban waste (Moyle et al. 2010). If present trends in altered flows and degraded habitat continue, California's rivers will be increasingly dominated by alien species, from bass to clams, with many fewer desirable natives, such as salmon and river mussels.

Declining aquatic ecosystems and native species will increasingly affect water management. Changing social values, reflected in state and federal endangered species and clean water legislation, have become embedded in all water management activities. But continued declines in native biodiversity are a stark indicator that current laws, regulations, and management are simply not working well. Fish, amphibians, and other aquatic organisms are losing the contest for water and habitat.

Additional native species will almost certainly be listed as threatened or endangered under the federal or state Endangered Species Acts. Moyle, Katz, and Quiñones (2010), for example, indicate that 17 unprotected species of fish should qualify for immediate listing as threatened or endangered, with others rapidly approaching that condition. Agencies responsible for water management will become increasingly bound to act to prevent extinction and promote recovery of listed species. Future necessary actions, under a changing climate, cannot be known today with high confidence but have potential to disrupt water management operations at all scales, particularly when cold water is necessary for maintaining fish populations. Although more water is not always better for fish, especially if not accompanied with habitat restoration (Hanak et al. 2010), increased environmental demands for flow are likely, simply to keep up with or compensate for changing conditions.

Scientific and Technological Progress

Advances in scientific knowledge and technological innovation will surely occur over the coming decades, as they have in the past. Some innovations—such as the ongoing introduction of new chemicals, discussed above—are likely to heighten water management challenges for human and environmental health. Others will help California cope with its water-related supply and demand problems, including reductions in water availability. Scientific advances should also lead to better understanding and tools for improving the health and functioning of the ecosystem. However, technology also has its limitations and is unlikely to provide a "silver bullet" solution for all of California's water problems (Hanak et al. 2010).

In this section, we briefly explore four areas where advances are likely: (1) treatment technologies for expanding potable water sources; (2) technologies and management approaches for improving efficiencies in water use; (3) technologies for measuring water use; and (4) advances in ecosystem management.

Treatment Technologies

Water treatment makes it possible today to safely and affordably supply drinking water from a wide range of previously disparaged water sources. Reuse of treated wastewater for nonpotable uses such as landscaping is now common in many parts of California, several Southern California agencies have indirect potable reuse by recharging groundwater with highly treated wastewater, and discussions continue regarding more direct potable reuse of water (California Department of Water Resources 2009). Desalination of brackish water is now affordable and is used by urban agencies in inland Southern California. Desalination of seawater, while still very costly, is becoming potentially affordable as an incremental urban water supply in California (California Department of Water Resources 2009; Hanak et al. 2010).

However, new treatment technologies are likely to have limits. As noted above, even as new wastewater and reuse technologies are developed, new chemicals of environmental and public health concerns arise to challenge these technologies. Water treatment also has fundamental physical and economic limits. For example, the most efficient large seawater desalination plants currently use about 4.5 kilowatt hour/cubic meter ($670/acre-foot for energy alone at recent industrial sector energy prices in California), and it seems unlikely that these plants will be able to reduce their energy use by more than 20 percent.[22] Real energy prices are likely to rise in the future. Capital and siting costs of these facilities are also substantial, as well as the sometimes significant costs of environmentally safe disposal of "waste" salt and brine.

Efficiency in Water Use

As discussed in Chapter 2, agricultural water use in California continues to become more efficient, primarily through increases in crop yields. Yields are likely to continue to progress in the decades to come.

Irrigation technology and management tools can help improve water quality, and this will become increasingly important as California works to reduce the flow of polluted agricultural runoff into streams and groundwater basins (Letey

22. See Semiat (2008) on desalination energy use. Energy prices are from the U.S. Energy Information Administration (www.eia.doe.gov/electricity/epm/table5_6_a.html). Recent industrial rates in California are on the order of $0.12 per kilowatt hour. Commercial sector rates are higher (over $0.16 per kilowatt hour).

et al. in press). In areas prone to soil salinization, such as the west side of the San Joaquin Valley, reductions in drainage from irrigation efficiency improvements have already greatly reduced salt loads in local soils and receiving waters (Wichelns, Jouston, and Cone 1997; Wichelns and Cone 2006; Shoups et al. 2005).

However, irrigation technology has less potential to create net water savings, because it generally does not reduce net agricultural water use (Box 2.1). Irrigation improvements can actually *increase* net water use by crops, by allowing either more intensive use of irrigation water on a given field (which raises both yields per acre and net water use per acre) or more extensive use of "saved" water on nearby fields that were previously less irrigated. Net water savings are more likely in areas where drainage water cannot be reused, such as where fields drain to brackish or saline aquifers or water bodies. Such savings have been the basis of water transfer agreements between the Imperial Irrigation District, whose crop runoff drains into the Salton Sea, and urban agencies in Southern California. Irrigation technology also can provide solutions to environmental water problems. But to create net water savings from farming in many parts of the state, reductions in crop acreage will be required. Some of this will happen naturally, as farmland is displaced by urban growth. Water marketing also provides an opportunity to compensate farmers and the local economy for reductions in acreage of low-value crops.

As in agriculture, improvements in urban water use efficiency can have water quality benefits. Inefficient landscape irrigation (generally less efficient than on-farm irrigation) is an important factor in polluted urban runoff. And even though the urban sector uses far less water than agriculture, urban water use efficiency actions—both indoors and outdoors—have a greater potential for net water savings. In the state's heavily populated coastal areas, most indoor water use savings result in net water savings, because most treated wastewater is discharged into the ocean. Improvements in outdoor water use efficiency, such as shifting from thirsty lawns to more drought-tolerant plants, can significantly reduce outdoor water use, especially in the hotter inland areas. Technological advancements in irrigation technology, including the use of "smart" irrigation control systems that use weather information to determine when plants need water, have the potential to significantly improve irrigation efficiency and reduce runoff from urban landscaping (Hanak and Davis 2006).

The introduction of more efficient indoor plumbing devices, such as low-flow toilets and showers, have already significantly reduced per capita urban use since the early 1990s (Chapter 2). Additional improvements in indoor plumbing (including more efficient appliances) as well as landscape planting changes, higher urban densities, and improvements in landscape irrigation have the potential to considerably slow growth in urban water use (California Department of Water Resources 2009; Gleick et al. 2003; Hanak and Davis 2006; CALFED 2006). With the mid-range population projections noted above at today's use rate (roughly 200 gallons per person per day [gpcd]), gross urban water demand would roughly double by the end of the century (Figure 3.8). A moderate conservation effort (20 percent by 2050 and 30 percent by 2100) would significantly lessen demand growth, and a more aggressive conservation effort (30 percent by 2050 and 40 percent by 2100) would keep gross urban demands roughly constant. These efforts would result in water use levels falling to 140–160 gpcd by 2050, and 100–140 gpcd by 2100. Lest this seem unreasonable, it is worth recalling that urban water use in the early 2000s in other developed economies with similar climates was 80–130 gpcd in Australia, 84 gpcd in Israel, and 76 gpcd in Spain (Food and Agricultural Organization of the United Nations, undated).[23] In Chapter 6, we explore the potential for aggressive urban conservation efforts to reduce pressures on the Delta and facilitate adaptation to climate change.

Figure 3.8
Successful conservation efforts could significantly slow urban water demand growth

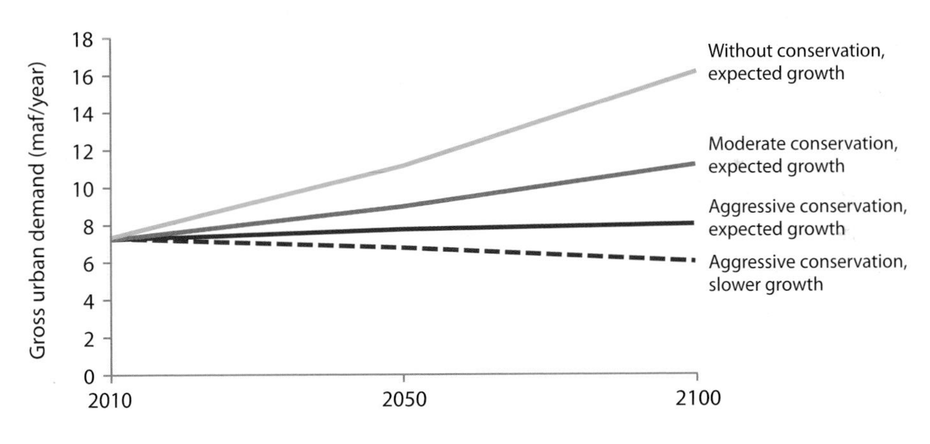

NOTES: Expected population growth scenarios are from Sanstad et al. (2009): 59.2 million in 2050 and 85.3 million in 2100. Slower growth projections are 51.7 million and 64.6 million, respectively (unpublished estimates from Hans Johnson 2009). Moderate conservation assumes 20 percent reduction by 2050 (160 gpcd) and 30 percent by 2100 (140 gpcd). Aggressive conservation assumes 30 percent reduction by 2050 (140 gpcd) and 50 percent reduction by 2100 (100 gpcd).

23. The low estimate for Australia is from www.nwc.gov.au/www/html/2765-national-performance-report-2008-09---urban-water-utilities.asp?intSiteID=1. Urban water use in Australia has been further reduced in recent years in response to prolonged drought.

Measurement of Water Use

Advances in the use of remote sensing technologies are likely to be useful both for raising farm water use efficiency and for improving water accounting. Federal satellite data show promise for accurately estimating crop evapotranspiration on the scale of a farmer's field. This method has the potential to inform farmers and water managers about water use accurately, at relatively little cost compared to metering and on-farm measurement techniques currently available (Allen et al. 2005, 2007). From a regional and statewide water accounting perspective, this method could help improve water use estimates in areas where data collection is hampered by the lack of reporting requirements for some categories of water use. For areas not served by surface water, remote sensing of crop water use gives a direct estimate of net groundwater use as well.

Ecosystem Management

In recent decades, California has seen remarkable improvements in understanding of the state's aquatic ecosystems, compared with the Hydraulic Era when most of the state's water management infrastructure and institutions were designed and constructed. As described in Chapter 5, this knowledge provides an improving basis for shifting the focus of ecosystem management toward approaches that aim to restore ecosystem function at fairly large scales, using concepts such as the "natural flow regime" (which aims to mimic natural conditions, albeit with lower flow volumes). However, there is still much to learn about how ecosystems and species will respond to improved water management actions, particularly with rapidly changing conditions.

New approaches to ecosystem management under changing conditions will require continued, large-scale experimentation aided by computer modeling. This task is complex, because experiments, especially on a large scale, often yield ambiguous results.[24] Also, as with hydrology, the past is not always a good predictor of the future with many ecosystems. Linking human and natural systems, combined with changes in climate and influxes of alien species, creates novel, dynamic ecosystems with no historical analog. Thus, efforts to restore ecosystem functions and attributes involve hitting a moving, only partially visible target. Finally, ecosystem changes are often nonlinear and interrelated. Declines in habitat quality or abundance reduce ecosystem resiliency, with the result that even small changes in conditions can lead to abrupt system collapse

---

24. An example is the decline of delta smelt and the somewhat chaotic efforts for its recovery (Bennett 2005).

and reorganization to a new state (Walker and Salt 2006).[25] Such thresholds or tipping points are difficult to predict. Taken together, these factors suggest that efforts to improve conditions for California's native aquatic species will necessarily involve trial and error, and that success is far from guaranteed.

Seemingly Inevitable Changes

One of life's charms and curses is that the future is inherently uncertain. We find the drivers of change discussed above compelling, but it is likely that some will be less important than we envision and that others might more than take their place. Other potential influences include changes in social preferences among water management objectives, including a tightening—or radical loosening—of endangered species regulations; major changes in energy policy or costs; and destructive geologic events, such as proximate or global volcanic eruptions that alter climate conditions or devastate regional landscapes.

Predicting changes with certainty is clearly impossible, although change itself is certain. California has always been changing, often quite dramatically, and water management in California is no exception. A list of the dozen most likely changes affecting California water, in order of their likely importance, would include:

1. Greatly expanded efforts to maintain "natural" ecosystems and native species as a water management goal, given increased numbers of both endangered and alien species, placing increasing pressure on providing water for human consumption;
2. Transformation of the Delta and water management as a result of sea level rise, earthquakes, and permanent flooding of western and central islands, reducing the viability of the Delta as an urban and agricultural water source;
3. Population growth and expansion of the urban footprint, displacing portions of agricultural land, altering water use, and raising floodplain risks, particularly in the Central Valley;

25. For instance, the Delta's ecosystem seems to have abruptly shifted in the 1980s, driven by increasing water exports from an already highly altered system, exacerbated by invasive species and pollutants (Moyle and Bennett 2008). Likewise, the Eel River ecosystem shifted from a shaded cold water system to a more exposed cool water ecosystem, less friendly to salmon and steelhead, as the consequence of massive human-caused erosion and introduction of an alien predator (Yoshiyama and Moyle 2010).

4. Declining financial support for water management from traditional state and federal sources;
5. Degradation of infrastructure, including levees, dams, and water treatment facilities, with increasing replacement costs;
6. Increasing average air and water temperatures, leading to decreasing snowpack, declining available water, changing natural vegetation, and increasing environmental water demands in reservoirs to maintain cold water for salmon and steelhead habitat below dams;
7. Rising expenses for water and wastewater treatment as water quality standards continue to diversify and become more exacting and as understanding of the negative effects of increasingly diverse and abundant contaminants increases;
8. Reductions in per capita urban water use (gross and net);
9. Reductions in irrigated agriculture as a result of urbanization, the flooding of Delta farmlands, salinization, increasingly costly groundwater overdraft, and cutbacks in Delta water exports in the western San Joaquin and Tulare Basins;
10. Globalization of California's economy, with continued growth in its service economy and continued shifts to higher-value perennial crops;
11. Increasingly compromised groundwater basins, as a result of overdraft and declining groundwater quality; and
12. Increased investments in (or retreat from) current shorelines and reexamination of coastal management as a result of sea level rise.

Other changes are likely but less certain. One possibility is that, despite population growth, total human water use in California might decline over time through the combined effects of lower per capita urban water use and reductions of irrigated agricultural land. Other changes, perhaps more significant, are likely to arise with little warning or to be evident only in retrospect. Thirty years ago, few could have predicted the ubiquity of information now available through the Internet. Two years ago, few preparations were in place to manage European air travel in the event of volcanic eruptions in Iceland.

A major uncertainty for water management is what will happen to overall precipitation levels with climate change. In contrast to most other drivers examined here, there is uncertainty about not only the magnitude but also the direction of change. A drier climate will exacerbate water scarcity arising from reductions in the snowpack, and a wetter climate will lessen scarcity but exacerbate flood risks.

Decisionmaking in the face of uncertainty about the future is inevitable for California water management. But the challenge is not new: Water managers have always faced uncertainty, often with less sophisticated technical tools than are available today. For those decisions whose usefulness depends greatly on uncertain outcomes (such as new surface storage to accommodate changes in precipitation), it would be wise to wait for greater certainty (Chapter 6). However, for many decisions, awaiting certainty can become an excuse for maintaining a deteriorating status quo. Such procrastination can turn the "precautionary principle" into a potentially dangerous "inaction principle" when maintaining the status quo means continued loss of environmental services, biodiversity, and other water management benefits. Fortunately, sufficient certainty often exists to make better choices.

Some changes reviewed in this chapter can be addressed individually, but many will require more integrated and comprehensive solutions. Part II of this book describes several approaches for managing simultaneous changes and increasing the adaptive capacity of water management systems to achieve multiple goals.

Part II

New Directions for a Changing Future

There is a certain magic about the number 21 in our society, and perhaps the 21st century will be an age of maturity by comparison to the adolescent centuries of wild growth and disorder that preceded it.

Kenneth Boulding, 1990

Part I of this book examined the history and current situation of California water policy and identified the many changes in natural, physical, and economic conditions that water policy will need to contend with in the future.

Part II presents some promising new directions for California water. In Chapter 4, we begin with an overview of major challenges that will require strategic shifts in water policy: (1) resolving the environmental and economic crisis in the Sacramento–San Joaquin Delta, (2) reversing the decline of native fish and aquatic ecosystems across the state, (3) reducing major flood risks, (4) protecting the quality of water sources, and (5) enabling California's water management network to respond more effectively to changing conditions. In most of these cases, not only will pursuing status quo policies slow progress, it will make conditions worse. In all of these cases, state (and sometimes federal) actions will be needed to move in a better direction, although local institutions will be vital in crafting on-the-ground solutions.

The three remaining chapters then discuss major changes in approach to California water policy that will provide a basis for addressing these and other challenges to economically and environmentally sustainable water management. In Chapter 5, we look at new directions for addressing California's looming environmental management crisis and examine approaches that reconcile environmental and human uses of water and adjacent lands. Current environmental regulation and management has largely failed to protect native species and ecosystems. But return to pre-development conditions is impossible. Reconciliation of environmental, economic, and social objectives will require more forceful efforts to essentially rebuild large parts of the water management system.

In Chapter 6, we focus on new directions for addressing California's water supply, water quality, and flood risks, using more integrated portfolios of management actions. Portfolio-based resource management, widely applied in the energy sector, can create a more diversified, flexible, and sustainable water system. California has begun some portfolio management efforts in the water sector, but a wider range of tools and better mechanisms for integrating actions at the regional level are needed to make these efforts more effective.

In Chapter 7, we discuss our third suggestion for improving California water policy—managing water as a public commodity. This approach, which again finds its model in the energy sector, uses regulated market mechanisms to improve the flexibility and responsiveness of water management to support human and environmental water use. Treating water as a public commodity offers more promise of economic and environmental success than does relying on traditional water projects, contracts, and regulations.

4 Urgent and Fundamental Challenges

CALIFORNIA DEPARTMENT OF WATER RESOURCES

Subsided cropland behind a Delta levee (Twitchell Island).

The need for change bulldozed a road down the center of my mind.

Maya Angelou, *I Know Why the Caged Bird Sings*

Changes, and the corresponding challenges they present, are inevitable for California's water system. The already fragile condition of the state's aquatic environment, flood control system, key parts of its water supply infrastructure, and the quality of its water sources will be further taxed by the drivers of change discussed in Chapter 3. Water management will need to change in response to these challenges. Failure to respond will lead to continued broad deterioration in the system's economic and environmental performance.

California has successfully adapted to many past water challenges, despite the unavoidable delays and controversies involving changes to the status quo. Some changes, such as the organization of groundwater users in Southern California and the improvements in agricultural and urban water use efficiency in recent decades, have occurred incrementally and have largely been initiated at the local level, in response to local pressures. Other more strategic changes have required state and federal leadership (Chapter 1). Examples include the creation of a comprehensive flood management system for the Central Valley, the widespread introduction of wastewater treatment in the 1970s and 1980s under the Clean Water Act, the shift toward addressing water management's harmful effects on native species through the Endangered Species Acts and other laws in the 1970s, and the launching of a water market to help cope with droughts in the early 1990s.

In each of these cases, state or federal intervention was needed because decentralized approaches were unable to resolve the problems on their own, for one or more reasons: (1) the scale of the problem was too large for local agencies to resolve (e.g., Central Valley flood control); (2) external pressure was needed to address the negative spillover effects of water management (e.g., new environmental regulations); or (3) existing state or federal laws and agency practices were getting in the way of local innovation (e.g., the water market).

Today, several major challenges facing California water will require strategic reform, with state and federal initiative: (1) resolving the Sacramento–San Joaquin Delta's water supply and environmental problems; (2) reversing the decline of native fish and aquatic ecosystems across the state; (3) preventing major increases in exposure to flood risk; (4) protecting source water quality through improved management of nonpoint source pollution and new chemicals introduced into the marketplace; and (5) effectively integrating state and regional storage and distribution systems with local water demands and supplies. In most of these cases, continuing to make incremental changes within the status quo policy framework will not only slow progress, it will make conditions worse. Success in these five strategic areas is fundamental to an economically and environmentally viable future for California's water system.

This chapter summarizes these five major challenges and how they affect the foundations of California water policy. While highlighting the need for state and federal leadership on these issues, we recognize the considerable difficulties governing bodies face in today's policymaking environment. To its credit, the state's administrative and legislative leadership passed two significant water reform packages in recent years—the first in 2007, addressing flood management in the Central Valley, and the second in 2009, addressing a range of water supply issues, including Delta governance, water use efficiency, and improvements in monitoring and reporting groundwater and surface water. However, in both cases, legislative negotiations reflected deep divides and strong resistance to change among stakeholders, preventing more significant reforms.

Our interviews with a wide range of California water experts revealed widespread concern over the capacity of state and federal agencies to address major challenges facing the state (Null et al. 2011). Problems cited include a lack of authority in particular areas, a lack of political support or will to exercise already broad existing authority, and a lack of adequate implementation capacity in many agencies. In Part III of this book, we explore options for bolstering the capacity of state and federal governments to assert the leadership needed to adapt to change.

Five Areas in Need of Strategic Reform

The Delta

The Sacramento–San Joaquin Delta—the hub of California's water supply network—provides a stark example of how incremental approaches to reform can lead to continued deterioration rather than progress. More than 20 years after the listing of Sacramento winter-run Chinook salmon in 1989, conditions for native species in this region are at all-time lows (Moyle, Katz, and Quiñones 2010). Meanwhile, the region's role as a conduit for high-quality water for cities and farms is more compromised than at any time since the Central Valley Project began pumping water from the southern Delta in the early 1950s. Risks of catastrophic levee failure are growing, and the pumps are operating under accumulating regulatory cutbacks to address native species declines. Over time, freshwater exports through Delta channels will become increasingly unreliable, and ultimately infeasible, as a result of sea level rise and island failures (Chapter 3).

Conditions in the Delta worsened during the CALFED decade (mid-1990s to mid-2000s), when policy discussions focused on making incremental improvements rather than fundamental changes in Delta management (Chapter 1). Strategic change, in this case, requires a system overhaul. Two basic options are available. Rather than continuing to route export water through the Delta, an alternative conveyance system is needed, either around or under the Delta, so that flows within the Delta itself can be managed to better support native species. Alternatively, the state needs to plan for greatly diminishing and ultimately ending Delta water exports (Lund et al. 2010; Moyle et al. 2010).

Major efforts are now under way to pursue the first option, by developing new conveyance infrastructure that would allow continued use of the Delta as a water supply hub, along with comprehensive flow and habitat investments to support the Delta ecosystem. Under the Bay Delta Conservation Planning process, export water users are working with state and federal fisheries agencies, under the auspices of the California Natural Resource Agency, to establish a new habitat conservation plan for the Delta that would accomplish these goals. Senate Bill (SB) X7-1, part of the 2009 legislative package, established several new governance components to provide broad oversight of Delta management, including a Delta Stewardship Council (which will oversee the development of a comprehensive plan for water and land use in the Delta) and a Delta watermaster within the State Water Resources Control Board (SWRCB) (who will oversee Delta flow management).

But a high probability remains that controversy and expense will eventually eliminate the Delta as a major water source.[1] This risk is greater if senior state and federal leaders do not press for a comprehensive solution. Ending exports entirely would have some merit for the Delta ecosystem, by reducing the amount of water diverted from the system and ending the harm caused by the pumps. But it also would pose great hazards in terms of loss of political interest and funding for environmental reconciliation in the Delta. In Chapter 6, we provide new modeling insights regarding the effects on California's economy of long-term cutbacks in Delta water exports. We find that local, decentralized efforts to reduce urban water use can help reduce the overall costs of Delta cutbacks. However, losing the ability to move water from northern and eastern California to points south and west would still be very costly for the state's economy, with major implications for San Joaquin Valley agriculture. These costs will be particularly high if California's future becomes significantly drier, as predicted by some climate models.

Fish and Aquatic Ecosystems

The Delta is just one manifestation of a widespread crisis for native aquatic ecosystems in California. Statewide, harmful water and land management practices have left a legacy of severely degraded wetland, riverine, and estuarine ecosystems. As a consequence, native fish species have been on a downward spiral. Similar trends are evident for terrestrial and riparian species that depend on functioning riverine and wetland habitat.

Regrettably, conditions for native fish species have largely continued to deteriorate despite regulatory protections under state and federal environmental laws passed in the 1970s. State and federal environmental safeguards were needed because of inherent conflicts between traditional water development projects and environmental protection. Thus, providing water and cheap power for farmers in the upper Klamath River Basin in Oregon can conflict with protecting endangered salmon in the lower river in California, as well as maintaining fisheries (Box 2.4; Doremus and Tarlock 2008). Statewide, contention over releases of water from dams to protect fish and enhance fisheries is

1. Madani and Lund (2011) describe how various parties' reluctance to compromise may prevent a negotiated solution—a game of "chicken" that leads to continued decline and a worse overall outcome for both water supply and environmental values.

Fish kills are common in areas where pollution, dams, and algae create poor water quality, such as in the Klamath River. Photo by Sarah Null.

common, because these releases can come at considerable cost to urban and agricultural water users.

The effectiveness of environmental regulations has been limited by the piecemeal approaches to recovery that have become the industry standard. Water management today tends to view aquatic ecosystems as a series of incremental constraints to be handled as cheaply as possible in the short term, rather than as a sustained, coherent objective. Even in the best of projects, the goal is to reduce water development effects on ecosystems, not to halt or reverse their decline. Mitigation efforts seek only to compensate for negative effects, not to sustain native ecosystems. This "no net losses in habitat" approach has rarely worked. Piecemeal, species-by-species mitigation measures have proven to be a poor and perilous substitute for environmental management that focuses on fostering functioning ecosystems.

As discussed in Chapter 5, a new approach is needed in which natural aquatic environments are protected and managed on a systematic basis. Rather than focusing principally on individual species, management will need to focus on improving the functioning of ecosystems in which native species once thrived. Given the likelihood of even greater conflicts among water management objectives with a warmer (and possibly drier) climate, this approach also will need to balance economic and environmental objectives at a broader scale. This means, for instance, perhaps managing some whole watersheds largely for natural values, while other watersheds primarily serve economic purposes. Many watersheds would continue to be managed for multiple purposes. This balancing will require many critical decisions, big and small, to be made every year: managing flows in regulated rivers, saving cold water for fish, preventing the introduction of new invasive species, reducing contaminant loads, changing land use practices to limit erosion and keep development away from rivers, moving back levees to allow wider riparian areas to receive floodwaters, removing dams, and so forth.

Such a strategic shift in aquatic environmental management will require strong leadership by state and federal regulatory agencies, which must become willing and able to assert their authority in a more decisive and systematic manner. For instance, the Department of Fish and Game has substantial authority to deal with many key environmental issues (e.g., requiring fish releases from most dams via § 5937 of the Fish and Game Code). But this agency generally lacks the independence, clout, and resources to do more than nibble at the edges of real protection. Likewise, the SWRCB has seldom used its power to adequately regulate flows in streams for fish and other aquatic organisms.

Flood Risk Management

Flood management is another area where incremental improvements can make matters worse (Kelley 1989). The 2007 legislative package on flood management in the Central Valley attempted to reduce problems in several areas: (1) It doubled the required level of urban flood protection (from one-in-100-year flood protection required by federal law up to one-in-200 years) (SB 5); (2) it required that cities and counties, which have local land use authority, incorporate flood risk considerations in their general plans and establish community protection goals (Assembly Bill [AB] 162); and (3) it aimed to correct some faulty incentives for building in the floodplain introduced by the 2003 *Paterno v. State of California* decision (see Chapter 1), by making these local agencies share liability with the state for flood losses on lands they approve for development in high-risk areas (AB 70). The move to encourage more integration of flood considerations in land use planning is laudable. But the doubling of the urban protection standard is likely to prolong the basic weaknesses of federal flood policy: It will promote some strengthening of existing flood defenses but ultimately encourage more development of flood-prone lands (Chapter 6). Even if these efforts reduce the *frequency* of flooding, they are likely to increase

Urbanization on Central Valley floodplains increases risk to lives and property. Photo by Rand Schaal.

overall flood *risk*—or the economic consequences of flooding—by continuing to encourage population growth and economic activity behind levees.

As described in Chapter 6, a new flood management policy is needed that supplements reductions in the frequency of flooding with reductions in the vulnerability to damage when inundation occurs. Such a policy will lead to more differentiation in levels of required protection, depending on the extent of economic losses to be avoided. As part of this strategy, flood management should also return to an approach that California used with success in the early 20th century—allowing greater flows on floodplains, with the use of bypasses and flood easements on agricultural land (Chapter 1; Kelley 1989). In addition to mitigating flood risk, such an approach also can improve aquatic and terrestrial habitats and in some cases enhance groundwater basin recharge. Although the state government can lead in effecting this shift, key federal agencies (notably the U.S. Army Corps of Engineers) will need to participate.

Any effective flood management approach also will require a major change in funding and liability frameworks. The major gap between funding needs and availability, despite roughly $5 billion in recent state bonds for flood works, implies continued structural unreliability for decades to come (Chapter 2). Moreover, despite the passage of AB 70, financial incentives for floodplain development persist in many areas, as local governments face few short-term risks from flood failures and stand to gain from increased tax revenues from new development.

Pollution from urban runoff is a major cause of beach closures. Photo by Mark Ralston/AFP/Getty Images.

Protecting Source Water Quality

Great strides have been made since the late 1960s to reduce pollution from urban wastewater facilities and industrial plants, often known as "point" sources. However, "nonpoint" sources of pollution from urban and agricultural runoff still pose major problems. Moreover, new and more exotic water quality threats such as pharmaceuticals have emerged. These threats are likely to grow as the range of chemicals employed in the economy continues to expand. The economic value of new chemicals must be weighed against their potential for harming public health and the environment.

The presence of these contaminants raises the costs of treatment for drinking water, and treatment itself cannot remove all potentially harmful substances. Chemical treatments such as chlorination, used to protect drinking water from pathogens, can create carcinogenic "disinfectant by-products" in the water—trading an acute health risk for a chronic one. By improving and protecting source water quality, less disinfection is needed, concentrations of disinfection by-products are greatly diminished, and less expensive drinking water treatment is required (Chen et al. 2010). Moreover, treatment does not solve problems for fish, birds, and other aquatic and riparian organisms that depend on the quality of water within rivers, lakes, and estuaries; for them, source water protection is the only solution.

Source protection is another area where incremental approaches are not working. A weak regulatory framework, which puts the onus for demonstrating environmental harm from chemicals on the regulatory agency and requires little disclosure from industry, has made the federal Toxic Substances Control Act ineffective at monitoring and tracking chemicals that should be regulated. And nonpoint source pollution control efforts under the Clean Water Act have focused largely on monitoring and best management practices, not on actual effectiveness in limiting discharges. As we discuss in Chapter 6, a regulatory approach is needed that places more burden for disclosure on industry and that requires performance-based outcomes for dischargers of polluted runoff.

Water Supply Management

To make the most of increasingly tight water supplies, California also will need to pursue strategic reform in managing its statewide and regional water storage and distribution systems. As discussed in Chapter 2, the state has a highly interconnected network of surface storage and conveyance facilities. This network is linked, in many places, to groundwater basins that are major sources of water for agricultural and urban users. Many groundwater basins have unrealized potential to serve as complementary, low-cost sites for storing water for dry years (California Department of Water Resources 2009). More integrated and flexible management of the network would permit California to cope better with variable precipitation, a shrinking snowpack, and shifting water demands (Tanaka et al. 2006).

As discussed in Chapters 6 and 7, considerable progress toward integrated system management has occurred incrementally in the past few decades, with the rise of active groundwater banking systems in some parts of the state, improvements in coordination between the Central Valley Project and the State Water Project (run by the federal and state governments, respectively), and the rise in water marketing. However, two major obstacles remain to achieving more efficient and environmentally beneficial management: (1) the lack of comprehensive groundwater management in many areas and (2) the lack of transparent and workable rules for transferring water among users. In contrast to the other challenges discussed above, this is an area where incremental actions, spurred by local agencies, can make some headway in the direction needed. But progress will be slower, and the system less effective, without strategic policy shifts and state and federal actions to remove these barriers.

Monitoring and managing groundwater

Almost alone among western states, California provides for no state-level regulation of groundwater (Garner and Willis 2005; Legislative Analyst's Office 2010). Comprehensive groundwater management schemes—in the form of adjudicated basins (which apportion the rights to use basin waters) or special management districts (which charge pumping fees to help regulate water levels)—now exist in much of urban Southern California and in Silicon Valley (Figure 4.1). In these regions, serious problems of overdraft and salinity intrusion threatened urban water supplies, spurring water users to find solutions from the legislature (the case of special districts) or from the courts (the case of adjudication) (Blomquist 1992). Each local adjudication typically required more than a decade.

Elsewhere in California, groundwater management is much more ad hoc. In many places, groundwater is managed, often quite effectively, by setting surface water prices below the cost of local groundwater pumping. This encourages more surface water use in wet years, which allows groundwater basins to recharge; pumping can then increase in drier years when there is less surface water available (Vaux 1986; Jenkins 1992). But this type of informal integration is becoming increasingly stressed by reduced surface water availability and higher surface water costs.

Local monitoring networks have also increased in many places, in response to localized overdraft problems (e.g., the Sacramento Regional Water Authority) or the potential for groundwater banking with external parties (e.g., Kern County).[2] Since the early 1990s, the state has encouraged the formation of voluntary basin management plans and provided bond funding to support monitoring wells and basin modeling studies. However, resistance to more comprehensive groundwater management remains strong in most rural counties, as witnessed by the failure of the 2009 legislative water package to require more than minimal concessions that counties monitor groundwater levels voluntarily.

As discussed in Chapter 6, the absence of groundwater monitoring and regulation has prevented the development of groundwater banking and limited water marketing in many rural counties, while contributing to groundwater mining in several major groundwater basins, particularly in the Tulare Basin. The failure to integrate groundwater and surface water management, despite their hydrological connection, has also reduced flows in rivers and lessened groundwater support

2. On the Regional Water Authority, see Hanak (2003). On Kern County, see Thomas (2001) and Hanak (2003).

Figure 4.1
Comprehensive groundwater schemes are concentrated in urban Southern California and Silicon Valley

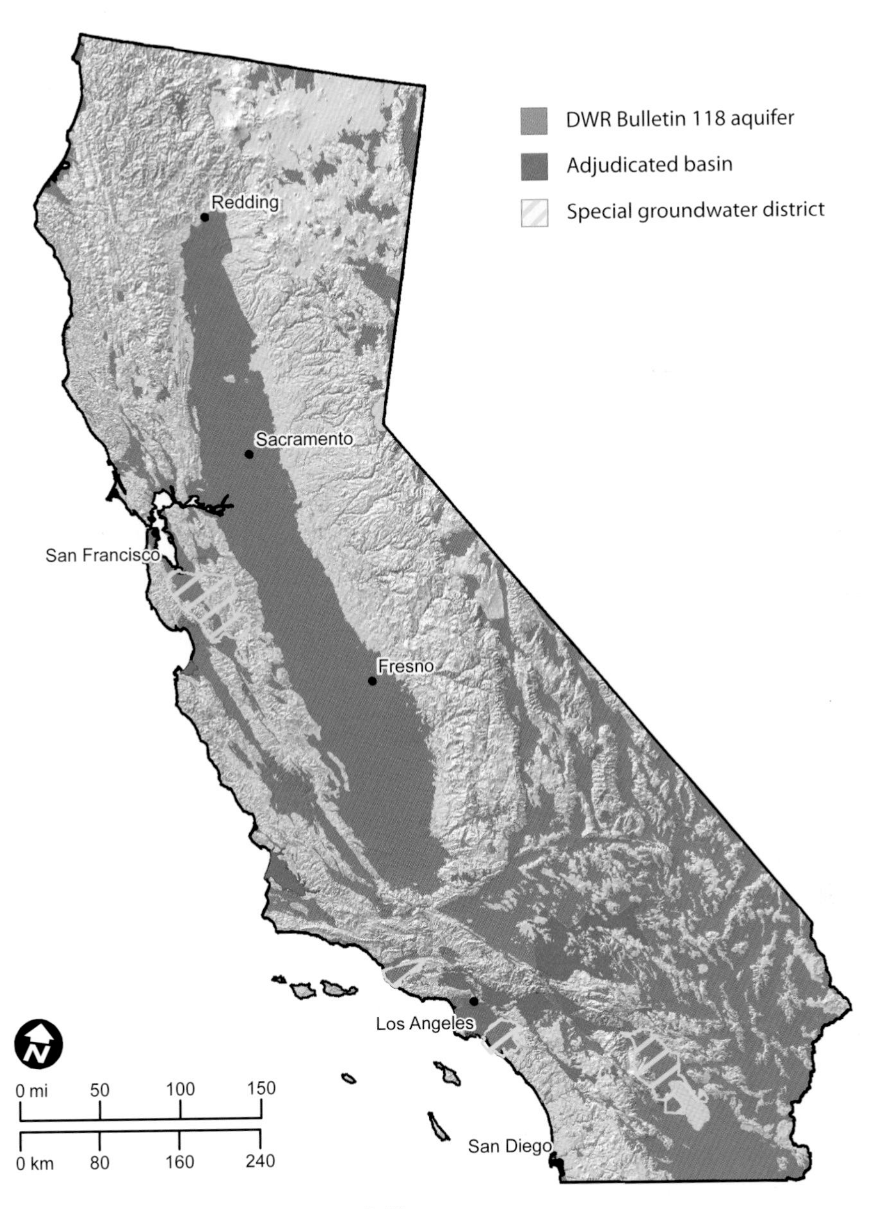

SOURCE: California Department of Water Resources (DWR).

NOTES: The map shows all groundwater basins (blue), all 22 adjudicated groundwater basins (red), and four special groundwater management districts (Coachella Valley Water District, Fox Canyon Groundwater Management Agency, Orange County Water District, and Santa Clara Valley Water District), all of which exercise authority to levy pump charges. (For a list of adjudicated basins, see www.water.ca.gov/groundwater/gwmanagement/court_adjudications.cfm.) In the Scott Valley (far north on the map), the adjudication included both ground and surface water rights.

for riparian and wetland habitats (Chapter 7, Box 7.2) (Howard and Merrifield 2010; Hall 2010). Climate change, sea level rise, and increased demand will exacerbate poor basin conditions in many areas (Chapter 3).

These pressures may eventually stimulate additional adjudications in some areas. However, our interviews revealed a broad consensus—including among agricultural interests—that state intervention is needed to spur more rapid reform in regions where the economic and environmental costs of delay are great (Null et al. 2011). We propose a framework of cooperative federalism, wherein the state sets enforceable deadlines for local parties to establish comprehensive basin management plans (Chapter 9).

Facilitating water markets

The past 20 years have seen the rise of water markets in California, making it possible to reallocate scarce water supplies during droughts and to accommodate longer-term shifts in water demands (Chapter 6). The state played a major role in launching the market, through enabling legislation in the early 1980s and the establishment of drought water banks during the early 1990s. Since then, the state and federal governments have been major market players, as purchasers of environmental water. They were also brokers of the most extensive package of long-term transfers, involving the transfer of more than half a million acre-feet of Colorado River water from farms to cities under the Quantification Settlement Agreement in the early 2000s.

However, market transactions appear to have leveled off since the early 2000s, despite recent drought conditions, which should have spurred increased sales. As we discuss in Chapter 6, the market's flexibility to serve as a drought response tool has been hindered by the fragmented nature of water rights and contracts, the absence of effective groundwater regulation, and the lack of clarity regarding the type and extent of environmental mitigation required. To meet the water challenges of the 21st century, the state needs to develop a more streamlined, transparent system for water marketing, with a clearinghouse to facilitate transactions between parties. In Chapter 7 we discuss options for creating such a clearinghouse, drawing on examples from the energy sector. Although many market participants in local and regional water agencies would likely support such a shift, the changes involved also are likely to meet resistance from various other—or "third"—parties that have opposed market development. Thus, the state—in partnership with the federal government as a major water rights holder—will once again need to significantly shape these new market institutions, also encouraging broader mitigation approaches to address third-party effects.

Pathways Forward

California's highly decentralized system of water management does relatively well with incremental solutions. Broad stakeholder involvement and decentralized authority often lead to careful (if noisy) crafting of small, useful changes. However, these same conditions can prevent significant, strategic changes from being made, even when they are broadly beneficial (Madani and Lund 2011). Some fundamental, strategic changes are needed to address major economic and environmental challenges facing the state's water system. State and federal governments will need to spearhead these changes, because local incentives are not sufficiently aligned, and local authority is not sufficiently strong, for strategic changes to happen through a purely decentralized process.

The Local Role

With the right policy directions and incentives, local institutions have crucial roles in crafting and implementing on-the-ground solutions to the major water management challenges facing the state. For instance, local entities—working together—will be better able than a state agency to determine workable operating rules for groundwater basins. The same is true for meeting performance standards for nonpoint source pollution. In both cases, the state should set a policy target and time line for local entities to develop a workable plan. In addition, local entities—working together—will often be able to make the best decisions on how to manage and integrate water supply portfolios most effectively and flexibly, combining a range of tools including water use efficiency, wastewater treatment and reuse, coordinated use of ground and surface water, stormwater management, and water marketing. In such areas, state and federal actions—including effective incentives, technical support, and regulations—can help motivate, maintain, and accelerate the pace of action but are not always essential to progress.

One major weakness in the current capacity of local entities is geographic and functional fragmentation, which impedes effective coordination and integration of water management actions. To address this, we propose the creation of regional stewardship authorities. These authorities would coordinate water supply, water quality, flood management, land use, and ecosystem actions at the scale of watersheds, providing a venue for integrating local planning to ensure that resource management actions occur at the appropriate scale. Chapters 5 through 7 discuss the role these entities could play in a variety of water management areas, and Chapter 8 describes how the entities might be structured.

Consequences of State and Federal Inaction

Of course, there is a strong possibility that state and federal governments will fail in at least some of the strategic action areas outlined here, in which case only incremental solutions will be available. Decisionmakers at all levels need to be prepared for such contingencies.

In the case of the Delta, such a failure spells missed opportunities for more effective management, greater likelihood of losing additional native species, and billions of dollars in near-term costs to deal with supply interruptions from catastrophic levee failures. But, as shown in Chapter 6, state and federal failure to resolve the Delta's problems, while very expensive, does not spell disaster for California's economy. The long-term economic losses will be concentrated regionally, as farm activity and related employment are reduced in the southern Central Valley. Urban water agencies are likely to respond with greater emphasis on local opportunities to cope with scarcity, including water conservation, wastewater reuse, desalination, and enhanced local storage. State and federal governments can facilitate useful incremental actions through legislation that strengthens the hand of local agencies, such as the new target to reduce urban water use by 20 percent by 2020 (adopted as part of the 2009 water package). Where available, financial incentives can also support local efforts, such as recent federal stimulus grants to support recycled water development.[3]

In the case of flood management, a failure to change course toward more risk-based policies and greater environmental use of floodplains is more problematic, because it implies increasing flood risk exposure for many homes and businesses. This problem will be compounded by the lack of financial resources to bring protections beyond the new 200-year minimum in urban parts of the Central Valley. As the example of the Sacramento Area Flood Control Agency, described in Chapter 6 (Box 6.6), shows, local initiative can make considerable headway on its own, but there are financial and geographic limits to the effectiveness of decentralized approaches.

3. California's local agencies were very successful in tapping federal stimulus funds for recycling, with $132 million in awards, and 26 out of a total of 27 projects funded (Environmental News Service 2009).

Perhaps the greatest problem from a failure of state and federal leadership is inadequate ecosystem protection across the state. Ecosystems are changing rapidly as a result of increased human demand for water, invasive species, harmful land management practices, and climate change. Without a strategic shift in the basic approach, California risks losing many of its remaining native aquatic and riparian species and the distinctive habitats they require. Management needs to focus on beneficial ecosystem function and prioritize conservation dollars to achieve maximum benefit. As described in Chapter 5, this shift cannot be accomplished without a major effort by state and federal governments to reorient resources and, in some cases, refocus regulatory action.

In the following chapters, we elaborate on these themes and outline policy changes, both large and small, that can help California meet the goals of more efficient and environmentally beneficial water management in the decades to come.

5 Reconciling Ecosystems: Reversing Declines in Native Species

CALIFORNIA DEPARTMENT OF WATER RESOURCES

> Food grows where water flows.
>
> Congress created dust bowl.
>
> No water = no barley = no beer.
>
> People are more important than fish!
>
> Signs along rural California highways, early 21st century

Free-flowing water in California has generally been regarded as something to extract, pollute, contain, or otherwise modify for human use. Not surprisingly, given California's rapidly growing human population and economy, wild organisms that depend on natural streams, wetlands, and lakes are in sharp decline, reflecting a decline in the quality and abundance of natural aquatic habitats. These losses bear witness to California's history of large-scale land and water development with scant concern for environmental needs (Chapter 1). Only since the 1970s has California really addressed the negative consequences of water and land development. For example, the construction of Friant Dam in the 1940s dried up long sections of the San Joaquin River and only recently has a monumental effort begun to restore flows (and fish) to the river. Recent efforts to recreate the San Joaquin River—albeit in a much reduced and controversial form—reflect a growing understanding that free-flowing waterways have high economic, aesthetic, and environmental values.

In this chapter, we (1) document the decline in California's native fish species, as indicators of deterioration of aquatic environments, (2) describe valuable ecosystem services that are being lost as a result of this deterioration, (3) discuss three general conservation strategies—reservation, restoration, and

A Chinook salmon, swimming upstream.

reconciliation—to create long-term solutions, (4) focus on reconciliation as a way to deal with major environmental problems, and (5) discuss legal means to achieve reconciliation. Then, we provide some guidelines for crafting policies and regulations to reconcile human and environmental uses of water.

Fish Versus Water Supply: The Fish Are Losing

The best documented indicators of declining aquatic environments in California are fish (Moyle and Williams 1990; Moyle 2002; Howard and Revenga 2009). Of 129 kinds of native fish in California, 5 percent are extinct, 24 percent are listed as threatened or endangered species, 13 percent are eligible for listing today, and another 40 percent are in decline (Figure B). In other words, over 80 percent of the native fishes are extinct or imperiled to a greater or lesser degree. The number of imperiled species is increasing rapidly. Since the first statewide assessment in 1985, fish species have been listed under state and federal Endangered Species Acts (ESAs) at a rate of about one species per year, with 31 listed by 2010. Most native fishes are endemic only to California (60 percent) or to the interstate waters of California, Nevada, and Oregon (19 percent). Thus, their decline is largely due to factors in California, mostly related to human water and land management.[1] Clearly, environmental management actions in recent decades have been far from sufficient to reverse these declines.

An analysis by Richter et al. (1997b) indicates that the loss of freshwater biodiversity in the western United States primarily results from altered hydrologic regimes, pollution (especially nonpoint source pollution), and invasions of alien species. Three quite different examples illustrate this well: Chinook salmon, delta smelt, and pupfish (Moyle 2002).

Chinook Salmon

Chinook salmon (*Oncorhynchus tshawytscha*) once dominated the Central Valley's rivers, as well as the Klamath, Eel, and other larger coastal streams. Statewide, it is likely that 3 million to 4 million large (9- to 90-pound) fish returned to spawn each year after two to four years in the ocean. The salmon returned in distinct runs, named for the time of year they entered fresh water: fall, late-fall, winter, and spring. The runs for each river and for each season

---

1. Declines in fish populations, of course, are also caused by natural factors such as droughts and weak upwelling in the coastal ocean. But the fish have always made it through such conditions in the past. What has changed is the human modification of habitats, which now exacerbate, or make it much harder to recover from, natural causes of decline.

were genetically distinct, reflecting a long history of adaptation to California's diverse environments. The diversity of the spawning runs and life histories meant that virtually all accessible habitats in the larger rivers were saturated with fish, with migrating or spawning adults found somewhere in the state during most months of the year.

Today in the Central Valley alone, the winter run is listed as endangered, the spring run as threatened, and the late-fall run as "special concern" (qualified for listing). The Central Valley fall-run population, which sustained the commercial and recreational salmon fishery for decades, has collapsed (fewer than 40,000 fish in 2009) and could be considered for listing. In addition, some local runs are now extinct, such as the spring and fall runs in the San Joaquin River. Although many factors have contributed to the decline of salmon, the biggest single cause was construction of dams, starting in the late 19th century. California's dams, large and small, denied winter-run Chinook access to *all* their upstream spawning and rearing areas, barred spring-run Chinook and late-fall Chinook from more than 90 percent of their upstream spawning areas, and kept the fall run from perhaps 70 percent of their historical spawning and rearing areas (Yoshiyama et al. 2001). Likewise, in the Klamath and Trinity Rivers, dams denied salmon access to hundreds of miles of spawning and rearing streams (Hamilton et al. 2005) (Figure 5.1).

Unfortunately, dams are not the only problem, just the biggest. Salmon declines have been exacerbated by levees that deny access to floodplain rearing habitats, alteration of flows and habitat in estuaries, sedimentation from mining and logging, pollution from agricultural and urban sources, introduction of alien predators and competitors, water diversions, and general decline of habitat and water quality. These factors make the salmon more vulnerable to natural episodes of adverse conditions, such as drought in fresh water and reduction in coastal upwelling and other conditions in the ocean (Moyle, Israel, and Purdy 2008; Lindley et al. 2009).

In the Central Valley, most salmon and steelhead runs have persisted because cold water released from dams in summer (principally for irrigation) replaced some of the lost upstream habitat and because of hatcheries, constructed to mitigate lost habitat. Winter-run salmon now spawn at locations far below their natural habitat, where water is maintained at required cold temperatures by the release of cold water stored in the very dam (Shasta) that bars them from their far-larger natural spawning grounds. Hatcheries focused on sustaining fisheries primarily by rearing fall-run Chinook salmon, especially following

Figure 5.1
Dams and diversions have cut off access to high-quality spawning and rearing habitat for salmon and steelhead

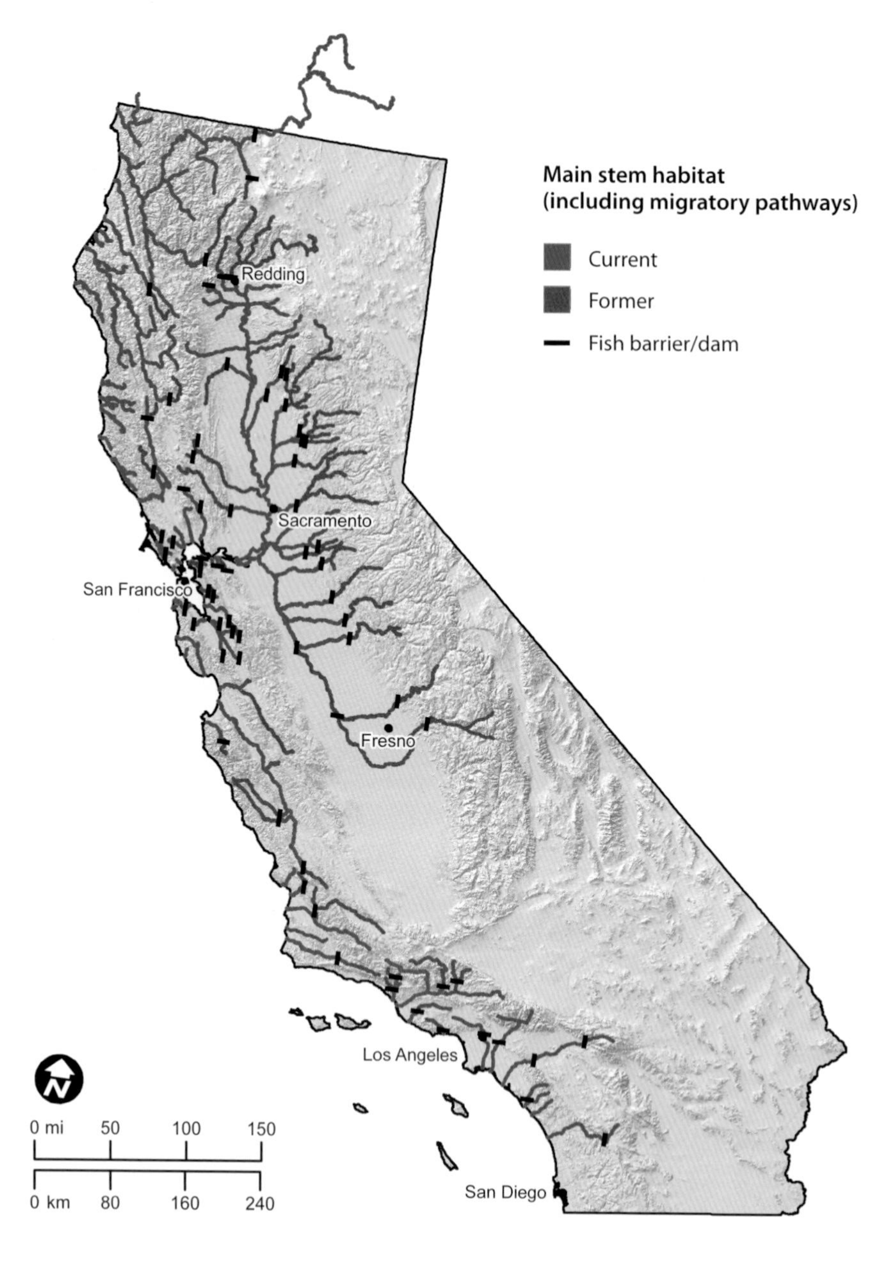

SOURCE: Moyle, Israel, and Purdy (2008).

NOTE: The map includes only habitat in larger rivers and major tributaries; the actual number of miles of stream cut off is much higher than shown.

the construction of Shasta Dam in the 1940s. Hatcheries annually produce millions of juvenile salmon, which, until recently, provided several hundred thousand adult salmon each year for the fishery and returns to the rivers, hiding in part a long-term decline in wild salmon abundance (Yoshiyama et al. 2000).

The hatchery strategy has had other, unintended consequences. Hatchery fish appear to have replaced naturally spawning salmon, rather than supplementing them as originally intended (e.g., Williams 2006). As a consequence, in the Central Valley, Chinook salmon have lost much of their genetic and ecological diversity.[2] The descendents of hatchery fish are less fit for survival in the wild, especially under adverse conditions such as those created by increased diversion of water, poor water quality, alien species, and less favorable ocean conditions. The result has been a collapse of fisheries and the creation of salmon populations whose abundance now increasingly depends on the hydrologic serendipity of a series of wet years combining with favorable ocean conditions (Lindley et al. 2009).

Delta Smelt

The delta smelt (*Hypomesus transpacificus*) is the most controversial endangered fish species in California today because it is a small endemic fish that lives in the hub of California's water distribution system, the Sacramento–San Joaquin Delta. Court decisions have required some reduction in exports to protect smelt populations, so the smelt have become scapegoats for major cutbacks in water deliveries to farmers in the southern Central Valley, even when the principal cause is drought (Hanak et al. 2010). Delta smelt are extremely vulnerable to changes in their habitat because they are found only in the upper San Francisco Estuary, have a mostly one-year life cycle, have a low reproductive rate, and depend on zooplankton in open water for food (Bennett 2005). Until the early 1980s, delta smelt were one of the most abundant fish in the upper estuary, but their population abruptly crashed, resulting in their listing as a threatened species in 1993 (Moyle 2002). Their decline, which hastened again in the early 2000s, coincides with increased export pumping from the Delta, as well as the decline of other open-water, or pelagic, fish species (Figure 5.2) (Feyrer, Nobriga, and Sommer 2007; Sommer et al. 2007).

---

2. On genetic diversity, see Williamson and May (2005) and Barnett-Johnson et al. (2007); on ecological diversity, see Carlson and Satterwaite (2010).

Figure 5.2
Populations of the Delta's open-water fish species have plummeted

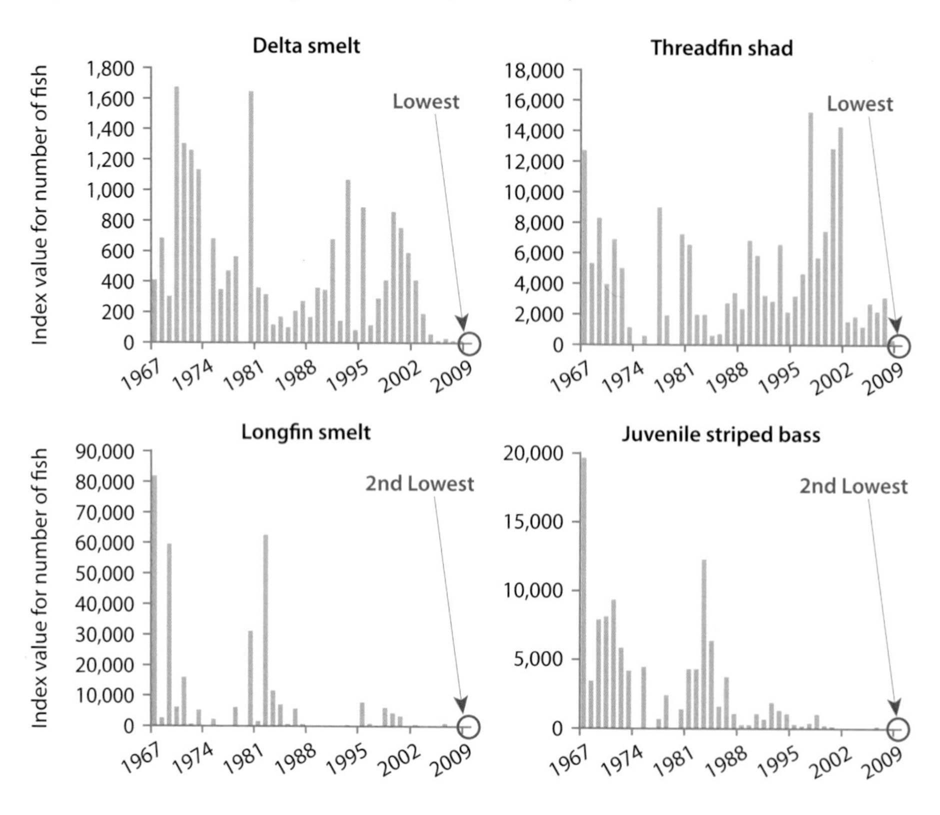

SOURCE: California Department of Fish and Game.
NOTE: The graphs report the indices for the fall midwater trawl.

The delta smelt's importance in affecting the timing and volume of Delta exports has caused some to seek a single cause of their decline other than water exports. This presumes that if such a cause can be found and fixed, delta smelt would recover and exports could continue or even increase. Single causes often suggested include entrainment in the export pumps of the southern Delta, predation by alien species such as striped bass, reduction in food supply by alien clams, the effects of ammonium from sewage treatment plants, the toxic effects of pyrethroids and other agricultural chemicals, and blooms of toxic algae. The problem with the single cause theories is that any or all of these factors can affect smelt populations at one time or another or in one place or another. As

Pupfish in desert environments are highly vulnerable to extinction from competition for water resources. Photo by Jacob Katz.

Bennett (2005) and Moyle and Bennett (2008) show, the problems facing the smelt are systemic: Since the 1980s, there has been a *regime shift* in the Delta ecosystem, so it functions less like an estuary (with strong upstream-downstream gradients) and more like a confused lake, with channels dominated by rooted aquatic plants and regular movement of water across the Delta, toward the pumps. This environment is increasingly hostile to the estuary-adapted smelt, making the smelt more vulnerable to such factors as toxins and food supply reductions (Moyle et al. 2010).

Pupfish

Pupfish (*Cyprinodon*) are the opposite of salmon and smelt in almost all respects. Pupfish are small (1–2 inches long) and spend all of their short lives (6–18 months) in the warm springs and river backwaters of southeastern California deserts (Moyle 2002). Of the eight varieties of pupfish native to California, one is extinct, two are listed as endangered, and the rest are considered highly vulnerable to extinction because their distribution is limited to deserts where water is in high demand. Thus, the Owens pupfish (*C. radiosus*) became endangered after the City of Los Angeles developed the Owens River and its hydrologically connected groundwater for municipal supply, altering most pupfish habitat. Likewise, desert pupfish (*C. macularius*) became endangered because of alterations of the Colorado River through dams, diversions, pollution from agricultural return water, and groundwater pumping. The Tecopa pupfish (*C. nevadensis calidae*) went extinct when the warm springs it inhabited were converted to a spa. Pupfish also are exceptionally vulnerable to predation by introduced fishes, which thrive in human-altered waterways as well as in pristine desert spring pools.

Other Aquatic Species

Studies in Europe and other countries indicate that little-studied mollusks, aquatic insects, and other aquatic organisms face problems similar to those of native fishes (Balian et al. 2008). This is no doubt the case in California as well, reflecting the altered state of freshwater environments. Loss of aquatic biodiversity is a worldwide crisis regarded as more severe than the destruction of rainforests because it is so pervasive (Moyle and Leidy 1992; Helfman 2007; Magurran 2009). California is arguably on the leading edge of global freshwater faunal endangerment in terms of threats to the entire fauna, so solutions here (or a lack thereof) can provide examples with global implications (Leidy and Moyle 1998; Howard and Revenga 2009).

Bringing Fish into Water Management: Ecosystem Services

There are many reasons to protect desirable fish and other organisms, including their potential scientific and medicinal benefits, their effects on other species of plants and animals that inhabit the same ecosystem, and stewardship for its own sake (Norton 1987; Rolston 1994).[3] These values—including the idea that it is wrong to allow species to go extinct through human actions—are expressed in the federal Endangered Species Act of 1973. Historically, the design, construction, and operation of California's water supply and flood management infrastructure were based on promoting economic development, principally through traditional uses of water for agriculture, manufacturing, and urban activities. The evolution of societal values, exemplified by the Wild and Scenic Rivers Act, the Endangered Species Act, and the Clean Water Act, changed how water has been allocated and delivered for these traditional economic

---

3. Desirable species are defined here as mostly native fishes that require an ecosystem that functions like the original ecosystem. Desirable species therefore are indictors of ecosystem "health," and maintaining or increasing their abundance can be a goal of management. Thus, in the Delta, the native delta smelt, tule perch, and Chinook salmon are desirable species because they thrive in a functioning estuary. The striped bass, an alien species, can also be regarded as desirable because it also requires a functioning estuary to persist, and it supports a valuable fishery (see Moyle and Bennett 2008).

uses (Chapter 1). This societal change has created ongoing tension between the economy and the environment, where allocations of environmental water or investments in habitat for organisms are viewed as "costs" associated principally with regulatory compliance, without recognizing corresponding benefits.

As discussed in Chapter 2 (Box 2.3), these perceptions stem, in part, from failure to adequately incorporate the value of *ecosystem services*—benefits that ecosystems provide to humans—in assessments of water-related activities. Ecosystems are important not only to support specific species, but also for the broader set of services they provide (Daily et al. 2009). As highlighted by the National Research Council (2005) and the Environmental Protection Agency (EPA) Science Advisory Board (2009), explicit monetary and nonmonetary evaluation of ecosystem services provides the best approach for translating various management actions into how they affect human welfare.[4] By bringing to light the high value of services provided by natural systems, such an approach can guide water resource design, implementation, and operation, leading to better stewardship of the environment (Arthington et al. 2009). Systematic evaluation of services improves the analysis of tradeoffs and complementarities among alternative uses of ecosystems by a wide range of stakeholders. Finally, and perhaps most significantly, clearly articulating linkages among ecosystem functions, the services of such functions, and how these services affect human well-being is necessary to move beyond the simplistic and misleading "farmers versus fish" perception that often dominates public debate over water management (Hanak et al. 2010).

There are many examples of complementarities, where restored or conserved ecosystem functions support native biodiversity while enhancing social and economic values (Brauman et al. 2007). In California water management, such mutually beneficial actions are perhaps best illustrated by efforts to manage floods. As described further in Chapter 6, modern approaches to flood management seek to store and convey water on floodplains and bypasses, rather than relying exclusively on dams and levees to "control" high flows.

4. Strict adherence to using ecosystem service valuation in benefit-cost evaluation of projects may produce undesirable results. For most projects, provisioning services are both more easily quantifiable and often of higher monetary value than other services. Thus, a benefit-cost evaluation can favor large, capital-intensive projects, such as dams and levees that maximize agricultural and urban water supply and hydropower, at the expense of poorly monetized regulating, cultural, and support services, such as benefits to species and open space (Box 5.1). In addition, many current and projected projects are specifically designed to restore ecosystem functions damaged by historical water management activities. Typical examples include reservoir reoperation to support cold water fishes, dam removal, the restoration of degraded physical habitat in rivers and streams, and the creation of wetland habitat. Since these do not often improve high-value provisioning services, they may not meet the ecosystem services-based benefit-cost test. Yet such projects are often essential for restoring ecosystem function.

Components of this approach include setback levees that increase the area inundated in wet seasons; flood bypass areas that divert flows onto floodplains, usually through weirs; and changes in reservoir operation that promote increased frequency and duration of floodplain inundation. Box 5.1 describes some benefits and costs from expanding floodplains. Done properly, this approach to flood control simultaneously restores a valuable array of ecological characteristics that support native species while providing a range of other valuable services (Opperman et al. 2009). Reintroducing seasonal inundation often restores the productivity of food webs to support native fishes within, around, and downstream of the floodplains. Floodplain inundation can also reestablish wetland and riparian woodlands and the array of native animal and plants that rely on them.

5.1

Ecosystem services and floodplain restoration

Many ecosystem services that improve human well-being arise from restoring floodplain functions. This restoration also can have significant costs. The challenge in ecosystem service valuation is to systematically compare these tradeoffs and identify actions with the greatest benefit. Some of the costs and benefits are discussed below, using the classification system from the Millennium Ecosystem Assessment (2005) (see also Box 2.3).

Provisioning services. Benefits include increased production of commercially harvested fish, increased operational flexibility for water supply, increased groundwater recharge, and more flexibility to adapt to climate change. Costs include loss of traditional economic land uses (including urban development and farm activities that are incompatible with seasonal flooding) and potential reductions in water supply from higher evapotranspiration and required releases to maintain floodplain ecosystem function.

Regulating services. Benefits include reduced flood stage and associated reductions in flood damages or costs to upgrade flood infrastructure, reduced maintenance for flood infrastructure, improved habitat for aquatic and riparian wildlife, improved water quality resulting from nutrient cycling, improved soil fertility, lower air temperatures, and improvements in air quality. Costs include maintaining flooded regions, controlling invasions by nonnative plants and animals, and compensating landowners for flood losses.

Cultural services. Benefits include increased native biodiversity, ecotourism and recreation, open space, education opportunities. Costs include increased oversight and patrolling of recreation areas.

Wintering snow geese on the Yolo Bypass. The bypass provides valuable ecosystem services in addition to flood protection. Photo by California Department of Fish and Game.

A prime example of this approach in action is the Yolo Bypass (Sommer et al. 2001). Initially designed to provide flood protection to Sacramento residents, the area supports seasonal agriculture, diverse habitat for fish and waterfowl, and recreational areas for bird-watchers, anglers, and hunters. Recently, interest has grown in expanding the aquatic ecosystem functions of the area, while also managing the floodplain for groundwater recharge. Any expansion in the flooded area will need to consider potential losses of agricultural or other economic activity and compensate landowners accordingly.

General Strategies for Recovering Freshwater Biodiversity

The provision of ecosystem services requires healthy ecosystems, usually characterized by high levels of native biodiversity, as indicated by the abundance and diversity of native fish species. However, any strategy to protect native freshwater fishes and their ecosystems must be simultaneously local, regional, and statewide because of the enormous environmental diversity in the state and the high degree of local endemism (Moyle and Yoshiyama 1994). Protection of pupfish, smelt, and salmon require radically different approaches that are best taken under an umbrella strategy for maintaining the array of aquatic diversity statewide.

Although the state and federal Endangered Species Acts allow for ecosystem-based management strategies through federal Habitat Conservation Plans (HCPs) and state Natural Community Conservation Plans (NCCPs), these efforts are usually undertaken in response to crises, not to prevent them. As the number of listed species increases, so will the number of crises, including conflicts among actions to protect listed species. To maintain biodiversity into the future, a general ecosystem-based conservation strategy will be needed that both prevents crises and deals with ongoing ones. Here, we discuss such a strategy and highlight some examples of the approach. The obvious state agency to take the lead in developing and implementing such a strategy is the Department of Fish and Game (DFG), working closely with the State Water Resources Control Board (SWRCB). The relevance of both agencies was illustrated when the state legislature required that each agency come up with criteria to provide freshwater flows through the Delta to reverse the trends in delta smelt and other endangered species (Box 5.2).

5.2

Flows for the Sacramento–San Joaquin Delta

The Sacramento–San Joaquin Delta Reform Act of 2009 (Senate Bill X7-1) directed that the SWRCB come up with recommendations for new flow criteria for the Delta ecosystem (State Water Resources Control Board 2010b). The board, citing its responsibilities under the public trust doctrine, developed flow criteria, mainly to protect endangered fish, without attempting to balance water needs for other purposes. The board concluded that there was good scientific evidence that higher flows were needed, although the exact amounts were controversial. Key recommendations were that flows needed for ecosystem function were (1) 75 percent of unimpaired Delta outflow from January through June, (2) 75 percent of unimpaired Sacramento River inflow from November through June, and (3) 60 percent of unimpaired San Joaquin River inflow from February through June. Depending on how these flow recommendations were implemented, they would greatly reduce Delta export pumping, with perhaps greater reductions for upstream and indirect diversions from the Delta.

The new law also required that DFG come up with "quantifiable biological objectives and flow criteria for the species of special concern in the Delta" (California Department of Fish and Game 2010a). DFG proceeded to do so for 34 species, mostly threatened or endangered plants, insects, fish, birds, and mammals. The DFG flow recommendations are very similar to those of the SWRCB. The two agencies are in general agreement that current water management provides inadequate flows through the Delta to sustain the endangered species, especially fish.

A general conservation strategy will need to combine three distinct approaches: reservation, restoration, and reconciliation. Although the first two have a role in conservation, in today's world most species are most likely to be protected through reconciliation, which recognizes how completely humans dominate the natural world (Rosenzweig 2003). These approaches differ from more technological approaches, such as artificial propagation (e.g., fish hatcheries, captive breeding programs) that have often been relied on with little success.

Reservation

Reservation is the strategy of protecting species in relatively pristine areas (reserves or preserves) where natural processes dominate, isolated from most interference from human activities. This strategy is reflected in language such as "protecting the best of what is left" and, for salmon streams, protecting "salmon strongholds." Although protecting the most pristine areas is highly desirable, few pristine areas remain and they are small in total area, so they cannot protect most biodiversity.[5] For protecting aquatic organisms, an added difficulty is that entire watersheds must be protected because stream processes and fish movements, from headwaters to stream mouth, are interconnected. Thus, small watersheds are more likely to be eligible for reserve status than large ones, where the economic costs of designating a reserve are also likely to be larger. Overall, few opportunities exist for establishing fully functioning aquatic reserves in California, although some possible examples exist, such as the Clavey River, a relatively pristine tributary to the Tuolumne River, and much of the Smith River, by the Oregon border. Some small de facto reserves exist, such as Salt Creek, completely within Death Valley National Park, or Elder Creek, Mendocino County, completely protected within the University of California's Angelo Coast Range Reserve.

Restoration

Restoration returns a damaged ecosystem to a more desirable condition, ideally requiring minimal continued human intervention to sustain its desirable species and characteristics. A restored system generally bears a close resemblance to the original system. For aquatic systems, restoration under this narrow definition is most likely in streams and other water bodies that are not damaged

5. Information in this paragraph draws from Moyle and Yoshiyama (1994) and Moyle and Randall (1998).

irreversibly by dams, diversions, channelization, and other changes. Ideally, restoration efforts also should encompass an entire watershed. Dam removal is often a major component of large-scale restoration projects, but the effects of removal can be complex and hard to predict (see the next section). A major problem with aquatic restoration efforts in California is that most waterways contain alien fish species, invertebrates, and amphibians that can interfere with native species. The most adaptable alien species rarely disappear after major restoration efforts.

Even in a region as large as the Sierra Nevada, few opportunities exist for real watershed restoration; most opportunities are at high elevations and require eradication of alien species (Moyle and Randall 1998). Thus, the Dye Creek watershed, Tehama County, is entirely within The Nature Conservancy's Dye Creek Preserve. Despite its remarkably intact riparian woodland and abundance of native fish and frogs, full restoration will require eradication of nonnative green sunfish, bullfrogs, wild fig trees, and pigs, all possible but very difficult (especially pig removal). Knapp, Matthews, and Sarnelle (2001) document how removing trout from Sierra Nevada lakes that were originally fishless not only brings back endangered frogs but recreates an aquatic ecosystem that interacts with the surrounding terrestrial ecosystem.

Reconciliation

Reconciliation recognizes that humans so completely dominate the planet that conservation of species and their habitats depends on integrating native ecosystem functions into ecosystems shaped by human activity. Such ecosystems are often largely new in many aspects of their structure and function and require continual human management. For example, maintaining native fish in rivers below dams in California requires not only minimum flow releases from the dam but releases with appropriate temperatures and volumes on a schedule that follows the natural flow regime. Thus, restoration flows in Putah Creek in Solano and Yolo Counties are less than 5 percent of the annual natural flow volume, but because the flow regime follows the natural seasonal pattern, a group (assemblage) of native fishes dominates much of the creek (Marchetti and Moyle 2001). Alien fishes remain but in low numbers in native fish reaches. Native birds and plants also have benefited from the flow regime, but active removal of invasive shrubs and trees has been required in some areas, and bird populations have been enhanced through the use of bird houses (Truan 2004).

The creek is a narrow ribbon of habitat in an agricultural landscape. The habitat looks "natural" but requires continual human input to keep it that way. Putah Creek is thus a reconciled waterway that supports many native species.

One of the best-known "restoration" efforts in California is Rush Creek, a tributary to Mono Lake. Rather than being a restoration project, Rush Creek is actually a good example of a reconciliation project. Rush Creek had been allowed to dry up completely through diversion to support Los Angeles's Owens Valley Project (Chapter 1). Following a key court decision, diversions were reduced, and extensive channel improvements and re-vegetation efforts were undertaken to restore the stream and its riparian habitat. This effort also restored the trout fishery, which, in fact, was the main legal reason for restoring the stream. Ironically, Rush Creek was originally without fish, so the restored stream supports populations of nonnative rainbow trout and brown trout, which undoubtedly have had effects on the reconciled ecosystem (Kondolf 1998).

The San Joaquin River "restoration" effort noted in this chapter's introduction is also an attempt at reconciliation. The reconciled river—roughly 150 miles from Friant Dam to the Merced River confluence—will support two runs of Chinook salmon, a natural assemblage of native fishes, and birds and mammals requiring riparian habitats once the new flow regime is established. But the ecosystem will bear only modest resemblance to the original river ecosystem. Much of the channel will be between levees, and nonnative fish, amphibians, and invertebrates will dominate some sections, especially those that still receive agricultural drain water. Yet there will be a living river again, flowing down the once-dry streambed.

A common aspect of these three examples of reconciliation is the presence of alien species as significant parts of the ecosystem. The aliens include not only fish species but also invertebrates such as clams, crayfish, and scuds (small shrimplike crustaceans), as well as plants, which may have replaced native species or else have added complexity to the ecosystem. Most of these species cannot be eliminated, because they are fully integrated into the ecosystem and some, such as brown trout in Rush Creek, may even be considered desirable species. Thus, management plans for reconciled ecosystems must first include designation of which desirable species should be the focus of management and then determine which alien species can be lived with and which species will require control measures. Reconciled ecosystems usually require continuous management.

A Systematic Approach to Protecting Aquatic Biodiversity in California

California has 140 major types of aquatic ecosystems, distinguished by zoogeography, endemism, and geomorphology (Moyle and Ellison 1991). For broadest protection of the state's aquatic biodiversity, each ecosystem type requires at least one protected/managed example, including unique systems such as Mono Lake and the upper McCloud River. An important reason for such protection is that, given the nature of California's environment, most of the ecosystem types are likely to support endemic species, including many species of invertebrates and plants. Unfortunately, even the best examples of most of these ecosystem types have already been altered by humans, many irreversibly, so the basic reconciliation strategy is to designate selected examples for protection and management of their remaining natural values, including endemic fish and invertebrates. Ideally, multiple examples of each type (or the most valued types) should be protected to provide redundancy (Moyle and Sato 1991). Where possible, the examples should be protected as reserves or restoration areas, but in reality most protected systems will need to be compatible with fairly sustained human use and will require adaptive management approaches to sustain desirable characteristics in a rapidly changing world.

Reconciled aquatic ecosystems of diverse quality, from a native biodiversity perspective, will necessarily dominate conservation programs in the future. However, strategies to protect aquatic biodiversity still typically focus on increasingly ineffective strategies such as setting up relatively small protected reserves or finding areas that can be restored to near-pristine conditions.[6] In an effort to use largely reservation and restoration strategies as a basis for conservation, Moyle and Yoshiyama (1994) and Moyle (2002) recommended a five-tiered approach to prevent further loss of aquatic biodiversity in California, with each tier requiring a different, increasingly difficult, scale of action:

1. Protect endangered species and their habitats.
2. Maintain habitats that support clusters or assemblages of native species with similar habitat requirements; the clusters often contain species that are or could be listed under state and federal ESAs.
3. Protect distinctive habitats such as spring systems or isolated small streams.

6. See, for instance, Nyman (1999) and Chadderton, Brown, and Stephens (2004).

4. Manage watersheds in wildlands for natural characteristics as much as possible.
5. Recognize bioregions (large areas with common natural features and common flora and fauna) and develop landscape-level strategies for maintaining biodiversity within them.

Moyle (2002) thought that under this approach, watershed protection and management (Tier 4) was likely to pay the greatest dividends in native biodiversity persistence in the long run. Unfortunately, this is extremely difficult to accomplish, given the scale of effort needed, because there are few watersheds of any size that do not suffer from heavy human use. Using a set of semi-quantitative criteria specifically designed for the Sierra Nevada, Moyle and Randall (1998) ranked nearly 100 watersheds according to their conservation value, as part of the Sierra Nevada Ecosystem Project. The most highly ranked watersheds would qualify for reservation or restoration. The rankings have been largely ignored, because highly ranked watersheds seemed obvious to most people and were already receiving attention (e.g., Deer Creek, Box 5.3) while the scores of some low-ranking watersheds were disputed by people who lived

5.3

Balancing reservation, restoration, and reconciliation in Deer Creek

Deer Creek, Tehama County, is a tributary to the Sacramento River with high aquatic conservation value (Moyle and Randall 1998). The aquatic ecosystem is largely dominated by a complex assemblage of native fish species (including threatened spring-run Chinook salmon and Central Valley steelhead) and amphibians. Although the creek has no major dams, there is a diversion on its lower reaches, which also are partially channelized to protect agricultural fields. Most of the watershed is a patchwork of public and private timber and grazing lands, with limited public access (partly because of its rugged topography). In the foothill reach, the creek flows through the Ishi Wilderness Area. Close to the headwaters is a large meadow system being restored from the effects of grazing, after being acquired by The Nature Conservancy as part of its Lassen Foothills Project. One small tributary, Cub Creek, is protected by Lassen National Forest as a Research Natural Area. The watershed is a patchwork of land with different degrees of protection and intensity of use. But the natural values of the watershed are largely maintained by private landowners (mostly ranchers and timber companies) through the Deer Creek Watershed Conservancy, with some assistance from public funds. The result has been that Deer Creek continues to support a flora and fauna dominated by native species (e.g., Baltz and Moyle 1993).

there (e.g., South Yuba River).[7] Thus, Tier 5, bioregional management, becomes the most likely general strategy for maintaining aquatic biodiversity, using reconciled ecosystems and waterways, mixed with a few reserves and restoration sites.

The reality is that the characteristics of aquatic areas likely to qualify for reservation or restoration are so demanding that few such areas exist or can be established (Table 5.1). This does not mean California should give up on them; just the opposite is true. Aquatic ecosystems that bear close resemblances to unaltered systems will become increasingly valuable, for protection of rare plants and animals and as a source of material for improving reconciled ecosystems. At the same time, the aim should be to manage as many reconciled systems as possible in ways that protect remaining native biodiversity, while maintaining a close resemblance in structure and function to undisturbed ecosystems. This approach not only will enhance biodiversity, but will provide society with valuable ecosystem services such as clean water and recreation.

Pragmatically, any effort to systematically protect aquatic biodiversity will include watersheds with conservation values ranging from high to low, with low-scoring watersheds being more integrated into human dominated landscapes (Doppelt et al. 1993). Such an effort will also need some form of groundwater management because many California streams have springs as sources and many

Table 5.1
Which approach for which ecosystems?

Characteristic	Reservation	Restoration	Reconciliation
Size	< 50 km^2	< 50 km^2	> 50 km^2
Hydrologic regime	Natural	Natural or restorable	Altered
Diversity of aquatic habitats	Low	Low	Low to high
Natural biological integrity (biodiversity)	High	Restorable to high	Low to high
Percent native fish species	100	90–100 or restorable	Various
Percent native riparian species	100	75–100	Various
Dominance of alien species	None	Low	Low to high
Importance of rare habitats	High	High	Low to high
Importance of endangered species	High	High	Low to high
Compatibility with human usage	Low	Low to moderate	Moderate to high
Protective management required	High	High	Adaptive

SOURCES: Characteristics of reserved or restored ecosystems are from Moyle and Yoshiyama (1994); Nyman (1999); and Moyle (2002).

NOTE: In reality, the three basic management strategies each represent part of a spectrum of actions, albeit a spectrum dominated by reconciliation.

7. P. Moyle, unpublished observations.

stream reaches can go dry if groundwater contributions are lost as a result of excessive aquifer pumping (Howard and Merrifield 2010). Given limited conservation dollars, some kind of prioritization for protecting and managing aquatic ecosystems is inevitable, and it is preferable that this be done explicitly. The highest investments would be in areas with the greatest potential for maintaining natural values, usually determined by some measure of native biodiversity. This would include larger reserve and restoration areas, reconciled systems that most resemble historical systems, and unique human-dominated ecosystems with significant natural values, such as the Sacramento–San Joaquin Delta (see below). The Nature Conservancy's Lassen Foothills Project is a good example of where investment is going into reconciled ecosystems with high natural values, resulting in significant ecosystem protection (Box 5.3). On the other hand, the Salton Sea may be an example of misplaced priorities for conservation dollars (Box 5.4).

5.4

Should the Salton Sea be saved?

The Salton Sea, at 35 miles long and 9 to 15 miles wide, is the largest "lake" in California. It was created in 1905 when the entire Colorado River broke through a small irrigation diversion and flowed into a desert depression, the Salton Sink. By the time the flow was shut off (1907), the sink was filled with water (Hundley 2001). Initially, it was an extraordinarily productive ecosystem, producing huge numbers of fish and supporting vast flocks of migratory and breeding waterfowl. Over the years, the sea became increasingly salty, although it was kept from reaching lethal levels for fish by inflows of heavily polluted irrigation and urban drainage from both the United States and Mexico. However, as less fresh water flowed into the sea because of more efficient water use, salinities increased which, combined with other factors, caused massive die-offs of fish and birds (Hurlbert et al. 2007). Elaborate schemes to "save" the sea by diking, pumping, and drying some areas have been proposed, at great cost in money and water (www.saltonsea.water.ca.gov). This is a case where "no action" might be the best alternative, especially if it allowed more water to be returned to the river to "restore" wetlands in Mexico's Colorado River delta. That delta, now largely dry, was once a major, productive ecosystem that supported many of the same bird species that now use the Salton Sea. It can be argued that saving the Salton Sea and restoring the Colorado River delta are independent issues, but they both depend on water from the overallocated Colorado River. Most water reaching the lower river is diverted for cities and agriculture. Although myriad legal issues are involved in water allocation in this region, a process to prioritize allocation of the little water available for ecosystem purposes would seem beneficial.

The Salton Sea is rapidly becoming too saline to support fish and many other kinds of life. Photo by David McNew/Getty Images.

The coordination of ecosystem reconciliation with local, regional, and statewide objectives will require considerable attention by local entities. Local leadership is often provided by local watershed groups (Putah Creek, discussed above) or regionally active conservation groups (e.g., The Nature Conservancy—Box 5.3). These groups typically work with local interests to reconcile other water and land uses and native ecosystems. Although such efforts are helpful, they might be greatly expanded and made more coherent with state and national objectives through creation of regional stewardship authorities, discussed in more detail in Chapter 8. These authorities could coordinate local ecosystem reconciliation activities in conjunction with other water and environmental management activities.

Reconciling the Delta

The examples of Putah Creek, Rush Creek, and the San Joaquin River described above are reconciliation efforts that rely principally on reintroducing water into existing stream channels that are then modified to improve ecological performance. For much of California, particularly in heavily urbanized areas or areas that have been intensively farmed, the physical changes to the landscape are so great that reconciliation efforts involve the development of wholly new, even novel ecosystems. Perhaps the best example of this is in the Sacramento–San Joaquin Delta.

The Delta was historically a 700,000-acre tidal freshwater marsh. Reclamation of land from the marsh involved constructing 1,100 miles of levees and then draining the lands behind them to allow crop production. Cultivation caused the land behind the levees to sink, principally as a result of oxidation of the Delta's peat soils. This process removed more than 2 billion cubic yards of soil from the Delta, creating deeply subsided islands—many more than 25 feet below sea level—surrounded by a network of fragile levees. As discussed throughout this book, and examined in detail in Lund et al. 2007, 2010, fixing the Delta to balance ecological and water supply goals is essential for California water management. But the Delta cannot be restored. There is insufficient fill or funds to bring all marshes back. Moreover, given the new blend of native and alien species, restoring the Delta to its original physical condition would not restore its historical biological condition.

The only alternative for the Delta is a reconciliation strategy that blends the needs of humans and the ecosystem in a landscape and hydrology that has irreversibly changed. One concept of a reconciled, "eco-friendly Delta" is shown in Figure 5.3. This new Delta, described in more detail in Lund et al. 2010, seeks to accommodate inevitable future changes (higher sea level, earthquakes, additional permanently flooded islands, and changing inflows as a result of climate shifts), seeks to maintain substantial and profitable agricultural use of Delta lands in ways that support native wildlife, and creates or improves aquatic habitats and functions needed to support desirable fish species (tidal marsh and open water habitat, along with variable hydrology and salinity). Most important, this reconciled Delta is strikingly different from the historical Delta. It supports new, novel habitats (flooded islands) that have no natural equivalent, as well as species of plants, invertebrates, and vertebrates from all over the world.

Reconciliation Strategies

Conservation by reconciliation requires actions that create better conditions for desirable species, usually by partially reversing previous large-scale actions by humans. Reconciliation actions do not bring back pristine or even historical conditions; rather, they create environments that support the long-term existence of native species, recovery of endangered species, and provision of ecosystem services. A list of potential actions appears in Table 5.2, along with a summary of positive and negative aspects of each tool from an environmental management perspective. Here, we present expanded examples of four important reconciliation actions: reducing contaminants, reducing the effects of alien species, reoperating or removing dams, and changing fish hatchery operations.

Figure 5.3
A reconciled, "eco-friendly" Sacramento–San Joaquin Delta would have multipurpose land and water uses

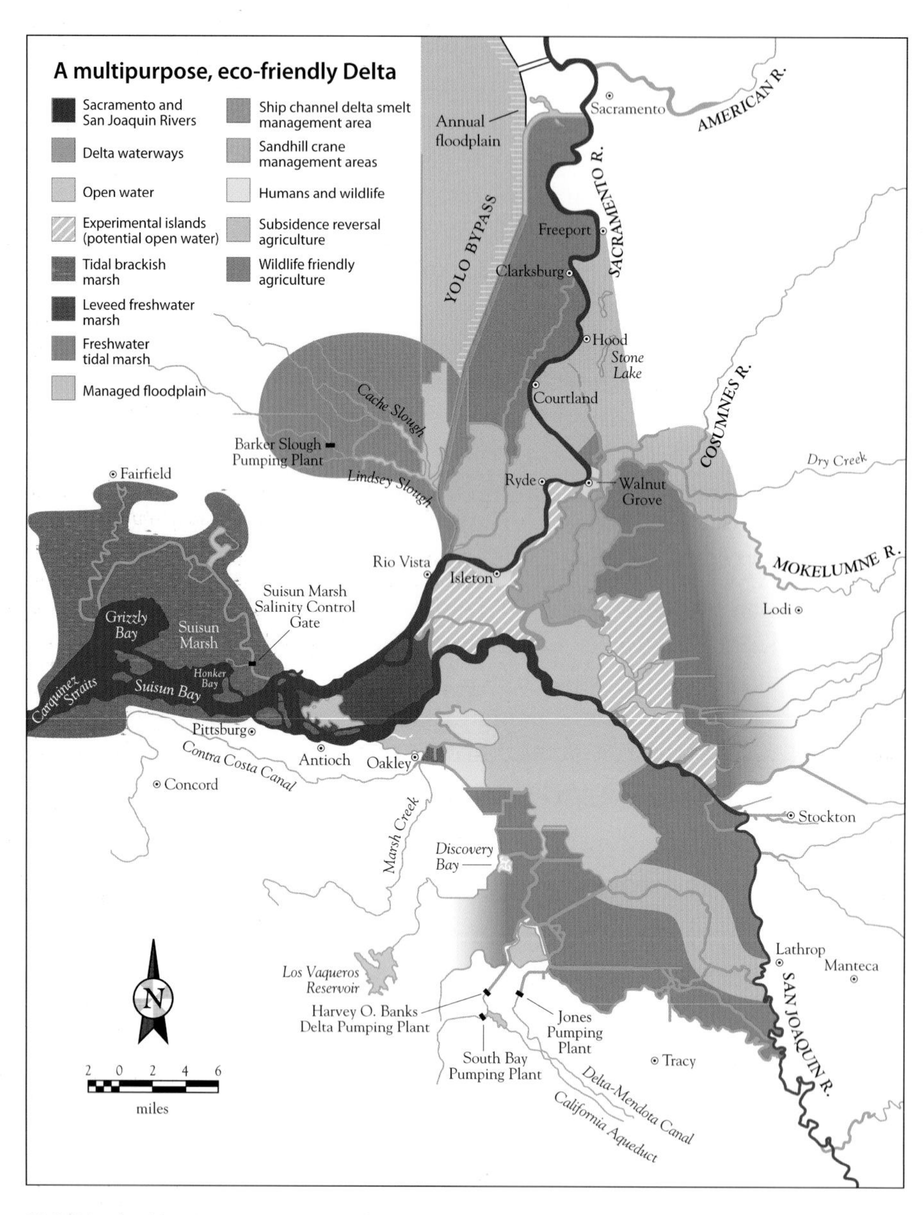

SOURCE: Lund et al. (2010).

NOTES: The map shows land and water use in a reconciled "eco-friendly" Delta. This conceptual Delta accommodates rising sea level and declining levee reliability by allowing flooding of islands (Suddeth, Mount, Lund 2010), creating new fresh and brackish water marsh habitat and floodplain habitat, promoting agriculture that provides habitat for wildlife, and restricting urbanization.

Table 5.2
Some tools for reconciling aquatic ecosystems

Tool	Positives	Negatives
Dam removal	Access to upstream areas, reduced alien species, improved downstream habitat	Loss of control of flows, especially cold water; loss of barriers to invasion
Dam reoperation	Flows to favor native species, downstream habitats	Reduction in water for other environmental purposes; requires habitat restoration as well
Estuary ecosystem-based management	Improved survival of estuarine-dependent species, including salmonids in both Delta and coastal systems	Reduced abundance of some desirable species, especially game fishes
Fisheries management improvement (including law enforcement)	Improved populations of many ecologically important species (salmon, sturgeon, etc.)	Tendency to substitute short-term actions for long-term changes
Floodplain recreation and management	Improved spawning and rearing habitat for native fish species, including salmon	Less water available for other environmental purposes in some years
Hatchery reoperation; conservation hatcheries	Improved survival of wild salmon and other fish; extinction prevention	Reduction in total salmon and steelhead numbers (temporary)
Invasive species prevention, eradication, management	Reduced "surprises" in ecosystem management; improved populations of native species; fewer listings of threatened and endangered species	Creation of public attitude that all alien species are bad, when many serve important ecosystem functions
Nonpoint source pollution reduction	Increased abundance and diversity of fish species, improved water quality for humans and other species	May result in reduced flows if polluted water sent elsewhere
Public education	Improved ecosystem function because of greater public engagement	People can love favored places to death
Scientific studies and monitoring expansion	Better understanding leads to improved management	Lack of complete information provides reason to delay taking action
Urban and industrial waste discharge improvement	Increased abundance and diversity of fish species, improved water quality for humans and others	Loss of some nutrients for ecosystems
Water diversion management (fish screens, etc.) improvement	Reduced loss of fish and aquatic life to diversions; improved stream flows; fewer "hardened" banks	Overoptimistic expectations of positive effects on fish populations
Watershed-based citizen groups (support)	Groups can be local "watchdogs" for stream alteration; monitoring; conducting habitat restoration; local education	Danger that restoration efforts can be misdirected without proper expertise
Watershed and stream habitat improvement	Improved terrestrial and aquatic habitats for native species; improved fish populations	Species tradeoffs, such as reductions of nonnative game fishes

Table 5.2 *(continued)*

Tool	Positives	Negatives
Wetland and riparian restoration and management	Increased habitat for aquatic and riparian organisms including fish and birds	Reduced dryland habitats
Wildland management (logging, fire, grazing, etc.) improvement	Reduced sediment in rivers, improved riparian cover, can counter effects of climate change	Increased frequency of fire; reduced populations of nonnative game animals (pigs)

NOTES: The positives and negatives are environmental, not economic. The most potent negative arguments—not noted in the table—relate to short-term costs of implementing measures.

Reducing Contaminants

No laws have made California's waterways more habitable for fish and usable by humans than the Clean Water Acts of 1972 and 1977 and their state counterpart, the Porter-Cologne Act of 1969. These statutes set high water quality standards to make all waters swimmable and fishable by regulating discharges of pollutants into navigable waterways. These regulations led to the construction of improved sewage treatment plants statewide, as well as general reductions of discharges from factories and other "point" or fixed sources. The result was a dramatic improvement of water quality, as once feculent rivers and estuaries became usable for recreation again and capable of supporting fisheries. This success story, however, has been limited for several reasons:

- Nonpoint source pollutants from agriculture and urban areas, including pesticide and nutrient runoff, continue to cause problems. Agricultural runoff, the biggest nonpoint pollution source in California, is still loosely regulated, with farmers in most regions required to comply only with best management practices (Chapter 6).
- "Legacy" contaminants from previous eras, such as heavy metals and PCBs, are causing problems in some waterways; their presence can greatly delay or increase the costs of large-scale environmental projects (e.g., removal of dams with mercury in reservoir sediments) (Chapter 3).[8]
- Thousands of new, unregulated chemicals are present from many sources, especially pharmaceuticals and personal care products. The chemicals, labeled Constituents of Emerging Concern, can be harmful in barely detectable concentrations (Chapter 3; Guo et al. 2010).

8. PCBs (polychlorinated biphenyl) were widely used as fluids in transformers, capacitors, and coolants. Because of PCB's toxicity and classification as a persistent organic pollutant, PCB production was banned by Congress in 1979. Toxic effects include endocrine disruption and neurotoxicity.

- Population growth has increased wastewater volumes and pollution loads, even though discharge concentrations are lower.
- Increasing water diversions reduce the ability of natural flows to dilute pollutants. Spills of oil and chemicals occasionally occur, as material is moved across and along streams and rivers by pipelines, trains, and trucks.

These factors sometimes result in direct kills of fish and invertebrates, as happened in the Southern Pacific Railroad Cantara spill of metam sodium in 1991, which killed most organisms in the upper Sacramento River above Shasta Reservoir (Hanemann 1992). More often the harm is more subtle, manifesting as increased mortality rates of small juvenile fish weakened by exposures; failures of eggs to hatch because of contaminants passed from the mother; tumors and other environmental diseases; or feminization of male fish, reducing reproductive capacity (Adams 2002). Similar effects can occur in humans exposed to contaminants, so treating water for drinking has become more complex and expensive. To help address these multifaceted problems, the State Water Resources Control Board and regional boards have set water quality standards (e.g., minimum dissolved oxygen levels, maximum temperatures, sediment loads) for most California streams and estuaries, based on § 303(d) of the Clean Water Act, but the standards are increasingly difficult to meet (Chapter 6; Mumley et al. 2003).

Legacy effects of mining are particularly worrisome because most large sites continue to leach toxic metals into the environment, even if treated by the U.S. Environmental Protection Agency as Superfund Sites. Thus, Sulfur Bank Mine on the edge of Clear Lake (Lake County), abandoned in the 1950s, continues to add mercury to lake food webs (Eagles-Smith et al. 2008). Likewise, Iron Mountain Mine on the Sacramento River continues to leach large amounts of copper, cadmium, and zinc into Keswick Reservoir on the river and has considerable potential for disaster from a catastrophic failure of Spring Creek Dam, an earthen structure that holds back a concentrated soup of toxic leachates (Mount 1995; Brown and Moyle 2004). Water emerging from the mine is the most acidic ever measured.[9] The mine and reservoirs are now the subject of one of the largest remediation efforts ever attempted, using federal stimulus funds under the American Recovery and Reinvestment Act of 2009.

9. The pH −3.6 (http://toxics.usgs.gov/topics/rem_act/iron_mountain.html).

Although there are no easy solutions to these problems, reduction of contaminants will likely require:

- ▷ Continuing investments in new water and sewage collection and treatment facilities;
- ▷ Reducing inputs of contaminants of emerging concern into waste streams and waterways by changing the availability, use, disposal, and treatment of these chemicals by individuals and corporations;
- ▷ Managing and reducing nonpoint source pollutants from agriculture and other sources, such as city storm drains;
- ▷ Managing watersheds to reduce sediment from logging, road-building, and other land-altering actions;
- ▷ Undertaking large-scale efforts to reduce the legacy effects of past human actions, especially mining; and
- ▷ Making large investments in education, regulatory agency staff, and enforcement staff to prevent and reduce future problems.

A common theme of the above actions is the continued need for money to pay for remediation, to benefit human and ecosystem health. The Sacramento region, for example, is facing costs of $800 million to upgrade its sewage treatment plant to remove ammonium, which has negative effects on the Delta ecosystem, and another $1.2 billion in other upgrades (www.sacdeltasolutions.com/pdf/costs-v-benefits.pdf). Although many of the costs of remediation will need to be met by increases in fees to wastewater dischargers, creative financing will also have to be considered, such as a surcharge on products containing contaminants of emerging concern to pay for cleanup costs and research to reduce their use. A model for this might be the surcharge California has instituted to cover the costs of safely disposing of electronic waste (Chapter 7).

Reducing the Effects of Alien Species

All aquatic and terrestrial environments in California contain alien species, many of which have altered habitats and contributed to the decline of native species (Chapter 3). Aquatic environments seem particularly susceptible to alien invasions. For example, the San Francisco Estuary contains at least 250 alien species, with the number increasing by four to five new species per year (Cohen and Carlton 1998). Several of these species, such as the overbite clam, Brazilian waterweed, and the fish species Mississippi silverside and largemouth bass, have contributed to major ecosystem changes that threaten native species. Similar problems have been recorded for habitats as diverse as North Coast rivers, Sierra Nevada lakes, desert springs, and Southern California creeks.

For aquatic systems, fishes are the best-studied alien species. Alien fishes have been introduced in large numbers, they often dominate California's aquatic ecosystems, and many are important game fishes. In their review of fish introductions into California, Moyle and Marchetti (2006) found that 50 of 110 species known to have been introduced became established. Introductions were made to directly benefit humans for food, sport, biological control, or forage for other fish, or as by-products of such human activities as aquaculture, shipping, fishing, and movement of water through canals. These introductions include some of the fish species most familiar to the California public: various sunfishes, basses, and catfishes, as well as common carp, goldfish, brown trout, and mosquitofish.[10]

Many of these familiar fish species were intentionally distributed into the state's many isolated watersheds by fisheries agencies in the 19th and early 20th centuries (Moyle 2002). In addition, species native to some watersheds have been moved to others, especially rainbow trout and Sacramento perch. These introductions, while done for noble reasons (e.g., improve fishing, provide food, mosquito control), have often imposed unanticipated harm on native fish and fisheries (Moyle, Li, and Barton 1986). Introductions of trout into hundreds of alpine lakes have caused the collapse of native amphibian populations (e.g., Knapp, Matthews, and Sarnelle 2001) and likely declines of native birds (Epanchin, Knapp, and Lawler 2010), while introductions of alien trout species into streams of the eastern Sierra Nevada have nearly eliminated native cutthroat trout. In the lower Colorado River, predation by alien fish species keeps native minnows and suckers from spawning successfully, resulting in extinction for species not maintained by hatcheries. Redeye bass, adapted for small streams, have basically eliminated native fishes in streams where they were introduced (e.g., Cosumnes River, Santa Margarita River). In the Eel River, invasion of Sacramento pikeminnow has suppressed the recovery of salmon and steelhead populations (Box 5.5). To prevent a similar disaster by alien northern pike to

10. Scientific names of species mentioned in this section are overbite clam (*Corbula amurensis*), Brazilian waterweed (*Egeria densa*), Mississippi silverside (*Menidia audens*), largemouth bass (*Micropterus salmoides*), common carp (*Cyprinus carpio*), goldfish (*Carassius auratus*), brown trout (*Salmo trutta*), western mosquitofish (*Gambusia affinis*), rainbow trout (*Oncorhynchus mykiss*), Sacramento perch (*Archoplites interruptus*), cutthroat trout (*O. clarkii*), Sacramento pikeminnow (*Ptychocheilus grandis*), redeye bass (*Micropterus coosae*), northern pike (*Esox lucius*), mud snail (*Potamopyrgus jenkinsi*), tule perch (*Hyterocarpus traski*), hitch (*Lavinia exilicauda*), Chinook salmon (*Oncorhynchus tshawystscha*), coho salmon (*O. kisutch*), California roach (*L. symmetricus*), zebra mussel (*Dreissena polymorpha*), quagga mussel (*D. rostriformis*), and Shimofuri goby (*Tridentiger bifasciatus*).

5.5

Alien species, floods, dams, and salmon in the Eel River

The Eel River is the third largest watershed in California, flowing into the ocean just south of the city of Eureka. It flows through the steep, highly erodible hills of the Coast Ranges. The watershed was originally covered with forests of redwood and Douglas fir. The only major dams in the system are Scott Dam (Pillsbury Reservoir, 1930) and Cape Horn Dam (1908) on the main stem, which together form the Potter Valley Hydroelectric Project. This project produces power and diverts some water to the Russian River.

During the 19th and early 20th centuries, in wet periods with good ocean conditions, the Eel River probably supported runs of well over a million salmon and steelhead (800,000 Chinook salmon, 100,000 coho salmon, and 150,000 steelhead), with about half that number in less favorable years (Yoshiyama and Moyle 2010). In the 1930s to early 1950s, the river attracted salmon and steelhead anglers because of the abundance of large fish. Today, the river supports, on average, about 3,500 fish total (±1,000) per year (1,000 Chinook, 500 coho, 2,000 steelhead). Present numbers are more than a 99 percent decline from historical abundance, with no sign of improvement. So, what happened?

From 1860 to 1960, a continuous, if slow, decline of fish resulted from overfishing and watershed disturbance from logging, grazing, and road-building. Disturbance of the fragile soils and rocks on steep hillsides resulted in fine sediment filling in gravel spawning areas and loss of rearing habitat in forested tributaries, stream edges, and the estuary. At the same time, Scott and Cape Horn dams prevented migration to parts of the watershed on the main stem of the Eel, as did reduced flows from the diversions to the Russian River. Habitat degradation and loss of fish intensified after World War II as logging increased and became mechanized with virtually no regulation, making hill slopes more susceptible to erosion. Then came the great storms and floods of 1955 and 1964, which, acting on a highly disturbed landscape, caused massive landslides and erosion. In most stretches, the river became shallow, meandering across an open plain of sediment, with little habitat for salmon and steelhead. This alteration created excellent habitat for the predatory Sacramento pikeminnow, introduced in the early 1980s into Pillsbury Reservoir, apparently by fishermen using juveniles as bait (Brown and Moyle 1997). The new conditions were also perfect for California roach, a small introduced minnow favored as prey by pikeminnow. Thus, the damage done to the watershed by logging, grazing, and dams became exacerbated by natural off-the-charts rain events, setting it up for invasion by a predatory alien. The pikeminnow spread rapidly through the watershed, preying on roach, lampreys, and small salmonids. The large population of predatory fish continues to suppress salmon and steelhead populations. Undoing some of the damage by removing Scott and Cape Horn Dams (Box 5.6) probably would not benefit salmonids much until a way is found to control pikeminnows. Some recovery of salmonids will occur, however, if watersheds, especially those in the coastal fog belt, are allowed to return to the stable, complex cold water habitat that pikeminnow tend to avoid.

Central Valley salmon populations, the Department of Fish and Game spent millions of dollars eradicating the illegally introduced pike from two reservoirs on the Feather River (Moyle 2002).

Today, fisheries agencies in California no longer condone introduction of species and actively oppose bringing new species into the state, although planting trout in some alpine lakes is still approved. All new introductions, therefore, result either from illegal introductions by anglers and aquarists or as a by-product of other activities, such as the transport of mud snails on the boots of anglers or the introduction of tule perch, shimofuri goby, and Sacramento hitch into Southern California reservoirs by way of the California Aqueduct.

Invasive alien species clearly can undo or diminish habitat management actions taken to protect desirable fishes, including releasing more water from dams. New disruptive species are still becoming established in California with a high enough frequency to cause alarm. For instance, quagga and zebra mussels have just invaded California and they have considerable capacity to alter ecosystems and disrupt water project operations by clogging canals and intakes. The cost for their control may run into the hundreds of millions of dollars, as it has in the eastern United States and Europe (Leung et al. 2002).

Because problems with aquatic invasive species cut across agency and jurisdictional boundaries, regulation and control actions must be coordinated with at least 14 state agencies and numerous federal agencies, with the Department of Fish and Game taking the leadership position (California Department of Fish and Game 2008). A comprehensive policy, with funding for enforcement, monitoring, and research, is needed to reduce the effects of alien species that are already present as well as the likelihood and effects of new invasions. Such a policy should include such actions as:

- ▹ Adopting the 163 prioritized actions recommended in DFG's (2008) *California Aquatic Invasive Species Management Plan* as well as the recommendations to manage invasive species made by the Ecological Society of America (Lodge et al. 2006);
- ▹ Requiring that agencies aggressively act to prevent new invasions, such as including 24-hour inspections of boats at the California border and enforcing no-tolerance limits for alien species in the ballast water of ships and other vectors;

- Creating and enforcing an approved ("white") list for pet, aquaculture, and bait organisms allowed for sale; permissible organisms would lack characteristics of successful invaders (Moyle and Marchetti 2006); and
- Creating an invasive species response team, with DFG as the lead agency, to react quickly to new, potentially harmful invasions, modeled on the oil spill response team; the team would require regular funding and sufficient authority to rapidly act when needed (California Department of Fish and Game 2008).

Reducing the Negative Effects of Dams

California has thousands of dams and diversion structures, each one contributing to loss of aquatic ecosystem function in some way. The dams range from small earthen dams on seasonal waterways, which create ponds for local use, to large dams, such as Shasta and Oroville, which are central to California's water supply system. Dam construction on free-flowing streams began in California in the 1850s, accelerated during the late 19th century in response to demands of hydraulic mining and logging, and peaked from 1900 to 1982 as irrigated agriculture and urban areas developed (Yoshiyama, Fisher, and Moyle 1998) (Figure 5.4).

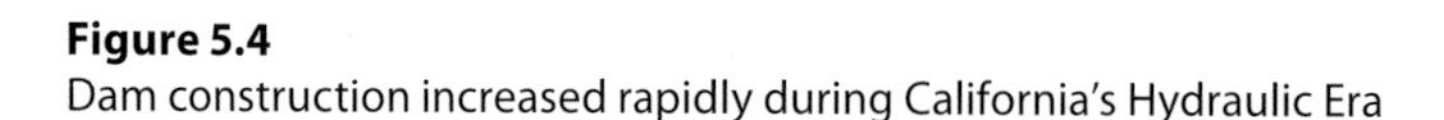

Figure 5.4
Dam construction increased rapidly during California's Hydraulic Era

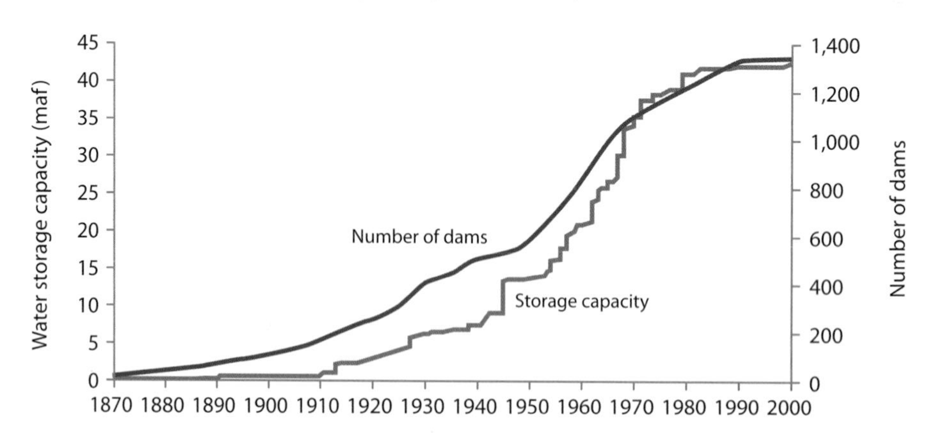

SOURCE: Authors' calculations using data from the California Department of Water Resources Division of Dam Safety.

NOTES: The figure shows dam construction and storage capacity from 1870 to 2000. Of dams built between 1850 and 1869, only 17 exist today, with a total storage capacity of 0.034 maf.

Today roughly 1,400 dams are large enough for state safety regulation (Chapter 3). Combined, these dams can impound up to 42 million acre-feet of water, or about 60 percent of the state's average annual runoff (Chapter 2; Mount 1995). Most dams were built with little consideration for their effects on fish, although legally they were required to provide adequate flows for fish downstream of the dam or fish passage around it (Box 1.3). As noted above, dams have dramatically reduced salmon and steelhead habitat in the state.[11] This loss of habitat is a major cause of fishery declines and endangerment of native species.

For salmon and steelhead, the main historical mitigation method has been hatcheries (discussed below), which have largely failed to sustain fisheries (Williams 2006; Moyle, Israel, and Purdy 2008). Recently, increased attention is being paid to either removing dams that harm fish or modifying their operations to improve fish habitat.

Reoperation of dams

The reoperation of dams is often seen as a means to help restore native ecosystems and species below dams while maintaining most economic benefits of one or more dams within a river system. Many researchers have developed methods to establish "environmental flows" in regulated rivers (Richter et al. 1997a; Tharme 2003; Acreman and Dunbar 2005). A particularly useful approach has been application of the natural flow regime concept, which can shift fish and invertebrate populations in a regulated river toward a diverse community of favored species, without requiring large amounts of water (Poff et al. 1997). The natural flow regime for Putah Creek, described above, features a permanent base flow, spring spawning flows for native fishes, and a fall pulse flow for salmon (Moyle et al. 1998). The success of this project, which was based on application of § 5937 of the Fish and Game Code (Box 1.3), formed the basis for the flow regime being applied to restoring the dry San Joaquin River.

The Federal Energy Regulatory Commission (FERC) relicensing process for dams with a hydroelectric component provides a major opportunity for reconciling ecosystems with the operation of dams (Gillilan and Brown 1997). Today, California is in a period of FERC relicensing, with approximately 150 FERC-licensed dams scheduled to be relicensed over the next 15 years. The

11. As shown above (Figure 5.1), dams or reduced flows exclude Chinook salmon from over 1,000 miles of former habitat (Yoshiyama et al. 2001). Likewise, dams on the Klamath River deny access of salmon and steelhead to several hundred miles of upstream habitat (Hamilton et al. 2005).

original licenses were granted 30 to 50 years ago, when there was little concern for the effects of dams on fish and stream ecosystems. FERC is now more willing to require changes to dam operations as requested by federal fisheries agencies. Thus, the agreement to remove four dams on the Klamath River began in the FERC relicensing procedure, in which the agencies requested that the dams be modified to allow voluntary passage of anadromous fish. Economic analyses suggested that removal was less costly (Box 2.4).

Adding new environmental flow requirements below FERC dams during relicensing is particularly important because the U.S. Supreme Court has ruled that releases from such dams are exempt from state laws such as § 5937 of the Fish and Game Code (*California v. FERC* 1990). Yet even with likely changes to the operation of FERC-regulated dams, there will still be hundreds, perhaps thousands, of dams that do not provide adequate flows for fish, as required under § 5937 of the Fish and Game Code and potentially other laws (such as the public trust doctrine and the reasonable use doctrine of the state constitution). The following actions should be taken to better integrate the presence and operation of dams in reconciled or restored native ecosystems. New regional stewardship authorities could coordinate these activities, liaising with the Department of Fish and Game as the lead state agency and working with the State Water Resources Control Board and local agencies and water users to:

- ▹ Create a database of *all* dams in California, to determine the extent to which dams modify California streams and do not comply with state law.
- ▹ Require flow releases for fish below all dams that currently do not comply with the law.
- ▹ Reexamine flow releases below all large federal, state, and local dams to determine if they should be modified to be more compatible with environmental management goals.
- ▹ For series of dams on tributaries to large rivers (e.g., dams on the Stanislaus, Tuolumne, and Merced Rivers), find ways to operate flow releases in a coordinated manner, to increase downstream benefits to fish.
- ▹ Improve methods for determining environmental flows, and the monitoring that should follow setting of flow releases, so that they are more likely to create conditions favorable to fish.

- ▷ Assess, below all dams, how reductions in flow have altered habitat quality and develop and implement mitigation measures (e.g., gravel enhancement for spawning).

Dam removal

Roughly 600 dams have been removed across the United States over the past 20 years, and California has been a national leader in the number of dams removed (Pohl 2003; Doyle and Havlick 2009; Heinz Center for Science, Economics, and the Environment 2002). So far the dams being removed are small, such as mill dams on streams in the eastern states or sediment-filled diversion dams in the west, such as Seltzer Dam on Clear Creek in Shasta County (Poff and Hart 2002). Such dams typically have little or no value for water supply, hydropower production, or flood control but have large effects from blocked fish passage (Heinz Center for Science, Economics, and the Environment 2002). They can also be relatively inexpensive to remove. Age contributes to dam removal: small, older dams sometimes have reservoirs filled with sediment, are subject to failure, no longer effectively serve purposes for which they were intended, and require significant rehabilitation to function well again.

However, large functioning dams also are being examined for removal because of the potential to contribute to recovery of endangered fish populations, especially anadromous fishes such as Chinook salmon and steelhead. Such removals are controversial because of the high costs of dismantling these structures, loss of hydropower and water supply, and uncertain benefits to fish (Stanley and Doyle 2003; Quiñones et al. 2011). Thus, the proposed removal of three hydropower dams on the Snake River, a tributary to the Columbia River, has generated huge arguments over cost and benefits, with fish biologists on both sides of the issue (National Research Council 1996; Gregory, Li, and Li 2002). Nevertheless, removal of two medium-size dams on the Elwha River in Washington State is scheduled to begin in 2011 (www.nps.gov/olym/nature-science/elwha-ecosystem-restoration.htm).

Although any dam removal is likely to be controversial, new approaches are being developed to systematically evaluate costs and benefits. Because dams both impair river systems and provide economic benefits, decisions on removal are rarely easy, in part from lack of a systematic, scientific decision-making process (Poff and Hart 2002). Kuby et al. (2005) applied a multiobjective optimization model to examine a network of 150 dams on the Willamette

River Basin in Oregon. Their preliminary results suggest that removing just 12 dams would have high benefits to salmon, with low loss of hydropower. Such a regional approach is especially promising because it recognizes that many river systems have multiple dams, often operated jointly. A joint evaluation can help determine where economic and ecological values are highest. A regional approach is particularly needed in California, where coordinated management of geographically extensive and diverse water sources is necessary. Null and Lund (2006) found that regional solutions and reservoir reoperation would allow removal of the O'Shaunessy Dam in San Francisco's Hetch Hetchy system, restoring an upstream river valley, albeit at considerable cost and with little benefit for native fish species.

Pejchar and Warner (2001) provide 36 questions that to help assess whether a dam merits removal, and they recommend systematically evaluating all dams using these criteria. The questions fall under seven general headings (pp. 566–67):

- "Is the dam currently degrading habitat quality and quantity?"
- "Will removal of the dam restore habitat quality and quantity?"
- "Is the dam fulfilling its original intended function?"
- "Does the dam pose a current or potential safety hazard to human lives and property?"
- "Is there stakeholder support for dam removal?"
- "Would the Endangered Species Act play a role in dam removal?"
- "Is funding available [for removal]?"

The economic values for retaining the dam also should be considered. Dams with low economic values for traditional purposes and good potential based on the above criteria are likely to be excellent candidates for removal. Some sizable dams would meet most criteria for removal (Box 5.6). The complexity of dam removal suggests that it should be accomplished within a larger regional ecosystem reconciliation context, even though the agency owning the dam should be responsible for removal. Regional stewardship authorities could be charged with such coordination and with convening an interagency group with appropriate expertise.

One factor that challenges demand for dam removal (including removal of Klamath dams) is the increasing demand for hydropower as "clean" energy. The roughly 400 hydropower plants in California currently produce about

5.6

Low-hanging fruit? California dams ripe for removal

Matilija Dam, Ventura River. Built in 1947, its reservoir quickly filled with sediment, making it nonfunctional. It blocks access of endangered southern steelhead to key spawning and rearing areas. The sediment also is needed to slow beach erosion. The dam has been lowered but cost of removal has stalled the removal process.

Rindge Dam, Malibu Creek. Same problems as Matilija Dam.

San Clemente Dam, Carmel River. Regarded as seismically unsafe, this dam is slated for removal rather than repair, to allow better access of endangered steelhead to upstream spawning and rearing areas. The cost of removal is estimated at $83 million, with sediment removal from behind the dam a major factor.

Englebright Dam, Yuba River. Built in 1941 to contain debris from gold mining, it blocks access of salmon and steelhead to the three forks of the Yuba. It is now about half full with sediment. Water supply, power, and recreational benefits of the dam are relatively small, but large amounts of mercury in the sediments complicate sediment removal.

Dwinnell Dam, Shasta River. Dwinnell Dam provides water for a small irrigation district and town and creates a small warm reservoir (Shastina) at the center of a large (1,200+) second-home/retirement-home subdivision. The dam diverts cold water and blocks access of endangered salmon runs to prime spawning and rearing habitat. Removal of the dam could restore the Shasta River, allowing it to become the most salmon productive of all tributaries to the Klamath River.

Iron Gate, Copco 1 and 2, and J.C. Boyle Dams, Klamath River. This sequence of four hydroelectric dams blocks access of endangered salmon and steelhead to cold water in the river and upper basin. Although the power revenue generated is considerable, the fish are in desperate condition and removing the dams may be more cost-effective than providing passage over them. These dams are slated for removal as part of a settlement among the power company, fisheries agencies, Indian tribes, and environmental groups, concluded in early 2010 (Box 2.4).

Martis Creek Dam, Martis Creek (Truckee River). The U.S. Army Corps of Engineers considers this flood control dam as one of the most unsafe dams in California. The dam also causes problems for fish by dividing the creek into two sections and warming up the creek below the dam, although the dam affects only extreme high flows.

Removal of Matilija Dam would improve habitat for endangered southern steelhead. Photo by Jacob Katz.

15 percent of the state's electricity, although much of this energy is from power plants at a handful of large multipurpose dams (Chapter 2; www.energy.ca.gov/hydroelectric/). Hydropower generally requires a dam or a way to divert water to run it through a powerhouse. Although most run-of-river hydropower dams are small and store little water, they can still block fish access to upstream areas and significantly reduce flows and water quality immediately downstream. Although some increases in hydropower output can be achieved with more efficient operation and modernization of existing facilities, pressure to construct more small dams, especially on high-gradient streams, is likely to continue.

Funding dam removal

More dams will be removed in California as environmental and safety benefits become more apparent. But because removal costs are high, especially on large dams, a source of funding is needed. A retirement surcharge on all existing dams may be a suitable way to fund these removals. If removing some dams to aid fish recovery reduces pressures to remove the remaining dams, such a fee could be a cost-effective form of environmental mitigation, albeit one that encourages specialization of river uses. Dam removal or replacement is an inevitable part of the cost of any dam, just as remediation of mining sites is part of the cost of mining (but often is not paid for by mining interests). Today, most dam removal projects are at the expense of taxpayers, not those who benefited directly from decades of dam operation.

Dams have finite lifetimes, even if such lifetimes are very long. Some California dams have had useful economic lives as short as 25 years (e.g., Matilija Dam, Ventura River, Box 5.6), and others will likely provide significant storage capacity for more than a thousand years. Nevertheless, as a matter of ensuring intergenerational equity and providing proper incentives for decisionmaking, the operation of a dam should generate revenues to fund the eventual retirement of the dam and rehabilitation of the dam site (Palmieri, Shah, and Dinar 2001). Similarly, California's Surface Mining and Reclamation Act requires that mine operators set aside a bond sufficient for restoring the mine site after operations have ceased.

Few examples exist of policies that address funding for dam retirement. One example is the Penobscot River Restoration Trust, which has bought three dams from Pennsylvania Power and Light with the intention of eventually removing them (www.penobscotriver.org/). Funding sources for the purchase include private fundraising and federal grants. The trust may use proceeds from the sale of power from the dams to help pay for dam removal. The funding proposal for removal of the Klamath dams includes $200 million from electricity ratepayers (mostly in Oregon) and public funding from California to cover up to $250 million in additional costs.[12] The water bond now slated for the 2012 ballot includes provisions to cover California's public funding obligations for this deal. To set up an alternative structure that relies on dam retirement fees for dam owners and beneficiaries, rather than on taxpayer funds, removal or repair of existing low-value or unsafe dams could be used to help estimate the costs and appropriate fee levels.

Dams will continue to be a major factor altering rivers and other waterways in California, and reoperation or removal of dams will be major ways to improve habitat for fish and other aquatic organisms into the indefinite future.

Salmon and Steelhead Hatcheries

When dams were built and blocked salmon and steelhead spawning streams throughout California, the decline in fisheries was largely regarded as the price of progress. The negative effects were recognized, however, and the legal code of California, even in the 19th century, contained a law that said owners of dams must provide passage over dams for fish or provide sufficient flows below dams to support fish populations. The law was generally ignored. Although this law

12. The decision to rely on taxpayer funding if costs exceed $200 million was based on a desire to minimize rate shock to customers (Public Utility Commission of Oregon 2010). The secretary of the Department of the Interior must estimate costs and determine whether to proceed by March 2012.

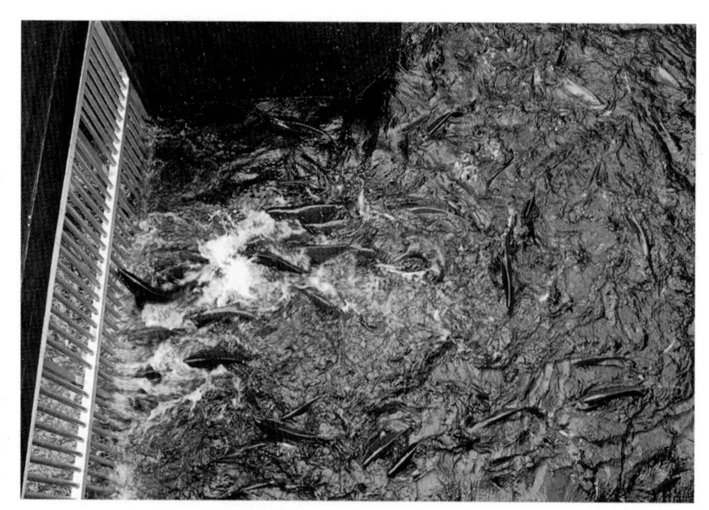

Chinook salmon trying to enter Nimbus Fish Hatchery. Hatchery salmon can overwhelm less abundant wild salmon. Photo by Peter Moyle.

remains on the books (as § 5937 of the Fish and Game Code; Box 1.3), it continues to be widely ignored, with notable recent exceptions of actions restoring flows to Rush Creek, Putah Creek, Trinity River, and the San Joaquin River. One factor that made it easy to ignore this and other salmon and steelhead protection laws was the idea that fish hatcheries (starting in 1872) could replace upstream spawning and rearing habitat (Yoshiyama 1999).

Hatcheries can be regarded as a reconciliation strategy because their goal is to release fish back into the wild, maintaining populations large enough to support fisheries. However, hatcheries are a strategy that has not worked well. They allow salmon and steelhead to be taken from the wild, spawned artificially, and have the fertilized eggs kept under controlled conditions. After a few months, small juveniles (alevins) hatch and are then reared in troughs or ponds for three to eighteen months. The assumption is that hatcheries do better than nature by greatly increasing the survival rates of embryos and juveniles, enabling millions of small fish to be released into streams every year. Thus, it should be possible to replace many miles of lost spawning and rearing habitat with a few hatcheries. The failure of this approach is indicated by the fact that of the 20 kinds of salmon and steelhead in California most endemic to the state, 16 are in serious trouble and some are on the verge of extinction (Moyle, Israel, and Purdy 2008). Even the Central Valley fall-run Chinook salmon—the mainstay of the hatchery program—has experienced major declines in abundance in recent years, causing fisheries to be closed or curtailed.

There are two general reasons why this has happened. First, hatcheries evolutionarily select for genetically uniform fish that thrive in hatcheries but do poorly in the wild, especially when environmental conditions are not optimal. Second, so many hatchery fish are produced that even with poor survival they can reduce the survival of wild fish, through competition for limited resources, predation, and hybridization (Williams 2006). Thus, when huge numbers of fat, unwary, hatchery juvenile salmon are suddenly released into rivers below dams, they can literally overwhelm the small and timid wild fish, pushing them from their rearing habitats and making them more vulnerable to predation. Such interactions can exist at all phases of the life cycle, including during ocean feeding and on the spawning grounds. In addition, because only a few returning adults are needed to provide spawners for hatchery production, in theory harvest rates on fish from a hatchery population can be extremely high. Because fishermen cannot tell hatchery salmon from wild salmon, much less distinguish hatchery salmon from individuals from endangered runs, the harvest rates of wild salmon then become unsustainable, further decreasing their numbers.

The reliance on hatcheries has left salmon and steelhead spawning in Central Valley rivers, and most likely in the Klamath and other coastal rivers, overwhelmingly of hatchery origin with a much more genetically homogeneous population (Lindley et al. 2009). Such fish are presumably less adapted to persisting through adverse conditions in both fresh and salt water (e.g., physiologically less capable of surviving on less food, more sensitive to changing ocean conditions, less able to avoid predation). The recent collapse of the Central Valley fall-run Chinook salmon population, for example, may result from a low diversity of responses to unfavorable ocean conditions (Lindley et al. 2009). Hatchery fish essentially lack the resilience and adaptability to persist for long in the real, rapidly changing world (Schindler et al. 2010; Carlson and Satterwaite 2010). Even with many fish being produced from hatcheries, the long-term result is likely to be loss of the fish and the fisheries they support. This loss of returning salmon causes serious damage to stream and riparian ecosystems that depend on the annual influx of salmon nutrients and breaks the implicit promise made to fishermen and coastal communities that dams would not destroy their livelihoods.

Californians must decide whether they want salmon around in the future, beyond a few boutique runs maintained at great expense in a Disneyland atmosphere. Maintaining diverse salmon and steelhead populations will require a radical rethinking of attitudes and policies that will improve flow regimes and habitats below dams, in conjunction with a comprehensive retooling of hatchery management. Such major steps should be taken in the context of a broader reconciliation strategy for salmon and steelhead, probably funded by surcharges on dam beneficiaries and managed by the Department of Fish and Game. Some possible changes:

- ▹ Recognize that most hatcheries maintain fisheries, not wild salmon and steelhead. Therefore, hatcheries should be located in places where released hatchery fish interfere minimally with wild fish (e.g., close to the coast), using fish so domesticated that they have few interactions with wild fish.
- ▹ Employ specially managed restoration and recovery hatcheries to keep populations from going extinct while habitat restoration is in progress.
- ▹ Improve flows below all dams on streams that historically supported anadromous fishes.
- ▹ Increase access to former spawning areas above dams through dam removal, installation of volitional passage structures (e.g., fish ladders), and similar actions.
- ▹ Engage in large-scale stream restoration to improve habitats for spawning and rearing of salmon and steelhead.
- ▹ Protect and enhance sources of cold water for stream flows, from spring systems to cold water pools of reservoirs.
- ▹ Develop intensive fish management strategies that favor wild salmon and steelhead, starting with marking all hatchery fish to distinguish wild from hatchery individuals, as is done in the Pacific Northwest. The strategy should emphasize the "portfolio effect," which maintains a diversity of life history strategies to buffer against environmental variability (S. Carlson, UC Berkeley, personal communication; Schindler et al. 2010).
- ▹ These same policies should apply, where appropriate, to native nonanadromous fish species.

Reconciliation and Environmental Laws

A reconciliation strategy for native species and their ecosystems requires a great deal of management and operational flexibility, along with considerable political and financial support. Changing environmental conditions, arrivals of new invasive species, and incorporation of new knowledge into management all require the ability to adjust course through time. The management of species is governed by numerous laws that provide guidance and, in some cases, severe restrictions on management. Three of these laws— the federal Clean Water Act and the state and federal Endangered Species Acts—can potentially constrain options for managing ecosystems in a changing world.

The Clean Water Act

Section 303(d) of the federal Clean Water Act requires that the SWRCB (usually through the regional boards) set water quality standards throughout California to support beneficial uses. By establishing total maximum daily loads (TMDLs) of pollutants, the board seeks to limit pollution entering the waters from all sources, including nonpoint sources. The goal is to protect and to restore water quality to meet a variety of economic, recreational, and ecological uses.

The same regulations prohibit the board from revising water quality standards in any way that would degrade existing water quality. These antidegradation regulations are targeted at those waters that meet or exceed current standards. Their purpose is to protect pristine and relatively unimpaired waters and to prevent backsliding once water quality objectives are met.

Managing changes in conditions consistent with the antidegradation regulations will be challenging for state and federal regulators. In the case of the Delta and many upstream water bodies, it may not be possible to protect all existing designated uses. Sea level rise will make it increasingly difficult to maintain salinity standards in the Delta with reservoir releases; a severe earthquake could have even more severe effects on salinity levels in the Delta (Lund et al. 2010). Regional warming of the Sierra Nevada will cause water temperatures in streams to exceed state standards (Null et al. submitted). This risk is especially acute for some species of fish, such as the various species of smelt that inhabit the Delta and salmon and steelhead throughout the state, which require relatively cool water flows during migration and spawning (Chapter 3).

It may become necessary in the future to adopt a policy of stream specialization, by which some streams are managed principally to protect fish and others are managed principally for water supply. In the former, water quality standards would focus on maintaining flows, temperatures, and other water quality criteria to protect fish habitat; in the latter, where changes in hydrologic conditions are likely to overwhelm current standards, the emphasis would be on maximizing water available for agricultural and urban use (or perhaps for hydropower generation).

The antidegradation requirements of the Clean Water Act were enacted in 1977, before the concept of changing climate conditions had become mainstream science. Congress therefore did not consider the likely consequences of climate warming on stream flows, water quality, and water supply. Although EPA's antidegradation regulations provide some flexibility for states to lower water quality standards "to accommodate important economic or social development in the area in which the waters are located," any such change must "assure water quality adequate to protect existing uses fully" (U.S. Environmental Protection Agency *Water Quality Regulations* § 131.12(a)(2) undated (e)).

Indeed, EPA has explained that "no activity is allowable under the antidegradation policy which would partially or completely eliminate any existing use.... Water quality should be such that it results in no mortality and no significant growth or reproductive impairment of resident species. Any lowering of water quality below this full level of protection is not allowed" (U.S. Environmental Protection Agency undated (d)). Accordingly, California would be prohibited from lowering water quality standards in any individual river (or other body of water) governed by the antidegradation laws if the change could harm native fish species or eliminate fish as a designated use.[13]

Under these constraints, the SWRCB and regional boards' only option is to try to ensure the protection of *all* existing fish species, regardless of the futility or costs of doing so. This dilemma may ultimately merit congressional review to reconsider the restrictions of existing antidegradation regulations and to modify the antidegradation policy to allow California and other states to alter water quality standards or eliminate designated uses where such changes are needed to facilitate reconciliation and adaptation in the face of the hydrologic realities of climate warming. The new regulations should not lightly permit the lowering of TMDLs or the elimination of designated uses. But where state water quality regulators can demonstrate either that it is futile to try to maintain a particular designated use or that water quality adjustments are necessary as part of a broader reconciliation strategy to improve the overall

13. The EPA regulations do allow states to set different standards for cold water and warm water fishes (U.S. Environmental Protection Agency *Water Quality Regulations* § 131.10(c) undated (e)). Thus, in some situations, it may be permissible for California regulators to conduct a use attainability analysis that would allow a degradation of water quality to protect warm water, but not cold water, fish species. However, for the reasons stated in the text, this change would not be permitted if it would harm an existing cold water fish species.

protection of designated beneficial uses, the law should be flexible enough to enable such changes.

The Endangered Species Acts

The federal and state Endangered Species Acts have become focal points in many of California's water controversies because they may require water to be allocated to fish (and other aquatic species) that previously was allocated to agricultural and urban uses. The number of species being listed under state and federal ESAs in California is increasing (with removals from the list rare), which suggests that most water decisions in the future, large and small, will involve one or more endangered species, especially fish (Chapter 3). With few accommodations and rare exceptions, the Endangered Species Acts prohibit the taking of species that are on the verge of extinction and place severe restrictions on human use of the species' critical habitat. The overriding mandate of the statutes is to ensure the survival and propagation of listed species, regardless of the costs or benefits to human endeavors. Endangered species controversies are usually acute, because by the time a species becomes threatened or endangered, the ecosystem it inhabits is often so degraded that it may be impossible to restore either the species or the ecosystem to its former state.

The resulting water shortages and lowering of water supply reliability raise questions of fairness and efficiency of allocation. In some cases, water users have responded with lawsuits challenging implementation of the statutes or claiming that the regulatory disruption of water supplies is a taking of property or a breach of contract.

Yet the statutes have protected native species that otherwise could have become extinct. In California, these species include several kinds of salmon and steelhead that migrate through the Delta, green sturgeon, delta smelt, and various pupfishes and minnows (Taylor, Suckling, and Rachlinski 2005). Moreover, in two of California's most complex and long-standing water controversies—the Delta and the Klamath River—the regulatory mandates of the ESAs have spurred broader environmental protection and reconciliation efforts.

Looking ahead, endangered species administration, and possibly the laws themselves, will need to adapt to meet several key challenges. Three aspects of the acts, in particular, will bedevil California water management in the future: the tendency of agencies to focus on single-species management, historical focus on single actions and single sources of stress, and the potential need for endangered species triage.

Single-species management

The heart of the federal ESA lies in §§ 7 and 9. Section 7 requires that all federal agencies consult with either the U.S. Fish and Wildlife Service (USFWS) or the National Marine Fisheries Service (NMFS) to ensure that federal actions do not jeopardize the existence of species protected under the act or harm critical habitat. Section 9 prohibits anyone from "taking" an endangered species without a permit, including modifying habitat in a way that could lead to injury or death of an endangered species.[14] Under § 10, however, the government can grant an "incidental take permit" to any persons who wish to take an action that may incidentally take a species, if they prepare an adequate Habitat Conservation Plan. The California ESA does not require consultation, but it prohibits taking of a listed species unless authorized by an incidental take permit from DFG.

Because these laws focus on preserving individual species on the brink of extinction, this sometimes leads to conflicts with efforts to manage other species (National Research Council 1995; Rosenzweig 2003). These conflicts have played out in the biological opinions covering coho salmon and two species of suckerfish in the Klamath Basin (National Research Council 2004) and are the focus of considerable attention and litigation within the Delta.

Despite the focus in practice on individual species, both the state and federal ESAs allow comprehensive, multispecies management actions that can address, at least in part, the problems of single-species management. The HCP process of § 10 of the federal act and the NCCP program of the state act allow regulators and regulated parties to negotiate a long-range habitat management plan to recover listed species (Presley 2011; Thompson 1997b). California has substantial experience on land with regional HCPs or NCCPs that encompass multiple species and a large area of habitat. Development of regional HCPs or NCCPs is a complex task that can require years of scientific study and negotiation. As of mid-2010, only eight NCCP's had been approved in California (many of these are also regional HCPs); most have been relatively simple in scope; all have focused on terrestrial systems not affected by water management (California Department of Fish and Game 2010b).

To date, the vast majority of HCPs nationwide, and NCCPs in California, have focused on land conservation and protection of terrestrial species. Of the 127 HCPs approved from January 1, 2001, through July 31, 2003, for example,

14. Although the "take" prohibition of § 9 applies only to species listed as "endangered," by rulemaking the USFWS and NMFS have extended this proscription to most threatened species as well under § 4(d) of the act.

only seven dealt with aquatic environments (Thompson 2006). Several HCPs in the past decade, however, have addressed the protection of salmon and steelhead, as well as other fish species, threatened by the modification of rivers and streams in the Pacific Northwest. These HCPs have focused on Portland's Bull Run watershed, hydroelectric projects on the mid-Columbia, Tacoma's Howard Hanson Dam, and Seattle's Cedar River watershed.

At the time of this writing, California's largest and most complex HCP-NCCP effort is under way. Known as the Bay Delta Conservation Plan, its purpose is to develop a comprehensive habitat management plan for the Delta. The basic goals of the plan are to recover numerous listed species while allowing for continued export of water through the State Water Project and Central Valley Project.[15] The complexities of this plan are extraordinary, including the large and diverse array of urban, agricultural, and environmental interests involved in negotiations. Unfortunately, the basic goals may be impossible to achieve, given recent recognition by the SWRCB and Department of Fish and Game that much higher flows through the Delta are needed if populations of endangered fish are to recover (Box 5.2). If this basic problem can be overcome, the plan could become a national model for HCPs in aquatic ecosystems. If not, the problems of the Delta are likely to continue to deteriorate, to the detriment of both the ecosystem and the people who depend on it.

Multiple stressors

A long-standing problem of the federal and state ESAs has been their focus on responding to particular projects and proposed actions, and the resulting failure of the USFWS and NMFS to adequately account for and address the many sources of harm to protected fish species. Instead, the focus has been on factors easily controlled by the act—mostly water operations linked to federally authorized projects that are subject to the interagency consultation requirements of § 7. The fisheries agencies routinely emphasize restrictions on how water is managed by these projects, regardless of other factors that limit recovery (although flow *is* often a "master variable" that interacts with other stressors). As agency personnel involved in these consultations routinely point out, their options under § 7 consultations are limited to federal actions and other activities authorized or funded by the United States. For fish, this aspect of the act tends to warp priorities for habitat management away from

15. Bay Delta Conservation Plan documents can be found at http://baydeltaconservationplan.com/default.aspx.

comprehensive ecosystem approaches to simply managing flows. Not only does this focus create high potential for controversy, as regulated water users resent the nonconsideration of other actions, it also reduces the prospects for success in maintaining native species.

The agencies' tendency to focus on those actions subject to § 7 has played out repeatedly in California, particularly in the Klamath Basin and the Delta. In both cases the biological evidence is clear and abundant: The decline of listed species is caused by multiple stressors, some of which are not directly affected by federal project operations and facilities (National Research Council 2004; Brown and Moyle 2004). There is authority under both the federal and state ESAs, as well as state and federal water quality laws, for the fisheries agencies and the SWRCB (and the regional boards) to take a broader approach to the problem of multiple stressors. Yet, to date, the agencies have not been successful in addressing the multiple-stressors problems outside the HCP-NCCP process, in part because of their unwillingness to exercise the broader authority they possess (Hanneman and Dyckman 2009). A recent action by the Central Valley Regional Water Quality Board suggests some movement in this direction. In October 2010, the board issued a draft permit to the Sacramento Regional Wastewater Treatment Plant to clean up discharges, especially ammonium, that harm the Delta ecosystem.

Managing changing conditions

As with the Clean Water Act, the ESAs were enacted before legislators and policymakers recognized the risk of climate change. The focus of the acts is on protecting habitat critical to the survival of species and to reducing actions that could lead to "take" of species. The statutes did not anticipate that changing conditions might make it unfeasible to preserve and recover all species in the future. Increasingly, scientists are recognizing that ecosystems of the future in any given place may be quite different from those today, requiring different management strategies to protect endangered species (e.g., West et al. 2009). Even if a particular species is unlikely to survive because of changes in temperature, arrival of invasive species, or loss of potential habitat from sea level rise, the law lacks provisions that allow regulators to make tradeoffs or to prioritize ecosystem investments that might ensure the survival of one species over another—a form of endangered species triage.

For example, the largest and most genetically distinct population of spring-run Chinook salmon in the Central Valley (listed as a threatened species) lives in Butte Creek, Tehama County. Studies by Thompson et al. (submitted) indicate that climate change will cause increases in water temperature that will drive the population to extinction within 80 years, if not sooner. It is unclear how this population can be saved without transferring it to a new location (e.g., the San Joaquin River). But the rarer a species becomes, the more difficult it becomes to take such risky conservation measures as relocation.

Given the pace and nature of change in California's aquatic ecosystems caused by climate warming, it is certain that this issue will become prominent in water resource management. The issue of delta smelt and coho salmon, two fish species that may be destined for extinction as self-sustaining wild species despite heroic efforts to save them, is explored in Box 5.7.

Under the federal Endangered Species Act, there is only one means of formally allowing the extinction of a species. Section 7 of the act authorizes convocation of the Endangered Species Committee, a cabinet-level, interdepartmental group that is colloquially known as the "God Squad" because it has the power to authorize other agencies to take actions likely to jeopardize the continued existence of a species. Through an elaborate process, the committee can grant an exemption for a specific federal action if it determines that (1) no alternative actions would save the species, (2) the benefits of the action outweigh the benefits of actions to save the species, and (3) the action is in the public interest. If the committee issues an exemption, the statute also requires that participating agencies employ "reasonable mitigation and enhancement measures" to attempt to preserve the species. These measures may include "live propagation, transplantation, and habitat acquisition and improvement."

Although the federal ESA thus allows for relaxing its protection in highly limited circumstances, it does so in a manner that presumes (and requires) that all feasible efforts be undertaken to attempt to keep the species alive. The act does not contemplate—even in its God Squad exception—that there may be circumstances in which the best policy is to allow some species in some rivers or estuaries to become extinct because the alternative is fragmented, inconsistent, and possibly futile efforts to preserve *all* species that may put every species at greater risk of extinction. The God Squad exemption process was established to address intractable conflicts between species preservation and economic activity rather than conflicts among species protection strategies. It therefore is ill-suited to the dilemma of biological triage discussed here. The California ESA has no provision comparable to the God Squad (or any other means of addressing the problem discussed here).

5.7

Must we think about species triage?

The number of species that qualify for listing as threatened or endangered under the federal and state Endangered Species Acts is increasing rapidly. Flow reduction and alteration caused by water project operations, pollution loading from municipal and industrial use, return flow from irrigated agriculture, sedimentation from logging, alien species introductions, pollution from abandoned mines, and now climate warming have increased stresses on California's aquatic species and reduced or altered their habitat. The problem is especially severe in fresh water, as the rapid increase in threatened fishes in California indicates (Figure I.2). The question thus arises: Can we save all species? Stated more bluntly: Should we devote large amounts of resources to try to save species that may become extinct no matter what we do?

The two species of fish most likely to become extinct in the wild are coho salmon and delta smelt. Bringing coho salmon back from brink will likely require massive investments in restoring watersheds up and down the California coast, especially those with sources of cold water in the summer (Moyle, Israel, and Purdy 2008; National Marine Fisheries Service 2010). Delta smelt are confined to the San Francisco Bay and Delta Estuary and are currently the center of a major conflict over how much freshwater inflow the species needs to persist.

If extinction in the wild of species such as coho salmon and delta smelt is determined to be inevitable, then serious consideration of hitherto unthinkable options may be required. One option involves biological triage in which listed species deemed the least likely to survive projected inevitable changes are taken off species-specific life support. The purpose would be to allow aquatic systems to be managed to better protect the more resilient (but still declining) species in human-dominated ecosystems, using resources available for conservation in the most cost-effective manner. Under this scenario in the Delta, Chinook salmon, green sturgeon, and splittail would be favored for conservation actions. In coastal streams, the focus would be on Chinook salmon, steelhead, and cutthroat trout, which have less demanding cold water requirements than coho salmon. The regulatory focus then could shift from species-by-species protection, to ecosystem-based management designed to maximize the ecological services provided to the ecosystem as a whole. A major problem with this approach, however, is the "shifting baseline," in which species allowed to go extinct slip from societal memory and the next endangered species also becomes seen as expendable. Eventually all the species become, one at a time, subject to the same triage process. Thus, triage is an ugly idea and should be invoked only after extraordinarily careful analysis and under powerful regulations.

In the future, the federal and state governments may need to consider creating an Endangered Ecosystem Committee that, in contrast to the federal Endangered Species Committee, would have authority to allow federal and state agencies, in protecting entire ecosystems, to triage species that are unlikely to survive even with massive governmental and private intervention. Relying on the best available science, the committee would evaluate (1) the probability of survival of listed species in a given ecosystem, (2) the probability that other species in the system will be listed without significant change in management, and (3) effects of proposed management actions on both types of species. The committee could then determine which management actions would have the greatest benefit to the most species and to the ecosystem as a whole. Agencies whose actions could otherwise violate the federal and state ESAs would be able to petition for an exemption if they furnished an appropriate plan to manage the ecosystem for overall habitat, species protection, and enhancement.

The time to adopt a limited policy of species triage is not here yet. But there is a need to anticipate this dilemma of species protection. Properly designed and prudently administered, endangered species triage might allow the fisheries agencies and other environmental regulators to focus on integrated ecosystem management and aggregate species recovery, without the statutorily mandated diversion of inordinate resources (and political capital) to species with low probabilities of long-term persistence. Many coastal salmon populations, for example, are likely to persist only as small, "boutique," highly subsidized runs (Lackey, Lach, and Duncan 2006). Mandatory devotion of substantial resources to conserving these species may both be futile and detract from the recovery of other species that are on the verge of extinction.

Managing with Uncertainties

We began this chapter with the premise that the environment has generally been short-changed in water management. Society has overlooked the many economic and social benefits of environmental water and has therefore been reluctant to manage water for environmental purposes. There is also a tendency to think that California's water system can just be modified in many small ways to preserve native species—the best indicators of the environmental quality of the state's aquatic systems. In some ways this is true, in that many small changes will be important to the success of species and ecosystem recovery efforts. However, success will often require far more radical and strategic changes in water and land use, including increasing flows in rivers, reconnecting floodplains with rivers, and removing dams. This means that creating more favorable conditions for aquatic biodiversity and the ecosystem services of free-flowing water will be difficult, expensive, and time-consuming. The difficulty is compounded by the high uncertainty of success for specific actions, given ecosystem complexity, gaps in knowledge of how to manipulate many key processes, and, most important, continuing change in climate, invasive species, and other conditions in California (Chapter 3). As a result, a flow regime or water quality target that seems adequate today may not provide the same services in 20 to 30 years. Aiming at a moving target in semi-darkness means that there will be many misses. We recommend using these basic guidelines for making decisions related to improving environmental conditions given this uncertainty:

- Use the principles of adaptive management as expressed by Holling (1978), Lee (1993), and others, which treat management actions as experiments, with appropriate hypotheses, documentation, monitoring, and knowledge integration and experimental design using modeling.
- Work *with* environmental variability rather than trying to fight it (Beechie et al. 2010; Moyle et al. 2010).
- Understand what desirable species require. Most aquatic species are highly adaptable, within limits. So understanding the limits is important, especially in relation to climate change.
- Be willing to accept large-scale change to ecosystems. Humans now irreversibly dominate California's ecosystems. To support native organisms and ecosystem services, it is necessary to think in terms of creating "new" ecosystems that may differ greatly in appearance from existing and pre-development systems (West et al. 2009).
- Focus on preventive actions where possible to avoid such unpleasant surprises as invasions of new species, effects of new toxins, and imperilment of additional species.
- Be explicit about the likely outcomes of large-scale management actions, including statements on uncertainties (Beechie et al. 2010).
- Base decisions on a strong program of solution-oriented scientific research and monitoring, to provide a reliable source of knowledge, recognizing that increased knowledge can also bring increased

uncertainty (Healey, Dettinger, and Norgaard 2008). Yet decisions can and must be made despite uncertainties.

- Involve local watershed groups to generate community support for projects, to act as environmental watchdogs, and to provide energy and labor for restoration projects.

It is becoming apparent that current environmental management will ultimately cause the loss of species and native biodiversity, through timid and incoherent management of ecosystems. More ambitious efforts at reconciling native ecosystems with a major and even predominant human presence will sometimes lose those species with low probabilities of survival, but a well-considered and energetic approach will offer a better chance of sustaining more native species.

Working Toward Reconciliation

The development of water supply, flood control, and hydropower throughout California has degraded aquatic and riparian ecosystems for native species. Today, only a handful of the state's rivers, streams, lakes, and estuaries are relatively unaffected by water management activities. These changed ecosystems are less capable of supporting native biodiversity, as indicated by the declining populations of native fish species, most of which are found only in California. The ever-increasing number of fishes listed under the federal and state Endangered Species Acts means that water decisions in California will be increasingly constrained by the need to save and recover native fishes.

Current approaches to address the decline in native fish species are not working. To improve effectiveness and reduce future conflicts, a multipronged effort focusing on reconciliation is needed. This will involve new approaches and new policies at the federal, state, and local levels and substantial financial investments. To more effectively design, implement, and improve ecosystem reconciliation efforts, it will be necessary to revitalize and focus scientific and technical efforts. Although basic research will remain important, more focused, solution-oriented efforts are needed. At the state level, the effort also will require real leadership, beginning with the governor and the legislature, although most of the on-the-ground decisions related to management will likely be made by the Department of Fish and Game and the state and regional water boards, supported by numerous other agencies including the Department of Water

Resources, the Department of Forestry and Fire Protection, and the Department of Food and Agriculture. New regional stewardship authorities could help coordinate state, local, and regional actions at the scale of watersheds (Chapter 8).

Today, management to support endangered species is often simply viewed as a cost to water operations and is generally undervalued as a result. To create a more accurate picture, water and land development projects should consider the economic value of the many services that healthy ecosystems provide and their contribution to human well-being, as well as the benefits to endangered species. This reconciliation approach is also compatible with continuing changes in California's economy, which is becoming less dependent on water as an input into economic growth (Chapter 2). A range of activities can be considered reconciliation strategies, including levee setbacks to promote floodplain inundation, nonpoint source pollution reduction, invasive species management, and more. Dams, one of the main causes of aquatic species decline, should be a central focus of reconciliation strategies, including dam reconstruction, reoperation, and in some cases removal.

Reconciliation strategies, however, are constrained by current environmental laws. Most significant are the state and federal laws for clean water and endangered species protection. The federal Clean Water Act and the state Porter-Cologne Act prohibit the state from allowing water quality to decline in ways that affect existing beneficial uses. Under a reconciliation strategy, the best option for the state or the ecosystem is not necessarily to maintain existing uses but rather to adjust to changing conditions. For instance, reimposing variability to suppress invasive species and support native species would likely harm some current beneficial uses and be incompatible with current legislation (Moyle et al. 2010). This is likely to be a major issue as climate change and invasive species alter ecosystems and may require amendment to the statutes.

The current implementation of state and federal Endangered Species Acts constrains reconciliation activities in three ways: They concentrate on single-species management, instead of ecosystem-based approaches; they focus on project operations that are federally authorized or funded rather than addressing multiple sources of ecosystem stress; and with one rarely used exception in the federal statute (the God Squad), they have no provision for allowing species to go extinct, whether as part of a species triage strategy or as a result of changing conditions, such as climate warming. The first two of these problems can be addressed with more flexible approaches under existing law. The third problem may eventually require amendment of the statutes.

There are many ways to make California's natural environment better for the coming generations. Here, we have presented some that are both ambitious and doable. One option that we do not like to consider is continuing to stumble along on the same dark path. If management continues as it is today, California will see the disappearance of iconic fish species such as salmon and steelhead from most of the state's waterways. Aquatic environments will become increasingly homogenized, supporting mainly nonnative, tolerant species such as common carp, red shiners, swamp crayfish, tubifex worms, and semi-domesticated ducks. The cost of such services as provision of clean water to drink, places to swim, and fish to eat will rise, or these services will become increasingly unavailable, at the cost of human health, wealth, and well-being. California has long borrowed from its environmental future and the debt is coming due. Paying this debt now will create a more livable, sustainable, and prosperous state. Putting this debt payment off until later will be much costlier, as the natural environment that makes California special slips away.

6 Orchestrating the Management of Water Scarcity, Quality, and Flooding

MARCIO JOSE SANCHEZ/ ASSOCIATED PRESS

The plan is nothing. Planning is everything.

Dwight Eisenhower

Growing demands on California's finite and variable water supplies make scarcity a permanent consideration in water management: Managers will always be preparing for shortages, even in very wet years. Impairments in water quality add another dimension to the problem, raising the costs of treating drinking water and wastewater, damaging farmlands, and threatening native ecosystems. And, despite chronic water scarcity, California is also highly vulnerable to flooding in the wettest years. These problems will increase as California's population and economy continue to grow and the climate changes, and they will become more severe and costly if water is not managed well.

Effective management of scarcity, water quality, and floods will involve the orchestration of thousands of management actions at local, state, and federal levels. Just as orchestral music requires many instruments to be played well in combination to provide greater harmony and broader appeal, orchestrated water management employs different water management instruments to satisfy diverse water management objectives.

This chapter reviews institutions and options available to manage water scarcity, quality, and overabundance to meet current and future challenges, with a focus on the direct human uses of water in the urban and agricultural sectors. The chapter begins with a brief discussion of the idea of portfolio-based planning—a useful way to think about how to combine water management actions for greater effect. We then examine California's use of the diverse set of tools available in each of three areas—supply, quality, and flood management—and look at opportunities to better integrate actions to achieve multiple goals in combination. Throughout this discussion, we illustrate how management will

Friant Dam on the upper San Joaquin River

need to adapt to changing conditions in the natural and physical environment. In particular, we present new modeling results that show how a dry form of climate change and a loss of Delta exports may affect California's economy and how aggressive increases in urban water conservation might help offset some of these costs. We also highlight areas where controversies, tradeoffs, and institutional and legal barriers pose particular challenges for adopting promising actions.

Orchestrating Activities Through Portfolio-Based Planning

Most people are familiar with the use of portfolios in financial management to balance risks and returns through diversification. This concept also has become well accepted in many areas of infrastructure planning and operations, ranging from water to energy (Hobbs 1995; Awerbuch 1993) to transportation (Johnston, Lund, and Craig 1995). The general notion is to employ a complementary mix of options—including supply-side, demand-side, and operational tools—to provide more cost-effective service that is reliable under a wide variety of conditions and able to serve multiple purposes.

Complementarities between some options can reduce costs and increase system reliability. For example, an inexpensive water conservation option may help avoid expensive expansions in supplies (sometimes called an "avoided cost"). But extreme levels of water conservation can be more expensive than judicious use of other water management activities. Similarly, coordinated, or "conjunctive" use of surface and groundwater storage allows surface water purchased cheaply in wet years to be stored underground and retrieved for use in drier years, when surface water is more costly. In these cases, neither option would work as well alone. As with a financial portfolio, it is common for some components to do well when others do poorly. For instance, surface water storage does poorly during long droughts, whereas groundwater is more resilient to droughts. Likewise, recycled wastewater and desalinated seawater are relatively expensive options, but, with significant prior investment, they are available even under extreme drought conditions.

Reliance on a variety of management techniques makes systems more stable when faced with such operational disturbances as droughts, floods, adverse legal rulings, and mechanical breakdowns. It also makes them more resilient to longer-term planning and policy uncertainties from changing climatic, population, economic, and regulatory conditions.

The Water Supply Portfolio

Table 6.1 lists many of the options available to water managers seeking to balance supplies and demands. Options for expanding usable supplies include both traditional methods, such as surface storage, conveyance, and water treatment, as well as more contemporary methods, such as improvements in operational efficiencies, conjunctive use of ground and surface waters, stormwater capture, and wastewater reuse. Keeping water usable by protecting water sources from pollutants is another tool receiving attention. Water demand management options include improvements in water use efficiency (e.g., low-flow plumbing fixtures and irrigation techniques to get "more crop per drop"), as well as reductions in water use below desired levels (denoted here as "shortages"). Often, some amount of shortage is less expensive than the cost of additional supply. Various general tools (pricing, water markets, taxes and subsidies, water markets, and public education) can motivate water users and water agencies to implement both supply- and demand-side options.

Each option provides different benefits, and each entails costs (Table 6.2). The financial costs of most options vary considerably depending on location and water availability conditions. For instance, local water transfers in Northern California agricultural areas can make some water available for $50 per acre-foot or less, but farmers south of the Delta during the recent drought were paying $500 or more for some water used by high-value crops. Similarly, cost ranges for new supply facilities, such as surface storage or recycled water, depend on the specific opportunities at different locations. Only a few options—such as low-cost water transfers, some agricultural efficiency measures, some conjunctive use, and conserving water by fallowing—are viable alternatives for most farming activities. Urban water agencies are more likely to employ a wider range of options, even though some options are costlier than many existing, but finite, supplies.[1]

1. Water utilities typically face supply costs (not counting treatment and delivery to customers) in the range of $100 to $650 per acre-foot (af), though, as noted in Chapter 3, these costs are rising for many reasons. Utilities that pump local groundwater typically have lower supply costs than those using surface water transported over long distances. In 2010, wholesale costs for untreated water from the Metropolitan Water District of Southern California, which now uses tiered rates to encourage member agencies to conserve and develop local sources, were $484/af for the first tier and $594/af for the second tier. Wholesale rates for untreated water from the San Diego County Water Authority, a member of Metropolitan, were approximately $650/af. Wholesale rates from the San Francisco Public Utilities Commission, which sells water to many Bay Area utilities, were approximately $825/af.

Table 6.1
Water supply system portfolio options

Demand and allocation options
Urban water use efficiency (water conservation)*
Urban water shortages (permanent or temporary water use below desired quantities)*
Agricultural water use efficiency*
Agricultural water shortages*
Ecosystem demand management (dedicated flow and nonflow options)
Ecosystem water use effectiveness (e.g., flows at specific times or with certain temperatures)
Environmental water shortages
Recreation water use efficiency
Recreation improvements
Recreation water shortages
Supply management options
Expanding supplies through operations (affecting water quantity or quality)
Surface water storage reoperation* (reduced losses and spills)
Conveyance facility reoperation*
Cooperative operation of surface facilities*
Conjunctive use of surface and groundwater*
Groundwater storage, recharge, and pumping facilities*
Blending of water qualities
Changes in treatment plant operations
Agricultural drainage management
Expanding supplies through expanding infrastructure (affecting water quantity or quality)
Expanded conveyance and storage facilities*
Urban water reuse (treated)*
New water treatment (surface water, groundwater, seawater, brackish water, contaminated water)*
Urban runoff/stormwater collection and reuse (in some areas)
Desalination (brackish and seawater)*
Source protection
General policy tools
Pricing*
Subsidies, taxes
Regulations (water management, water quality, contract authority, rationing, etc.)
Water markets, transfers, and exchanges (within or between regions/sectors)*
Insurance against drought
Public education

NOTE: Options represented in the CALVIN model (see the text) are denoted by an asterisk.

Table 6.2
Operational characteristics and cost ranges for some portfolio options

Method	Operational pros and cons	Illustrative cost range ($/af)
Demand and reallocation		
Water transfers	**Pros:** Flexible tool for lowering costs of dry-year shortages and enabling long-term reallocation of supplies as economy shifts **Cons:** Potential economic harm to selling regions	50–550
Agricultural water use efficiency	**Pros:** Reduces total stream diversions and pumping; enables farmers to raise yields and limit polluted runoff. **Cons:** May not generate net savings that make water available for other users; net use reductions often require fallowing (Box 2.1)	145–675 (per acre-foot of net use reduction)
Urban water use efficiency	**Pros:** Savings can often occur without loss of quality of life; high net savings possible in coastal areas and with landscape changes; some actions also save energy **Cons:** Requires implementation by large numbers of consumers; can be especially difficult for outdoor water uses, which depend on behavior as well as technology	225–520 (per acre-foot of gross use reduction)
Supply management		
Conjunctive use and groundwater storage	**Pros:** Flexible source of storage, especially for dry years **Cons:** Slower to recharge and harder to monitor than surface storage	10–600
Recycled municipal water	**Pros:** Relatively reliable source in urban areas **Cons:** Public resistance can preclude potable reuse	300–1,300
Surface storage	**Pros:** Flexible tool for rapid storage and release **Cons:** Potential negative environmental impacts; small value of additional storage with a drier climate	340–820+ (state projects)
Desalination, brackish	**Pros:** Can reclaim contaminated groundwater for urban uses **Cons:** Brine disposal can be costly	500–900
Desalination, seawater	**Pros:** "Drought-proof" coastal urban supply tool, especially useful in areas with few alternatives **Cons:** Potential environmental costs at intakes and for brine disposal; sensitive to energy costs	1,000–2,500

SOURCES: Water transfer cost data are from the authors' estimates; cost data for the surface storage low estimate (Sites Reservoir), agricultural and urban use efficiency, recycled municipal water, and desalination are from the California Department of Water Resources (DWR) (2009); conjunctive use cost data are from the California Department of Water Resources (2005b); the cost data for the surface storage high estimate (Temperance Flat Reservoir) are from the authors' calculations using estimates in U.S. Bureau of Reclamation (2008).

NOTES: Costs are illustrative and vary widely with local conditions. For conjunctive use, the costs of water for banking may be additional. For most options other than water use efficiency, cost estimates do not include delivery. For water transfers, conjunctive use, and surface storage, cost estimates do not include treatment. For agricultural use efficiency, cost estimates are for subsidies needed to implement measures that are not locally cost-effective and refer only to actions yielding net water savings. Many costs from DWR sources are from studies in the early to mid-2000s and may have increased with inflation. Some figures are rounded.

In some cases, it will be less expensive to endure temporary or even permanent shortages than to provide additional supplies. However, planned shortages can be controversial, particularly when water users had more abundant supplies in the past. The controversies are especially intense when agricultural or urban users' supplies are cut for reallocations of water to the environment. But environmental water users have tended to face disproportionately high shortages during droughts, with cuts of 50 percent or more relative to wet years, versus 10 to 30 percent for agricultural and urban users (California Department of Water Resources 2009 public review draft).

Orchestration will often be more effective at the regional scale. When local agencies within a region coordinate their activities, they can benefit from economies of scale for some investments and create a more balanced portfolio. Coordination at the watershed and basin level is required for some tools to be effective, such as groundwater basin recharge, water markets, source protection, and most large infrastructure projects.

Progress in Decentralized Portfolio Management

In recent decades, many local and regional urban water agencies have moved toward more diversified portfolio approaches, with greater emphasis on tools that stretch available water supplies to complement existing surface and groundwater sources. Thus, pricing, subsidies, public education, and landscape watering ordinances have been used to encourage urban demand reductions, and investments have been undertaken to augment usable supplies by desalting brackish groundwater, treating recycled wastewater, reducing operational losses, building interties (or interconnections between water distribution systems) to allow utilities to manage their supplies jointly, and recharging groundwater basins with surface water and captured stormwater. In the agricultural sector, water use efficiency techniques have become widespread in areas facing chronic shortages. In addition, as described further below, an active water market has developed within the state, enabling temporary and longer-term reallocation of water from lower-value (mainly agricultural) activities to higher-value activities in farming and urban sectors and to the environment. This market has been combined, in some areas, with active groundwater recharge (or "banking") to balance supplies across wetter and drier years (Box 6.1).

The state has promoted these shifts through legal reforms (e.g., to facilitate water marketing, to require low-flow plumbing fixtures), direct intervention (e.g., as a broker in the water market), and subsidies for some nontraditional

6.1

Effective portfolios: the whole exceeds the sum of its parts

In addition to providing benefits from diversification, portfolio tools can often work together to increase the overall effectiveness of individual tools, as the following examples illustrate:

Proceeds from water marketing were used to support investments in agricultural water conservation in the Imperial Irrigation District (Gray 1994a) and to support flood management investments in Yuba County (Water Education Foundation 2007).

Reservoir reoperation—allowing greater releases of dry-year storage—has been used to increase groundwater infiltration and storage in the Friant-Kern Canal service area (Vaux 1986).

Urban water conservation has increased water storage in the East Bay Municipal Utility District's reservoirs and Southern Californian aquifers.

Water markets have provided incentives for changes in operation and groundwater banking in Kern County and Southern California (Pulido-Velázquez, Jenkins, and Lund 2004; Harou and Lund 2008).

Recycled water has augmented water supply reliability and reduced discharge of treated wastewater to the environment in Orange County (www.gwrsystem.com).

activities (e.g., water use efficiency investments and recycled wastewater plants). Often, these subsidies have sought to encourage collaboration among local agencies, most notably through the Integrated Regional Water Management (IRWM) program, which has allocated more than $2 billion in general obligation bond funds to these efforts since 2000.[2]

Efforts to diversify water supply portfolios and increase coordination have helped improve California's ability to cope with scarcity (Chapter 2). Nevertheless, major technical and institutional challenges remain to integrate these wide-ranging options into a coherent set of activities at local, regional, and state levels.

Technical Gaps in Portfolio Analysis

Determining how to combine options cost-effectively requires sophisticated analytical support and computer modeling.[3] Some local and regional agencies already

2. Proposition 13 (March 2000) provided $235 million in local assistance grants to the Santa Ana Watershed Project Authority. Proposition 50 (November 2002) set aside $500 million to fund competitive grants for projects consistent with an adopted IRWM plan. Proposition 84 (November 2006) provided $1 billion for IRWM planning and implementation. Proposition 1E (November 2006) provided $300 million for IRWM stormwater flood management.

3. See Jenkins and Lund (2000) and Lund and Israel (1995a) for some examples from the research literature.

employ decision support tools to develop their portfolios. The Metropolitan Water District of Southern California, for example, uses a set of simulation models to develop a wide-ranging portfolio of water sources, storage facilities, water conservation activities, as well as wastewater reuse, water marketing, and other options suitable for meeting regional demands over a wide range of wet and dry years (Metropolitan Water District of Southern California 2010). The San Diego County Water Authority has employed optimization modeling to identify and integrate a similarly wide range of water management actions (San Diego County Water Authority 1997). However, in many cases, investment choices are being made without the benefit of integrated decision support.

The technical gap may be most pronounced at the level of statewide planning. Although the last two issues of the *California Water Plan Update* (Bulletins 160-05 and 160-09) have emphasized integrated portfolio approaches to water system planning, neither exercise used portfolio modeling tools to quantify effective combinations of options. Instead, the plans discuss potential water supply benefits of a range of options one-by-one, often without quantitative estimates of supply potential or costs. The plans acknowledge the complementarities among some options but make no attempt to quantify how they might interact and the relative roles each might have in cost-effective regional and statewide water management under different future scenarios.[4]

The lack of integrated decision support will not stop innovation in water supply management, but it can lead to misjudgment of the actual savings potential from some options and a failure to recognize the benefits of others. It also deprives policy discussions of promising integrated alternatives for consideration and can muddle these discussions with unnecessary technical controversies.

Modeling Insights

To illustrate the value of integrating water supply management options statewide, we provide some results from the CALVIN model (Jenkins et al. 2004; Pulido-Velázquez, Jenkins, and Lund 2004). Computer models of water systems are commonly used in water management because they can explicitly represent what is known about complex systems, thereby providing a platform for

4. See, for instance, the discussion of resource management strategies in Bulletin 160-09 (pp. 18–19 of the executive summary and Volume 2; California Department of Water Resources 2009). DWR does use its Least-Cost Planning Simulation model to examine promising portfolios of water management activities within the Southern California and San Francisco Bay metropolitan areas (Hoagland 2010), but it does not currently have capabilities to do this type of analysis for the state.

exploring problems and solutions. This computer model combines economic and engineering representations of most major elements of California's water supply system, identified by asterisks in Table 6.1, such as water markets, pricing, reoperation and coordination of reservoir and aquifer operations, water conservation, water recycling, and desalination. CALVIN seeks least-cost ways to serve urban and agricultural water demands throughout most of the state while meeting environmental flow requirements (see Figure 6.1 for geographic and system coverage).

This model has provided insights into how California's water system can adapt to a wide variety of strategic opportunities and challenges (Jenkins et al. 2004; Pulido-Velázquez, Jenkins, and Lund 2004; Null and Lund 2006; Tanaka et al. 2006, in press; Medellin-Azuara et al. 2008b; Harou et al. 2010). In general, CALVIN has highlighted the value of tools that enhance the flexibility of the water system and make the most of existing system assets. Accurate price signals and a well-functioning water market are important for encouraging demand reduction and reallocation of water from lower- to higher-value uses. Integrated system operation—which treats all major groundwater basins, surface storage reservoirs, and conveyance facilities as part of a larger network—facilitates water marketing and makes it possible to better exploit the potential for conjunctive use of groundwater and surface water and the wide range of integrated options. In this integrated system, conveyance is generally the most valuable system asset, in the sense that it is far more valuable to expand or enhance some interconnections, to facilitate conjunctive use and marketing, than to build new surface reservoirs.

All modeling has limitations. The CALVIN model idealizes water management in three important ways. First, it generally assumes that managers do not face institutional barriers to implementing the most cost-effective decisions. As a result, it can understate the costs of some adaptations (for example, if cumbersome administrative procedures or local political pressure in the source region prevents the use of water transfers, leading to greater shortages in other regions) (Tanaka et al. in press). Second, it assumes that managers have perfect foresight of hydrologic conditions. As a result, it somewhat understates some of the higher cost elements of a water supply portfolio as hedges against risk and overstates the benefits of reoperations, particularly for flood management (Draper 2001). Third, by representing water recycling and seawater desalination with average costs per acre-foot, when their initial investment costs are in fact large and irreversible, the model often understates the costs of using these options.

Figure 6.1
The CALVIN model includes most of California's water supply system and water demands

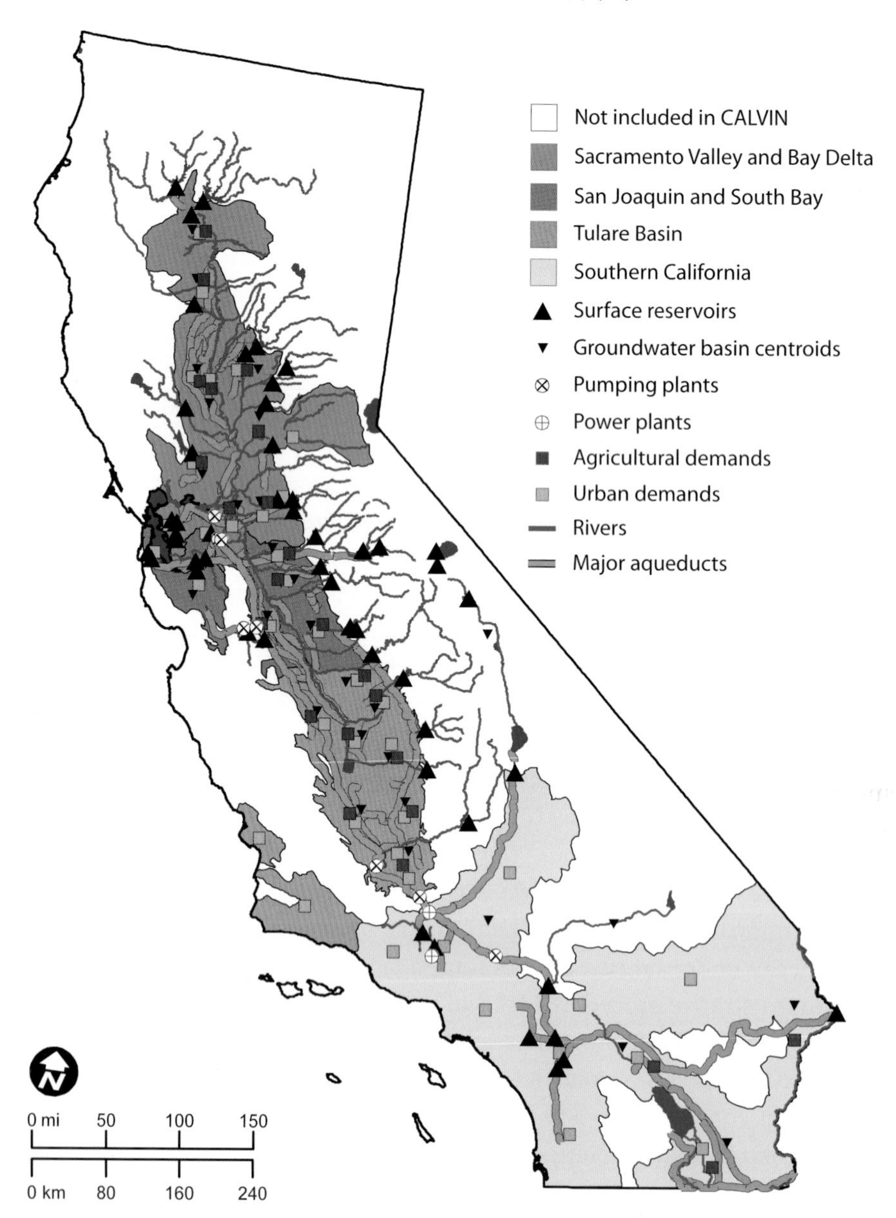

Effects of climate change, cutbacks in Delta exports, and urban conservation

The model gives insights into water management possibilities for a variety of future scenarios, including changes in hydrology, demands, technology, system assets, and policies and regulations. Here, we explore the implications of two major management challenges that California may well face by the mid-21st century: (1) significant restrictions in water supply from the system's hub in the Sacramento–San Joaquin Delta and (2) drier overall conditions resulting from climate change. In looking at adaptation options, we consider how a major behavioral and technological shift—a major successful urban water conservation effort—could help California cope with these challenges. We look at urban, rather than agricultural, conservation as an explicit policy tool, because most agricultural water use efficiency efforts do not result in net water savings without extensive fallowing (Box 2.1; Chapter 3). The model does project large reductions in net agricultural water use from fallowing under some conditions, as this is a relatively cost-effective way to respond to shortages.

To examine these changes, we compare a base case with historical conditions for climate, Delta exports, and urban water use with scenarios where urban water use is cut by 30 percent and Delta exports are restricted (Table 6.3).[5] The reductions in Delta exports reflect increasing restrictions on pumping operations arising from native species declines as well as physical collapse of the system from widespread levee failure (Lund et al. 2010). Two climate scenarios are considered: historical climate conditions and a warm-dry type of climate, as employed in the state's most recent biennial assessment of the potential effects of climate change (Adams et al. 2010). As noted in Chapter 3, although most studies agree that temperatures in California will rise, there is no consensus on whether California's climate will be drier or wetter. This drier scenario provides a moderately extreme climate test of the state's water system.[6]

One important, and somewhat unrealistic, assumption is that this leap in urban water conservation is achieved for free. In reality, such conservation would incur significant up-front costs, at least in a transition period where

5. More complete results appear in Ragatz 2011. Previous CALVIN results have looked separately at the effects of climate change (Tanaka et al. in press; Medellin-Azuara et al. 2008b; Harou et al. 2010) and cutbacks in Delta exports (Lund et al. 2010, Tanaka et al. in press).

6. Other studies have shown that the reduction in stream flow in this climate change scenario is more problematic for water management than the increase in temperature, because existing surface reservoirs are able to absorb much of the additional early runoff associated with reduced snowpack and earlier snowmelt (Connell 2009). Given California's fairly large reservoir capacity, wetter climates tend to have much lower water supply costs but could easily have much greater flood management costs (Tanaka et al. 2006; Zhu et al. 2007).

Table 6.3
Assumptions for 2050 water management scenarios

Scenarios	Climate	Urban water use (gpcd)[a]	Delta exports range	Costs per acre-foot of new supply technologies (2008 $)
Base case	Historical climate	2000 levels (221)	Full exports only (pre-2007 operating rules)	Desalination: 2,072 Recycled wastewater: 1,480
Policy changes with historical climate	Historical climate	30% reduction (154)	Full to zero exports	Desalination: 1,628 Recycled wastewater: 1,480 for new plants 518 for existing plants
Policy changes with warm-dry climate	+8.1°F and −26% stream flow	30% reduction (154)	Full to zero exports	Desalination: 1,628 Recycled wastewater: 1,480 for new plants 518 for existing plants

SOURCE: Ragatz (2011).

NOTES: The model assumes 2050 land use and population from Landis and Reilly 2002, with 65 million residents. Urban water use includes conveyance losses. The 30 percent reduction applies to residential and commercial uses but not to industrial uses, and the cuts are split proportionately between indoor and outdoor uses. The historical climate assumes conditions from 1922 to 1993. For other assumptions, see Ragatz (2011).

[a]Gallons per capita per day.

existing water users change plumbing, appliances, and landscaping to lower water-using technologies and plants (Table 6.2; Hanak and Davis 2006). However, by allowing energy as well as water savings, many indoor conservation measures can actually save costs over the longer run.[7] Following a transition period, the assumption of no additional costs would be consistent with a shift in behaviors and tastes such that the new norms do not constitute a great overall hardship. Other advanced economies with semiarid climates, such as Spain, Australia, and Israel, where per capita urban water use is much lower, provide some models for California in this regard (Chapter 3).

Key findings

This modeling exercise yields important insights about the potential roles of conservation, infrastructure investments, and new water supply technologies in California's future. Perhaps the most striking finding is the potential role of urban conservation in managing climate change and reductions in Delta exports.

---

7. See Cooley et al. (2010) for some examples, including low-flow showerhead replacement, more efficient front-loading clothes washers, faucet aerators, and a variety of commercial appliances.

1. **Urban conservation can significantly reduce pressure for Delta exports.** With a historical climate, the demand for Delta exports would drop from 5.7 million acre-feet (maf) (the base case), to 3.9 maf in response to 30 percent urban conservation. The savings are reduced with a warmer and drier climate: the base case demand for Delta exports is higher (6 maf, essentially full pre-2007 capacity), and conservation reduces export demands only to 5.4 maf.
2. **Urban conservation can free up some supplies for agricultural uses.** This effect is particularly pronounced under a drier climate (Figure 6.2). Given the high economic value of urban water use, which would likely increase following 30 percent urban water conservation, climate change and reductions in Delta exports have little, if any, effect on urban water deliveries. Almost all additional shortages from climate change and reductions in Delta exports are borne by agricultural water users, many of whom would still have incentives to sell water to urban users.
3. **Urban conservation can significantly reduce operating costs and generate energy savings.** Conservation reduces pumping for long-distance imports of water to Southern California from the Delta and the Colorado River (Figure 6.3).[8] Reductions in Delta water exports capacity further decrease water operation costs, mostly because less water is available to pump and treat. However, a drier climate increases use and costs for water reuse and seawater desalination. Although these results doubtless understate the initial costs to the urban sector of achieving conservation, the operational savings from conservation are likely to be durable.
4. **A warmer, drier climate raises the costs of Delta pumping cutbacks substantially.** Drier conditions raise the costs of shortages by at least $1 billion per year for each scenario (to see this, compare each pairwise orange and green bar in Figure 6.3). With a warmer, drier climate, the added costs of a complete

8. With full exports, this conservation scenario reduces state and federal project energy use by 40 percent; if Delta exports are ended altogether, energy use goes down by more than two-thirds (Bates 2010a).

shutdown of the pumps more than doubles, jumping to $2.8 billion/year, more than wiping out the cost savings from the urban water conservation program (compare the orange bars in the base case and the no export scenarios in Figure 6.3). Increases in water shortages occur primarily in the agricultural sector, as water-short urban users purchase water from farmers with more secure rights (Figure 6.4). The costs to the statewide economy would be even higher if these transfers were blocked.[9] These results highlight the value of building alternative conveyance—either a peripheral canal around the Delta or a tunnel underneath the Delta—to allow continued movement of water to urban and agricultural water users.

5. **Delta pumping cutbacks and a drier climate reduce the value of new surface storage.** Delta cutbacks, on their own, substantially reduce the value of expanding Northern California surface storage, because it becomes increasingly difficult (and ultimately impossible) to move water to water users south and west of the Delta. A warm-dry climate, on its own, has a similar and more widespread effect, because most reservoirs rarely fill.[10] Even with a warmer-wetter climate, with more precipitation and earlier runoff, expanding conjunctive use and groundwater banking appears more cost-effective than expanding surface storage (Tanaka et al. 2006). Conjunctive use projects south of the Delta also become more difficult with Delta pumping cutbacks and with a warm-dry form of climate change, as it is harder to obtain water for aquifer recharge. Delta pumping cutbacks also raise the value of new conveyance interties in regions south and west of the Delta, to better employ available supplies.
6. **Delta pumping cutbacks and a drier climate make recycled water and desalination more valuable.** The 30 percent reduction in urban water demand, by itself, would lead water agencies to dramatically reduce new investments in these

---

9. In a scenario using historical hydrology and base case demands, the loss of the ability to transfer water with a Delta shutdown increased costs by $700 million/year, or 47 percent (Lund et al. 2010; Tanaka et al. in press).

10. For results with Delta cutbacks on their own, see Ragatz (2011) and Tanaka et al. (in press). For a warm-dry climate on its own, see Ragatz (2011); Tanaka et al. (2006); Medellin-Azuara et al. (2008b); and Harou et al. (2010).

> more expensive water sources (Figure 6.4), although use of most existing water recycling plants would likely continue.[11] A drier, warmer climate plus an end of Delta exports encourage a significant increase in water reuse and desalination statewide, even with 30 percent urban water conservation. Nevertheless, water recycling and desalination remain a small proportion of statewide water supplies.

In sum, these results suggest that a major effort in urban water conservation—along the lines now being sought under legislation passed in 2009—can lessen the brunt of Delta export cutbacks and the costs to the economy from a warmer, drier climate.[12] However, even with substantial additional urban water conservation, a drier, warmer climate makes continued Delta water exports much more valuable, highlighting the value of new conveyance infrastructure to permit these exports to continue. Decisions about other major infrastructure investments also depend on these outcomes. In particular, it may be prudent to defer costly expansions of surface storage and focus on improving the ability of the existing system to work in an integrated manner, with the expansion of groundwater banking, select interties, and water marketing institutions.

Of course, even if the state and federal governments succeed in implementing a long-term solution that allows substantial Delta exports from a peripheral canal or a tunnel under the Delta, it will take 10 to 25 years before such facilities can be completed and operational. This implies a potentially long period of diminished water supplies for Bay Area and Southern California cities and southern Central Valley agriculture, with environmental pumping restrictions and the threat of a complete shutdown of the pumps from a major earthquake. Tools to enhance flexibility—such as infrastructure and institutions to facilitate water transfers and exchanges—can help reduce agricultural and urban scarcity costs. In addition, early efforts to achieve conservation gains, along with other investments to stretch local resources (e.g., groundwater banking, stormwater capture, wastewater reuse), can help build resiliency within urban areas.

11. Although model results show decreased use of water recycling from projected current levels with 30 percent urban water conservation, the sunk costs of existing recycling plants and other wastewater disposal and water supply reliability considerations are likely to support continued use of existing water recycling plants.

12. A model run with a 40 percent reduction in urban water demand, with a warm, drier climate and no Delta exports, largely amplifies the effects of a 30 percent urban demand reduction. Total costs remain higher than for the base case of historical climate and full export capacity, but the cost savings from 40 percent conservation (assuming it is free) more than make up for the cost of lost Delta exports compared to a base case with a warm, dry climate (Ragatz 2011).

Figure 6.2
Urban water conservation would reduce agricultural water losses from reduced Delta water exports and a drier climate

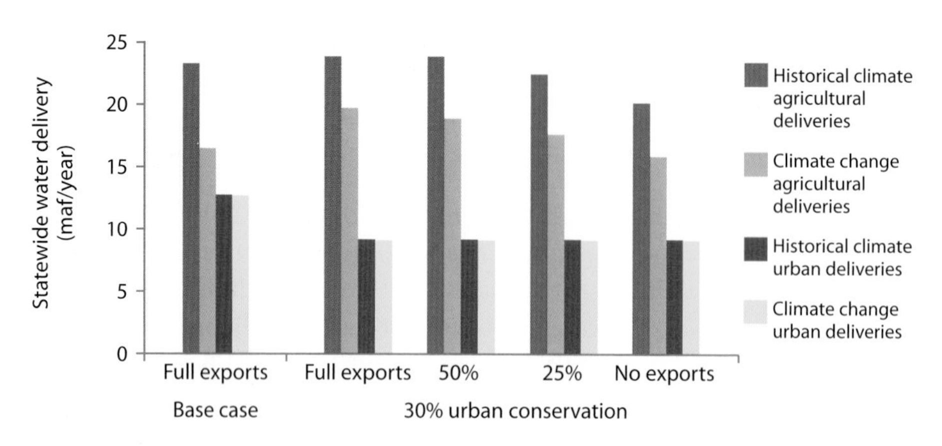

SOURCE: Ragatz (2011).

NOTES: The figure shows conditions in 2050. See Table 6.3 for scenario assumptions.

Figure 6.3
Ending Delta water exports would be particularly costly with a drier climate

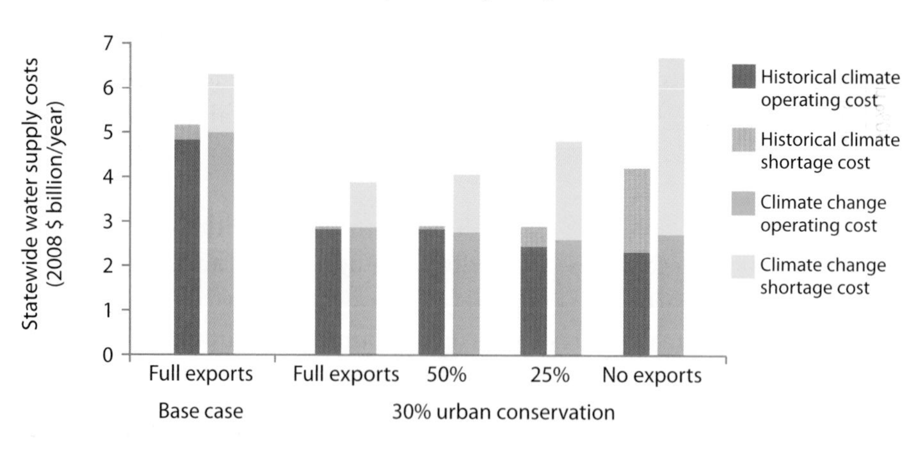

SOURCE: Ragatz (2011).

NOTES: The figure shows conditions in 2050, in 2008 dollars. See Table 6.3 for scenario assumptions.

Figure 6.4
Ending Delta water exports and a drier climate would greatly reduce agricultural water deliveries south of the Delta

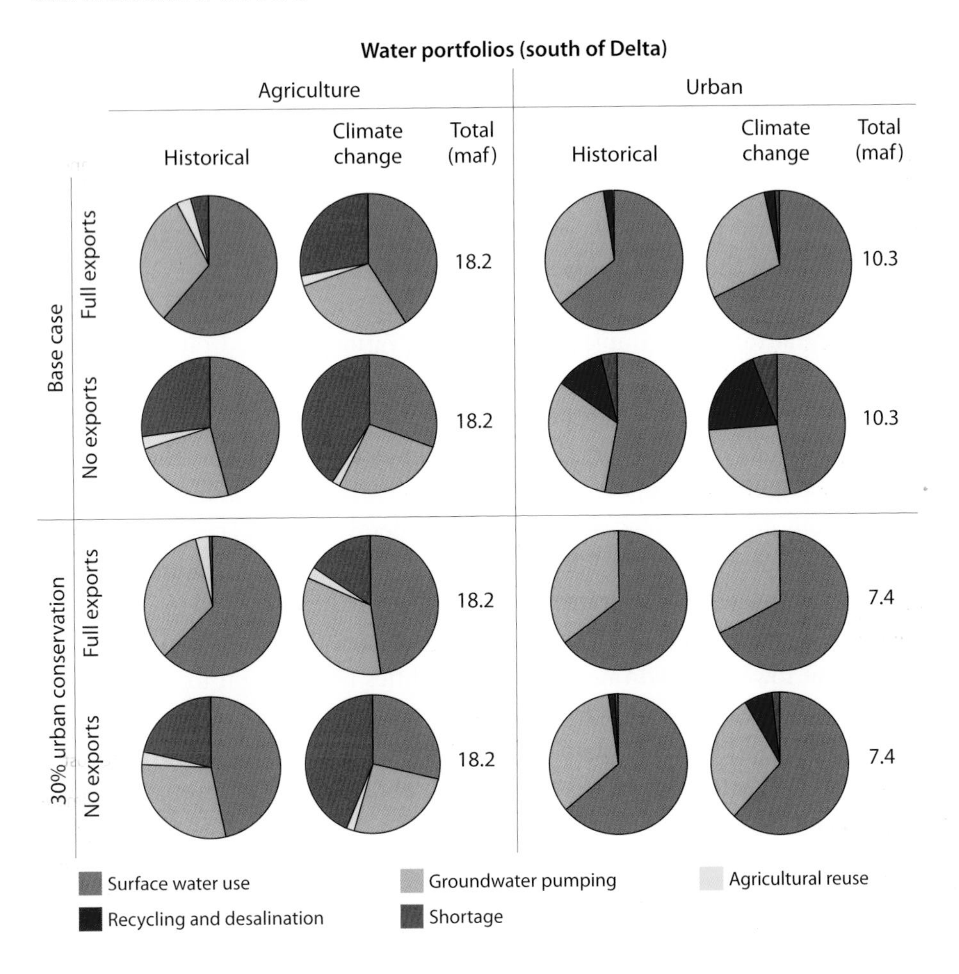

SOURCES: Ragatz (2011); Tanaka et al. (in press) (for base case without exports).

NOTES: The figure shows annual conditions in 2050. See Table 6.3 for scenario assumptions.

Overcoming Institutional and Legal Hurdles to Portfolio Management

The modeling results presented above highlight the importance of linking management actions together, often over great distances, as part of a portfolio approach. To strengthen water supply portfolios in the near and longer term, it will be necessary to overcome several important institutional and legal hurdles.

Here, we highlight issues in three key areas: water pricing, groundwater management, and water transfers.

Water pricing: an underutilized tool for water conservation

A variety of nonprice tools can encourage conservation: plumbing and appliance standards, landscaping ordinances and restrictions (e.g., limits on the planting of lawns and use of outdoor watering), rebates to encourage new technology adoption, and public education (Table 6.1). Water pricing should be an important part of any conservation effort, because it can reinforce the effectiveness of the many nonprice tools.[13]

Since the early 1990s drought, California's urban water agencies have made important advances in implementing conservation-oriented rate structures. In particular, many agencies have shifted from uniform to increasing block or tiered rates, which bill higher per gallon charges when water use exceeds the threshold of one or more tiers (Hanak 2005b). Another reform—the switch to volumetric billing—has begun in the many Central Valley communities that traditionally did not bill by use, as a result of federal and state laws that require a phase-in of water meters. By 2006, roughly half of California's population lived in a service area with tiered rates, and fewer than 10 percent lived in communities with unmetered rates.[14] Over the past few years, there has been additional movement toward tiered rates, as urban utilities have sought to change consumer behavior in response to drought conditions and restrictions on Delta pumping. In addition, the state's large investor-owned utilities have recently adopted tiered rates as part of a California Public Utilities Commission effort to promote conservation (Box 6.2).

In broad terms, tiered rate structures provide incentives to conserve (Hewitt and Hanemann 1995; Olmstead, Hanemann, and Stavins 2007; Hanak 2008). However, there have been debates about the extent to which different rate structures can meet a variety of potentially competing objectives: economic efficiency, revenue stability, political feasibility, and ability to cover utility costs (Hall 2009). From an efficiency perspective, water users should face a price signal corresponding to the marginal cost of new supplies, which typically exceeds the average cost of existing supplies. Yet if utilities charge everyone this long-run marginal cost, they raise too much revenue (Brown and Sibley

13. We thank Michael Hanemann and Darwin Hall for discussion of many of the points raised here.

14. Authors' estimates, using rate structure information from the water rate survey by Black and Veatch (2006). These percentages are virtually unchanged from 2003 (Hanak 2005b).

In much of Southern California, integrated management of groundwater and surface water is now well established. Photo by Steven Georges/Press-Telegram/Corbis.

1986). From a political feasibility perspective, water rate structures need to be perceived as fair, which argues for transparency and simplicity. And from a revenue perspective, utilities need to be able to cover their fixed costs—typically a high component of overall costs—even if water use declines. (Structuring rates in this way is known as "decoupling," which has been a standard feature of electricity rates in California for several decades.)

A particular type of tiered rate structure—often known in California as an "allocation-based" structure—can meet all these objectives. Allocation-based rates set tiers at different thresholds for different subgroups of ratepayers, so the volume in the base tier corresponds roughly to the amount of water an efficient household would need to use. Households using more face a higher price per gallon (corresponding to the marginal cost of water). The subgroups are defined based on readily observable factors that affect water use: household size, lot size, and climate zone, and the threshold can be adjusted across seasons to reflect the higher outdoor water requirements of plants in hotter, drier months. Utilities set the lower-tier price to recover fixed costs, and they can use additional revenues from the higher tiers to fund new supplies, including conservation programs. This system is transparent, and it sends a salient price signal to water users, because the conservation objectives embodied in the threshold are meaningful, tailored to expectations of what water users with similar characteristics should be able to do. If the prices for the tiers are allowed to vary with drought conditions, this structure also allows utilities to meet their revenue requirement when water use declines (Hall 2009).

Allocation-based rate structures have been successful for several Southern California utilities since the early 1990s, including the City of Los Angeles and the Irvine Ranch Water District (Orange County), and in the past few years they have been adopted by several others, including the Eastern Municipal Water District and the Coachella Valley Water District (Riverside County) and the Rincon del Diablo Water District (San Diego County).[15]

In contrast, most tiered rate structures in California do not vary tiers by customer groups, making it harder to send salient price signals to most water users (thereby generating an efficiency loss). In addition, with calls to restrict water use in the recent drought, many utilities found that they were unable to cover costs as water sales fell—evidence that they were relying on revenue from their upper tiers to cover fixed costs. The subsequent need to raise rates when customers have been reducing water use raises political problems for utilities. Such problems could be avoided if utilities had the flexibility to implement a drought rate structure, whereby prices in the tiers are adjusted in advance to drought conditions (as Los Angeles does; Hall 2009). With an allocation-based structure, tiers also can be adjusted over time to encourage progressive conservation. For instance, Irvine Ranch recently reduced its base allocation to encourage higher outdoor water use efficiency. Effective communication with the public is an important part of such programs. This includes not only information on why unit prices may need to rise when water use declines but also information on which conservation actions can most effectively reduce water use. A recent survey for the Association of California Water Agencies found that a strong majority of the state's residents support the idea of reducing household water use (Fairbank, Maslin, Maullin, Metz & Associates 2010). But this same survey found that most homeowners underestimated the dominant role of landscape irrigation in total water use.

As California moves to implement an aggressive urban water conservation program, more utilities should consider using allocation-based rate structures. Opponents of this approach often voice concerns over the costs of implementation, given higher data needs. But advances in information technology have brought down the data costs of establishing allocations for different lot sizes:

15. Some of these utilities use more than two tiers; Hall (2009) and Michael Hanemann (personal communication) argue that a simpler system, with just two tiers, is preferable.

Digitized parcel maps are readily available for most counties, as are climate maps that reflect outdoor watering needs. And customers can have the option to declare household size. Another objection sometimes raised is that it is "unfair" to give larger base allocations to residents with larger lots (many of whom have higher incomes). Allocation-based rate structures are not "fair" in the sense of treating everyone exactly the same. But they end up being fair in a broader sense, because each group of customers ends up paying about the same average price per unit of water. By grouping customers more homogeneously by factors such as lot size and location, it is possible to send a meaningful price signal to all water users, to encourage efficient water use.[16]

Recent experience with investor-owned utilities (Box 6.2) also suggests that the state could benefit from conducting periodic rate reviews of publicly owned water utilities from the standpoint of conservation objectives (Chapter 8). Such reviews could provide an impartial technical analysis, helping to depoliticize rate-setting and helping utilities to maintain a solid financial footing while encouraging water use reductions.

6.2

Conservation-oriented rate reform by investor-owned utilities

Privately owned water utilities serve roughly one-fifth of California's households. In contrast to public sector water suppliers, private utilities have rate structures regulated by the California Public Utilities Commission (CPUC). Because they are less constrained by local politics, however, private utilities often can make policy changes more rapidly. Past rate-setting rules adopted by the CPUC restricted private utilities from adopting conservation-oriented rate structures. In 2006, roughly half of the state's population lived in areas with tiered water rates, but no private water utility had this type of rate structure. Following a policy change that year at the CPUC, accompanied by legislation requiring that private utilities review rates within a short time frame, all 10 major private utilities will have adopted tiered rate structures by the end of 2010. This rate reform includes careful attention to the principle of "decoupling," long used in the energy sector, so that utilities can cover their fixed costs even if water use falls considerably. Lack of decoupling has been problematic for many public sector utilities implementing tiered rates.

16. Utilities can establish lifeline rates to subsidize low-income households who cannot afford full water rates (something already done in some areas). To address equity concerns, utilities can also look to their policies regarding fixed service fees. Utilities that cover a portion of their fixed costs with a fixed fee usually charge higher fees for larger meters, which require a higher level of service (higher water pressure). For the smallest meters (3/4 in.), utilities could also waive the meter fee and rely entirely on commodity charges. With lower fixed charges, the higher tier will typically need to be higher.

Filling the gaps in groundwater management

Increased integration of surface water and groundwater is essential for portfolio management of California's water resources. Water banks use available space in aquifers to store imported surface water both to recharge the aquifer and for subsequent pumping for local and export uses.

Blending imported surface water with local groundwater recharge raises a variety of difficult administrative and accounting questions, however. As a group, landowners overlying the basin have superior rights to pump the local (or "native") groundwater up to the so-called "safe yield" of the basin relative to any other users. Importers, meanwhile, have exclusive rights to the surface water they import and store in the basin (*Los Angeles v. San Fernando* 1975; Kletzing 1988). To implement a groundwater banking project, it is necessary to have an effective means of measuring inflows (both imports and local recharge) and outflows (including pumping for local uses and for export). It is also necessary to anticipate possible effects of the project on local storage availability. Sometimes, importing water benefits local users by raising the level of the groundwater table, which reduces pumping costs. But in other cases, imported water may harm local users by displacing storage capacity in the aquifer that would have captured local recharge, to which they have superior rights. Water quality also may be an issue if imported supplies contain higher levels of salts than the local water or if recharge from overlying surface sources contains pollutants that would contaminate water recharged from other sources.

The creation of water banks has been hampered by several lingering legal uncertainties. These include the archaic separation of surface water rights and groundwater rights systems, as well as questions about local landowners' rights to exclude others from using the aquifer space beneath their lands for storage of imported water.

These problems have largely been overcome in Southern California's adjudicated groundwater basins, where monitoring and accounting systems exist and there is clarity on who has rights to withdraw water from the aquifer (Figure 4.1). Banking is also relatively straightforward in the state's few special groundwater management districts, where a single agency is responsible for managing recharge and has authority to charge pump fees to cover the costs. In some other areas—notably Kern County—active groundwater banking systems have been established based on looser arrangements, which include careful monitoring and an agreement with neighboring groundwater pumpers that withdrawals from the bank will not harm local parties (Thomas 2001; Hanak 2003). Such schemes can work if local pumpers outside the scheme cannot cause significant drawdown of the aquifer, jeopardizing the stocks of banked water funded by others. But generally, more comprehensive basin management mechanisms are needed to increase conjunctive use operations in the state, an issue we return to in Chapter 7.

A related problem arising from the disjunction of surface and groundwater rights systems is the inability of water managers and state regulators to protect surface water resources from being undermined by groundwater pumping. This has been a problem in a variety of watersheds around the state, including the Shasta, Cosumnes, Russian, and Santa Clara stream systems, where combined surface and groundwater extractions have lowered stream flows to the detriment of water quality, fisheries, and consumptive users alike (Hall, 2010; Howard and Merrifield 2010). As described in Chapter 7, in the absence of legislative response to these problems, the reasonable use mandate of Article X, § 2, of the California constitution and the public trust doctrine may be employed to bridge this historical divide between the surface and groundwater rights systems.

Water marketing: getting past the growing pains of adolescence

State and federal legislation passed in the 1980s and early 1990s paved the way for California's water market. New state laws clarified that transferring water is a beneficial use (to lessen sellers' fears that they might lose the rights to use water in subsequent years), extended "no injury" protections against negative "third party" impacts on fish and wildlife (to ease concerns of environmental managers and stakeholders that water movements would negatively affect the quantity and quality of environmental flows), and required that owners of conveyance facilities lease space for transferred water if they had excess capacity (Table 2.7). The federal Central Valley Project Improvement Act of 1992 also encouraged water marketing.

These legal changes, along with active participation in the market by both state and federal agencies, helped jumpstart an active water market in the early 1990s, when California was in the midst of a major drought (Israel and Lund 1995; Gray 1996; Haddad 2000; Hanak 2003). The market continued to grow when the rains returned, and by the early 2000s, the annual volume of water committed for sale or lease was on the order of 2 million acre-feet, with roughly 1.5 million acre-feet moving between parties in any given year (Figure 6.5).[17]

17. Figure 6.5 reports transactions between water districts. In addition, many water districts have established active water markets within their own jurisdictions, so that local users can trade among themselves as water demands and supplies change (Archibald et al. 1992; Thompson 1993; Carey, Sunding, and Zilberman 2001).

Figure 6.5
California's water market grew in the 1990s but has flattened since the early 2000s

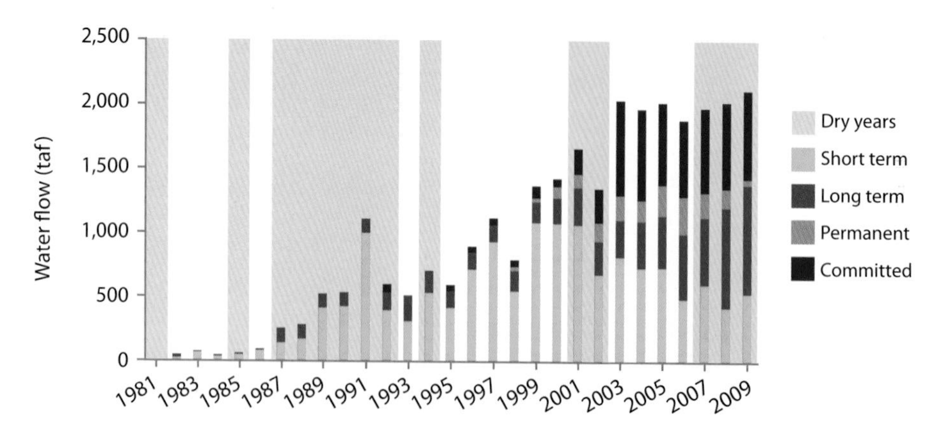

SOURCE: Hanak (2003) for 1981–2001; authors' updates from various sources for 2002–2009.

NOTES: The figure shows actual flows under short- and long-term lease contracts, estimated flows under permanent sale contracts, and the additional volumes committed under long-term and permanent contracts that were not transferred in those years. The database includes transactions between water districts, federal and state agencies, and private parties that are not members of the same water district or wholesale agency (for a description of methods, see Appendix A in Hanak 2003).

Consistent with the relative share of agricultural water use in the state's overall supply, farmers have always been the primary sellers in California's water market. But over time, there have been shifts in the nature of contracts and the uses of purchased water. During the 1990s, the market consisted primarily of short-term (single-year) transfers, with long-term contracts constituting only about 20 percent of total volumes. By the end of the 2000s, long-term and permanent sales accounted for most of the volume traded. Along with this transition, farmers have declined in importance as buyers, constituting only 22 percent of all contractual commitments in the 2002–2009 period and only 34 percent of actual flows (Figure 6.6). Water purchases for environmental flows and wildlife refuges have remained important in this decade (one-fifth of all commitments and one-quarter of all flows), but the major increases have been by urban agencies, which now account for nearly half of all commitments (more if one includes agencies with mixed water uses) and 37 percent of flows. Long-term contracts among water districts that use Colorado River water have accounted for a substantial share of this growth: With the conclusion of the Quantification Settlement Agreement (QSA) in 2003, over 600,000 acre-feet

Figure 6.6
Urban water purchases now account for at least half of the market

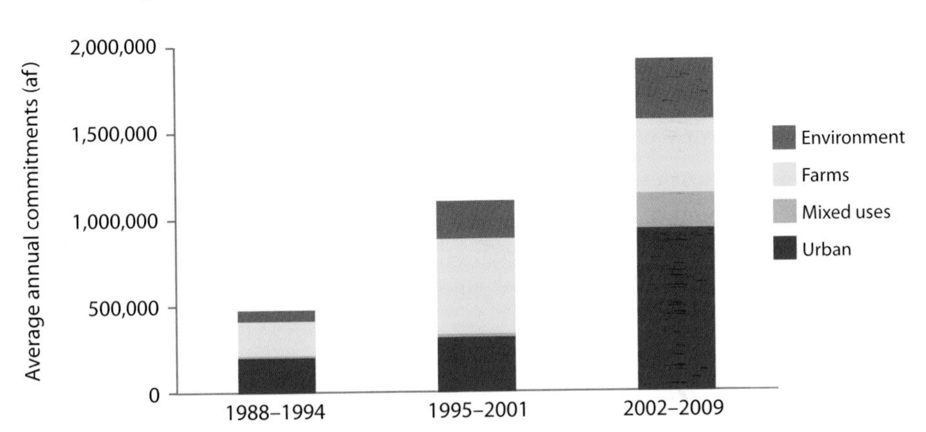

SOURCES: Hanak (2003) for 1988–2001; authors' updates from various sources for 2002–2009.

NOTES: The figure shows shares of all committed transfers (short-term flows and contract volumes for long-term and permanent sales). Mixed uses denote purchase by agencies with both urban and agricultural uses, such as the Coachella Valley Water District and the San Luis Delta Mendota Water Authority.

of farm water transfers are now committed, mostly to urban users.[18] Urban agencies within the Central Valley have also made local purchases from agricultural agencies, and some Southern California urban agencies have successfully purchased agricultural contract water from SWP contractors in the San Joaquin Valley. These long-term transfers have been made possible through a combination of system efficiency improvements (e.g., canal lining and operational improvements), agricultural land retirement, on-farm irrigation efficiency improvements (where improved efficiency generates net water savings, such as Imperial Irrigation District), and releases of water from surface and groundwater reservoirs (e.g., from Yuba County).

The growth of long-term and permanent transfers—which generally involve more complex negotiations and more in-depth environmental documentation—is a sign that the market is maturing. Long-term commitments are

18. See Chapter 2. The new transfer agreements from the early 2000s include the movement of 303,000 af/year of water from the Imperial Irrigation District (IID) to the San Diego County Water Authority and the Coachella Valley Water District, two canal lining projects that will move nearly 96,000 af/year of conserved water from IID and Coachella to San Diego and the San Luis Rey Indians, and the movement of up to 111,000 af/year from the Palo Verde Irrigation District (PVID) to the Metropolitan Water District of Southern California. The QSA also recognizes an existing transfer of 110,000 af/year from IID and Metropolitan, in place since the late 1980s. In addition to these long-term agreements, some temporary transfers have taken place between PVID and Metropolitan during the recent drought.

particularly important for supporting economic transitions. By law, urban water agencies need to demonstrate long-term supplies to support new development, and transfers can provide this assurance. Long-term commitments for environmental flows provide flexibility for environmental managers and reduce the conflicts associated with regulatory alternatives to market-based transactions. Long-term commitments to make temporary supplies available—such as the recent 25-year transfer agreement between the Yuba County Water Agency and the Department of Water Resources—enhance operational flexibility. (In this transfer agreement, supplies are made available annually to a pool of State Water Project (SWP) and Central Valley Project (CVP) contractors, who can bid on available volumes.)

Despite these positive market developments, there is also evidence of overall weakening in market momentum. Overall trading volumes have leveled off since the early 2000s; excluding Colorado River transactions, both committed and actual flows have declined since 2001. This trend is particularly worrisome because drought conditions in the last few years should have boosted sales.

A variety of impediments—some long-standing and some new—appear to be at work (Hanak in press). One new problem relates to conveyance infrastructure. Water markets require an ability to move water from sellers to buyers (Israel and Lund 1995). California's sophisticated supply infrastructure has made it possible to transfer water either directly or through exchanges throughout most of the state's demand and supply areas (Figures 2.6, 6.1). However, the Delta is an important conveyance hub for north-to-south and east-to-west transfers, and new pumping restrictions since late 2007 have impeded both movements.

Other obstacles reflect legal and institutional impediments. Because California does not regulate groundwater at the state level, the no injury protections for other legal surface water users (including fish and wildlife) do not extend to groundwater users. This omission has spurred the development of county ordinances restricting water exports in many rural counties that lack more comprehensive forms of groundwater management (Hanak and Dyckman 2003). Local groundwater ordinances have restricted direct sales of groundwater as well as transfers based on conjunctive use (selling surface water and pumping groundwater), and they have also restricted the development of groundwater banks in some places (Hanak 2003, 2005a). Although these ordinances were a useful stop-gap measure to prevent harm to local users, they are less efficient than comprehensive basin management schemes, which address locally generated overdraft as well as problems related to exports.

Another local concern in source regions has been the potential effects on the local economy of fallowing or land retirement. These "pecuniary" effects are not proscribed under state law, which generally views such changes as a natural consequence of shifts in the economy—much as a new freeway might affect local businesses for better or for worse.[19] However, fallowing conducted for sales to the drought water banks in the early 1990s generated local concerns, and many agricultural water districts disallow fallowing-related transfers unless the water is going to other lands leased or owned by the same farmer. Because fallowing of low-value crops is one of the most efficient and effective ways to make new net water available for other uses, continued local resistance will remain an obstacle to market development. In two long-term transfers of Colorado River water that involve fallowing (from Palo Verde Irrigation District and Imperial Irrigation District), buyers have supplied mitigation funds to address community effects. Agreement on the size of the mitigation fund was particularly contentious for the transfer from Imperial, and the community has had difficulties determining how mitigation funds should be spent.[20] Developing templates for such mitigation payments will be important for managing economic transitions (Chapter 9). These programs should consider not only residents who may become unemployed as a result of fallowing but also the potential increase in social service costs and reduction in tax revenues for counties in the region where fallowing is occurring.

Another market obstacle relates to environmental protections. Over time, transfers have been subjected to additional environmental restrictions, beyond the requirement of no injury to environmental flow conditions. For instance, under the 2009 drought water bank program operated by DWR, fallowing of rice fields was restricted to protect the habitat of the giant garter snake, a listed species that now depends on artificial wetlands created by irrigation water. Use of diesel pumps for groundwater-substitution transfers was also restricted because it was deemed to violate Clean Air Act rules, which farmers are normally exempt from when they operate pumps for their own activities.

19. State law does require public hearings on transfers that will exceed 20 percent of local water use, however (§ 1745.05).

20. In 2007, IID and the San Diego County Water Authority came to an agreement that roughly doubled and capped the amount paid by San Diego for socioeconomic mitigation at $40 million and that increased the price San Diego would pay IID for the water (Imperial Irrigation District and San Diego County Water Authority 2007). Under the agreement, IID also will put $10 million into the fund and is responsible for any additional socioeconomic mitigation. The community-based, volunteer local entity established to disburse funds disbursed just $3.5 million before it was disbanded in 2008. The IID board is now serving as the local entity and has recently begun soliciting applications for mitigation funds (Lusk 2008; www.iid.com/index.aspx?page=199). In the case of the Palo Verde Irrigation District transfer to the Metropolitan Water District of Southern California, the community is just now beginning to develop guidelines for allocating the mitigation fund (initially set at $6 million, now worth over $7 million with accumulated interest) (W. Hasencamp, personal communication).

Uncertainties over the terms of these new restrictions, combined with the inability to move water through the Delta in the spring, depressed drought water bank activity: Fewer than 80,000 acre-feet were acquired, whereas the goal was several hundred thousand acre-feet (Hanak in press).

As discussed in Chapter 7, new mechanisms are needed to clarify and streamline environmental reviews for water transfers, particularly for medium-term agreements that create flexibility to transfer water quickly in the event of drought- or regulatory-induced shortages. Water market development also will benefit from greater integration and more uniform treatment of the various types of water rights and contracts. Current rules heavily favor transfers between agencies within the same large project (CVP, SWP, Colorado River), resulting in less efficient reallocations for short-term water management and long-term economic shifts.

The Water Quality Portfolio

California water policy discussions often focus on water supply, to the neglect of water quality. Yet there are very direct connections between the two: When water quality is impaired, it becomes less valuable as a supply source. Drinking water treatment costs increase with higher levels of contaminants, and agricultural production can be damaged by high concentrations of salts. Contaminated waters also pose threats to the environment. As described in Chapter 3, some water quality threats are growing as a result of sea level rise and rising salinity in the Delta, increasing numbers of chemicals released into the environment, and the limited effectiveness of measures to control polluted runoff from farms and urban areas.

Federal and state regulatory standards apply to the purity of potable water supplies and to the control of pollutants entering water bodies. A wide range of options are available for meeting these quality goals, falling into three broad approaches: source control (restricting the use of contaminants), pollution management (including collection, treatment, and discharge management), and pollution response (limiting the harm from spills and discharges) (Table 6.4). Water quality managers and regulators typically rely on many of these tools in combination.

Source Control

The most direct approach to reducing contaminants in water is source control, which limits or eliminates contaminants at the source. As noted in Chapter 3,

Table 6.4
Water quality management portfolio options

Source control
Prohibition of contaminants (e.g., DDT, polychlorinated biphenyls [PCBs])
Restricted use of contaminants (e.g., regulated pesticides such as pyrethroids)
Registration and risk assessments for new chemicals (e.g., nanometals)
Pollution management
Collection and treatment
Collection of contaminated waters (sewerage and drainage water)
Treatment of waste and drainage water
Treatment wetlands (buffering effects)
Natural biodegradation
Disposal
Dilution
Discharge timing shifts
Discharge elimination and reduction (water reuse)
Contaminant concentration and sequestration (e.g., landfills)
Discharge regulations and standards
Discharge fees and price incentives
Markets (cap and trade)
Pollution response
Treatment before use (e.g., drinking water treatment)
Restricted downstream uses and warnings (e.g., fish consumption warnings, boil water advisories, beach closures)
Spill response and containment
Public health responses (monitoring and treatment of disease outbreaks)

tens of thousands of industrial and agricultural chemicals are already in use, and hundreds of new chemicals are registered each year. Newly developed or imported pesticides, or chemicals to be newly used as pesticides, are covered by the Federal Insecticide, Fungicide, and Rodenticide Act (FIFRA). This act requires that new pesticides be registered and tested for their effects by their manufacturer and charges the Environmental Protection Agency (EPA) with setting use standards. The Toxic Substances Control Act (TSCA) gives EPA the authority to require registration, testing, and regulated use of new chemicals, except for food, drugs, cosmetics, and pesticides. It is designed to prevent very hazardous chemicals from being manufactured and sold.

Both FIFRA and TSCA seek to identify chemicals or substances that may be harmful if they enter water bodies, providing an important regulatory function for source control. However, the efficacy of these acts, and the state programs that administer them, is subject to dispute. The least effective is TSCA. Under TSCA, EPA, rather than the manufacturer, must prove that a new chemical or substance causes harm and warrants regulation. In addition, before EPA can issue regulations, an extensive cost-benefit analysis is required to demonstrate "unreasonable risk." For this reason, in the 45 years since its enactment, TSCA procedures have found only five chemicals that present an unreasonable risk. In addition, TSCA requires that EPA provide the public with information on chemical production and risk, but the act prohibits disclosure of confidential business information. As outlined in a critical review of TSCA by the U.S. Government Accountability Office 2009, 95 percent of notices of new chemicals provided to the EPA have some information that is claimed to be confidential. Although the standards for regulation under FIFRA and TSCA are similar, the FIFRA process is somewhat different, leading to more thorough analysis of potential harm. Under FIFRA's licensing procedure, a great deal of testing is required by the manufacturer before a license application can be submitted. This distinction reflects the greater concerns about toxicity with pesticides, which are designed to be widely applied to kill some organisms, than with chemicals in general.

Source management of toxic contaminants is a major challenge for California as manufacturing increases in complexity (Chapter 3). One model for source reduction policy has been recently adopted by the European Union. Known as the Registration, Evaluation, Authorization and Restriction of Chemical substances program (REACH) (http://ec.europa.eu/environment/chemicals/reach/reach_intro.htm), it differs from the TSCA principally by shifting the burden of proof, and the associated costs, away from the public and to the manufacturers. Under REACH, manufacturers are required to evaluate the risks of new and existing chemicals before registering them, with different levels of testing for different quantities of chemical production.

One of California's most successful efforts to date at regulating harmful substances has been Proposition 65, which prohibits the discharge of toxic substances that cause cancer or developmental harm into drinking water or onto lands that allow toxics to pass to drinking waters. This law also requires that businesses post warnings of listed toxic substances. The California Office of Environmental Health Hazard Assessment has listed 834 chemicals under this law (and subsequently delisted 11 of them) (oehha.ca.gov). Proposition 65, like the REACH program, shifts the burden of proof to businesses using toxic products. It relies on multiple data sources to establish a California list of toxic substances. And it provides for private enforcement, because anyone can sue to enforce Proposition 65. However, Proposition 65 is limited in its scope, because chemicals can appear on the list only if a government (federal, state, or international) has tested it and found it to cause cancer or reproductive harm in humans.

Currently, the California Department of Toxic Substances Control is promoting a Green Chemistry Initiative that builds on some components of the REACH program and Proposition 65 (www.dtsc.ca.gov/pollutionprevention/greenchemistryinitiative/index.cfm). The program seeks to accomplish the following goals: (1) create an online product ingredient network, based on manufacturers' disclosures;[21] (2) create a complementary online toxics clearinghouse, with known information about ecological and public health properties of chemicals made available for use in the state; and (3) encourage the development of manufacturing chemicals and processes that reduce effects on the environment. By making information on product ingredients and properties available to the public, this initiative could, like Proposition 65, create incentives for manufacturers to limit the use of harmful chemicals. This effort is in its most nascent stages but holds promise for source reduction of toxics.

Pollution Management

Most water quality management centers on controlling the amount and type of pollution that enters the state's surface and groundwater through collection, treatment, and management of discharges. For "point" sources of pollution, such as urban sewage and industrial waste, collection and treatment are generally required before disposal into water bodies. On-site retention and treatment is a growing practice for some "nonpoint" sources, such as urban stormwater. Natural buffering systems are also gaining in use. Wetlands, for example, can help filter certain contaminants from nonpoint sources of pollution and further "polish" wastewater discharge. For some contaminants, disposal can be timed to limit damage. For instance, salt discharges from agricultural areas can sometimes be held for discharge during winter storms, which dilute the concentrations of salt in the receiving waters. Similarly, some pesticides are prohibited during some seasons to help ensure that they degrade naturally before their remnants discharge into water bodies. Irrigation efficiency technologies and drainage flow management are also useful tools for reducing polluted discharges from farms.

21. Manufacturers of products sold in California would be required to tell the state what the ingredients are, and the state would disclose publicly anything considered nonproprietary.

Better source control and pollution management are priorities for policy attention. Photo by Fred Greaves/Reuters/Corbis.

Regulations governing the discharge of pollution into water bodies, under both the federal Clean Water Act and the state Porter-Cologne Act, have traditionally distinguished between point and nonpoint sources. When these laws were passed in the 1960s and 1970s, the focus was on point sources of pollution, such as factories and wastewater treatment facilities. The laws consequently emphasize regulation of point sources. This focus, along with generous federal financial support to upgrade wastewater treatment capacity in the 1970s and 1980s (covering up to 90 percent of costs), has tremendously improved the quality of water discharged from point sources (Sax et al. 2006; Salzman and Thompson 2010).

Regulators began to shift their attention toward nonpoint sources in the late 1980s and early 1990s, initially for construction activities and urban runoff in large municipalities (>100,000 persons), and since 2003 for runoff from smaller communities (>50,000).[22] In California, agricultural runoff in some regions has been subject to "waivers of waste discharge," as long as farmers engage in water quality monitoring and implement prescribed best management practices. Although the goal of addressing nonpoint sources is laudable, the efficacy of current approaches is limited. Whereas point sources are generally subject to strict numerical and technology-based standards, most nonpoint sources are

22. Because these programs involve the issuance of stormwater permits under the National Pollution Discharge Elimination System, urban runoff is legally identified as a point source, despite its nonpoint character.

required only to follow various management practices—without quantitative requirements to ensure effectiveness. In addition, the regional water quality control boards responsible for oversight generally have neither the resources nor the inclination to support rigorous enforcement programs.

Partly as a consequence, nonpoint pollution is now a primary source of water quality impairment in California. The federal Clean Water Act provided that the nation's waterways would all be fishable and swimmable by 1983 and that the nation would eliminate all discharges of pollutants by 1985. In 2004, however, 93 percent of California's river miles, 93 percent of California's lake acreage, and 98 percent of its estuarine square miles were listed as impaired (U.S. Environmental Protection Agency undated (a)). Agricultural runoff and other nonpoint sources of pollution are among the top five sources of pollution for California's rivers and streams, lakes, and estuaries (U.S. Environmental Protection Agency undated (a)). Point sources of pollution do not rank in the top five for any of these waterway types and, indeed, do not rank among the top ten sources for rivers and lakes (although they rank eighth for estuaries).

Another weakness in water quality laws is the failure to effectively integrate water quantity decisions (Hanemann and Dyckman 2009). Hydrologic modification of waterways through water diversions, dams, reservoirs, and river channelization has both degraded water quality and limited the natural ability of rivers and wetlands to restore water quality. Water supply facilities and operations are a major source of impairment in California waterways—ranking second for estuaries (behind natural sources) and third for rivers and lakes. However, federal and state water quality laws do not directly regulate most hydrologic modifications of the state's waterways.[23] Courts have split on the question of whether dams must obtain Clean Water Act permits for their discharges.[24]

Pressured by lawsuits, federal and state regulators in the last two decades have begun to address impairment by developing quantitative limits on the discharge of specific pollutants. Such limits, known as total maximum daily

23. Indeed, in passing the federal Clean Water Act, Congress declared, as a matter of policy, that "the authority of each State to allocate quantities of water within its jurisdiction shall not be superseded, abrogated, or otherwise impaired by this Act."

24. Dams that simply impound and release water in the same river do not need a permit, even though they alter or degrade water quality (*National Wildlife Federation v. Gorsuch* 1982). In contrast, dams that divert water from one watershed for release into another may be required to have a permit (*South Florida Water Management District v. Miccosukee Tribe of Indians* 2004; *Catskill Mountains Chapter of Trout Unlimited v. City of New York* 2001). Recent EPA regulations exempt all water transfers that move water between watersheds if the transferred water is not subjected "to intervening industrial, municipal, or commercial use" (U.S. Environmental Protection Agency undated (c)).

loads (TMDLs), can address a wide range of problems—chemicals, biohazards, sediment, trash, even temperature—alone or in combination—and can involve both point and nonpoint sources. Some TMDLs, such as temperature and sediment, also can affect water supply decisions. California's regulators have a goal to establish over 400 TMDLs, of which over 120 are under development (State Water Resources Control Board 2010d). Lawsuits are driving the implementation schedule in several regions.[25]

The development of TMDLs raises numerous issues. Performance-based standards are clearly needed to remediate some water quality problems, where technology standards and best management practices are falling short. However, TMDL implementation costs can be quite high, and the law does not require balancing the benefits to be gained with the costs of achieving the standards.[26] The question of costs and tradeoffs is particularly pertinent where targets are being set for legacy contaminants, such as mercury, where background levels meet or exceed generic standards, making it difficult, if not impossible, to comply with TMDLs. In these cases, a Use Attainability Analysis can be conducted, and if standards cannot be achieved at reasonable cost, they can be revised. In practice, however, conducting a Use Attainability Analysis is costly and time-consuming, and few are conducted. Numerous uncertainties also arise in the methods used to set TMDLs and apportion responsibility for meeting water quality standards (Box 6.3). With climate change, temperature and temperature-dependent standards will become increasingly difficult to meet.

These considerations suggest the need for greater flexibility in implementing TMDLs. One important change is to modify the procedures for conducting a Use Attainability Analysis, to make it more useful and less cumbersome. This flexibility will be especially important where regulators are operating under court-imposed deadlines to establish TMDLs, as these deadlines reduce administrative flexibility to prioritize TMDLs and informally factor in cost and feasibility considerations.

A second change, which is already encouraged by the federal Environmental Protection Agency, is to adopt and implement water quality trading programs. The idea behind pollution trading is that some dischargers may face lower costs

---

25. California is operating under three consent decrees covering most of the North Coast Region, all of the Los Angeles Region, and Newport Bay and its tributaries in the Santa Ana Region. Additional statewide suits are under litigation (State Water Resources Control Board 2010d).

26. Hanak and Barbour (2005) describe the debates concerning the cost of implementing a trash TMDL in Los Angeles County, which one study put at $102 billion.

6.3

Klamath River TMDL uncertainty

The adoption and implementation of TMDLs is a costly, politically charged exercise. To achieve water quality standards set forward by a TMDL, responsibility is apportioned among various landowner groups, water management facilities, or any other point or nonpoint sources that degrade water quality to levels below conditions necessary to support beneficial uses. In many cases, the TMDL evaluations are based on water quality modeling, with the potential for large errors that can apportion responsibilities inequitably or, worse yet, set TMDLs that can never be achieved.

The North Coast Regional Water Quality Control Board (2010a, 2010b) recently adopted a TMDL for the Klamath River in California that sets standards for temperature, nutrients, organic material, dissolved oxygen, and algal toxins. The upper half of the Klamath River (above the Shasta River) derives the bulk of its flow from upper Klamath Lake. This lake was naturally rich in nutrients (eutrophic), before land use changes, such as logging, grazing, and the draining of marshes for agriculture, augmented the nutrient load. Internal cycling of nutrients maintains the lake in a hypereutrophic state today and will do so for many generations regardless of efforts to reduce nutrient inputs (National Research Council 2004). The water that leaves the lake and flows down the Klamath River, particularly during the summer, is warm and contains high levels of nutrients and organic material and low levels of dissolved oxygen—all factors harmful to the river's salmon.

A series of reviews of the water quality model used to develop the TMDL highlighted multiple significant problems (Rounds and Sullivan 2009, 2010). Most notable is the model assumption that water quality in upper Klamath Lake will dramatically improve in the future, to a level unlikely to have occurred even in pre-European times. Continued use of this model has the potential to perpetuate conflict over water management in a basin already well known for conflict and to erode confidence in the institutions responsible for water quality regulation.

of reducing pollution than others. Most trading programs are based on a "cap and trade" principle, where the caps are the maximum pollution loads that would allow water bodies to meet their water quality standards. Within this cap, polluters are allowed to trade initial allocations in a market setting. The allocation of the total load, also required as part of the TMDL, can function as the initial allocation for a trading program. The value of a trading approach is that it promotes regional cost-effectiveness, innovation, and alignment of financial benefits with pollution reduction.

Pollution trading has been effective under the Clean Air Act to reduce sulfur dioxide emissions—largely from coal-fired electricity-generating plants (Burtraw et al. 2005). The EPA estimates that the savings from water quality trading in the United States as a whole could exceed $900 million (U.S. Environmental Protection Agency 2004). The experience in cap and trade of nonpoint pollution in Australia suggests that market-based tools can help address salinity and a variety of other water quality issues (Young 2009).[27]

As with other pollution trading, water quality trading raises issues that must be overcome. A prerequisite for implementing market-based instruments is a clear scientific understanding of the relationship between production practices and water pollution. This is particularly germane to nonpoint sources of pollution, where discharges cannot be directly measured. In addition, reducing discharges at one point on a waterway may not be equivalent to reducing discharges by the same amount somewhere else—requiring complex scientific evaluations of whether particular trades between distant pollution sources are appropriate. Where a particular pollutant (e.g., the discharge of toxins) has significant localized effects, moreover, trades can lead to localized health problems or "hot spots"—making these pollutants less suitable for trading. These issues notwithstanding, the potential gains from trade suggest that the careful analysis required to set up trading schemes is worth the effort.

The TMDL requirements of § 303(d) of the Clean Water Act have provided an impetus for the recent rise in pollution trading initiatives in the United States (Ribaudo 2009). Nationally, the number of trading programs increased from eight to almost 100 between 1995 and 2008. To date, most trading programs are only pilot projects, and just one, involving the Long Island Sound, has been responsible for 80 percent of the trades (Salzman and Thompson 2010). Most programs address nitrogen and phosphorus but some also include heavy metal and other pollutants (Breetz et al. 2004). Point/nonpoint trading systems for nutrients exist on 15 waterways (Ribaudo and Nickerson 2009).

Although California has been slow to embrace water quality trading, it offers the potential to help tackle numerous contaminant problems in the state cost-effectively, including salt, nitrate, nitrogen, phosphorus, and pesticide discharges. Indeed, a trading program among nonpoint source discharges has existed in the Grasslands region of the San Joaquin Valley since 1998. This program was

27. Australia is also moving in the direction of much more rigorous measurement of nonpoint sources of pollution. See Murray-Darling Basin Authority (2008).

the result of the Central Valley Regional Water Quality Control Board's 2001 promulgation of a TMDL for selenium in the lower San Joaquin River and issuance of the first waste discharge requirement for nonpoint source pollution in the United States. The cap on selenium loading has helped to meet the TMDL for most years during the program's existence, and the opportunity for trading selenium allowance among the participating dischargers has both enhanced farm operational flexibility and encouraged compliance (Breetz et al. 2004; Karkoski and Young 2000). Water pricing—with tiered rates set to encourage greater irrigation efficiency—has also been an effective component of the region's efforts to reduce selenium discharges (Wichelns, Jouston, and Cone 1997; Wichelns and Cone 2006).[28] The Grasslands' trading program is a model for the use of market-based trades as part of an integrated water quality regulatory strategy.

California should build on this model for managing nonpoint sources. The agricultural waiver program has established important building blocks for moving beyond monitoring and best management practices toward performance-based outcomes. Farmers are now organized in groups to conduct monitoring under the law. The next step would be to establish water quality targets these groups of farmers should collectively meet for specific contaminants in farm runoff within a well-defined area (e.g., a stretch of a river) and allow them to determine how best to meet the targets. Such an approach reduces the administrative costs of regulation and provides incentives to farmers to find least-cost approaches for complying with the standards.

Finally, for some contaminants, it may be appropriate to consider introducing surcharges on products sold, both to discourage overuse and to help fund mitigation efforts. California already does this in the case of some pollutants, such as electronic waste and old tires.

Pollution Response

The third approach to water quality is pollution response. For municipal water systems, it has long been standard practice to treat raw surface water to limit damage to human health from inadequacies or failures in upstream collection and treatment of wastes. Wellhead treatment of groundwater (which typically did not require treatment beyond chlorination) is now used in some areas where nitrates and other contaminant concentrations are too high. These actions are regulated

28. Tiered pricing is also used to limit chemical-laden urban runoff from overwatered landscapes by the Irvine Ranch Water District. Some of the proceeds from the higher-tier revenues are used to fund stormwater retention areas.

under the federal Safe Drinking Water Act and the state Porter-Cologne Act, which require that utilities meet maximum contaminant limits or cease using contaminated sources. As discussed in Chapter 3, the number of regulated contaminants in drinking water is growing and will continue to grow, raising the costs of water supply treatment and compromising some water sources for municipal uses.

A second damage reduction strategy is to restrict uses of contaminated waters. Restrictions or warnings for recreational or fishing uses downstream from contaminated discharges can help avoid harmful human contact with the contaminants, as can beach closures in the event of sewage spills and stormwater discharges. In much of California, warnings are often posted on rivers and estuaries to reduce the potential public health effects of long-term accumulation of mercury and other contaminants in the environment. Although this strategy can protect public health from contaminants that are unavoidable or too costly to contain, restricting downstream uses is obviously a less-than-ideal approach to overall contaminant management.

Finally, few viable options exist for protecting fish, other aquatic organisms, and birds and riparian species once harmful pollutants have been discharged into the state's waterways. As described in Chapter 5, contaminants are a major contributing factor in the degradation of the state's aquatic ecosystems. The growing costs of treatment for human uses and the high environmental costs of contamination both underscore the importance of strengthening upstream actions, including better source control and better pollution management, as priority areas for policy attention.

The Flood Management Portfolio

Floods are a different sort of water problem. Floods occur infrequently, arrive rapidly, dissipate quickly, and can impose significant damage and loss of life. Yet these rare, short-lived events require vigilant preparation and planning. The nature of flooding—long periods of tedious attention to detail punctuated by brief moments of frenzied terror—creates significant challenges to sustained maintenance, governance, funding, and public attention.

Options

As with water supply, many options are available for flood management (Table 6.5). Combining a range of actions can provide higher levels of flood protection at a lower overall cost to the economy and the environment (White 1945; Lund 2002; Needham et al. 2000; Woodall and Lund 2009).

Table 6.5
Flood management portfolio options

Preparatory actions
Protection
Levees (peak accommodation)
Flood walls and doors (peak accommodation)
Closed conduits (peak accommodation)
Channel improvements (peak accommodation)
Reservoirs (peak reduction and duration extension)
Channel bypasses (peak accommodation)
Sacrificial flooding (peak reduction)
Flood easements (for bypasses and areas designated for sacrificial flooding)
Vulnerability reduction
Relocation of vulnerable human activities
Floodplain zoning and building codes
Floodproofing: raising structures, sacrificial first floor, watertight doors
Flood warning systems
Flood insurance and reinsurance
Flood risk disclosure
Public and policymaker education
Response actions
Protection
Levee and flood wall monitoring (structures and seepage)
Sandbagging of levees and flood walls
Flood door closure
Reservoir operation
Vulnerability reduction
Issue warnings and evacuation calls and emergency mobilization
Recovery actions
Flood insurance and reinsurance
Reconstruction and repair
Relocation to reduce future flood vulnerability

Preparatory actions

The typical long periods between floods allow for significant preparations to both protect land from inundation and reduce vulnerability to human and economic losses when inundations occur. Traditional preparatory flood protection options include levees, dams, bypasses, and channel improvements that prevent floodwater from reaching vulnerable areas. Flood protection actions work in one of two ways: by containing the flood peak flow within a designated channel ("peak accommodation") or by storing water to shift part of peak flows to a later time (which extends a flood's duration at a lower flood peak). In some areas, water from smaller floods also can be spread and infiltrated into the ground to reduce downstream flood peaks and volumes. Infiltration is usually ineffective for larger floods, however, because soils tend to be saturated before they arrive.

Flood protection actions are the most traditional management activities and are often called "structural" measures. California relies heavily on levees, in addition to a major bypass system in the Sacramento Valley and numerous reservoirs (Figure 2.13) (Galloway et al. 2007; Kelley 1989). Levees are designed to accommodate flood peaks, but they weaken as they become saturated during longer-duration floods. Flood storage reservoirs reduce peaks by temporarily storing peak flows to extend flood duration. Broader bypass channels are used to accommodate larger peaks and reduce peaks somewhat. In some cases, floods can be directed to lower-value or more easily repaired areas, such as recreation fields or agricultural lands. This reduction of flood protection at one location to increase flood protection elsewhere is sometimes called "sacrificial flooding." Flood easements are agreements with landowners to allow for the occasional flooding of areas in bypasses or areas predesignated for sacrificial flooding. The Sacramento Valley bypasses relied on one-time payments to incorporate farmland into these systems. For future expansions of such easements, compensation could also be set up as smaller annual payments to landowners and to local governments (which lose tax revenues when land cannot be developed).

Because it is impossible to prevent all floods, reducing vulnerability is also an important part of a flood management portfolio. Like seatbelts for car crashes, actions to reduce vulnerability to floods decrease damage and loss of life from inundation, rather than prevent inundation. Individuals can undertake some actions to reduce vulnerability on their own, for instance, by flood-proofing structures, purchasing flood insurance, and heeding flood evacuation warnings. However, some key management actions are regulatory in nature, in the interests of public health and safety. Floodplain zoning and building codes are important policy tools, as are mandatory insurance requirements by lenders and flood warning and evacuation systems. Vulnerability reduction is often more cost-effective than extreme levels of flood protection.

Education of the general public and policymakers also helps reduce flood risks by keeping attention on actions to protect against floods and reduce vulnerability during the often long periods between floods. An underutilized education tool is flood risk disclosure, which can encourage both insurance uptake and public willingness to support flood protection investments.[29]

29. In preliminary work using national data, we find that the introduction of a state requirement to disclose at the time of sale that a property lies within a 100-year floodplain increased insurance uptake in these zones by nearly 15 percent.

Response actions

Flood response actions occur just before and during floods to improve or extend structural flood protection through sandbagging and enhanced inspections of levees, reservoir operations, and closure of operable flood structures. Flood warnings and evacuation can greatly reduce loss of life and damage and economic disruption from floods. Effective flood responses typically require preparatory actions and investments, such as installation of warning and evacuation systems, as well as periodic (annual) testing and exercises.

Recovery actions

Recovery tools focus on addressing disruptions from flooding. Preparation to repair damaged transportation infrastructure, businesses, and homes can shorten the time to recovery and reduce the overall costs of the flood. Flood damage also sometimes presents an opportunity to reconstruct in less vulnerable ways, such as elevating structures in the floodplain or removing structures to less flood-prone locations. In some cases, it is preferable to rely on structural investments until they are destroyed by a flood, and then abandon these sunk costs or relocate the activity to a more sustainable location (Suddeth, Mount, and Lund 2010).

Disconnected Water and Land Use Management

The disconnect between water and land use management presents a major challenge for flood management. Comprehensive flood management inherently implies joint management of water and land, but this integration is often missing in practice because of institutional fragmentation. Land use decisions are primarily the prerogative of city and county governments, which have strong local economic development objectives and often rely on fees and taxes from newly developed properties for revenues. Their interests are aligned with those of the owners of undeveloped land, who stand to gain from land sales. Hence, local incentives are strong to allow urbanization of floodplains. Floodwater, meanwhile, is traditionally managed by flood control agencies at the local, state, and federal levels. Even at the local level, the county agencies responsible for flood protection typically have little authority over the land use decisions of the individual jurisdictions within their area of responsibility.

This disconnect creates perverse incentives, since the jurisdictions authorizing development are not responsible (and potentially not liable) for flood damages. This divergence of incentives became particularly acute following the 2003 *Paterno v. State of California* decision, which found that the state was liable for all damage caused by failure of "project levees" within the state-federal flood control projects, including the large Central Valley Project (Chapter 1; for a map of project levees, see Figure 2.13). Thus, the state is now liable for damages even when locally built and maintained levees within these projects fail.

Faulty flood perceptions by residents and policymakers magnify the problems of managing land and water together for floods. Since most rivers already have some sort of flood channels, levees, and reservoirs, local residents often feel protected, even when a substantial residual risk remains that floods will overwhelm the capacity of existing infrastructure (Box 6.4).

Faulty flood risk perceptions have also restricted the availability of funding for flood management (Chapter 2). Thus, aside from the addition of flood warning systems, there has been little sustained effort to keep California's flood infrastructure system up to date with changes in land use, updated hydrologic data, and technical advances in flood management.

Finally, flood management today and into the future is heavily influenced by land-related policy choices made over a century ago (Chapter 1). For example, the massive quantities of hydraulic mining sediment from the Sierra Nevada in the latter 19th century led flood planners to place levees close together to promote scouring of sediments and their movement downstream. These riverfront levees ended the frequent floods that supported riparian corridors and floodplain wetlands and spurred urban and agricultural development behind them. Today, these riverfront levees promote scouring (requiring more frequent maintenance), increase flood stage (as a result of confinement of flows), and, because of the development behind them, reduce the flexibility to move levees back from the river to improve flood protection and restore river and floodplain environments. In Southern California, Los Angeles's choice in 1915 to channelize its main river allowed development up to its concrete-lined banks. Both choices—close levees to manage hydraulic mining sediment and channelization of the Los Angeles River—created a legacy that affects management today (Kelley 1989; Gumprecht 1999). The choice to crowd rivers, rather than leaving them room to adjust their shape, support habitat, and convey floods, has been repeated in all major urban areas of California (Mount 1995).

Until recently, flood management in California has been successful enough to allow sustained inattention to growing flood risks. Elected officials could almost rely on not having to worry about floods for their terms of office.

6.4

Flood risk and residual risk

Perception and calculation of flood risk are both important for managing floods. "Flood risk" is formally defined as the likelihood of flooding multiplied by the magnitude of damage (vulnerability) if flooding occurs. "Residual risk" is the flood risk that remains after management actions are taken to reduce flood frequency (protection) and flood vulnerability (damage). Because flood warning and evacuation systems are typically highly effective, such calculations usually are made only for economic losses, with potential for loss of life estimated separately.

As an example, consider the homes constructed in the Natomas area of Sacramento County. The depth of flooding likely to occur in this area approaches 22 feet, meaning that structural damage will be severe, leading to a total loss of some structures (as occurred in New Orleans). A typical home may sustain losses of $300,000 or more as a result of deep flooding. In 2000, the system of dams and levees that protected Natomas offered only a 1-in-70-year level of protection. This translated to an approximate $4,300 annual risk of flooding (= $300,000/70), and triggered requirements for mandatory flood insurance and restrictions on future development. Work since that time has led to an approximately 1-in-100-year level of protection, removing restrictions on development and requirements for flood insurance. Yet the annualized residual risk for the same home remains high—approximately $3,000/year. The goal of a 1-in-200-year level of protection for the Natomas area will lower annual residual risk of flooding to $1,500/year.

When flood policy focuses on flood frequency standards without considering flood risk, this can lead to unintended consequences. A community of 1,000 Natomas-area homes (each with $300,000 damage in a flood) with a 1-in-70 annual chance of flooding has a total flood risk of $4.3 million/year (= 1,000 × $300,000/70). Raising the level of flood protection to 1-in-100 per year reduces this risk to $3 million/year ($3,000/year per household). However, if achieving the higher level of flood protection—which meets National Flood Insurance Program standards and avoids development restrictions—increases the number of homes to 5,000, the resulting increase in vulnerability overwhelms the increase in protection and raises residual community flood risk to $15 million/year (= 5,000 × $300,000/100). Thus, even with increased flood protection, development-motivated local land use decisions can increase flood risks and state taxpayer liability for flood damages.

However, California faces increasing flood management challenges, with an extensive legacy of short-sighted flood infrastructure decisions, growing human and economic activity in floodplains, growing state liability for flooding, diminished long-term federal and state funding, continued separation of land and flood management, and climate change. To its credit, the state recently enacted some of the nation's most progressive flood legislation to manage these issues in the Central Valley (Chapters 1, 2, 4). But even these new laws are unlikely to significantly reduce tension between local and state flood management objectives or to effectively limit flood risk. A review of the problems in the current flood management portfolio helps to explain why.

Problems with the Current Flood Management Portfolio

Any portfolio, whether financial or otherwise, needs to be balanced. Flood management in California has had a historical tendency to overinvest in a few tools to increase flood protection, without regard to flood vulnerability. The unintended consequence of these investments is often an increased, rather than a decreased, flood risk. The underpinnings of this problem lie in the policies used to manage risk (Box 6.4).

The main policy instrument for setting flood protection standards in California and the nation is the National Flood Insurance Program (NFIP), administered by the Federal Emergency Management Agency. Communities participating in the NFIP—almost all floodplain communities in California—must restrict new development to elevations at least one foot above the expected water level of the flood with a 1-in-100 chance in any given year (the so-called 100-year flood) (Box 6.5). These requirements, and the precise maps that apply the policy on the ground, are used to define Special Flood Hazard Areas that limit land uses and require flood insurance.

The NFIP policies and maps exert a strong influence on local land use plans, which often seek to barely meet NFIP minimum standards to avoid flood insurance requirements and land use restrictions. Yet this policy has not significantly reduced flood damages (King 2005). In many areas, it has actually increased overall risk by promoting floodplain development.

Current policy failures in managing damaging floods are numerous and complex (Carolan 2005), but can be summarized into the following seven reasons:

1. **Uniform flood frequency standards.** By setting a uniform standard for a frequency of flood protection, NFIP policies fail to include the economic consequences of flooding (flood vulnerability). For example, a 100-year flood in the Natomas area of Sacramento has substantially more risk than a 100-year flood in the town of Modesto, because of the depths of inundation and the value of property behind the levees.

6.5

The 100-year flood

The National Flood Insurance Program requires that communities develop protection from the so-called 100-year flood. The term "100-year flood" is one of the most misunderstood in all of water management. It is the flood with a 1 percent probability (or 1-in-100 chance, thus the name 100-year flood) of being equaled or exceeded in any given year. This does not mean that the 100-year flood will occur every 100 years. Rather, it just means that there is a 1-in-100 chance that it will occur in any given year. Indeed, in some unlucky cases so-called 100-year events have occurred in successive years and occasionally several times within the same year.

Hydrologists use a statistical analysis of the historical record of flows to estimate the flood with the 1 percent probability of occurring. From this analysis, a curve is developed that depicts the relationship between flood magnitude and flood probability: Small floods have a high probability of occurring in any year and large floods have a low probability. What is lost during most debates about who should or should not be included within the boundaries of the 100-year flood zone is the large uncertainty about the 100-year flood itself. Confidence intervals—which indicate the uncertainty of estimates—are always very large for flood probability curves. Thus, a bright line defining the boundaries of the 100-year flood will always be controversial and is hardly warranted.

In addition, every time there is a large flood, the values used to calculate the 100-year event change. An increase in large floods tends to shift the flood probability curve upward. This is why both the 100-year flood and the 100-year floodplain tend to grow after large floods, creating a demand for ever-larger flood protection structures.

2. **Current flood standards too low.** For most floodplain communities, the federal minimal standard of flood protection is insufficient, with high residual flood risks often borne by the state rather than by local authorities and residents. A 200-year standard—which will soon be required for new development in the Central Valley—has many of the same problems as the 100-year standard, because it largely disregards potential damages from flooding and the fact that conditions are rapidly changing. By contrast, Dutch flood standards are 1-in-10,000 years for major urban areas (Box 6.7).
3. **Precise, but inaccurate, flood maps.** Special Flood Hazard Area maps define the precise geographic location and depth of the so-called 100-year flood, but errors in estimates can be

California has relied too heavily on weak levees to protect against flood risk. Photo by California Department of Water Resources.

large, and the statistics are recalculated following large floods (Box 6.5). Large floods in California in 1955, 1964, 1986, and 1997 increased the estimated size of 100-year floods in the Central Valley and North Coast (Box 6.6). The complexity of flow on floodplains and the need for precise topographic data further reduce the accuracy of floodplain maps. Yet the maps legally define which land parcels are "in the floodplain" and which are out, setting insurance rates and land use restrictions.

4. **Neglect of changing conditions.** Methods for calculating the 100-year floodplain exclusively use past hydrology to predict future flood frequency (Milly et al. 2008). This assumption ignores changing conditions within watersheds (typically changes in land use and levees that increase flow peaks) and ongoing changes in climate that will increase flood magnitudes (Chapter 3).
5. **Increased flood elevations from levees.** Levees, particularly those close to rivers, further their own demise. Riverfront levees confine flows to a narrow channel cross-section, eliminating or restricting the flood storage and conveyance functions of floodplains. This significantly raises flood elevations and increases scouring of the levees, raising the likelihood of catastrophic flooding of protected areas (Brookes 1988).

6.6

Updating flood protection in the Sacramento area

The Sacramento metropolitan area is routinely cited as one of the most at-risk areas nationally for catastrophic flooding. Sacramento chose early in its history to promote the construction of levees closely adjacent to the American and Sacramento Rivers to maximize economic development on adjacent floodplains. These close levees failed frequently in the 1800s and early 1900s, initiating a cycle of levee strengthening and enlarging after each flood (rather than rethinking the wisdom of urbanizing the floodplain).

The U.S. Army Corps of Engineers determined that construction of a multipurpose dam on the American River, upstream of the Sacramento, would provide sufficient flood control to support development of the city. Statistical analysis of the short hydrologic record at the time showed that Folsom Dam, in conjunction with downstream levees, would protect against the 500-year flood. This turned out to be one of a number of misjudgments about flood control for Sacramento. A series of floods occurred after the dam was built, culminating with one in 1986 that came within inches of overwhelming the city. When the statistics of flood probability were recalculated, the 500-year level of protection had been reduced to a 60-year level of protection, putting Sacramento land use under the National Flood Insurance Program's proscriptions.

In 1989, the city, its surrounding unincorporated areas, reclamation districts, and counties formed the Sacramento Area Flood Control Agency (SAFCA). This program has accomplished many things including working with the U.S. Army Corps of Engineers to upgrade levees along the American River and the Sacramento River to meet NFIP minimum standards, purchasing additional flood storage behind Folsom Dam, gaining congressional authorization and funding to modify the Folsom Dam spillway to improve performance during floods, and securing more than $400 million in state bond funds to upgrade levees on the Sacramento River. To accomplish this, SAFCA required extensive local support to meet cost-sharing agreements. Thanks to an effective outreach program, property owners in the region overwhelmingly supported assessing themselves to cover these costs, and development interests agreed to impact fees to offset future flood control needs created by new developments.

By most measures, SAFCA is a success in tackling its flood issues. The irony is that much of this could have been avoided by an earlier commitment to land use planning that avoids flood hazards rather than relying on very expensive, environmentally damaging infrastructure solutions.

6. **Flood memory half-life.** Perception of risk directly changes pressure for improving flood management. Longer periods of time since a natural disaster reduce the perception of risk—a phenomenon referred to as the "flood memory half-life." The problem is well in evidence in Californian's flood insurance coverage behavior, which peaked soon after the 1997 floods—the last large floods within the state—and has declined ever since (Figure 6.7).
7. **Environmental costs.** Flood management infrastructure has imposed a significant and lasting toll on the environment. Thousands of miles of levees have disconnected rivers from their floodplains and prevented the natural adjustments of river channels, altering two fundamental processes needed to sustain river ecosystems (Florsheim, Mount, and Chin 2008). Dams have further enforced this separation. Although conflicts today are often mostly about how much water to extract from the environment, rarely does the discussion turn to how little environment is left as a result of flood management.

These seven factors combine to make it difficult to effectively manage flood risk sustainably with the present mix of policies.

Figure 6.7
California flood insurance coverage has been falling since the 1997 floods

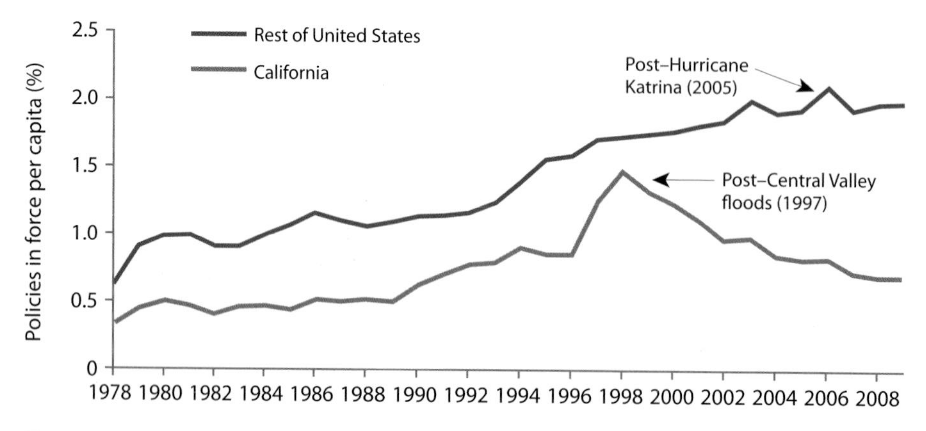

SOURCE: Authors' calculations using flood insurance data from the National Flood Insurance Program and population data from the California Department of Finance and the U.S. Census.

NOTE: The figure shows insurance policies in force from 1978 to 2009.

Updating the Flood Portfolio

To effectively manage future flood risk, California should move away from overdependence on the NFIP to guide flood planning and design and move toward more risk-based approaches. With its 2007 legislative package, the state showed that it can go beyond federal flood policies. However, the change made then was incremental: Flood protection requirements in the Central Valley were doubled, but the emphasis continues to be on flood frequency rather than flood risk. To modernize flood protection, the state should fundamentally break with the NFIP approach and focus on risk.

A balanced flood management portfolio should contain the following key elements.

1. **Sustainable finance.** Flood protection is expensive and state and federal funding sources are inadequate (Chapter 2). Fee-based approaches, based on the value of structures at risk in floodplains and the likelihood and depth of a flood, would better allocate the costs of flood management to its beneficiaries.[30] Local funding is essential both for accountability and because federal and state funding will be severely limited well into the future. For decades, much of California has placed itself at risk every winter, waiting in vain for resurgence in federal flood control funding. It is now clear that federal funding is unlikely to be substantial or timely.
2. **Local responsibility.** Flood management needs to move from the assumption of state liability for flooding toward increased local responsibility for risk management. Although state flood legislation in 2007 created potential shared liabilities between the state and local communities that promote development in flood prone areas, the terms of this new law are sufficiently ambiguous that it is unlikely to compel communities to invest in reducing risk. Moreover, this legislation applies only to the portions of the Central Valley protected by the Sacramento–San Joaquin Flood Control Project. Two steps should be considered:

30. Under California law, "benefit assessments" are the appropriate vehicle. Today, benefit assessments in some areas (such as SAFCA) rely at least in part on the likelihood and likely depth of flooding, but this practice should be extended.

a. Develop mandatory risk-based flood insurance requirements for all properties within the 500-year floodplain.[31] As with fire hazards, mandatory insurance is the most direct way to reward local communities for their flood management investments and decisions, as well as to prepare to cover their residual risks.

b. Provide annual flood risk disclosures to all property owners within the 500-year floodplain. Disclosures can help maintain public awareness and increase the likelihood of maintaining insurance. These disclosures should include flood frequency and depth of flooding and can build on efforts recently begun with the flood legislation package of 2007, which requires that DWR provide annual flood risk notices to Central Valley landowners in areas protected by levees.

3. **Rebalanced portfolio.** Changing economic and climate conditions, along with improvements in scientific capabilities, should help improve the mix of flood management activities. Greater emphasis should be placed on:

   a. Vulnerability reduction: making structures less vulnerable to flooding, rather than focusing solely on reducing flood frequency;

   b. Better levee maintenance and reliability: conducting systematic periodic assessment, maintenance, and improvement of flood defenses;

   c. Reservoir reoperation: using new forecasting and modeling tools to operate multipurpose reservoirs for improved flood protection;

   d. Expanded flood bypass capacities and setback levees: making greater use of floodplains to store and convey floods, rather than relying on simply raising levees;

   e. Sacrificial flooding: allowing rare flood peaks to spill into some lower-value floodplain areas to reduce flood levels elsewhere;

---

31. Within the Central Valley, there is little difference between the 500- and 1,000-year floodplain, so a 500-year insurance mandate would effectively cover most structures at risk of flooding.

f. Expanded purchases of flood easements and outright land acquisitions: supporting the expansion of bypasses and areas available for sacrificial flooding; and

g. Mitigation payments to county governments: compensating local governments for the forgone tax revenues from forgone development of lands in new bypass and sacrificial flooding areas.

4. **Risk-based planning.** Current frequency-based planning should shift to risk-based planning to be economically viable. Risk-based planning ensures that investments in flood management create the greatest net reduction of risk and flood management cost. This approach, if done properly, helps prioritize investments of limited funds. When state and federal resources are invested in flood management, there is strong political pressure to "spread the money around" to appear equitable. Frequency-based flood management encourages diffuse investments because various stakeholders inevitably argue about what level of protection they should receive. By quantifying the costs and benefits of flood management, risk-based methods help focus on investments that are cost-effective. SAFCA (Box 6.6) provides a model for risk-based local assessments: Its fees have been based largely on flood depth, allowing it to raise more funds from areas with the greatest likely reductions in flood risks.[32]

5. **Adaptive capacity.** One consequence of frequency-based planning is emphasis on satisfying the minimum federal standard for level of protection. As discussed above, this standard, based on a short historical record, ensures future crises as changing conditions increase local flood vulnerability and exceed the design flood capacity. Communities that have invested in a 100-year level of protection must regularly undergo the disruption of being mapped in or out of the 100-year floodplain, with increases in insurance requirements, disruptions in economic development, and expensive "fixes" to meet the revised level of protection. To avoid this,

32. This differentiated fee structure fell within SAFCA's interpretation of Proposition 218 requirements.

risk-based planning must also incorporate the capacity to adapt to changing future conditions. This involves building more robust structures in some areas, providing room for the river in others, identifying locations for storing floodwater on floodplains, and negotiating changes in reservoir flood operations. As in the Netherlands, California should require periodic assessment of flood protection structures and flood vulnerabilities and hydrology, without waiting until after major floods have occurred (Box 6.7).

6. **Integrated environmental objectives.** It is not enough to simply seek to mitigate damage to the environment from flood management. Environmental mitigation approaches have failed to halt the decline of ecosystems and native species (Chapter 5). Rather, the goal of future flood management design, construction, and operations should be to *improve* ecological conditions to meet a broad range of environmental services provided by rivers and their floodplains. Improving services such as groundwater recharge, nutrient and pathogen reductions, recreation, improved soil moisture and fertility, temperature and airborne particulate reductions, commercial fisheries, and native biodiversity are compatible with modern flood management and should no longer be viewed simply as costs (Box 5.1). Recent flood management on the Napa River provides good examples of urban flood management that supports significant riparian and wetland environmental improvements (Box 6.8).
7. **Integrated water supply and flood management.** Better coordination of reservoirs for flood and water supply operations can expand both services (Georgakakos and Graham 2008). Particularly with climate warming—with more runoff in winter and less in spring—storing water for droughts in aquifers, rather than in reservoirs, provides more reservoir space to capture winter precipitation (Tanaka et al. 2006). Conjunctive operation of surface and groundwater for floods and water supply can also improve ecosystem function. For instance, seasonal flooding of parts of the Yolo Bypass and

other areas may improve spawning conditions for native fish while recharging groundwater basins and reducing flood risk in nearby urbanized areas.

These seven elements would go far toward meeting the challenge of managing floods for an expanding population and an uncertain future climate. Reform of California's flood policy should apply beyond the Central Valley to other flood-prone areas of California, including the Los Angeles Basin, the Bay Area, and North Coast Rivers. Regionally integrated approaches tailored to regional and local conditions will be best suited to implementing this strategy. The Netherlands—another developed economy with high flood risk exposure—employs many of these elements in its flood management (Box 6.7).

6.7

The Netherlands' approach to flood management

The Netherlands is a flood-prone region where flood management receives more attention and sustained funding than in California. Maintenance of flood structures is supported by taxes on local lands, and the national government supports national flood infrastructure. Regional flood standards are risk-based and determined by a national effort, with the levee reliability of each area determined based on a balancing of flood protection costs and flood damage vulnerability and frequency (Woodall and Lund 2009; van Dantzig 1956). Each levee undergoes a rigorous independent evaluation every six years, with systemwide plans developed every 12 years (Hessel Voortman, personal communication 2010). Although California has a levee certification process, there are no set frequency requirements for reevaluation of levees in California, just evaluations of maintenance to meet federal and state standards. Aside from the technical merits, periodic recertification of levees provides a consistent public policy reminder of the importance and condition of local flood protection infrastructure, helping to defeat the flood memory half-life. Dutch risk-based levee standards, explicitly balancing protection costs and risk reductions, also provide much higher levels of flood protection than are common in California. Major urban areas are protected to the 0.01 percent annual level (a 1-in-10,000-year flood), with more rural areas protected to lower levels. In recent years, growth of population and property values in the Netherlands, as well as anticipated sea level rise, has led to a call to raise these levels of protection (Eigenraam 2006; Voortman and Vrjiling 2004). Over time, Dutch flood management also has responded to changes in societal desires to improve ecological functions, with greater emphasis on developing more ecological "room for the river" (Deltacommissie 2008). Decades of attention to flood management have also led to significant scientific and technical advances (Disco and van der Ende 2003).

6.8

Flood protection with environmental benefits along the Napa River

The Napa River, which runs through downtown Napa, has a long history of flooding. Historically, the lowest reaches of the river meandered across a broad floodplain that merged with the tidal marshes of San Pablo Bay, part of the San Francisco Estuary. High flood flows on the river and its main tributary, Napa Creek, have subjected residents of downtown Napa to more than 20 significant floods since the city was founded. For more than a century, the town used traditional methods to manage floods, involving construction of levees, floodwalls, and dikes to constrain the river to a small footprint.

For many years, the town sought improvements in flood protection through Congress. Although Congress authorized a project for Napa in 1965, the residents refused to tax themselves to fund the local match. However, floods can be a great motivator. Following major floods in 1986, 1995, and 1997 that severely damaged the city, and a near-miss flood in 1998, the city passed a measure in March 1998 to fund a flood control project (highlighting the importance of the flood memory half-life; see the text).

The Napa River Flood Project's design is innovative. It restores a wide range of ecosystem services, including recreation and support for native biodiversity. Originally, the U.S. Army Corps of Engineers proposed a traditional approach involving enlarging existing levees and floodwalls and straightening the river. The city's residents resisted this effort and developed a plan to reduce flood risk while improving the natural functions of the river. This involved removing levees in the lowest part of the project and reconnecting the river to its historical tidal marsh. The project also included creating a flood bypass channel, replacing bridges to reduce constrictions, and giving the river room to adjust its channel without affecting flood infrastructure.

The project has received many awards and is held up as an example of restoring key ecosystem attributes while lowering flood risk. The project is not without its problems, however. It has not been completed, principally because of large delays in federal funding. In addition, the project, as currently designed, provides only the bare minimum 100-year level of protection required by the National Flood Insurance Program, a level of protection insufficient for urban flood control projects. Finally, there are no plans to adapt to rising sea level and changing runoff patterns in the basin. Floods will return to Napa and, although less frequent, may be more devastating.

Portfolios Across Sectors: Integrated Water Management

Many tools are available individually and collectively to address California's water supply, water quality, and flood risk problems. However, California is not making adequate use of some of the most cost-effective tools or mixtures of tools. To be more effective, these diverse tools also should be used across larger scales. Integrated, basin-scale approaches—which jointly consider supply, quality, floods, and related land use at the level of the watershed—are often necessary to reap the benefits of modern management tools. Integration needs to address two types of fragmentation that now plague California's decentralized system for water and land management. Geographic fragmentation results from numerous agencies making decisions that affect the whole watershed, and functional fragmentation results from numerous agencies making decisions on only one piece of the supply-quality-flood-land-use puzzle.

As noted above, the state has attempted to promote regional integration in recent years, primarily through the allocation of grants to agencies working in partnerships. Although this financial carrot approach has encouraged some new forms of cooperation and collaboration among local entities, it suffers from the need to distribute large sums of cash, which has kept the focus of partnerships on capital projects that agencies want to build.[33] To achieve real functional and geographic integration, California needs to develop a management framework that requires regional coordination in water and land resource planning. As we discuss further in Chapter 8, regional stewardship authorities, organized at the scale of the state's nine water quality basins, could provide this organizing framework. One prototype for this model is the Santa Ana Watershed Project Authority, which operates at the scale of the Santa Ana Regional Water Quality Control Board (Region 8) and which has aimed to integrate a wide range of water and land use planning functions (Box 6.9).

Information and Analysis: What Needs to Improve?

More comprehensive, integrated portfolio management requires better information and better analysis. Despite being a center of the world's emerging information economy, California does not have adequate information on water to meet current and future challenges. In addition, the state's policy and

33. To wit, it is sometimes said that IRWM, the acronym for Integrated Regional Water Management, stands for "I really want mine."

6.9

Santa Ana Watershed Project Authority

One example of the management of diverse interests at the watershed scale comes from the Santa Ana Watershed Project Authority (SAWPA), a joint powers authority established in 1974 to manage water supply and water quality in the Santa Ana watershed.

The Santa Ana watershed covers 2,800 square miles, making it the largest urban watershed in Southern California. This historically agricultural watershed, once filled with large dairies and fruit orchards, is undergoing rapid urban expansion. After many years of conflicts over changing demands for water quality and supply, the five large water districts that serve the watershed developed SAWPA. Initially, the goal was to deal with water supply and waste and stormwater treatment in an integrated fashion. Today, SAWPA's mission has expanded to include habitat restoration, invasive species management, and flood control, in recognition that these efforts are integral to the water supply and quality management missions.

SAWPA faces many challenges. To meet an annual water demand of approximately 1.4 million acre-feet, SAWPA and its member agencies have initiated some of the state's most progressive water recycling and reuse programs, with extensive conjunctive use of groundwater basins. The watershed has significant and widespread problems with high-salinity waters, which constrain recycling and reuse efforts. To manage this, SAWPA has coordinated and helped fund the state's most elaborate salt capture and removal system, the Santa Ana Regional Interceptor line. SAWPA has also initiated programs to capture, treat, and store urban stormwater. In addition, one of the largest flood control facilities, Prado Dam, is now operated as a water storage facility that recharges groundwater within Orange County. To address poor water quality on the main stem of the Santa Ana River, SAWPA members have developed extensive treatment wetlands. Finally, SAWPA has coordinated extensive efforts to manage invasive species (the giant reed, *Arundo donax,* in particular), and to improve aquatic habitat and recreation at the watershed scale.

No one within the Santa Ana watershed is under the illusion that SAWPA has resolved all of the watershed's problems. Many of its programs are either in the planning stage or relatively new, so their effectiveness cannot be evaluated. Yet this approach—coordination, cooperation, and integration of water agencies to pool resources and manage water at the basin scale—is one of California's best models for integrated water management.

decisionmaking processes are poorly prepared to use technical and scientific information. The problem partly stems from inadequate data collection, which reflects opposition by stakeholders who fear that making this information available will lead to an increase in regulation. This is the case with groundwater in much of the state, for instance.

But state agencies also put too little effort into analyzing and making available information that could easily be assembled. For instance, there is no centralized database for urban water and wastewater rate schedules, even though this information is publicly available. To date, analysts have relied on periodic reports from a private consulting firm, Black and Veatch, to understand trends and patterns in rate structures. The state could easily require that utilities report changes in rate structures and post this information; ideally, state analysts would also regularly assess rate structure trends. As another example, no centralized database exists on the state's water market. Instead, various state and federal agencies keep track of the transfers that they oversee, and a private firm, Stratecon, publishes information on some transfers in a monthly periodical, *Water Strategist*. Although it would be straightforward for the state to develop a centralized database on the water market, efforts to do so as part of the CALFED program foundered in the early 2000s and have not been renewed.

In general, improving water information will require more standardized data collection. Much detailed information exists at the level of decentralized water management entities. But given that much portfolio analysis needs to occur at regional and statewide levels, this information needs to become available in a standard format so that it can be aggregated to the appropriate scale. For example, estimates and projections of water demands, supplies, and costs should be done using common standards. Given the limited technical expertise available to the state in this matter, data collection standards and methods (including software) should probably be developed by a committee led by local and regional agencies, which will make most use of these data, with inputs from other interested parties.[34]

Fortunately, California does not need to start from scratch in this endeavor. The state already has a very useful tool for reporting on long-term urban water demand and supply planning—Urban Water Management Plans (UWMPs). These plans, prepared every five years by all large and medium-sized urban

34. A parallel is the development of many federal highway design standards, where state transportation agencies have played a leading role.

utilities (at least 3,000 connections) cover close to 90 percent of the population, and they require that utilities report on a standard set of issues.[35] Unfortunately, the ability to aggregate the data to the regional or statewide level is now hampered by nonstandard reporting (Hanak 2010). For example, demand reductions from conservation are not calculated in a standardized way in these plans, nor are the levels of confidence in projected new supply sources. With readily accessible, standardized information, UWMPs could form a useful foundation for regional integrated planning, along with flood management, water quality, and land use plans, as well as state water and resource plans. Similar efforts could apply to agricultural water supplies. Senate Bill X7-7, one of the bills in the water legislation package passed in 2009, requires that DWR develop standardized reporting forms for UWMPs and expands the number of agricultural agencies that will prepare Agricultural Water Management Plans. This effort is an important first step in improved data reporting, even though reporting private groundwater pumping is still not required by law. For this effort to be effective, DWR will also need to monitor the reports for data quality, not just completeness, as it currently does (Hanak 2010).

Of course, data without analysis are almost useless. Local, regional, and statewide modeling and analytical capabilities need to be further developed so that the cost and service performance of particular portfolio solutions can be better documented, understood, and explored (Rosenberg et al. 2007; Rosenberg, Howitt, and Lund 2008; Harou et al. 2009). Advances in modeling and analysis are continuous, with the optimal lifetime of an analytical tool being somewhere between five and 15 years, depending on the application. California should be upgrading and replacing old modeling software and methods much more quickly than it now does. These tools should represent and integrate many local, regional, and statewide options. With a proper state framework and information standards, high-quality local plans and information can be better integrated regionally, perhaps under the auspices of new regional stewardship authorities. Functioning regional plans can then become the basis for truly integrated resource plans and policies at the state level. Having such capability would entail some technical controversies but would dispel many myths and make it easier for policymakers to consider and explore the important technical and scientific aspects of California's water problems.

---

35. In addition, California's Urban Water Conservation Council, a membership organization, collects and analyzes data from its 233 water utility members to assess compliance with implementing agreed-upon urban water conservation practices. Although these data are posted online, they are not available in a format that facilitates analysis of trends or comparisons across agencies.

Priorities for Portfolios in Water Management

California is not helpless in facing its chronic problems of water scarcity, water quality, and flooding. More effective, robust, and cost-effective solutions to these problems are available by orchestrating a range of options at local, regional, and statewide levels. These "portfolio" solutions combine the strengths of individual options but require a higher level of analysis and integrated decisionmaking than is currently common in the state.

Water Supply Priorities

Water supply management has seen the most progress in implementing portfolio approaches, as numerous nontraditional tools have been tapped to cope with increasingly tight water supplies. Expanded efforts are especially needed in three areas: urban conservation, groundwater banking, and water marketing.

Urban conservation has the potential to play a major role in mitigating the effects of reduced export capabilities from the Delta and supply losses that may result from dry forms of climate change. Water rate reform, using tiered rates with variable base allowances, can promote conservation in a flexible and fiscally responsible way.

The state should also work to loosen institutional barriers to groundwater banking and water marketing, two essential tools for adapting to water scarcity. As discussed in Chapters 7 and 9, we propose that the state establish criteria for integrating groundwater and surface water and for managing groundwater withdrawals and allow local entities to develop implementation plans. In Chapter 7, we also discuss solutions to improve the functioning of the water market. These include streamlined environmental reviews and the creation of an independent system operator, modeled after the energy sector, to serve as a water transfer clearinghouse. With better-functioning water markets and more effective environmental reconciliation, agricultural water conservation will increase in response to water scarcity and incentives to transfer water to agricultural, urban, and environmental activities in which water has a higher economic value.

Water Quality Priorities

Water quality management in California has been most successful in reducing pollution from point sources (by treating wastewater and industrial waste) and in removing pollution from drinking water (by treating water before use). To reduce impairment and regain environmental and recreational uses of water bodies, California must make greater headway in two areas: preventing harmful chemicals from entering the environment and meeting performance targets for reducing discharges of nonpoint-source pollutants.

To meet the first goal, the state should continue to build on the successful model of Proposition 65, the Safe Drinking Water and Toxics Enforcement Act of 1986. Proposition 65 shifts the burden of proof to manufacturers, relies on multiple data sources, and allows private sector enforcement for some toxins that affect human health. The state's new Green Chemistry initiative, which seeks to make information available on chemical ingredients in products and to reduce the lifecycle effects of chemicals, is one promising avenue.

To meet the second goal, California should embrace water quality trading, which can help lower the cost of reducing nonpoint-source pollutants. California already has a successful model of trading to reduce selenium from agricultural runoff in the Grasslands area of the western San Joaquin Valley. As with groundwater management, local entities should be given the flexibility to develop implementation solutions to meet state performance criteria.

Federal actions also will be important for cost-effective water quality management. In particular, more flexibility is needed to enforce water quality standards under the Clean Water Act in cases where natural conditions such as nutrients and temperature preclude effective management solutions.

Flood Management Priorities

In the 2007 flood legislation, California broke with federal policy by setting higher protection standards for new development in the Central Valley. But the focus is still largely on improving flood protection infrastructure, using levees and reservoirs to limit the frequency of flooding. And despite $5 billion in recent state bond funds, California's flood protection system remains woefully underfunded.

To limit the growth of flood risk—or the average economic losses from flooding—California should focus more on reducing flood vulnerability. This means limiting the location of new development in flood-prone areas, improving building codes, expanding mandatory flood insurance requirements, and improving flood risk disclosure. Higher local contributions also are needed for flood protection investments, and properties facing higher risks should pay higher fees—a model already in use in the Sacramento area. To make the most of scarce flood investment dollars, both the state and federal governments should allocate funds based on cost-effectiveness, which depends not only on the costs of investments but also on the value of assets being protected.

The flood portfolio also should be expanded to include more environmentally beneficial protection measures, such as bypasses and levees set back farther from the river to expand the floodplain. Such tools can provide multiple benefits and are often cost-effective. They will require compensation of local landowners and local governments for the loss of revenues from forgone development.

Finally, flood policy should apply beyond the Central Valley to the many other flood-prone areas of California, including the Los Angeles Basin, the Bay Area, and the Central and North Coasts.

Integrating Actions

To realize many of the gains in water management, it will be necessary to overcome the geographic and functional fragmentation that characterizes California's highly decentralized system. Integration at the scale of watersheds, with coordinated planning of water supply and quality, flood management, and land use, is essential to meet objectives for human and environmental water uses. The current voluntary approach to integrated management—which entices local entities to collaborate in exchange for state bond support for infrastructure projects—is not very effective. As discussed further in Chapter 9, we recommend the creation of regional stewardship authorities, either replacing or supplementing existing regional water quality control boards, to coordinate and focus the efforts of local agencies.

Better information and stronger analytical tools will be needed to support these goals. The state has an interest in the collection and development of local, regional, and statewide information, as well as in regulations and incentives that foster the development of effective portfolios. Without such information and institutional prodding, water decisionmaking and conflicts will remain more difficult, expensive, and time-consuming to resolve. In the next chapter, we further explore ways to balance water management for economic and environmental sustainability, focusing in particular on using and strengthening the state's legal framework for water allocation and water system finance—keys to managing water as a public commodity.

7 Managing Water as a Public Commodity

CALIFORNIA DEPARTMENT OF WATER RESOURCES

> [F]ew public interests are more obvious, indisputable and independent of particular theory than the interest of the public of a State to maintain the rivers that are wholly within it substantially undiminished, except by such drafts upon them as the guardian of the public welfare may permit for the purpose of turning them to a more perfect use. This public interest is omnipresent wherever there is a State, and grows more pressing as population grows.
>
> Oliver Wendell Holmes, Jr., *Hudson Water Co. v. McCarter*, 1908

The preceding chapters highlight two central calls to action for California water policy. First, California must restore and strengthen the ecological functions of its watersheds, many of which are in serious decline and all of which face increasing risks from climate warming and other stressors. Second, California must improve its ability to respond and adapt to growing pressures on its water system from population growth, a changing economy, deteriorating infrastructure, rising costs of water pollution, deteriorating ecosystems, and shifts in precipitation and water availability with a changing climate.

To address these challenges, California must manage water comprehensively and in a way that recognizes both the public and private aspects of the resource. In some respects, water is a public good, with broadly shared benefits. Many environmental services provided by California's water resources are part of the state's collective heritage, owned by the public at large. The broad economic and environmental effects of storing, moving, and using water make it necessary to regulate these functions to protect public values. But water is also a commodity—an input into the production of goods and services, with a price and a market value—much like electricity or natural gas. Efficient use of water, for

The state's California Aqueduct and the federal Delta-Mendota Canal, side by side.

both economic and environmental purposes, requires an ability to adjust water use to changing conditions.

In fulfilling these two roles, water can be considered a "public commodity," the effective management of which must reconcile economic efficiency with protection of public values. In this chapter, we examine how California can better manage water as a public commodity to meet the needs of the economy and the environment. The overarching themes of this discussion are balance and flexibility. Striking a balance among competing uses and objectives is the core principle of managing water as a public commodity. Flexibility—or the ability to adapt—is essential for achieving this balance in the face of demographic, economic, and environmental changes.[1]

In the following discussion, we first review the legal framework for managing water as a public commodity. At its core, California water law—especially the foundational doctrines of reasonable use and the public trust—embodies the capacity for balance and flexibility essential for successful adaptation.

Second, we suggest changes in California's water rights system that would bring it into accord with hydrologic realities. These changes focus on two areas: (1) providing equal treatment for groundwater and surface water rights (particularly in areas where the current lack of formal groundwater management causes environmental harm or economic losses to other surface or groundwater users) and (2) providing incentives to incorporate riparian and pre-1914 appropriative surface rights-holders in the modern regulatory system. (Riparians, in particular, will have an interest in regularizing their rights with a warming climate.) These changes will need to be accompanied by better water accounting, which becomes increasingly important for improving management and reducing conflicts as water becomes scarcer.

Third, we examine mechanisms for strengthening the legal framework for water marketing. Although California's water laws provide a framework for facilitating water transfers, the slowdown in water market transfers since the early 2000s reflects procedural obstacles and concerns about the law's incomplete coverage of effects on groundwater users and the local economy in selling regions. We examine potential synergies between the reasonable use doctrine and water transfer law and suggest reforms of the environmental review process to streamline approvals while more broadly protecting public values.

---

1. Early notions for managing water in California along these lines can be found in Phelps et al. (1978).

Fourth, to address the problems of institutional fragmentation that hamper management of California's water grid, we explore the potential for California to learn from successful reforms in the energy sector. In particular, we suggest that California consider creating an "independent system operator" to more effectively manage water conveyance and water market transactions.

Fifth, again drawing on the experience of the energy sector, we recommend a "public goods charge" on water uses and specific environmental mitigation fees on the users of dams and chemical contaminants to cover the costs of improving the efficiency and reliability of California's water supply and distribution systems and the costs of ecosystem restoration, fish protection, and the other public benefits of the state's water resources systems.

Water as a Public Commodity: The Legal Framework

Fundamentally, the laws governing the management of California's water resources are more than capable of addressing the challenges identified in earlier chapters. The constitutional and common law bases of California water law, its overlay of regulatory statutes, and most aspects of water rights administration are compatible with the goal of managing water as a public commodity.

Putting the Reasonable Use and Public Trust Doctrines to Work

The foundations of California water law—the reasonable use mandate of Article X, § 2, of the state constitution and the public trust doctrine—both embody flexibility and responsiveness to change.

The doctrine of reasonable use requires that all water rights be exercised in a reasonable manner under contemporary conditions. As expounded by both the legislature and the courts, the doctrine evaluates not just the reasonableness of a particular use in isolation but also the broader public interest in efficient use and allocation of the state's water resources and protection of the ecosystems that are sources of the state's developed water supplies. The public trust doctrine complements the reasonable use directive by recognizing that navigation, protection of fisheries, commercial and recreational boating, and environmental protection and preservation are integral components of the reasonable use calculus and that the state has an obligation to preserve and protect these public trust uses in the administration of the water rights system to the extent feasible.

Both doctrines have deep roots in California water law. In a series of decisions dating back to the 19th century, the California Supreme Court recognized

Through the reasonable use and public trust doctrines, California's Supreme Court has consistently recognized that water law must be responsive to the needs of the state as a whole. Photo by Marc Moritsch/National Geographic Society/Corbis.

that the exercise of riparian, appropriative, and groundwater rights must conform to the requirements of reasonable use. In 1928, the voters enshrined the reasonable use doctrine in the California constitution (Box 1.4). The public trust in navigable waters was a component of English common law, which the legislature incorporated into California law in its first statute in 1850, although the Supreme Court did not expressly integrate the public trust into the state's water rights laws until its decision in the Mono Lake case in 1983 (*National Audubon Society v. Superior Court* 1983) (Box 1.2).

In defining and applying the reasonable use and public trust doctrines, the California Supreme Court has consistently recognized that the state's water laws must be responsive to the needs of the state as a whole, rather than favoring one set of water rights holders or water users over another. Moreover, efficient use and allocation of California's water resources must be consistent with contemporary demands, standards of use, hydrologic realities, and scientific understanding of the requirements of the ecosystems from which developed water supplies are taken. Indeed, the court has emphasized on numerous occasions that "[w]hat constitutes reasonable water use is dependent upon not only the entire circumstances presented but varies as the current situation changes" (*Barstow v. Mojave Water Agency* 2000).

The public trust doctrine similarly recognizes that existing uses and allocations of water are subject to reevaluation in light of contemporary knowledge about their effects on the ecosystems from which the water is taken. Thus, in *National Audubon Society v. Superior Court*, the court declared that in "exercising its sovereign power to allocate water resources in the public interest, the state is not confined by past allocation decisions which may be incorrect in light of current knowledge or inconsistent with current needs. The state accordingly has the power to reconsider allocation decisions even though those decisions were made after due consideration of their effect on the public trust" (*National Audubon Society v. Superior Court* 1983).

The flexibilities of the reasonable use and public trust doctrines vest significant authority in all levels of government to ensure that water rights are exercised in a manner that is reasonably efficient under contemporary conditions and does not cause significant negative spillover effects for other water users or the environment. This does not mean that environmental needs always take precedence over competing economic uses of water. As the Supreme Court made clear in *National Audubon Society v. Superior Court*, under Article X, § 2, "all uses of water, including public trust uses, must now conform to the standard of reasonable use." But as long as water planning, management, and regulatory decisions are the product of reasoned decisionmaking, based on a sound scientific analysis of ecosystem needs and due consideration of the needs of competing water users, the reasonable use and public trust doctrines afford water administrators broad and flexible authority to ensure that water use practices keep pace with changing conditions and that the allocation of water adequately protects water quality, fish, and other environmental uses.

Reallocating Water for the Environment

The reasonable use and public trust doctrines also address the potential of water rights to constrain the allocation of water to environmental purposes.

The California legislature has declared that "[a]ll water within the State is the property of the people of the State," but "the right to the use of water may be acquired by appropriation in the manner provided by law" (Water Code § 102). State and federal courts have long held that water rights, as well as derivative contract rights for water, are property rights within the meaning of the U.S. and California constitutions (Gray 2002a). One consequence of these decisions is that the government may not take or significantly impair existing water or contract rights without paying just compensation.

In several recent cases, federal courts have concluded that the United States may not implement the Endangered Species Act and other environmental laws without compensating water users for resulting water shortages. Although the courts found that the government had taken the water rights of the affected users (or breached its contractual obligations), each of these courts failed to consider the limitations imposed on all California water rights by the reasonable use and public trust doctrines. Some commentators have therefore argued that the cases were incorrectly decided and that the decisions do not provide useful precedent for future cases challenging the environmental regulation of California water rights (Box 7.1).

7.1

Recent takings and breach of contract cases in federal courts

Three recent federal court cases concluded that governmental restrictions on water rights constituted takings under the federal constitution, but they failed to consider the limitations that the reasonable use and public trust doctrines place on water rights and derivative rights to water use in California.

In *Tulare Lake Basin Water Storage District v. United States* (2001), the federal court held that restrictions on State Water Project (SWP) operations required by the Endangered Species Act, which caused shortages for some SWP contractors, constituted a taking of their property. The federal court ordered the government to pay the contractors approximately $26 million in damages. Although the court noted that California water rights law might itself preclude the appropriation of water under conditions that would imperil endangered species of fish, it declined to consider either the reasonable use or public trust doctrine as part of its analysis.

In *Casitas Municipal Water District v. United States* (2008), the federal court ruled that the U.S. directive that a local water district allow water to pass through a fish ladder was a taking of property. The releases of water were needed to support migration of steelhead, which are protected under the Endangered Species Act. The court reasoned that the United States had physically diverted the plaintiff's water for its own purposes—protection of the endangered fish. The court never addressed the question of whether California's reasonable use and public trust doctrines might limit the plaintiff's exercise of its water rights in a manner that could harm the protected fish.

In *Stockton East Water District v. United States* (2009), a breach of contract case brought by contractors within the New Melones Unit of the Central Valley Project (CVP), the federal court acknowledged that under California law it might be unreasonable or in breach of the public trust for the U.S. Bureau of Reclamation to operate the CVP in a manner that degraded water quality or endangered protected fish. The court refused to consider the effects of state law on the contractors' claims, however, because the federal government failed to establish a causal connection between the particular state mandates and the Bureau of Reclamation's inability to meet its obligations under the contracts.

As both human and environmental demands for water continue to rise relative to usable supplies, more such cases are likely in the future. Yet the reasonable use and public trust doctrines are likely to limit the ability of existing water users to successfully challenge regulatory actions that reallocate water to protect water quality, fish, and other environmental uses.

The California Supreme Court has long held that, under Article X, § 2, "no one can acquire a vested right to the unreasonable use of water" (*National Audubon Society v. Superior Court* 1983). The public trust doctrine similarly "serves the function in [California's] integrated [water rights] system of preserving the continuing sovereign power of the state to protect public trust uses, a power which precludes anyone from acquiring a vested right to harm the public trust, and imposes a continuing duty on the state to take such uses into account in allocating water resources" (*National Audubon Society v. Superior Court* 1983). Moreover, court or agency determination of whether a particular exercise of water rights is reasonable must consider the effects on the natural environment, and this determination may change over time as conditions vary in terms of hydrology, water demands, and species listed for protection and as scientific understanding of ecological functions and needs develops. The Court of Appeal stated this principle succinctly in describing the scope of the State Water Resources Control Board's (SWRCB's) authority over the Central Valley Project and the State Water Project in the Delta Water Cases (*United States v. State Water Resources Control Board [Racanelli]* 1986): "Here, the Board determined that changed circumstances revealed in new information about the adverse effects of the projects upon the Delta necessitated revised water quality standards. Accordingly, the Board had the authority to modify the projects' permits to curtail their use of water on the ground that the projects' use and diversion of the water *had become unreasonable*" (emphasis added).

Nevertheless, significant limits remain on the power of the state to encroach on existing water rights for environmental protection or other purposes. The California Supreme Court has held, for example, that neither the board nor the courts can ignore water right priorities in pursuit of other important objectives, including the allocation of water to correct conditions of aggregate overdraft or overuse of groundwater basins (*Barstow v. Mojave Water Agency* 2000). And the courts have recognized that water contracts create enforceable rights that the state and federal governments must honor unless conditions exist that either excuse nonperformance of the contract or render water service illegal or impossible (*O'Neill v. United States* 1995).

In all cases, water administrators must make individualized determinations of unreasonable use and base such determinations on evidence of inefficient use; wasteful or excessive use in relation to both supplies and alternative demands; degradation of water quality; or harm to fish, aquatic habitat, and other values protected by the public trust or other laws. But if the state has appropriately applied this principle of California water rights law to allocate additional water to environmental uses, neither water rights nor water contracts and other interests based on those water rights can block the necessary changes.

These overriding constraints on California water rights are central to the effective functioning and adaptation of California's water rights system. If the water rights laws are rigidly administered and enforced inconsistently with the more flexible directives of reasonable use and the public trust, the opportunities for responsive adaptation to changing conditions and corresponding institutional reform may be undercut.

Harmonizing Water Rights Administration

Although the foundations of California water rights law embody the adaptive flexibility needed for effective state water policy, two legal anachronisms could hamper efficient and sustainable water management and use: the disjunction between groundwater and surface water administration and the exemption of riparian, and pre-1914 appropriative rights from the permit and license jurisdiction of the State Water Resources Control Board. As described in Chapter 1, both anomalies result from decisions the legislature made when crafting the state's modern water code, the Water Commission Act of 1913. The legislature created a distinction between ground and surface water that is hydrologically inaccurate, and it decided to apply the regulatory jurisdiction of the Water Commission (predecessor to the SWRCB) only to nonriparian surface water uses commenced after the effective date of the statute in 1914.[2] These decisions were misguided at the time, and neither is justified today, when integrated water management under changing conditions requires greater consistency with hydrologic reality.

---

2. Two other categories of exempted rights are pueblo rights (established by some towns before statehood—see Chapter 1) and federal reserved rights (the authority of the United States and Indian tribes to claim water independent of the state water rights system to fulfill the purposes of national parks, national forests, and Indian reservations, and other federal lands that are reserved for specific uses (*Arizona v. California* 1963; *United States v. New Mexico* 1978). We focus this discussion on riparian and pre-1914 appropriative rights, as these are most significant in terms of volumes.

Equal Treatment for Groundwater

When the legislature enacted the Water Commission Act, it was well understood by geologists, policymakers, and courts that groundwater and surface water were usually hydrologically connected. In *Katz v. Walkinshaw* (1903), the California Supreme Court acknowledged that groundwater pumping may cause "an exhaustion of the underground sources from which the surface streams and other supplies previously used have been fed and supported. . . . The danger of exhaustion in this way threatens surface streams as well as underground percolations and reservoirs." The legislature's exemption of groundwater extraction (other than pumping from "subterranean streams flowing through known and definite channels") was a political choice, rather than a decision based on current scientific knowledge or sound water rights administration. Although there is evidence that the legislature intended to grant the Water Commission regulatory jurisdiction over the "pumping of groundwater that appreciably and directly affected surface stream flows" (Sax 2003), the statute has been consistently interpreted as not applying to "percolating" groundwater (which infiltrates from the surface)—regardless of the hydrologic relationship between such groundwater and surface water resources.

The legal divide between ground and surface water rights has contributed to a variety of water supply and water management problems. Expanded irrigation in the San Joaquin Valley and Tulare Basin in the late 19th century depleted rivers flowing from the Sierra Nevada, which in turn reduced recharge of aquifers and caused farmers without access to surface water to drill more and deeper wells. By the mid-20th century, these aquifers were in severe overdraft, with groundwater lowered by more than 400 feet in some places. The plummeting groundwater table caused some aquifers to compact, and in some areas of the San Joaquin Valley and the Tulare Basin, land elevations sank by more than 60 feet. Yet, there was no direct means to regulate surface water users to protect the groundwater or to regulate the aquifer mining caused by groundwater withdrawals (Chapter 1; Hundley 2001).

In Southern California, unregulated groundwater pumping depleted aquifers that supported the basins' meager streams and led to overdraft, legal conflicts, and saltwater intrusion as coastal aquifers fell below sea level (Blomquist 1992). Later in the 20th century, conflicts among surface and groundwater users appeared in regions as diverse as the Scott River on the North Coast and the Mojave River Basin in the high Southern California desert. During the

Vineyard management in Sonoma County will need to adapt to reduce the harmful effects of groundwater pumping on salmon and steelhead in the Russian River. Photo by Sonoma County Water Agency.

1988–1992 drought, groundwater users in Yolo County complained that transfers of surface water to the 1991 and 1992 drought water banks overdrafted local aquifers, as sellers of surface water pumped additional groundwater (Carter, Vaux, and Scheuring 1994).

Groundwater–surface water conflicts continue today in many coastal and inland stream systems, including the Russian and Santa Clara River Basins, where groundwater pumping has diminished stream flows to the detriment of surface water users and salmon and steelhead (Box 7.2). Similar problems exist on several inland rivers, including the Shasta River, where groundwater withdrawals threaten cold water springs that feed promising coho habitat, and the Cosumnes, where groundwater extractions have dewatered wetlands and riparian habitat (Hall 2010; Howard and Merrifield 2010). The lack of integrated rules for groundwater and surface water management also impedes more effective water marketing in parts of the Sacramento Valley (Chapter 6; Hanak 2003).

In addition, excessive pumping in many basins is creating acute management conflicts among groundwater users (e.g., Tulare Basin, Salinas Basin, Pajaro Basin), and overdraft has the potential to become a more serious problem in additional areas (including the San Joaquin Basin) with reduced water exports from the Delta (Chapters 3, 6). The lack of groundwater regulation is also an impediment to groundwater banking (Chapter 6). The lack of formal groundwater management could have dire consequences for future water supply

7.2

Groundwater use and river flow in the Russian River Valley

The Russian River occupies a large valley that supports numerous vineyards on its floodplains, hill slopes, and tributaries. Most water for these vineyards comes from either direct stream diversions or shallow groundwater wells. These wells take advantage of large alluvial deposits that store groundwater derived directly from stream channels and adjacent hill slopes. Given this close connection between the river and groundwater in the basin, high rates of groundwater pumping directly affect flows in the river and its tributaries.

The Russian River has three fish listed for protection under the federal Endangered Species Act: coho salmon, Chinook salmon, and steelhead. Juveniles of all three species rear in the main stem of the Russian River, particularly when dry conditions exclude them from the river's tributaries. Coho and steelhead spawn mainly in perennial tributaries.

The vines of the Russian River Valley bud in early spring and are highly susceptible to frost damage. Because wine grapes freeze at approximately 28°F, during severe cold periods, farmers spray a fine mist of water on the vines, which coats the grapes in ice, creates a protective temperature of 32°F, and thereby reduces frost damage. Heavy pumping of wells lowers local groundwater tables and abruptly reduces flows in adjacent channels.

In 2008, there were reports of stranded fish caused by rapid drops in flow during frost protection efforts. In 2009, the National Marine Fisheries Service and several other parties filed a complaint with the State Water Resources Control Board, arguing that although the frost protection actions may be legal under current water rights, they were harming listed species.

Acting under its authority to enforce Article X, § 2, the board has proposed to find the current methods of frost protection to be unreasonable (State Water Resources Control Board 2010c). The board has directed that a water demand management program be implemented that ensures that cumulative diversions do not lower flows to the level that harms fish.

Notably, the board has identified the pumping of closely connected groundwater as unreasonable use in its proposed regulations. This includes areas where wells pump water from "subterranean streams," from active channel sediments, and from what the board's consultant termed "Potential Stream Depletion Areas." The significance of these regulations is that they explicitly address a well-established hydrologic relationship between groundwater use and river flow.

management as the effects of climate warming become manifest. Reduced snowpack coupled with more frequent and intensive spring flooding will make water banking and conjunctive use more sought-after (Chapter 6; Connell 2009). Aquifer storage in the lower Sacramento River, in the San Joaquin and Tulare Basins, and in Southern California are likely to be especially valuable for such conjunctive management.

The most direct solution to these problems would be for the legislature to pass a statute that extends SWRCB jurisdiction to all groundwater extraction. The administrative costs of this transition would be substantial if the board were to exercise this authority directly. It would have to adjudicate (or readjudicate) each basin to determine hydrologically integrated surface water and groundwater rights, define the relative priorities, and then issue new water rights permits. A less costly alternative is for the board to use this authority to require that local water users establish effective management protocols. The board would set overall goals and a deadline for compliance and step in only if locals do not comply. This type of reform, where a higher level of government sets mandates for a lower level of government, is known as "cooperative federalism" (Chapter 9). It has the advantage of providing local users with more flexibility to establish cost-effective local rules.

This approach could be implemented incrementally, focusing first on basins where groundwater overdraft is impairing surface water uses or otherwise causing serious management problems. One model for local management is special water management districts with authority to quantify water rights, to regulate surface and groundwater extractions, and to impose pumping charges to reduce economic incentives to overdraft and to pay the costs of imported surface water supplies. The legislature has created these types of entities in several areas of California with mixed urban and agricultural use, including Orange, Santa Clara, and Ventura Counties, in response to local requests (Chapter 6; Schneider 1977).

Of course, political resistance to such reforms is likely from the beneficiaries of the regulatory status quo and groundwater users who fear or distrust government regulation. The difficulty of simply including mandatory well-level reporting in the 2009 water legislation suggests that significant legislative changes to regulate groundwater rights may be years away. If the legislature fails to act, the alternative is for the courts to step into the breach where possible. The courts have long exercised their common law authority over groundwater rights to adjudicate groundwater use and restrict the overdrafting of groundwater (*Katz v. Walkinshaw* 1903; Chapter 1). However, the expense of adjudications has deterred many groundwater users from filing suit. Article X, § 2, also provides authority for the courts to declare groundwater extraction unreasonable when it impairs surface water rights or harms public trust uses such as fish, water quality, and aquatic habitat. Thus, where evidence exists of groundwater pumping depleting surface streams (as in the Shasta River Basin), lowering the groundwater table that supports a surface river (as in the Santa Clara River Basin), or causing harm to other groundwater users (as in the Tulare Basin), courts have the power to regulate groundwater use to ensure that pumping does not cause unreasonable harm to other legal water users or to the public trust.

There are numerous precedents for the integrated management of ground and surface water rights under Article X, § 2, by the courts. Extensive monitoring of wells, regulation of withdrawals, and coordinated management of groundwater use occur in the 22 groundwater basins that have been adjudicated to date (Blomquist 1992; for a map, see Figure 4.1).[3] These adjudications include examples with explicit legislative direction, as with the Scott River system, and without, as with Los Angeles groundwater adjudication and the Mojave River.[4] The SWRCB's recent action to limit environmental damage from groundwater pumping in the Russian River Basin is also under existing authority, without explicit legislative direction (Box 7.2).

The reasonable use doctrine (and in some cases the public trust) thus can bridge the legal gap between surface water and groundwater rights systems in basins where combined surface and groundwater withdrawals harm water rights holders or the environment. This application of the reasonable use doctrine would build on the numerous cases in which the courts have already applied the reasonable use doctrine to limit individual or aggregate groundwater rights in basins where excessive pumping is harming other groundwater users (*Barstow v. Mojave Water Agency* 2000; Littleworth and Garner 2007). This case-by-case, basin-specific approach is not ideal, but it is often better than the consequences and conflicts of disintegrated water management. Legislation setting direction for integrated management would be preferable, but without legislative action the courts and, in some cases, the SWRCB may need to take the lead. Indeed, a series of basinwide integrated adjudications of ground and surface water rights may provide the impetus needed for legislative reform. Unless the legislature acts, courts may wish to consider how they might streamline basin

3. For a list of adjudicated basins, see www.water.ca.gov/groundwater/gwmanagement/court_adjudications.cfm.

4. On the Scott River, see Water Code § 2500.5, Schneider 1977, and California Department of Water Resources 2003. On Los Angeles, see *Los Angeles v. San Fernando* 1975; and on the Mojave River, see *Barstow v. Mojave Water Agency* 2000.

adjudications to make them a less expensive, more timely, and more effective procedure for addressing groundwater and integrated groundwater–surface water issues. The recent adjudication in the Beaumont Basin, located in a rapidly growing part of Riverside County, also provides a promising model for achieving speedy, low-cost adjudications through a nonadversarial process.[5]

Article X, § 2, also may be asserted to encourage more efficient local management of groundwater, including the establishment of groundwater banks. Local governments have jurisdiction to regulate groundwater extraction and use as part of their general police power (*Baldwin v. County of Tehama* 1994), and local water agencies have similar authority under Assembly Bill (AB) 3030. To date, most local governments and water agencies have exercised their authority over groundwater only to prohibit or restrict exports (Hanak 2003). Although legitimate local and regional interests are at stake—including protection of water rights holders, water quality, and prevention of overdraft and land subsidence—local interests should not trump statewide considerations. Given the importance of further development of groundwater banking to cope with scarcity and respond to a warming climate in California, it would be unreasonable for local groundwater restrictions to impede the statewide objectives of maximizing the efficient use and distribution of usable water resources. If the legislature fails to address this problem, the board, DWR, groundwater management agencies, or individuals acting through the courts may assert Article X, § 2, to pressure local governments and water agencies to take a more statewide perspective and in particular to allow the establishment of public and private groundwater banks—subject to local regulation but only such regulation as needed to protect legitimate local interests.

More Effective Regulation of Riparian and Pre-1914 Water Rights

The second anachronism of the Water Commission Act is the exemption of riparian rights and pre-1914 appropriations in the modern regulatory system. These water rights do not require a water rights permit, are largely unregulated, and represent a significant portion of California's surface water use.[6] As with

5. In this case, five water districts and 20 large overlying landowners reached a negotiated agreement, which the court then validated. The process took only 18 months and cost less than $700,000. Three newly elected members of the Borrego Water and Sewer District in the Borrego Springs area of San Diego County recently ran on a platform of pursuing a similar type of adjudication (www.smartvoter.org/2010/11/02/ca/sd/vote/brecht_l/paper2.html).

6. As discussed below, the exact volumes of diversions are not known because of incomplete and inaccurate reporting. We do not include pueblo rights in the text discussion because they are limited to a few cities and account for only a minute percentage of surface water use in California. Moreover, the pueblo water rights (both surface and groundwater)

groundwater regulation, incorporation of these rights into a modern water rights system also would ideally be accomplished through legislation. Yet, legislation compelling riparians and pre-1914 appropriators to obtain permits and licenses for their water rights is also unlikely to pass (or even to be seriously considered) for the foreseeable future. However, there may be ways short of compulsion to bring these long-exempted water users into the modern regulatory system.

Climate change will pose a substantial risk to riparian rights. As described in Chapter 3, natural stream flows in California will be higher in winter and lower in spring and summer as a result of climate warming. This shift is likely to diminish riparian rights, which are based on natural flow. Riparian water rights holders are entitled to divert only the natural flow of the river and cannot store water for more than 30 days, so winter flows are unavailable to them during the irrigation season.

One response to this dilemma would be to change the definition of natural flow to account for the predicted changes in runoff. But this response would be fraught with risks to California's overall water policies, as it would protect riparians from the effects of climate change at the expense of appropriators, which include California's major cities, most of its industrial and commercial uses, and much of its irrigated agriculture.

Another response would be to use the specter of the gradual loss of rights as an incentive to bring riparians into the modern regulatory system. The legislature could authorize willing riparians to petition the SWRCB to quantify their rights based on the board's assessment of reasonable present and future demands, taking into account not just the riparian's uses but also the available (shrinking) water supply available for all uses (consumptive and environmental). Once quantified, this would become each participating riparian's permitted or licensed water right, and the riparian would have all of the rights and privileges of other permittees and licensees. These would include the right to store water for later use, the right to use water on nonriparian lands, and the right to transfer water within or outside the watershed of origin. The converted riparian right likely would have greater economic value than the common law riparian right both because it would have greater certainty in the face of climate change and because of these expanded privileges of use and transfer.

---

of the largest pueblo, the City of Los Angeles, have been quantified and are subject to regulation under the final judgment in the *Los Angeles v. San Fernando* litigation.

Pre-1914 appropriators do not face the same threats from climate change, primarily because they may store water for later use, and so have less incentive to convert to a permit and license system. Nevertheless, pre-1914 appropriators could protect themselves by seeking clarity and quantification of their rights. The records of many pre-1914 appropriations are sketchy, as they are based only on notices of intent to appropriate, filed in county records offices, and on rates of actual (and continuous) diversion and use that are not always well documented. Pre-1914 water rights are therefore vulnerable to legal challenges that the quantity of the stated right may vastly exceed the quantity of right established by water use practice. Moreover, pre-1914 appropriators are subject to claims that their water use is wasteful, unreasonable, and perhaps in violation of the public trust, and the appropriators cannot rely on SWRCB evaluation and authorization to counter these claims. So, some pre-1914 appropriators may find it advantageous to join the regulatory system to enhance the security of their water rights relative to that of other permittees and licensees. This incentive may increase as California's available surface supplies diminish over time.

Better Water Accounting

The state's fragmented water rights system has contributed to serious gaps in water measurement and accounting. Most groundwater users have not been required to report water use to the state.[7] Although riparian and pre-1914 appropriative rights holders are required to report their diversions, there was no legal sanction for failure to file an annual statement of diversion and use until the legislature amended the Water Code in 2009 to establish civil penalties for failure to report (Water Code § 5107). Many did not report, and those who did tended to substantially overstate their diversions and use.[8] These gaps have led to difficulties in tracking water use trends, and they impede more effective management of water resources for economic and environmental purposes (Chapter 2; Little Hoover Commission 2010).

As water becomes increasingly scarce, it will become ever more important to measure and keep track of physical stocks and flows and their uses. Improved water accounting is essential for the effective administration of water rights, a key element of public commodity policy. In addition to better reporting, improved

7. Reporting is required in only four Southern California counties.

8. According to the State Water Resources Control Board (2003), the total water diversion and use indicated by reports submitted by riparian and pre-1914 users adds up to about five times current estimates of all urban and agricultural water use diversions, including groundwater, under all bases of right.

As supplies become scarcer, California must better track water use and flows, including groundwater. Photo by Bob Rowan/Progressive Image/Corbis.

accounting will require better quantitative representation of water flows and uses throughout California, in terms of both field data and hydrologic modeling. New technologies are improving estimates of net water uses from land surfaces and are making flow measurements in the field easier, but there will always be locations and times where water flows and uses are not or cannot be measured. Hydrologic modeling will be needed for such occasions. Better water accounting also requires real-time synthesis of water availability and delivery commitments to determine shortages to users and suggest improvements to operations. Periodic strategic synthesis also is needed to inform policymakers and system operators about longer-term issues and opportunities for water management.

In addition to strengthening water diversion and use reporting requirements for all surface water rights holders, the 2009 water legislation now requires that groundwater users report the elevation of their wells as a means of monitoring groundwater levels (Water Code §§ 5100–5107 and 10927–10936). These are but first steps toward the type of comprehensive measurement and accounting of water stocks, flows, and use that will be essential for improving water management.

Strengthening Water Transfer Law

Water transfers use voluntary market mechanisms to reallocate water in line with economic incentives. The state's water market is supported by a series of statutes introduced by the California legislature beginning in the early 1980s (Table 2.7) as well as the federal Central Valley Project Improvement Act of 1992, which encourages transfers by CVP contractors (Gray 1994a; Thompson 1993). Short-term (annual or seasonal) water transfers have become important for California's response to droughts and other acute water shortages, as they allow for the temporary movement of water from areas of relative abundance to areas of critical need. Long-term and permanent transfers from existing users reduce pressure to develop new water supplies, often a more financially costly and environmentally harmful alternative. Such transfers have grown in importance over the past decade, particularly for urban uses (Figures 6.5, 6.6).

Water transfers are consistent with the reasonable use doctrine. An important innovation of modern water transfer laws in California is that existing users may profit from conserved net water use. This allows water users to lease water to others without facing the "use it or lose it" provisions that normally apply to appropriative water rights. These financial incentives improve the efficiency of developed water allocation by encouraging transfers from relatively inefficient or lower-value uses to higher-value uses. Water transfers also can contribute to protecting the public trust by allowing users to transfer water directly to wetlands, water quality, fish, recreation, and other environmental uses (Gray 1996).

Although a market in both short- and long-term transfers has developed since the early 1990s, legal and institutional obstacles now appear to be limiting market growth (Chapter 6). Providing equal treatment for groundwater, as recommended above, would lessen some of these barriers. In addition, two areas of water transfer law would benefit from greater regulatory attention or legislative reform. The first involves the interplay between the regulation of water rights and water transfers, and the second is the relationship between water transfers and environmental review.

Water Transfers and Reasonable Use

There is an underappreciated synergy between water transfers and the reasonable use doctrine. Properly administered, the reasonable use doctrine can place constructive pressure on existing water users and encourage the profitable transfer of water from potentially unreasonable uses. One of California's earliest large water transfers resulted from this interplay between reasonable use and the market (Gray 1994a).

In 1986, the Imperial Irrigation District (IID) decided to conserve and transfer water following an unreasonable use determination by the state government.

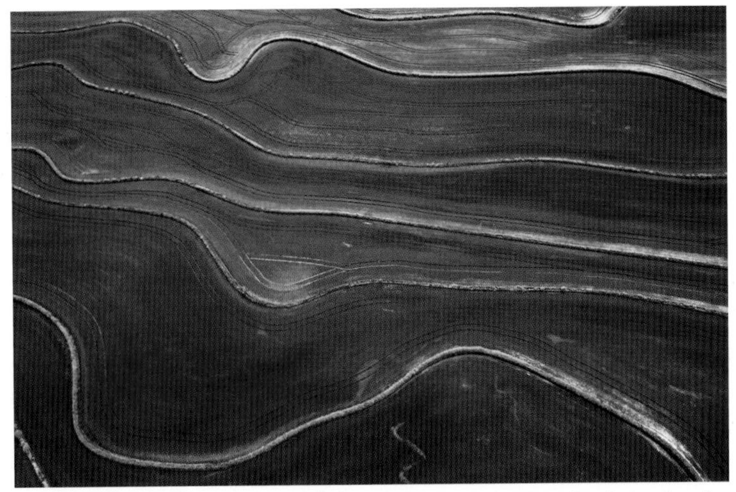

Sacramento Valley rice farms can be an important source of water transfers during droughts. Photo by California Department of Water Resources.

This application of the reasonable use doctrine induced IID to use water more efficiently, but the state also allowed the district to capture the economic benefits of these improvements by selling the conserved water to the Metropolitan Water District (MWD) for a 35-year period. This decision allowed IID to retain the value of its full water rights while maintaining reasonable use. MWD gained additional long-term water supplies at a lower price than alternative sources. And the state recognized that it is often better to achieve improvements in water use efficiency rather than to quibble over the financial equities of the case.

Although the government can use the reasonable use doctrine to help encourage water transfers by intransigent water users, the reasonable use doctrine can also undermine water transfers if not used carefully. Water markets (which encourage conservation through the incentive of being able to sell the conserved water) are in potential conflict with the reasonable use doctrine (which encourages conservation through command regulation). Rather than paying for conservation through the market, cities may be tempted to bring unreasonable use claims against other water users. More important, water users may worry about putting water up for sale if they may attract an unreasonable use claim as a result.

Water Transfers and Environmental Review

The legislature has exempted short-term transfers subject to the jurisdiction of the SWRCB (i.e., those lasting one year or less) from environmental review under the California Environmental Quality Act (CEQA) (Water Code § 1729). This exemption allows water to be moved quickly in response to acute shortages caused by drought, regulatory restrictions, or other contingencies. The exemption also recognizes that any potential harm to "third parties" (those who are not buyers or sellers in the transaction) from a short-term transfer will itself be short-lived. In contrast, long-term transfers must be preceded by CEQA review (usually in an environmental impact report [EIR]), because they often involve large quantities of water and their effects on the rivers and lands from which the water is transferred may last for many years.

Although the principle of streamlining environmental approvals for some transfers is sound, the practical distinction between short- and long-term transfers is not as clear-cut as implied by statute. The CEQA exemption for short-term transfers in the water code applies only to transfers subject to review by the SWRCB. Yet, many transfers can be accomplished without the board's approval, either because the transferor's water rights are not subject to board jurisdiction (e.g., pre-1914 appropriative rights) or because the transfer does not require a change in the transferor's permit or license (e.g., transfers between CVP contractors or between SWP contractors) (Gray 1994b). These short-term transfers are not categorically exempt from CEQA and therefore must be preceded by an EIR where the potential environmental effects may be significant. This has been true for the short-term transfers of water that the state has acquired for drought relief and environmental uses over the past decade, for instance.

To address these inconsistencies, to ensure that *all* major water transfers are subject to some environmental analysis, and to expedite and improve the quality of most environmental reviews, it would be desirable for the legislature to direct the SWRCB to conduct a comprehensive study and programmatic EIR for major sources of water transfers. This exercise could be done regionally, focusing on major river and stream systems most likely to sell water. As an alternative to conducting the analysis itself, the SWRCB could establish procedures or guidelines for such a programmatic EIR to be prepared by local water agencies interested in selling or purchasing water. The EIR (or set of region-specific EIRs) would examine the potential environmental impacts of transfers under a variety of hydrologic conditions, to enable the preapproval of a range of transfer volumes, depending on market conditions. Several recent long-term transfers provide useful models for such an approach, including the Vernalis Adaptive Management Plan along the San Joaquin and its tributaries, which involves the transfer of environmental water by six senior water rights–holding entities, and the Yuba Accord, which governs transfers from the Yuba County Water Agency to the Environmental Water Account and a pool of SWP and CVP contractors.

The analysis would assess the potential effects of transfers that currently require mitigation under state law (e.g., effects on other legal users of surface water, including fish and wildlife) as well as those currently excluded or only partially covered by state legal protections (e.g., effects on groundwater users and on the local economy) (Box 7.3). The following types of effects would be considered:

- ▹ **Surface water effects.** From what areas and in what amounts could water be transferred without significantly harming water quality, stream flows, and water supplies for other legal water users (including fish and wildlife)? (Mitigation is already legally required.)
- ▹ **Groundwater effects.** From what areas could water be transferred without significantly reducing groundwater recharge or exacerbating groundwater pollution? What limits and conditions should be placed on groundwater extraction to avoid or minimize these problems? (Mitigation should be legally required, to put groundwater on an equal footing with surface water.)
- ▹ **Fallowing effects on habitat.** In what areas could agricultural land be fallowed to make water available for transfer without jeopardizing the habitat for wildlife and waterfowl? (Mitigation is already legally required.)
- ▹ **Fallowing effects on the local economy.** In what areas could land be fallowed without significant long-term disruption of local economies and without imposing unreasonable social services costs on local governments? (Mitigation should remain optional, but buyers and sellers should be encouraged to develop funds to support the local economy when transfers cause significant unemployment and a loss in local tax receipts.)

The study and programmatic EIR would provide a consistent, more reliable, and less time-consuming basis for assessing surface water and groundwater effects (for which mitigation would be required), and to flag potential problems to the local economy in source regions (for which mitigation would be optional). Once completed, the state would have a hydrologic and ecologic map of regions likely to contribute to, or be affected by, future water transfers and all levels of government would be better prepared for managing such transfers.

7.3

Incomplete "no injury" protections under California water law

Current state law requires that water transfers avoid injury to other legal users of surface water, including fish and wildlife, which might be caused by a change in the place or purpose of use. These no injury protections are an important guarantee that transfers do not unreasonably harm other water users. Because of limitations on state authority over groundwater, these no injury protections do not extend to groundwater users—an unfortunate omission, which has led many counties to ban groundwater-related transfers (Hanak 2003). In addition, state law does not protect against the potential negative effects on local economies in water-selling regions when transfers are made possible by fallowing farmland, although it does call for public review of such transfers involving more than 20 percent of local water supplies (Water Code § 1745.05). To level the playing field and facilitate the development of California's water market, no injury protections should be extended to groundwater users. Parties involved in water transfers that cause significant unemployment and loss of local tax receipts from land fallowing should be encouraged to develop mitigation options to support the local economy in the selling region, as in the recent long-term transfers from the Imperial Irrigation District and the Palo Verde Irrigation District to urban agencies in Southern California (Chapter 6).

This template then could be applied both to transfers subject to review by the SWRCB and to those that are not. Transfers consistent with the analysis and findings of the programmatic EIR would be exempt from additional analysis under CEQA, except under extraordinary circumstances. For transfers requiring the board's approval, the information produced by the study would help to expedite the board's determination whether the proposed transfer would be likely to "injure any legal user of the water" or "unreasonably affect fish, wildlife, or other instream beneficial uses" (Water Code §§ 1725 and 1736). Transfers that could violate the limitations and conditions established in the study and programmatic EIR to protect third-party interests, as well as transfers to or from areas not covered by the study, would be permissible only following CEQA review (and, where required, approval by the board).

In addition to these changes, more comprehensive reforms in the management of California's water grid could reduce institutional barriers to water marketing and more flexible use of groundwater basins for storage, as described next.

Modernizing California's Water Grid

One of California's major assets is its extensive network of interconnected reservoirs, aquifers, rivers, and aqueducts, which makes it possible for water users in most of the state to access a wide range of portfolio management tools, including water transfers, surface storage, and groundwater banking. Current management of this system is an accident of history: Numerous vertically integrated independent water projects rely largely on their own supplies and conveyance infrastructure to meet demands of users within their service areas. Some improvements over the past few decades have helped to integrate the system. Notably, the Coordinated Operating Agreement between the CVP and the SWP has improved the joint operating efficiencies of the two largest projects. In addition, some local agencies have developed emergency sharing agreements. And the "wheeling" statute adopted in 1986 allows buyers and sellers to use water conveyance facilities owned by others to accomplish water transfers. Nevertheless, California's highly interconnected water system still functions in a fragmented manner.

Management of California's statewide water grid should be modernized to meet 21st century challenges. If it were possible to start from scratch today, with future needs in mind, California would create a more integrated system, with coordinated operation of major water storage and delivery infrastructure and nondiscriminatory access to supplies by human and environmental water users. To ensure unbiased protection of environmental values, the system would be operated by an independent and impartial entity, not beholden to any water utility.

We propose something short of full integration but well beyond current arrangements: to create an independent system operator (ISO) for the water grid that would focus, at least initially, on the backbone of California's water system—the CVP and SWP. Consistent with the policy of managing water as a public commodity, the purpose of this new system is to improve the efficiency of the distribution of the state's water resources while ensuring protection of public values.

This proposal builds on recent suggestions for changes in water governance, including removing SWP operations from the Department of Water Resources (DWR) and merging the operations of the SWP and the CVP (Little Hoover Commission 2010; Bates 2010b; King Moon 2009). Such proposals are commonly made to improve the operational efficiency of these projects (now encumbered by bureaucratic employment and contracting rules), with the side benefit of allowing the leaner DWR to become an impartial resource management agency.[9] Our proposal would achieve these goals but go further in considering the potential for a system overhaul that better incorporates market signals. Specifically, we endorse the Little Hoover Commission's proposal that the state create an independent wholesale water utility as a public benefit corporation to hold the water rights and assets of the SWP and to operate the project facilities. (In Chapter 8, we discuss related governance reforms for the non-SWP functions of DWR.) In addition, we propose the creation of an independent system operator to serve as a water market clearinghouse for the SWP, the CVP, and locally owned projects.

The model for this water ISO is California's existing electricity ISO, created in the mid-1990s as part of energy deregulation. Although some initial aspects of California's energy deregulation model worked poorly, contributing to the energy crisis in 2000–2001, the ISO has emerged as a successful new structure for electricity management in the state. The ISO is a nonprofit public benefit corporation, which operates—but does not own—most of California's high-voltage wholesale power grid (www.caiso.com). The ISO was created to accommodate a structural shift in electricity management, which separated generation and distribution facilities and introduced a market-based system of supply management. Before this shift, power utilities (much like today's water utilities) were vertically integrated and procured most supplies for their customers from their own generating facilities and transmission lines. California's three large investor-owned utilities (PG&E, Southern California Edison, and San Diego Gas & Electric), which together serve roughly two-thirds of the market, were required to divest themselves of some of their generating capacity and to participate in the ISO. The state's municipal power agencies (e.g., the Los Angeles Department of Water and Power, Sacramento Municipal Utilities District, Modesto Irrigation District), which serve roughly one-quarter of the market, were given the option to join.[10]

In the new ISO system, electric utilities buy and sell power produced by utilities and independent generators within and outside California through

9. The Department of Water Resources has had difficulties adequately remunerating and retaining staff, purchasing supplies, and contracting for services, particularly given state budget difficulties since the recent economic downturn.

10. In 2008, the investor-owned utilities provided 68 percent of retail electricity, the public agencies provided 24 percent, and nonutility service providers supplied the remaining 8 percent, primarily to large industrial customers. (California Energy Commission data, as reported in Griffin, Leventis, and McDonald 2010).

a combination of long-term and spot market contracts.[11] The ISO ensures the integrity of the grid—maintaining the minimum flows needed to avoid unwanted flow reversals, avoiding supply spikes that would exceed transmission capacity, and facilitating the ability of utilities to meet customer demands (i.e., avoiding brownouts or blackouts). It acts as a clearinghouse for purchases and sales, much as a bank does for deposits and loans. The ISO operates a set of short-term markets (day-ahead, hour-ahead, and five-minutes ahead), fulfills long-term contracts, and oversees industry plans to develop transmission infrastructure for the grid. The owners of generating and distribution capacity—not the ISO—are responsible for meeting the environmental regulations on facility siting and operations, including compliance with air emissions standards and environmental flow requirements for hydroelectric projects.

Independent grid operators similar to California's ISO, though nonexistent before the mid-1990s, now provide two-thirds of U.S. electricity deliveries (www.caiso.com). This model of management through organized, competitive wholesale energy markets generates consumer benefits through optimized use of the transmission system and lower wholesale prices (NERA Economic Consulting 2008). California's ISO also has become important for meeting the state's goals for demand management and clean energy through improved market access to new providers.

The ISO appears to be a successful model for maintaining independence while soliciting meaningful input from stakeholders. The ISO maintains stakeholder advisory groups on key operational and policy issues, and stakeholders are invited to weigh in on candidate lists for the ISO board. The lists—including at least four nonstakeholder professionals for each position—are drawn up by an independent recruiting firm, with final selection made by California's governor. The ISO's public benefit corporation status allows a flexible pay scale and rewards for meeting performance goals, factors that contribute to staff professionalism and cost efficiencies.

The proposed water ISO would be similar to the electricity ISO in several key respects: It would be a nonprofit public benefit corporation, with an independent board and comparable mechanisms for seeking stakeholder input, and would operate the water network without taking ownership. The water ISO would begin with the two major water projects—the SWP and the CVP—giving

11. A greater emphasis was placed on long-term contracts and capacity planning following the energy crisis, as exclusive reliance on spot markets left the system vulnerable to price spikes and market manipulation (Pechman 2007).

other local projects the option to join the system. As with the electricity ISO, facility owners would continue to assure maintenance and investment in the facilities, either directly or under contract with third parties. (For the SWP, the facility owner would be the new public utility, noted above.)

The scope of ISO market operations could be extensive or limited, depending on the extent of the state's willingness to revisit the underlying water rights and long-term water service contracts. In the limited alternative, the ISO would act as a central market (and perhaps operations coordinator) for voluntary water transfers employing any unused system capacity, after existing water rights and contract entitlements of water users, which would remain with their current owners. This could include forward markets for water purchases several months or years in advance, in addition to a daily or monthly spot market. Over time, a market might also develop for storage and quality attributes (e.g., a higher price for water with lower salinity). The advantages of this system would include operational efficiencies in grid management plus the ability of parties to transact through an impartial, arm's-length brokerage, which would establish market-clearing prices for water entering the market over several planning horizons. This might look something like the water market in Australia's Murray-Darling Basin, where private brokers operate through an electronic exchange. However, California's market would include important environmental safeguards that were excluded from the Australian market design but that are already part of California water transfer law, including protections of environmental flows and a requirement that only "real" physically available water—not "paper" legally available water—can be transferred to other parties (Box 7.4). Indeed, these protections would be strengthened by extending them to cover groundwater, as proposed above.

The second, more ambitious, alternative would make the water ISO much more like California's electricity ISO, which finds market clearing prices for *all* electricity that moves through the grid. Under this model, the ISO would not simply operate the CVP and SWP systems and a voluntary market; it would have authority to change how water is priced and allocated among the contractors, by establishing a market clearing price for the use of conveyance. Each year, the ISO would set the amount of water available for distribution after environmental requirements are satisfied. Rather than assert their water or contract rights to a specific water quantity and price, the participants would bid for delivery of available water (or available conveyance space). The ISO would then allocate water based on the highest to lowest bids over various time horizons.

7.4

The Australian water market

Several regions of Australia have water markets for short-term leases of annual allocations as well as permanent sales of water rights (or "entitlements") (Brennan 2006; Garry 2007). In the 2008–2009 water year, approximately 3.2 million acre-feet of water rights and allocations were traded, about 16 percent of nationwide entitlements (National Water Commission 2009). The largest volume of trading occurs in the southern part of the Murray-Darling Basin, where an active electronic exchange operates (www.waterfind.com.au/contact.html).

Water market development has been spurred by national water policy reforms. Following several decades of water scarcity, the Council of Australian Governments initiated a sweeping water policy reform process (Kendall 2011). Among other changes, the reforms gave financial incentives and legal support to Australian state governments to implement property rights reforms that facilitate water trading (Garry 2007; National Water Initiative 2004).

The property rights reforms separated water rights from land on which the water was used (something also possible in California for appropriative rights) and also allowed water rights to be traded even if they were not being exercised (something generally not possible in California, where only water that was in use within the past five years can be transferred). Australian water rights holders are also able to transfer the full diversion right, corresponding to "gross" water use (Box 2.1) rather than just the net water savings resulting from reduced use on the property. (In California, generally only net water savings can be transferred.) These conditions make it possible to sell water required to maintain environmental flows.

The clarity of property rights and lack of environmental limitations on water sales have allowed the Australian water market to evolve quickly and with lower transaction costs than in California. However, this market efficiency comes at a high environmental cost, which became increasingly apparent during the past record drought. To address this problem, the national government plans to spend over $3 billion in the next decade to purchase back environmental water and to invest over $5.5 billion in water savings whose yield will be shared between irrigators and the environment. Connor (2010) and Young (2010) call for modifying water allocations to reflect the value of environmental water.

This bidding system would allow the market—specifically the price that users are willing to pay—to direct the allocation of water among participating water users. Such a bidding system would likely result in a different allocation of water than would occur under existing CVP and SWP contracts and the various water rights held by other users that may choose to join the ISO. The highest bidders (most likely urban and industrial users, followed by high-value agricultural users) would be assured firm supplies in all but extraordinarily dry years, whereas lower bidders would obtain their water for less but with greater frequency of shortages.

Both ISO models would require authorization from Congress and the state legislature. The broader model, which creates a market for conveyance on all CVP and SWP supplies, would also need to address the issue of contract rights. Project contractors who received less water or face higher prices than under their existing contracts would have a valid claim that the government had breached their contract rights and would be entitled to compensation for the fair market value of the lost water or the difference in price between market and contract prices. To address this issue, federal and state legislation creating the ISO would need to authorize the condemnation of CVP and SWP contracts and establish some other process for awarding just compensation. Thus, the broader model, while conferring substantially more flexibility to the system, could also have significant up-front costs.[12]

Given the greater complexities of the broader model, we recommend beginning with the "ISO-lite" model that focuses on a voluntary transfer clearinghouse function. If California faces significant longer-term reductions in water supplies as a result of climate change, expansion of the ISO might become necessary. Severe long-term drought, with roughly a 90 percent reduction in supplies, was a major factor in the overhaul of the Australian system of water rights management and water marketing.

Because water operations have more direct and complex environmental consequences than electricity grid operation, the water ISO would be responsible for administering the system to comply with laws governing water transfers and wheeling, as well as water quality standards, endangered species limitations, and other environmental requirements applicable to the operation of facilities.[13] Water rights and contract holders would retain responsibility for environmental mitigation related to their own water development and use. Facility owners,

---

12. However, to the extent that the new system conferred additional value to water users (through increased operational efficiencies and flexibility), the net costs of the transition might be very low or negative. A major issue would be whether compensation should be based on the present value of full contract amounts or expected deliveries given hydrologic variability and changing environmental regulations. Although the latter method would appear consistent with the reasonable use and public trust doctrines, the federal appellate court decision in the Stockton East case (Box 7.1) held that making contract performance less reliable through new environmental restrictions is a breach of contract.

13. For this reason, the transfer of operational authority also would likely require revised biological opinions, as well as environmental review under the National Environmental Policy Act and CEQA unless the federal and state legislation creating the ISO were to declare otherwise.

likewise, would be responsible for permits and compliance with environmental laws related to the facilities themselves.

Under either model, a water ISO could interact with the electricity ISO in at least two ways. First, the ISO would buy and sell power from the energy ISO, thereby creating healthier incentives for energy efficiency. Currently, the projects subsidize water contractors by using revenues from hydropower sales to lower water delivery costs and, in the case of the CVP, charging contractors below-market rates for hydroelectric power produced by project facilities.[14] (This change would, for instance, raise the price of water delivery over the Tehachapis.) Under the new system, water conveyance (including energy costs) would be fully priced. Second, under either model, the energy ISO might pay the water ISO to schedule pumping and operation of hydropower releases as part of managing the electric grid.

In either model, the market operated by the ISO could be accessed by environmental managers and others wishing to acquire water for instream purposes (e.g., environmental and recreational flows). The reform also could provide environmental managers with revenue-raising options to lease out excess regulatory flows and bank the receipts. The market could then enhance the potential for flexible environmental flow management—which is important for the new approaches to ecosystem reconciliation discussed in Chapter 5.

Clearly, the benefits of this institutional change are closely tied to the fate of the Sacramento–San Joaquin Delta. As discussed in Chapter 6, if the present through-Delta conveyance system collapses and is not replaced with an alternative, many benefits of integration disappear, along with many other water supply management options available to the state. As long as conveyance limits Delta water exports, however, having a reliable and transparent market to manage scarce Delta export capacity can significantly improve the system's efficiency.

Assuring Funding for Public Benefits

In recent years, California has come to rely on an unreliable funding source—general obligation (GO) bonds—to support ecosystem programs and state planning and management functions (Chapter 2). GO bonds have also supported local and regional water projects that are primarily funded by ratepayers.

14. Central Valley Project electricity is heavily subsidized, relative to market prices. In 2002–2003, the project charged its contractors less than one-tenth the price PG&E charged to industrial water users (Sharp and Walker 2007). The SWP does not sell electricity to contractors at subsidized prices, but it uses project hydropower revenues to reduce water delivery costs.

Inadequate resources have been a theme in virtually all studies of the state agencies key to managing California's waters (e.g., Little Hoover Commission 1990, 2010). Yet increased support through the state's general fund seems unlikely in the current fiscal environment and unreliable in the long run. California needs to establish public funding sources supported by water users, as is now done in the energy and transportation sectors.

Public Goods Charge on Water Use

A statewide "public goods" charge (PGC)—a volumetric charge on all surface and groundwater used in the state—is a promising solution to the chronic underfunding of the state's water-related agencies and ecosystem programs. It would also provide a more efficient and equitable way to support local and regional water infrastructure.[15] A PGC could support (1) operations of state agencies directly related to overseeing water allocation and extraction, (2) scientific and technical activities to improve water management, (3) environmental protection and restoration needed because of water extraction, and (4) local and regional water infrastructure improvements.

A similar public goods charge for energy, passed by the legislature as part of its 1996 deregulation of the energy sector, collects roughly $800 million per year from a roughly 0.5 cent per kilowatt hour charge on electricity and a similar charge on natural gas.[16] This funding has gone to support energy use by low-income households (47 percent), increasing energy efficiency (28 percent), renewable energy sources (17 percent), and research (8 percent) (Kuduk and Anders 2006). These funds assure steady funding for state-of-the-art infrastructure, social goods, and research and development (Chapter 2) and have received high marks for supporting energy efficiency and the development of renewable sources (Griffin, Leventis, and McDonald 2010). Nationally, the federal highway trust fund, financed by a per gallon charge on fuel, supports roads, mass transit, and environmental cleanup associated with transportation projects.[17]

---

15. See Griffin, Leventis, and McDonald (2010) for an exploration of this idea for local and regional infrastructure support.

16. This amounts to a relatively small share of customer energy costs (e.g., 4 percent in the San Diego area—see Kuduk and Anders 2006). The surcharge on electricity was introduced as part of legislation restructuring electric utilities in 1996 (AB 1890) and renewed with specific legislation in 2000 (AB 995). In 2000, a consumption surcharge on natural gas was also introduced (AB 1002). The surcharge on electricity expires on January 1, 2012, and would likely require a two-thirds vote for renewal under the terms of Proposition 26 (see text below). These earlier bills all passed with high majorities: AB 1890 passed by unanimous vote of both houses; AB 995 and AB 1002 passed with 95 percent of all assembly votes, and 86 percent and 75 percent of senate votes, respectively (www.leginfo.ca.gov).

17. The ability of this fund to serve its various purposes is now challenged by several factors, including Congress's failure to index the per gallon gas tax to inflation—it has remained at $0.18 per gallon since 1993 (National Surface Transportation

By providing stable funding for the administration of statewide and regional water rights, planning, and quality programs, a PGC would reduce much of the disruption, delay, and inefficiencies resulting from irregular, bond-dependent, and increasingly stressed general revenue funds. Funding for research and development would benefit in similar ways.

PGC funds for ecosystem reconciliation would support habitat development for native species, long-term purchases of water for environmental uses, invasive species enforcement, reconciliation-oriented research, and other environmental management activities. This funding would partially compensate for damage to native ecosystems and species from water infrastructure and operations and, by improving conditions, it would also reduce environmental pressures on water deliveries. The administration of such funding would need to ensure sound mechanisms for allocation and oversight in support of effective ecosystem reconciliation.

PGC funding for water reliability would support water infrastructure, conservation, reuse, and other activities that materially improve the reliability of water deliveries throughout the state. These funds would provide incentives for local and regional water agencies to cooperate in developing integrated water management activities, along the lines of current bond funding. These funds would also support state water rights administration to improve the institutional reliability and security of water rights and contracts. The creation of a PGC would likely require a two-thirds vote of the legislature.[18]

Regional fees for water system management might be levied in parallel to the statewide public goods charge. For instance, Metropolitan Water District of Southern California instituted a stewardship fee on its wholesale water sales in the early 1990s to support a range of water supply reliability programs, including water use efficiency, recycled wastewater, and desalination projects.

A PGC also would help ensure that water users are paying a rate that better reflects the cost of their water use to society, including management and

---

Infrastructure Financing Commission 2009). California levies a similar fee on fuels to support transportation investments and maintenance and has faced similar challenges in recent decades.

18. Although the SWRCB has authority to impose fees to fund the board's issuance, administration, review, monitoring, and enforcement of water rights permits and licenses (see Water Code §§ 1525–1560), this authority applies only to surface water users within the board's direct permit and license jurisdiction. In contrast, the PGC proposed here would apply to all surface and ground water use. Creation of a PGC therefore would require new legislation, most likely with a two-thirds majority vote under Proposition 26 (enacted by the electorate in November 2010 (Cal. Const. art. XIIIA, § 3(a))). The PGC would likely not fall within the exemption set forth in Proposition 26 for charges "imposed for the reasonable regulatory costs to the State incident to issuing licenses and permits, performing investigations, inspections, and audits, enforcing agricultural marketing orders, and the administrative enforcement and adjudication thereof" (Cal. Const. art. XIIIA, § 3(a)(3)).

environmental protection and mitigation. Why should general tax revenue support administration and regulation of what is ultimately a utility service? Because water users are not currently paying a price that reflects these costs, they do not take these costs into account in making economic decisions, such as the appropriate level of water conservation.

Much as the federal highway trust fund taxes all highway fuel use to support federal highways built and maintained by state and regional transportation agencies, this approach to supporting statewide and regional water reliability would create financial incentives for local and regional cooperation in operations, planning, and infrastructure development. A major by-product of the federal highway fund is that it has provided incentives for states to agree on national data-collection and design and maintenance standards for roadways. The public goods charges in the energy sector have also fostered cooperation between utilities and local and regional governments in the use of energy efficiency grants (Hanak et al. 2008). These demand management programs and research and development activities funded through the program help to lower energy prices for all users.

Specific Fees for Specific Problems

In addition to a general public goods charge, some specific fees should be levied to address specific problems:

- A surcharge on chemical contaminants could help fund containment of source pollutants. Such a fee could be modeled after California's electronic waste fee, introduced by the legislature in 2003, and the fee levied on paint manufacturers to mitigate lead paint poisoning, introduced in the mid-1990s;[19] and
- A fee on beneficiaries of dams to help fund dam retirement actions (similar in spirit to the requirement under California's Surface Mining and Reclamation Act that mine operators provide a bond sufficient for restoring the mine site) and to fund programs to improve the condition of fish whose habitat is compromised by dams (Chapter 5).

19. On electronic waste recycling, www.calrecycle.ca.gov/electronics/act2003/. On the fee for lead paint mitigation, see Misczynski (2009). This regulatory fee was upheld by the California Supreme Court in *Sinclair Paint v. State Board of Equalization* (1997).

Other sources of state revenue also could help support work critical to the health of California's waterways. Recognizing the major effect of roads on aquatic ecosystems, for example, a small percentage of transportation mitigation funds might appropriately support the work of the Department of Fish and Game. As a precedent, 0.1 cent per gallon of the federal gas tax funds a Leaking Underground Storage Tank Trust Fund.

Until recently, these types of specific mitigation fees could be approved with a simple majority vote of the state legislature. However, with the passage of Proposition 26 in November 2010, they are also likely subject to a two-thirds vote by the legislature.[20]

Treating Water as a Public Commodity

Treating water as a public commodity—balancing the public benefits of water and its value as an economic input—is the most promising approach for meeting environmental and economic objectives both now and in the future, as water becomes increasingly scarce. Management flexibility is essential for achieving this balance. Fortunately, California water law, especially through the reasonable use and public trust doctrines, has the capacity for balance and flexibility.

Water management in California has already moved substantially in the direction of treating water as a public commodity, particularly through the development of the state's water market. However, several changes are needed to consolidate this trend. Foremost among these is to put groundwater on an equal footing with surface water—necessary to protect environmental stream flow in some systems, to reduce harm to other surface and groundwater users, and to facilitate the development of water marketing and groundwater banking—needed tools for adapting to increasing water scarcity. As discussed further in Chapter 9, there are good reasons for the state to play a leading role in guiding policy on this issue, while encouraging local water users to develop comprehensive management solutions within their watersheds. Establishing incentives for better legal and administrative definition and security of other water rights, including pre-1914 and riparian surface water rights, will also improve the functioning of the system, facilitating water transfers and groundwater

20. See Cal. Const. art. XIIIA, § 3(a). Before passage of Proposition 26, regulatory fees to fund "remedial measures to mitigate the past, present, or future adverse impact of the fee payer's operations" could be enacted by majority vote of the legislature (*Sinclair Paint v. State Board of Equalization* 1997). At the local level, such fees previously could be adopted by simple majority vote of the local agency's governing board. After Proposition 26, these fees are now subject to a supermajority vote of the general public within the local agency (Cal Const. art. XIIC, § 1).

banking. Improved water accounting—including better reporting, monitoring, and analysis of all types of water usage—is also fundamental to managing water more effectively for economic and environmental objectives.

California also needs to strengthen its water marketing law to allow the market to move beyond the growing pains of adolescence and continue to expand. Environmental reviews should be streamlined to improve efficiency, and their scope should be extended to ensure that the public values of the system are protected. A further change—establishing an independent water transfer clearinghouse, modeled after the state's electricity ISO—would allow California to benefit more from its complex network of storage and conveyance infrastructure and facilitate water marketing. This system currently bears the weight of a fragmented history of development by numerous federal, state, and local agencies.

Finally, California should draw on the experiences in the energy and transportation sectors to develop a more reliable, user-based source of funding for the public functions of the water system, establishing a public goods charge on water use and specific environmental mitigation fees.

The state legislature will have a pivotal role in driving these changes, as many will require or benefit from new legislation. This will not be easy, because those who benefit from the regulatory status quo are likely to resist change. However, if the legislature fails to act, both the courts and the State Water Resources Control Board have considerable existing authority under the reasonable use and public trust doctrines to further the goals of more efficient and environmentally beneficial water management. In particular, the courts can play an important role in furthering groundwater management. The board can also assume a leadership role on the integration of groundwater and surface water management in cases where groundwater pumping is causing environmental harm, as demonstrated by its recent actions in the Russian River Valley.

To institute reforms such as those outlined here and in previous chapters, California needs a more capable and nimble set of governance institutions and approaches to the reform process itself. Part III of this book examines promising alternatives in both areas.

Part III

Making Reform Happen

The anterooms of our legislative halls have been already too long blocked by the presence of those who mutually accuse each other of only selfish aims in connection with these irrigation questions, and who all denounce or suspect every one who does not agree with them and works with them exclusively. Full and fair consideration of the subject at the hands of any one is not received patiently by the active parties in behalf [*sic*] of the various interests at stake in this irrigation conflict. Members of legislature during the brief period of a session, amidst a multiplicity of other questions, cannot be expected to master the irrigation questions and act upon them under such circumstances.

William Hammond Hall, State Engineer, 1886

Parts I and II demonstrate the need for reforming water management in California. In this section, we discuss ways to make this happen. Reform must begin at the top, by improving the institutions that formulate and run the state's water system. Developing an effective water management system will be impossible if governing institutions cannot identify, formulate, implement, and enforce needed reforms. Institutions must also be able to adapt to the inevitable changes that will occur over time, including climate change.

Chapter 8 examines institutional improvements needed to make substantive reforms possible. Key steps include ensuring that policymakers and managers have adequate information and resources, providing for more integrated and coherent water management at all levels of government, relying more on expert agencies, and developing new mechanisms to help agencies protect the public trust.

Chapter 9 examines the process and procedures of reform, addressing several key questions:

- Is new legislation needed for reform, or does the existing complex of common law, statutes, and regulations already provide an adequate structure for implementing critical reforms?
- How can the knowledge and expertise of local agencies be used in designing and implementing reforms, while overcoming the common reticence of local agencies to adopt reforms?
- How can California overcome the almost inevitable political opposition that has prevented many needed reforms from being adopted in the past?
- Can the costs of reforms to vested interests be reduced or eliminated to lessen their opposition?
- What roles can public education, coalition-building, consensus processes, initiatives, and judicial actions play in promoting reforms?

Chapter 10 concludes with a summary of observations and recommendations.

8 Effective and Adaptive Governance

SARAH NULL

Once an organization loses its spirit of pioneering and rests on its early work, its progress stops.

Thomas J. Watson

This chapter discusses the institutional improvements needed if California is to achieve the reforms identified in the preceding chapters. Institutional inertia has impeded prior reforms, and even the best policies will fail if institutions are incapable of implementing them. Beyond today's reforms, governmental institutions must be able to identify and implement future reforms. Such adaptive capacity is particularly important, given the many inevitable changes that will occur in California's environment, economy, and society.

Information, Expertise, and Resources

The starting point for improving water management is to ensure that policymakers, managers, and judges have the information, expertise, and resources they need to identify, shape, and implement reforms. Without these fundamental building blocks of good governance, state policymakers and managers will be handicapped in shaping and implementing the dramatic improvements needed in California's water management.

Information

Although water agencies collect a multitude of information about the state's water resources and uses, policymakers and managers still lack key data and information for decisionmaking. Perhaps the most important missing data element is actual water diversions from surface waterways and groundwater aquifers. California is almost unique among western states in not collecting

Tuolumne River, in the Poopenaut Valley near Hetch Hetchy (Yosemite National Park).

The 2009 water legislation made some progress toward improving water use information. Photo by Justin Sullivan/Getty Images.

information on such diversions. California also lacks water quality information on many of its aquifers and waterways. California's local and regional water agencies track much of this information, such as water use and local hydrologic data. But these and other important data such as volumes traded in water markets, the value of water use in different activities, and the rates paid by different water users are unavailable to the public or not maintained in forms that are easy to access or use. Much of the problem is not the lack of data but the unavailability of data for analysis by other agencies or groups.

The 2009 legislature took an important step toward collecting better groundwater information when it passed Senate Bill (SB) X7-6, providing for monitoring and reporting of groundwater elevations. However, SB X7-6 addresses just part of the information gap confronting California water management. Congress also could support the U.S. Geological Survey and other federal agencies in collecting and analyzing data on key water issues, including the condition of groundwater aquifers and groundwater-surface water connections (Leshy 2009). Federal satellite data, for example, show promise for being able to accurately estimate crop evapotranspiration on the scale of a farmer's field, with potential to both inform farmers and water managers, at relatively little cost, and without inconvenience to farmers (Chapter 3). To aid analysis and enforcement, greater and more systematic state efforts are essential to assemble data from local, state, and federal agencies within a coherent framework. If

California knew what Californians know about water, management and policy-making would be much easier.

Policy Expertise

In addition to needing better water information, government officials must have the expertise and responsibility to use and analyze that information. For example, the California legislature needs synthesized data, information, and insights to help identify water problems and then evaluate and structure responsive policies. All legislatures need information, but data and information are particularly important where reforms deal with scientifically and factually complex issues, as is common for water policy.[1] State legislatures have far less data and information than Congress because (1) they generally have smaller staffs and lower budgets, (2) fewer "think tanks" and policy groups inhabit state capitals, and (3) term limits prevent legislators from developing expertise in policy subjects over time. Although stakeholders and interest groups can help fill the information gap, the information they provide can be biased to favor their positions, so-called advocacy or combat science (Chapter 2). More even-handed sources of information are generally in-house experts, major research universities, and independent think tanks.

A simple first step to reduce the legislature's information gap would be to create a full-time water analysis group within the Legislative Analyst's Office (LAO). Currently, the LAO has just one staff member with principal responsibility for water, along with a wider portfolio of natural resource topics. Given the importance of water in the state, a water analysis office within the LAO could usefully engage in long-term monitoring and study of California's evolving water challenges, providing the "expert capital" now in short supply within the legislative branch. The water analysis office would work with experts in state and local agencies to ensure that appropriate information is collected and evaluated and to summarize this information for the legislature. The office also would develop its own independent capabilities and analysis, and provide a form of technical institutional memory for a legislature subject to term limits. The LAO also might wish to create formal relationships with the state's major research universities, along with other expert research organizations and state agencies, to provide data and analysis on major water issues of immediate and longer-term interest to the legislature. This in-house service will better prepare legislators and legislative staff for timely and effective engagement in water issues.

1. On the general issue of legislative information needs, see Sabatier and Whiteman (1985); Lupia and McCubbins (1994).

The legislature also might consider adding scientific and technical water expertise to the Assembly Committee on Water, Parks and Wildlife, the Senate Committee on Natural Resources and Water, and other relevant committees. These committees are critical in identifying issues and developing and refining solutions to the state's water challenges. Creating a cadre of permanent water experts in these legislative committees and the LAO would provide the legislature with the "expert capital" needed to formulate effective policies and provide long-term institutional memory on water issues.

Expertise is also an issue for California's courts. The judges who have decided the vast majority of California's water cases have been generalists—trial and appellate judges with no specialized understanding or training in water issues. Several other jurisdictions have turned to specialized courts to resolve water and other environmental issues, on the theory that specialized judges can better understand the issues and develop a more effective and coherent body of law. Colorado, for example, uses specialized water courts to manage its water system (Sax et al. 2006). Australia's New South Wales has gone a step further and established a specialized Land and Environment Court with jurisdiction over environmental matters more broadly.

Although specialized judges can bring greater expertise to water disputes, any move toward greater specialization should also recognize the value of generalization. Judicial generalists often bring a broader perspective to water issues than specialists might, and they sometimes are more willing to question traditional solutions. One potential approach to combining the advantages of both a generalist court and water expertise would be to appoint a single judge, or a panel of judges, from the superior court bench in each county to hear all water cases; the judge or panel would periodically rotate (e.g., every five years). This approach would allow judges to develop expertise in the water field, while ensuring a fresh set of eyes on a regular basis. Colorado appoints its water judges from the regular bench, and water judges continue to hear other matters; indeed, for most Colorado water judges, water cases are only a small part of their caseload. There is little turnover, however, among Colorado water judges. California is already taking a step toward this model with the appointment by the Chief Justice of the California Supreme Court of judges to hear groundwater adjudications. Water judges or panels also could develop more efficient procedures for water cases, hopefully reducing the complexity, time, and cost currently associated with adjudications of groundwater and surface water rights (Chapter 7).

Courts could also benefit from specialized training in water science and economics. The Land and Environment Court of New South Wales provides its judges with professional development courses focused on relevant environmental knowledge, expertise, and skills, and requires that they attend such courses at least five days a year (The Land and Environment Court of NSW 2010). Subjects could range from scientific advances in hydrology to the potential effects of climate change on fresh water.

Both federal and state agencies, including the Department of Fish and Game (DFG) and the State Water Resources Control Board (SWRCB), also could make greater use of internal and external expertise. As noted above, governmental investment in science has not kept up with decisionmaking needs; state scientific and technical capacity has declined, hindering the scientific basis for policymaking. In this era of smaller budgets, agencies should look to augment their capacities with new science partnerships with universities and other agencies, such as the California Energy Commission (which funds a great deal of climate change research). The Interagency Ecological Program for the San Francisco Estuary is one model for statewide research and monitoring. Agencies might consider establishing permanent contracts and coordinating mechanisms to engage university scientists in responding rapidly to research needs. At a minimum, agencies should better develop and employ in-house scientific experts.

Agencies also might consider appointing scientific experts to more key positions. As environmental issues grow in complexity, increased expertise is needed to implement and enforce the state's laws. For example, the Department of Fish and Game might create a specialized group of wardens with more scientific backgrounds to investigate major violations of environmental laws, such as illegal diversions of water and stream alterations.

Adequate Resources: A "Public Goods" Charge

Effective water management also requires that agencies have adequate resources to carry out their current responsibilities and to meet future challenges. As discussed above, agencies responsible for managing and protecting California's waters have long been underfunded to the point of ineffectiveness. Inadequate resources have been a theme in almost all studies of state water agency effectiveness (e.g., Little Hoover Commission 1990, 2010). Yet increased state general fund appropriations seem unlikely for many years. The fluctuations and unreliability of general obligation bond funds also make them unsuitable for such a sustained task.

As described in Chapter 7, a statewide "public goods" charge seems the best financial solution to sustain capable attention by California's water-related agencies. Public goods charge revenues could be allocated to support (1) operations of state agencies directly related to overseeing water allocation and extraction and addressing the effects of water management on fish and wildlife, (2) environmental reconciliation and restoration efforts, (3) regional collaborations and infrastructure for integrated water management, and (4) scientific and technical activities to improve water management. This use fee is modeled after the existing public goods charge on energy in California and the federal highway trust fund, which supports road, mass transit, and environmental cleanup using fuel tax revenues. In addition, some specific fees should be levied to address specific problems: a surcharge on chemical contaminants to help fund containment of source pollutants (modeled after California's electronic waste fee) and a fee on beneficiaries of dams to help fund mitigation efforts for fish affected by dams and dam retirement actions (similar in spirit to the requirement under California's Surface Mining and Reclamation Act that mine operators set aside a bond sufficient for restoring the mine site). Other sources of state revenue also could help support work critical to the health of California's waterways. Recognizing the major effects of roads on aquatic ecosystems, for example, a small percentage of transportation mitigation funds might appropriately support the work of the Department of Fish and Game. Finally, existing funding programs could be improved. Our interviews with state and local water experts revealed problems in the administration of federal grant and loan programs, which could benefit from streamlined procedures (or, at a minimum, more active assistance on applications by agency staff).

Problems arise not only from inadequate funding but from imposing new responsibilities on already strapped agencies. The U.S. Army Corps of Engineers' vital domestic role, for example, has been seriously compromised by demands placed on it by the nation's overseas military operations; resulting staffing gaps are undermining federal responsibilities in flood management (Chapter 2).

Integration and Coherence

Good governance also requires integration and "coherence." Agencies must have sufficient breadth and internal coherence to address the challenges they confront. Fragmentation of agencies by geography, jurisdiction, and mission hamper California's ability to address many water challenges. Although

Better integration between water supply and flood management of reservoirs will become increasingly important. Photo by California Department of Water Resources.

decentralization can support responsiveness and innovation, fragmentation is generally inefficient and hinders coherent response. Valuable expertise and decisionmaking capability and perspective are split up, and potential efficiencies from combining management programs (e.g., water supply and water quality) or operating at a larger scale (e.g., regional treatment facilities) are lost. Geographic fragmentation can undermine the ability to plan and manage at a regional or statewide scale. Fragmentation also can undermine the sharing and development of expertise and information, magnifying the state's information problems discussed above.

Figure 8.1a shows the fragmented nature of current California water management. As discussed in Chapter 1, the legislature gave managerial authority to a single agency—the California State Water Commission—when it first created an administrative system for the state's water rights. At the same time, however, the legislature fragmented water administration by giving the commission authority over only post-1914 appropriative rights; all other rights (groundwater, pre-1914 appropriations, and riparian rights) were relegated to the courts. When California decided to build the State Water Project in the 1950s, the legislature further separated water management into two agencies—the Department of Water Resources (DWR) (with authority over the project and state water planning) and the Water Rights Board (with regulatory authority over the state's water rights system)—to avoid conflict between the state's roles as a water

Figure 8.1
Changes in state water governance structure would increase integration and adaptive capacity

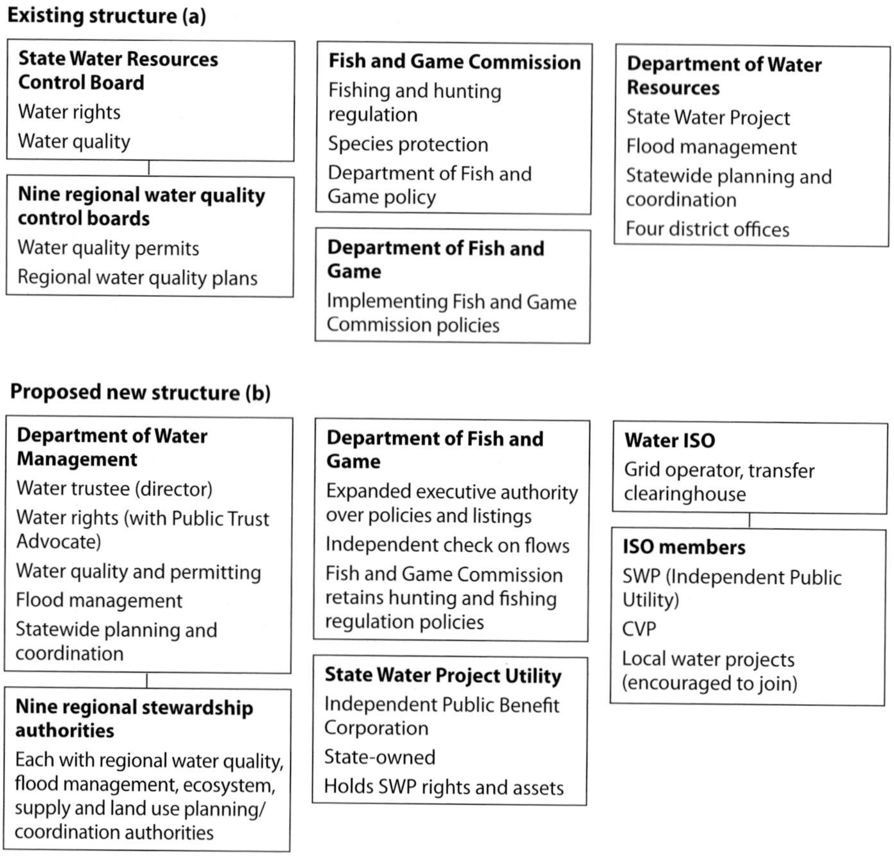

Existing structure (a)

State Water Resources Control Board
Water rights
Water quality

Nine regional water quality control boards
Water quality permits
Regional water quality plans

Fish and Game Commission
Fishing and hunting regulation
Species protection
Department of Fish and Game policy

Department of Fish and Game
Implementing Fish and Game Commission policies

Department of Water Resources
State Water Project
Flood management
Statewide planning and coordination
Four district offices

Proposed new structure (b)

Department of Water Management
Water trustee (director)
Water rights (with Public Trust Advocate)
Water quality and permitting
Flood management
Statewide planning and coordination

Nine regional stewardship authorities
Each with regional water quality, flood management, ecosystem, supply and land use planning/ coordination authorities

Department of Fish and Game
Expanded executive authority over policies and listings
Independent check on flows
Fish and Game Commission retains hunting and fishing regulation policies

State Water Project Utility
Independent Public Benefit Corporation
State-owned
Holds SWP rights and assets

Water ISO
Grid operator, transfer clearinghouse

ISO members
SWP (Independent Public Utility)
CVP
Local water projects (encouraged to join)

project designer and as adjudicator of water rights. In one of the few moves toward greater integration, the legislature combined water quantity and water quality regulation in 1967 to create the current State Water Resources Control Board, replacing the Water Rights Board. The Department of Water Resources, however, remained separate. Authority over water-related fish and game issues has been fragmented for over a century, stemming from the decision in the late 19th century to create two separate entities—the Department of Fish and Game and the Fish and Game Commission (FGC).

Local authority over water issues is similarly fragmented. Many watersheds, for example, are governed by many small agencies, each with jurisdiction over only a small fraction of the watershed and only one or a few aspects of water management (Chapter 2). Jurisdictional fragmentation can further undermine effective water management. For example, to decommission a dam on a salmon-critical stream, a dam owner is likely to need permission from several state agencies (e.g., Department of Fish and Game, Department of Water Resources), federal agencies (e.g., Fish and Wildlife Service, National Marine Fisheries Service (NMFS), U.S. Army Corps of Engineers, Federal Energy Regulatory Commission), and local authorities (cities, counties, local water authorities). Governing legislation, moreover, often gives these agencies quite different and sometimes even opposing missions, increasing the problem of coordinating among agencies on a shared decision or issue.

To improve the capacity of California's state and local institutions to manage water in a more integrated and coherent way, we propose institutional reforms to four functions of water management (supply, quality, floods, ecosystems):

- ▹ A new independent public utility to manage the State Water Project (described in Chapter 7);
- ▹ A new Department of Water Management, merging the water rights and water quality functions of the State Water Resources Control Board and the remaining planning and flood control functions of the Department of Water Resources;
- ▹ A new public trust advocate, to be housed within the Department of Water Management;
- ▹ A shift in responsibilities from the Fish and Game Commission to a reinvigorated Department of Fish and Game;
- ▹ New regional stewardship authorities, expanding on existing regional water quality control boards, to coordinate water quality, supply, flood management, and ecosystem management at the regional and state levels; and
- ▹ A water ISO to coordinate water market transfers (described in Chapter 7).

Figure 8.1b illustrates the basic proposed new structure of state and state-affiliated agencies and independent public-benefit corporations, key elements of which are described below.

One California Water Department

At the statewide level, combining the SWRCB with the nonproject functions of the Department of Water Resources can promote greater coherence and efficiency. As noted, the state created a separate Department of Water Resources only because of the potential conflict presented by the state's development and running of the State Water Project. If the State Water Project is separately managed by a public-benefit corporation, as recommended in Chapter 7, there is no reason to continue to maintain two separate agencies. Merger of the two agencies would allow better coordination of water management functions, increase the technical capabilities available to water rights and water quality regulators, and reduce inefficiencies. By contrast, there is no advantage to tying statewide water planning to the State Water Project. During the Hydraulic Era, when water planning was infrastructure planning, it made more sense to house planning and project operations functions in the same agency. But today, water planning should focus on a much wider and more integrated range of water management and policy activities, including regulation of water projects.

A new Department of Water Management would be an executive agency responsible for

- Administration and enforcement of water rights;
- Administration and enforcement of water quality laws, including continued oversight of regional permitting;
- Statewide water planning, and support and coordination of regional water plans, acting through regional stewardship authorities;
- Development of programs and policies to ensure that California's water is put to "reasonable" use and complies with the public trust doctrine;
- Management of grant and loan programs; and
- Oversight of dam safety and flood management infrastructure and programs.

As discussed below, a single executive official, rather than a council, should lead this new department. The current council structure slows decisionmaking and diffuses responsibility. To ensure the independence and objectivity of water rights administration, the adjudication of water rights should be delegated to administrative law judges, with the assistance of hearing officers.

This recommendation closely parallels the Department of Water Management proposed by the Little Hoover Commission 2010, with two exceptions. First, the Little Hoover Commission does not recommend that the new department have responsibility for administering water quality laws; we believe it is important to keep quality and quantity functions in the same agency. Water quality and quantity decisions are closely related, and California's merger of the two administrative functions is often held out as an example of integrated management (Sax et al. 2006). Indeed, even greater integration of quality and quantity decisions would be valuable. Second, the Little Hoover Commission recommends that the environmental-flow unit of the Department of Fish and Game be merged into the new Department of Water Management, but we recommend maintaining separate units and increasing the modeling capability within the new Department of Water Management. Separate units can help ensure the independence of environmental-flow analysis. If the environmental-flow analysis resides only in the new department, pressure might be placed on the unit to achieve the water department's desired outcomes, even if that is inconsistent with environmental protection. Rather than merging the unit, we recommend that (1) the Department of Fish and Game be revitalized (with, among other things, reinforced modeling capabilities), and (2) the Department of Water Management be required to request the views of the Department of Fish and Game before taking any major action that could negatively affect environmental flows. A similar system of advice and consultation works well with the Federal Energy Regulatory Commission (DeShazo and Freeman 2005).

An open question is whether the new department should be located in the Resources Agency or the California Environmental Protection Agency—or instead should be a separate agency. The Little Hoover Commission recommends locating the new department in the Resources Agency. However, placing the department in the California Environmental Protection Agency would promote coordination between water quality management and other pollution policies. At least one state, New Mexico, places its water department in its environmental agency rather than its resources agency (which focuses instead on energy and minerals). Given the role of water in California, a merged department would be sufficiently important to arguably justify independent, cabinet-level status. Several states, including Arizona and Idaho, have independent water agencies. More important than where the new department sits, however, is its combined jurisdiction, organization, and leadership.

California needs to strengthen the role of the Department of Fish and Game. Photo by Jeff Bernard/Associated Press.

More Coherent Regulation of Fish and Wildlife

The Little Hoover Commission concluded in 1990 that California "has an antiquated structure set up to protect the state's natural resources" and that this structure had proven incapable of "reacting either quickly, consistently, or adequately to the demands of our times" (Little Hoover Commission 1990). In the 20 years since this assessment, California's fish and wildlife have continued to decline. The threat to California's native fishes and the collapse of salmon populations indicate the continued inability of California's "antiquated structure" to deal effectively with conservation of aquatic resources (Chapter 5).

Fragmentation is again part of the problem. First, responsibility over fish and wildlife is divided between the Department of Fish and Game and the Fish and Game Commission, undermining the state's ability to effectively address fisheries and modification of the state's waterways. Most states unify fish and game protection in a single agency. Because the FGC is constitutionally mandated (Cal. Const., art. IV, § 20), the division cannot be completely eliminated. However, because the exact jurisdiction of the FGC is not constitutionally specified, the legislature could limit the responsibilities of the FGC to setting regulations for fishing and hunting, which was its initial jurisdiction. The other duties of the FGC (from managing commercial fisheries, to listing endangered species, to dealing with dams and diversions) are more appropriately handled by scientific experts and should be unified within DFG.

Second, there could be more coordination between DFG and the state agency responsible for water management (whether it be the existing State Water Resources Control Board or the proposed Department of Water Management). Both agencies have common goals but often do not work together effectively. As recommended above, the water agency should receive the timely views of DFG before taking major actions affecting fish and wildlife. The water agency also should establish mechanisms to increase administrative coordination with DFG. Both the water agency and DFG, for example, could coordinate their efforts to require and monitor environmental flows and conditions below dams.

Regional Stewardship Authorities

Greater integration and coherence is important not only at the statewide level but also within regions or watersheds. California encourages regional integration and management of water to a degree. Recent state law, for example, requires linkages between the planning activities of cities and counties (i.e., local land use authorities) and urban water suppliers and flood management agencies (Chapter 2). The state has also provided over $2 billion in bond funds to support Integrated Regional Water Management (IRWM) (Chapter 6). Although this funding has supported projects that multiple water agencies in a region already wanted to pursue, it has not yet served as an effective incentive for additional integration of multiple water management functions at the watershed scale.

To further encourage integration of water resource planning, the California legislature could create an affirmative structure for regional integrated planning and management. We propose creating nine regional stewardship authorities, coinciding with the jurisdictions of existing regional water quality control boards. As discussed below, the authorities would develop and manage integrated basin plans. The new authorities would coordinate and integrate staff from the various state agencies working on aspects of water management within the authority's region, and they would have authority to regulate dams under § 5937 of the Fish and Game Code. The authorities could replace the current regional water quality control boards (assuming these boards' current responsibilities) or supplement and coordinate with the existing boards. Leadership would reflect the broad responsibilities of the new entities. In some cases, local agencies and groups might jointly form regional authorities (similar to the Santa Ana Watershed Project Authority (SAWPA), Box 6.9) to perform these regional coordination functions, under authority and responsibility delegated by the state, with responsible oversight. This latter model reflects a "cooperative federalism" approach to water reform, discussed further in Chapter 9.

The authorities, much like the new Delta Stewardship Council, would be responsible for developing integrated basin plans that encompass water quality, flood control, groundwater management, and other local water resource development, as well as aquatic ecosystem management encompassing everything from local restoration projects to basinwide planning and management. These integrated basin plans would build on the existing basin plans developed by the regional boards, which focus on water quality for human and environmental uses, and incorporate additional water management functions (flood control, water supply), including broader ecosystem management.

Borrowing another idea from the Delta Stewardship Council, all local entities involved in water resources planning, including local land use authorities, water utilities, flood control and reclamation districts, and resource conservation districts, would be subject to a consistency requirement. Both the federal Coastal Zone Management Act and the transportation-planning requirements of the federal Clean Air Act provide models for an effective consistency process. All planning by local entities—such as general plans, urban water management plans, and flood-control plans—would need to be consistent with the broader regional plan to the maximum extent practicable. The regional plans also would be required to be consistent with the state planning policies overseen by the new Department of Water Management. Indeed, coordination of regional and watershed planning efforts would provide much of the basis for the statewide plan, maintaining decentralization, but reducing fragmentation. Various mechanisms could be used to enforce the consistency requirements. For example, state funding for local actions and planning could be contingent on a finding that the local entity is in compliance with the consistency requirement, local plans could be submitted to the regional stewardship authorities for approval (which could be automatic absent action by the authority), or aggrieved parties with standing could be permitted to challenge local actions on consistency grounds in state court.

The existing boundaries of the nine regional water quality control boards—defined to match the boundaries of broad watersheds—are largely appropriate to the scale of regional planning from an integrated resource management perspective.[2] This is a suitable scale for planning to occur, not only for water

2. DWR's hydrologic regions overlap those of the regional boards. The Central Valley board (region 4) consists of three hydrologic regions (Sacramento River, San Joaquin River, Tulare Basin), and the Lahontan board (region X) consists of two hydrologic regions (North Lahontan, South Lahontan). The South Coast hydrologic region is split into three regional boards (Los Angeles, Santa Ana, San Diego), corresponding to local watersheds (www.waterboards.ca.gov/waterboards_map.shtml).

quality but also for groundwater and surface water interactions, coordinated management of reservoirs and stormwater for flood management and water supply, coordinated development of recycled water use and brine disposal, and integrated management of flows and riparian habitat to support aquatic ecosystems. At present, of the 46 IRWM regions accepted by DWR (and hence eligible for bond funds), only three correspond to the boundaries of the regional boards (the Santa Ana River, the North Coast, and the San Francisco Bay Area). Even geographically small regions, such as San Diego and Los Angeles, contain multiple groups, and in many cases these groups have overlapping boundaries.[3]

Some types of management need to be more local, but even then the broader watershed approach can provide policy guidelines and help to set priorities for local projects. For instance, in an area like the Central Coast, where flood management must be for local streams, broader basin planning can develop principles that improve environmental and water supply functions (e.g., less riprap—or rocky armoring—on levees, expanded use of floodplain storage, improved groundwater recharge, improved logging practices). The basin planning approach also would make it possible to prioritize ecosystem reconciliation efforts and conservation dollars within particular areas and local watersheds. The authorities also could encourage and help fund projects of local watershed groups, recognizing that local involvement is essential for success at the regional level as well. Similarly, within the Central Valley, integrated groundwater and surface water management and some aspects of flood management will be needed for more localized areas, but this effort should be integrated at the broader watershed scale to take into account environmental flows into the Delta, water quality, and broader goals of water supply and flood management.

Local Integration and Coordination

Beyond the major structural reforms discussed above, the state should continue to encourage greater coordination among and, where appropriate, merger of, local water agencies. Given the increased complexity of water challenges and the abundance of agencies with often fragmented jurisdiction over water, a single agency may find that its jurisdiction does not extend to all issues or areas that

---

The Department of Fish and Game's seven regions also have a fair degree of overlap with the regional board regions (www.dfg.ca.gov/regions/).

3. For a map of accepted regions as of late November 2009, see www.water.ca.gov/irwm/docs/RegionalsAcceptanceProcess/IRWM_RAP_sizeE_final_decision_11_23_09.pdf. For more information about the regional acceptance process, see www.water.ca.gov/irwm/integregio_rap.cfm.

must be addressed to achieve effective reform. For instance, collaborative agreements between wastewater and water agencies are often needed to implement effective water recycling projects—as with the Orange County groundwater replenishment system project (Chapter 2).

Coordination and integration of local water agencies also can increase their ability to adapt to changes in conditions. Limited geographic or functional reach can restrict adaptation options (Thompson 2010; Folke et al. 2005). A small local water distributor with a single source of supply, for example, may have less ability to respond to a drought than a larger agency with multiple supply alternatives. Flood management agencies with the ability to exercise land use powers may be better able to respond to shifts in flood magnitudes and frequencies than agencies with only the ability to manipulate physical infrastructure. Joint powers authorities have been successful in many cases (such as SAWPA), but agency mergers and other actions also may be warranted.

Legislation that requires coordination—such as the 2001 "show me the water" laws requiring that cities and counties get the approval of the local water district before approving large new developments—can help in this regard, even when the broader lines of authority between agencies remain distinct (Hanak 2010).

Federal Fragmentation

Federal water management also suffers from unnecessary fragmentation. One of the best examples is the division of responsibility under the Endangered Species Act (ESA) between the National Marine Fisheries Service, which is housed in the Department of Commerce, and the Fish and Wildlife Service, in the Department of the Interior. For decades, this division did not exist, and the Fish and Wildlife Service handled freshwater, marine, and anadromous fisheries. In the late 1960s, however, President Richard Nixon moved management of anadromous and marine fisheries to the National Oceanic and Atmospheric Administration in the Department of Commerce. Merging the NMFS back into the Department of the Interior would promote greater coherence in federal protection of imperiled species.

Decisionmaking

A third issue is how to ensure that decisions are made in a timely fashion and with due regard for science and the public trust. The current committee structure of the State Water Resources Control Board, in which decisions are made by votes of the five board members, presents concerns on both counts. In many instances, the board's committee structure, combined with the requirement that most decisions come before the full board, slows and complicates decisionmaking. Because the board is quasi-adjudicatory, it also has been unwilling in some situations to commit to agreements negotiated through multistakeholder processes, undermining efforts to solve state water problems through such negotiations. However, in other situations, the board's appointed members have proven incapable of withstanding significant political pressure from water users and have encouraged parties to reach a compromise agreement rather than making politically difficult decisions. Sometimes, the committee structure has also diffused responsibility and reduced the accountability of individual board members.

The legislature should consider moving away from the current committee structure, whether it retains the current State Water Resources Control Board or replaces it with a unified Department of Water Management. In most western states, a single state engineer, rather than a multimember board, administers the water rights system. Replacing the current board with a "state water trustee," modeled after state engineers but with a modern emphasis on the official's responsibility to manage the state's water in compliance with the public trust, would address several major deficiencies of the current board structure. Like current members of the State Water Resources Control Board, the state water trustee should serve for a fixed term rather than at the pleasure of the governor. Smaller steps could address specific problems. For example, establishing an active network of administrative law judges or providing for decisions by delegated individual board members, without full board consideration except where the board chooses to convene as a panel, could help speed the current process. Such steps, however, would not eliminate the fundamental problems of a board structure.

The legislature should also look for ways to ensure that the water agency adequately considers the public trust interest in California water. The diffuse character of public benefits and the limited resources of environmental interests mean that the public trust is not always adequately represented in board proceedings. One potential solution is to establish a public trust advocate, modeled after the Division of Ratepayer Advocates at the California Public Utility Commission (Division of Ratepayer Advocates 2010). The public trust advocate would be responsible for evaluating major board proceedings for public trust implications and advocating for positions that promote the public trust. To promote independence, the public trust advocate could be appointed by the governor, with confirmation by the legislature, but serve for a fixed term rather than at the governor's pleasure. In addition to ensuring representation of public trust interests, a public trust advocate would also help provide for more deliberate and consistent development of public-trust principles in the board's work. Like the Division of Ratepayer Advocates, the public trust advocate also could be a source of information to the legislature. A public trust advocate would be a useful innovation whether the board remains independent or is merged into a Department of Water Management.

In interviews, we repeatedly heard that a major obstacle to effective, long-term reform by California administrative agencies has been political pressure from the legislature or governor. The state may wish to seek ways to shield state water authorities from the most pernicious pressures and provide them with sufficient autonomy to formulate coherent, long-term water policies. The short-term political objectives of water users and other stakeholders often are inconsistent with the long-term needs of a sustainable water system. Effective water management requires a consistent, long-term perspective, protected to a significant degree from short-term politics. When crises such as droughts hit, water managers need to keep long-term goals in mind and not simply respond to immediate political demands. Autonomy is particularly important where issues are technical and depend on scientific expertise, as in the protection of imperiled ecosystems and fisheries.

In similar situations, Congress and other legislatures have developed a variety of techniques to try to reduce political pressure on administrative actions. For example, the legislature can provide administrative appointees with fixed terms, so that they cannot be fired in response to political pressure. As noted above, we recommend that major water positions in California receive fixed terms. In the case of some administrative positions (e.g., members of the Federal Reserve Board who serve for 14 years), terms are longer than political cycles to help insulate the appointees from day-to-day political pressures. Councils with staggered terms also should provide greater protection from momentary political pressure, although this benefit must be weighed against the potential costs from council systems discussed above. Providing agencies with significant budgetary independence (e.g., through fee revenues that do not require yearly appropriations) also helps reduce the potential for disruptive political influence. In considering new administrative structures for water management, the California legislature should evaluate the potential benefits of these and similar mechanisms to ensure effective, long-term water management.

Adaptive Capacity

Governmental institutions should be able not only to address current challenges but also to adapt their policies and practices to changing conditions and demands. Government's adaptive capacity has always been important. Changes in the environment (including water conditions), the economy, population, technology, and other factors frequently require new policies and approaches. Government must be able to identify and respond to those changes on a timely and effective basis.

Climate change and the other drivers of change described in Chapter 3 make adaptive capacity all the more important today and in the future. Climate change alone will significantly affect water resources and demands: Mean temperature will change, extreme events such as droughts and floods will become worse and more common, and weather regimes themselves could shift (Duit and Galaz 2008). These changes will often be unpredictable, making it critical that agencies be able to adapt to events as they occur (Thompson 2010; Easterling, Hurd, and Smith 2004). The many other drivers of change in California water management impose similar demands for governmental adaptation.

Effective adaptation requires that governmental institutions have capacities to explore, create, and implement new policies (Thompson 2010). Institutions must gather, develop, and analyze information to identify changes in conditions and needs that may require new policies and practices. Institutions must also have sufficient creativity to be able to develop solutions to problems that have not been seen before. Creativity requires openness to new ideas and to dissent within an institution. Finally, institutions must be able to implement needed adaptations on a timely basis, which requires that they be capable, efficient, and coherent.

In addition to adopting the structural changes suggested above, California could improve its adaptive capacity in at least four additional ways. First, agencies can make modest investments that keep or expand the availability of future alternatives (Dobes 2008). For example, if a water supplier is building a treatment plant, the supplier can plan and construct the plant to permit future expansion—enabling the supplier to increase capacity in the future if changing conditions require it, without having to make potentially unnecessary investments today. Even the simple steps of planning options today and preparing environmental assessments of those options in advance of their implementation can increase the ability of agencies to respond to changes on a timely basis (Quay 2010).

Second, legislatures can enhance the adaptive capacity of agencies by not straight-jacketing agencies unnecessarily (Thompson 2010). Although reducing the risk of administrative abuse of discretion, strict legislative directives often reduce the ability of agencies to be efficient and effective and to modify practices in response to changing conditions. As discussed above, for example, the strict mandate in the Endangered Species Act that governments take no action that could jeopardize endangered or threatened species may become unworkable given significant climate change or additional invasive species (Chapter 5). Although the U.S. Fish and Wildlife Service might be able to better effectuate the goals of the ESA in some future cases by focusing on ecosystems and triaging among species, the ESA limits that option.

Third, the government should avoid unnecessarily locking in decisions for lengthy periods of time (Hallegatte 2009). Permits, licenses, and contracts can limit the government's adaptive capacity when they do not allow for modification during their terms, last for long time periods, and carry a presumption of renewability. Water users, whether dam operators or water recipients, have legitimate reasons to seek certainty. However, too often terms and conditions have erred in favor of certainty rather than agency flexibility, and flexibility has become necessary for adapting to change. The government therefore should reevaluate whether current terms and conditions for dam licenses, reclamation and other water contracts, and appropriation permits should be revised.

Finally, the government can promote adaptation to climate and other changes by enhancing the ability of markets to respond to changed conditions. Markets historically have been responsive to climate changes and have already begun to respond to current climate shifts (Thompson 2010). The government should therefore avoid erecting unnecessary barriers to market adaptation. Water markets, for example, can help regions adapt by allowing water-short regions and users to acquire water from regions or users who are better able to spare water (Chapters 2, 6). By promoting water markets, the government increases society's ability to adapt to changes in water availability (Phelps et al. 1978; Lund and Israel 1995b; Kiparsky and Gleick 2005; Luers and Moser 2006). As highlighted in Chapter 7, the state can take further steps to enhance California's water market—through streamlined environmental reviews and the creation of a water ISO to serve as a water transfer clearinghouse. In addition to participating in these reforms, the federal government can enhance water marketing by eliminating the types of crop subsidy programs that discourage water transfers. For instance, current rules disallow farmers from collecting crop payments for relatively low-value field crops (such as cotton) if they use the land to plant higher-value fruits and nuts—a discouragement of more efficient use of scarce water resources (Chapter 2). Further "decoupling" of federal farm subsidies—so that they do not create artificial incentives to produce particular crops—is part of a responsible federal water policy for the 21st century.

Improving Water Governance

Leadership is ultimately more important to California water management than is the structure of the state's water institutions. But structure matters. Existing and new policies to tackle California's water management challenges are less likely to be implemented effectively if governmental institutions themselves are ineffective. Institutional structure also helps determine a state's ability to identify needs for future reforms and to adopt those reforms on a timely basis.

Many of our recommendations, such as the creation of a new Department of Water Management and regional stewardship authorities, will require legislative action. Others can be undertaken today without new legislation. California courts, for example, can provide for greater expertise and training, local agencies can establish new collaborative partnerships, and agencies can increase their flexibility by anticipating and planning for changing conditions.

Our recommendations reflect five themes. First, adequate information, expertise, and resources are critical for making wise decisions and for knowing when adaptation is needed. Existing state agencies and the proposed Department of Water Management should ensure that adequate information is being collected and available to policymakers, stakeholders, and the public at large in a usable and useful format. Moreover, the legislature should require the submission of key information. Policymakers and managers need access to the expertise and resources needed to make and implement effective decisions.

Second, the most important reform for water-related agencies at all levels of government is to increase integration, coordination, and coherence. This will not only help improve current water management but also increase the state's adaptive capacity and ability to deal with changing conditions. At the statewide level, the State Water Resources Control Board should be merged with the nonproject functions of the current Department of Water Resources. As discussed in Chapter 7, the State Water Project should be managed as a separate and independent public utility. At the regional level, the legislature should create new regional stewardship authorities (either replacing or supplementing existing regional water quality control boards). The state also should continue to encourage, through financial and other incentives, integration and coordination among local water agencies.

Another major theme is that the state should move away from management through council structures and toward greater use of expert agencies. The council structure of the State Water Resources Control Board appears to diffuse responsibility and to slow and complicate decisions. Similarly, many decisions assigned today to the Fish and Game Commission are far more complex than is appropriate for a nonexpert committee of volunteers. All regulatory functions of the State Water Resources Control Board, whether it remains independent or is merged into a new Department of Water Management, should be headed by an appointed state trustee. The responsibilities of the Fish and Game Commission should be limited to setting hunting and fishing restrictions, with other responsibilities being reassigned to the Department of Fish and Game.

Fourth, the state system should develop structures and mechanisms to ensure that the public trust in water is better protected. The legislature, for example, should create a new public trust advocate, to be located either in a new Department of Water Management or in the State Water Resources Control Board if it is maintained as an independent entity. The Department of Fish and Game should retain authority over environmental flows, as an independent check on the authority of the State Water Resources Control Board to issue and oversee water use permits. Before making any major decision that could negatively affect aquatic resources, the board should consult with the Department of Fish and Game and take its views into account.

Fifth, governing institutions should take steps to improve their adaptive capacity. This includes taking actions that expand management opportunities in the future, avoiding strict legislative directives that overly restrict agency authority. One key institutional issue is to avoid unnecessarily locking in decisions for lengthy periods of time. Permits, licenses, and contracts can limit the government's adaptive capacity when they do not allow for modification during their terms, last for long time periods, and carry a presumption of renewability. Both the state and federal governments should reevaluate whether current terms and conditions for dam licenses, water contracts, and water rights permits should be revised.

These institutional improvements should make it easier for reforms and leadership to be more effective in managing water adaptively in a changing California.

9 Pathways to Reform

CALIFORNIA DEPARTMENT OF WATER RESOURCES

Delay always breeds danger; and to protract a great design is often to ruin it.

Miguel de Cervantes, *The History of Don Quixote of la Mancha*

Our previous chapters have suggested many reforms for California's water policy. Unfortunately, the history of the Golden State is littered with great ideas for water reform that were never adopted because they were poorly planned or badly executed. This chapter discusses how to design and promote effective reforms. The greatest obstacles to a more sustainable water system are political and institutional—not a lack of understanding regarding the need for reform or the nature of beneficial reforms. To be successful, reforms must not only be scientifically sound and rational but also be sensitive to political, economic, social, and institutional considerations (Cordova 1994).

Water reform efforts should keep in mind at least four truths. First, although crises often spur reform, California cannot afford to wait for crises to solve many of its water challenges. Second, federal, state, and local agencies often already enjoy the discretion and authority needed to implement reforms. The challenge generally is not the law but a combination of inadequate resources and lack of political will. Third, although local agencies and governments often have an advantage in designing and implementing reforms, they frequently need a mandate or nudge from the state or federal government to pursue a reform. Finally, the government has a variety of means available to address the problem of transition costs, which are generally the major source of political opposition to reforms. This chapter considers each of these particulars and looks at how proponents of reform can promote reform efforts.

The Jones Tract levee break in the Delta, summer 2004.

Waiting Can Be Costly

Reforms generally are costly and often depend on a precipitating crisis to overcome reluctance to enact them. Political scientists have suggested that successful policy reforms are more likely during political "honeymoons" (when new administrations take office with key reform plans and do not yet face a hostile legislature) and in response to crises (Williamson 1994). New political administrations sometimes enjoy considerable success at enacting bold reforms early in the first year or two of their administrations (Dinar 2000). Crises, however, have motivated most water reforms in California's history (Chapter 1). For example, saltwater intrusion in coastal aquifers of Southern California in the middle of the 20th century helped spur lawsuits among urban water agencies and the creation of groundwater management and replenishment districts (Blomquist, Schlager, and Heikkila 2004; Ostrom 1990). California droughts in the 1970s and 1980s encouraged development of both water markets and significant conservation programs (Archibald and Renwick 1998; Thompson 1993). The "burning" of the Cuyahoga River and similar catastrophic consequences of water pollution helped motivate congressional passage of the Water Pollution Control Act of 1972 (now the Clean Water Act [CWA]) (Salzman and Thompson 2010). Hurricane Katrina spurred a renewed focus on flood management in California. And recent court decisions have focused attention on the problems of the Sacramento–San Joaquin Delta.

However, waiting for a crisis before addressing water problems has substantial costs. First, by the time people realize there is a crisis, the problem may have generated unrecoverable costs or irreversible losses. For example, dewatering a waterway may lead to the extinction of a species. Overdrafting an aquifer can cause irreversible subsidence or saltwater intrusion or strand agricultural or residential developments that relied on the availability of groundwater (Sax et al. 2006). One could argue that in many cases, California is already facing a crisis, but the crisis is moving so slowly that policymakers and the public fail to recognize it.

Second, by the time a crisis is recognized, many of the best management options may be precluded or difficult to implement, and political positions might be too entrenched to overcome. For example, if decisionmakers wait to see if climate change actually leads to large floods that overpower current flood-control infrastructures, flood easements may no longer be viable because key floodplains have already become urbanized. Options for protecting fish species are generally far more constrained once a species is highly stressed and listed as threatened or endangered under the Endangered Species Act. A major criticism of the Endangered Species Act is that it pursues an emergency-room approach to species protection and acts too late to take the most effective actions (Chapter 5; Salzman and Thompson 2010). Finally, crises typically require quick action, whereas developing effective solutions may require careful and prolonged consultation and deliberation.

Coho salmon provide an example of problems from waiting too long to act. Coho salmon once supported large commercial fisheries yet have been moving toward extinction for at least 40 years, largely from logging, overexploitation, dams, and hatchery effects (Moyle, Israel, and Purdy 2008). The Department of Fish and Game and other agencies failed to deal with the decline until the mid-1990s (Brown, Moyle, and Yoshiyama 1994). The federal government finally listed California coho as threatened in 1996, and the state soon followed suit. Because the decline was so long-standing and deep, the recovery plan (National Marine Fisheries Service 2010) is more of an extinction prevention plan than a recovery plan (Miller 2010). More important, every small change to the few remaining coho salmon streams presents a significant problem with few options. San Geronimo Creek in Marin County, a small tributary to Lagunitas Creek, contains the last sustainable runs of coho in the region. Because it is one of the few streams where steps can still be taken to protect the coho, housing developments in the region are threatened, to the consternation of developers and local residents who cannot understand why efforts to save coho salmon must restrict their use of a tiny creek and its watershed (Miller 2010). Dealing with the decline of coho when they were still widespread would have made far more sense. Likewise, delaying timely action on the Sacramento–San Joaquin Delta provides myriad examples of potential losses of native fish species as well as many economic and recreational values (Lund et al. 2010).

Not every reform to California water policy needs to be immediate. In some cases, waiting may produce valuable information or new technologies or save on administrative expenses (Howitt 1995). For example, waiting for better information on whether the future climate will be wetter or drier before building new surface storage is prudent, because new storage is expensive and will have little added value in a drier climate with less water available to fill reservoirs (Chapter 6). Suggestions to delay water reforms, however, should consider and weigh the costs—financial, ecological, and social.

New Laws Are Often Unnecessary

In most cases, federal, state, and local agencies can reform water policy today without legislative action.[1] Moreover, agencies often have the expertise, experience, and understanding of stakeholder interests needed to identify, analyze, design, and implement effective reforms. However, agencies frequently lack the willingness, and sometimes the resources, to tackle reforms. Where agencies' jurisdictions are unclear or political opposition is significant, legislatures may still need to intervene, but these situations are more the exception than the norm. Courts also can help by reforming common-law rules, by reducing constitutional and other legal barriers to reform, and by providing a forum for reform negotiations among stakeholders.

Agency Authority

The history of California water policy provides many examples of the ability of agencies to pursue crucial reforms without new legislative authority. In the past, for example, the State Water Resources Control Board (SWRCB) has creatively used its authority and discretion under the "reasonable use" provisions of the California constitution and the public trust doctrine to address a variety of perceived water problems. The board, for example, has sought to abolish or limit unexercised riparian rights through stream adjudications (*Long Valley Creek Stream System* 1979), encouraged water conservation by declaring excess water use to be unreasonable (Imperial Irrigation District 1984), regulated the operation of federal dams to protect the state's environment (*California v. United States* 1978), and engaged (albeit fitfully) in efforts to increase water flows in the Delta (Hundley 2001; State Water Resources Control Board 2010b).

Current water challenges require similar creativity and willingness to exercise authority and discretion. The board's broad authority and expertise put it in a prime position to address many reform needs identified in earlier chapters. For example, it can bar illegal diversions and can use its reasonable use authority to promote greater water conservation (Chapter 7). Actions might include:

1. A recent example is the state controller's decision to require that local governments report salary information, in response to concerns over the lack of adequate local oversight. This information, now being made public on the controller's website, was gathered under the controller's existing authority to require financial reports (http://lgcr.sco.ca.gov/). This information may ultimately help spur some consolidation of small water districts, which often have high overheads because they must cover the costs of expensive senior management functions from a small ratepayer base. More generally, making information readily available in a comparable form for decentralized governing bodies may be a powerful tool for reform.

- ▷ Requiring use of tiered pricing systems, designed to encourage conservation, as a condition of continued use of an appropriation permit;
- ▷ Imposing conservation standards as a condition of continued appropriation;
- ▷ Requiring water users to increase the efficiency of their use by, for example, reclaiming and reusing wastewater by urban utilities; and
- ▷ Allowing at least limited participation of farmers in water markets within or outside a water district.

Similarly, the board can use its reasonable use power to impose additional terms—or conditions—on water rights permits designed to protect the state's environment (e.g., conditions addressing salinity problems or watershed protection). Finally, knowledgeable experts have argued, with considerable legal support, that the board can exercise its authority over "subterranean waters" to regulate any groundwater pumping that threatens material injury to consumptive or instream surface water uses (Sax 2003).

A state agency with significant authority over an important segment of the state's water supply—but one that is often forgotten—is the California Public Utilities Commission (CPUC). The CPUC regulates privately owned water utilities, which serve roughly one-fifth of California's households. An example of the CPUC's ability to pursue broad reforms is its recent promotion of tiered pricing structures (Box 6.2). The State Water Resources Control Board could follow the CPUC's lead by instituting a regular rate review for publicly owned utilities, to ensure that rates are consistent with reasonable use.

Federal agencies also can pursue many reforms under their current authority without congressional action. Faced with criticism of the federal Endangered Species Act (ESA) from property owners in the 1990s, the Clinton administration adopted several major administrative reforms to the act without seeking or obtaining congressional approval. These reforms include a "no surprises policy" (under which the government agrees not to seek further uncompensated protections from a property owner after issuing an incidental take permit, except in exceptional circumstances) and a safe harbor program (protecting property owners who voluntarily act to protect endangered species from any new obligations under the ESA) (Salzman and Thompson 2010). These reforms are now an accepted and established part of the ESA, even though they are not explicitly found in the act. Federal agencies also used their discretion under the ESA to participate in the Environmental Water Account, a water transfer mechanism that attempted to introduce a degree of flexibility into the operation of the ESA (Chapter 2; Thompson 2000).

As described above, the U.S. Fish and Wildlife Service today can use its authority under the ESA in a similar fashion to help reconcile environmental water needs with those of agricultural and urban users and focus on protecting ecosystems rather than just individual species (Chapter 5). It can use its latitude under the ESA to move away from a species-specific approach toward a focus on ecosystem protection. In particular, it can work with water users under § 10 of the ESA to develop multispecies habitat conservation plans focused on whole ecosystems. Where a sufficient number of species are listed in a particular ecosystem, federal agencies also can develop recovery plans that focus on broader ecosystem principles underlying the recovery of the species.

Judicial rules for reviewing administrative actions reinforce the latitude of administrative agencies under their governing statutes and other legal provisions. Under both federal and state law, agencies cannot stray from the requirements of clear legislative intent. However, where legislative language is ambiguous or silent on a particular issue, courts uphold agency decisions so long as the agency's interpretation of the statute is a "permissible" interpretation; the agency interpretation does not need to be the best or most reasonable interpretation in the eyes of the court (*Chevron, U.S.A., Inc. v. Natural Resources Defense Council* 1984). Courts, moreover, typically defer to an agency's expertise in the agency's application of the law to specific facts (Salzman and Thompson 2010).

The discretion and authority of local water agencies over local water uses and practices are often far greater than that of federal and state agencies. Local water districts control the largest percentage of California's water supply, including water for over half of the state's irrigated acreage. Like administrative agencies, local agencies have significant discretion to both supplement state water rules and modify them within their borders to better serve local needs (Thompson 1993). Local agencies have used this discretion to adopt numerous reforms—including local regulation of groundwater, development of local water markets, use of reclaimed water to recharge local groundwater basins, and adoption of conservation rate structures (Chapter 6).[2]

2. On groundwater regulation, see also Blomquist (1992); Anderson (1983); Anderson, Burt, and Fractor (1983); and Peck (1980). On local water markets, see Archibald et al. (1992); Thompson (1993); Carey, Sunding, and Zilberman (2001); and Israel and Lund (1995). On groundwater recharge, see Sax et al. (2006). On the adoption of conservation-oriented rate structures, see Hanak (2005b).

Despite their wide latitude, administrative and local agencies often have been reticent to exercise creative authority (Hundley 2001). The SWRCB has generally undertaken major reforms only in response to judicial or legislative pressure. In 1986, the California Court of Appeal criticized the board's failure to more aggressively address water quality issues in the Delta (Chapter 2). According to the court, the board was overlooking its "statutory commitment to establish objectives assuring the reasonable protection of beneficial uses . . . [which] grants the Board broad discretion to establish reasonable standards consistent with overall statewide standards" (*United States v. State Water Resources Control Board* 1986).

Efforts to reform California water policy must understand and address the reasons for the agencies' reticence. In some cases, agencies lack resources, time, and personnel to either evaluate or implement significant reforms. Given the increased complexity of water challenges and the abundance of agencies with some jurisdiction over water, a single agency may also find that its jurisdiction does not extend to all the issues that must be addressed to achieve effective reform. The governmental reforms suggested in Chapters 7 and 8 (particularly creation of adequate and reliable funding and increased collaboration among agencies) would help address these obstacles.

In other cases, however, agencies face significant political pressure not to challenge the status quo and need external mandates or pressure to justify acting (Hundley 2001). The threat of lawsuits if a reform is adopted can also deter agencies from adopting the reform, even if an agency feels confident that the courts will ultimately uphold the action, because lawsuits are costly and distract the organization from other duties.

Legislatures

In several settings, Congress or the state legislature may need to act to enable effective reform. In some cases, Congress or the legislature can further reform by giving agencies clear authority to engage in a needed reform. For example, although legal experts have argued that the SWRCB has authority to regulate all groundwater withdrawals (Roos-Collins 2009), groundwater users are likely to judicially challenge any effort by the board to do so—leading to a significant delay and expense—and the board currently lacks the resources needed to administer groundwater statewide. Only legislative intervention can provide a clear mandate and the needed resources (Chapter 7). The board also does not currently have authority to quantify riparian rights except in lengthy and costly stream adjudications.

Similarly, legislative revisions to the ESA and the California Endangered Species Act (CESA) may ultimately be needed to allow the triage of species as part of integrated ecosystem management that focuses on aggregate species recovery. As explained above, both ESA and CESA appear to incorporate sufficient discretion today to enable fish and wildlife agencies to focus on the protection of broad ecosystems and multiple species; many regional habitat conservation plans, as well as natural community conservation planning, already do exactly that. Neither ESA nor CESA, however, provide a clear mechanism under which the agencies could allow some species in a river or estuary to become extinct to protect more species in the aggregate. Congress designed the existing so-called "God Squad" to address species-versus-economy disputes, not unavoidable species-versus-species tradeoffs, and the CESA contains no system similar to the God Squad (Chapter 5). If such triage becomes necessary to effective species protection in the future, new federal and state legislation providing a mechanism for determining when it is appropriate to engage in triage (like the Endangered Ecosystem Committee described in Chapter 5) will be critical.

Even where an administrative agency appears to have the needed authority and is inclined to pursue a specific reform, the legislature may still find it useful to clarify the agency's statutory authority or signal legislative support for the reform through new legislation or oversight hearings. In the 1980s and 1990s, for example, the state legislature helped promote water markets by clarifying the authority of water districts to engage in such transfers and by expressly emphasizing the state's interest in promoting transfers (Chapter 2). In a similar fashion, the California legislature today could usefully clarify the State Water Resources Control Board's authority to regulate groundwater–surface water interactions, as well as provide guidance on how to engage in conjunctive management (Chapter 7).

Legislative intervention also may be needed to ensure that agencies have the resources needed to design and implement effective reforms. As described above, legislative enactment of a public goods charge or other sustainable revenue source is needed to ensure that the SWRCB, Department of Fish and Game, and other state agencies have sustainable funding (Chapters 7, 8).

In other cases, legislatures may need to set general or specific performance standards for water reforms, either because the legislature does not believe that the agency will otherwise implement reforms or because it concludes that the standard should be set democratically rather than by an expert agency. The state legislature for over a hundred years has established substantive environmental protections through such laws as the Porter-Cologne Act, the California Wild and Scenic River Act, the state Endangered Species Act, and the Fish and Game Code. The legislature also has adopted quantitative goals for urban conservation and recycling. Similarly, legislative direction on groundwater management, funding, and other issues is desirable.

Courts

Courts have often been the agent of change in California water law and remain critical players in reform efforts. Courts are the major arbiter of common-law doctrines such as the reasonableness rule and the public trust doctrine. In the case of groundwater, riparian rights, and pre-1914 appropriative rights, courts have primary authority. Courts also are the ultimate interpreters and enforcers of statutes, such as the federal and state Endangered Species Acts and water quality laws. Courts, moreover, have advantages as agents of reform. Largely insulated from political pressure, courts may be willing to act in some cases where the legislature would not and are more likely to pay attention to perceived principles than to relative political power in designing reforms (Thompson 1990).

However, courts also have limitations that make it essential that legislatures and administrative agencies also actively pursue reforms and not simply leave reform efforts to the courts. For example, courts have more limited fact-finding ability than legislatures as well as less expertise on complex issues, given legislative staff and committee processes. Courts also lack funding or staff to implement and enforce reforms that require long-run administration. More important, courts are reactive; they cannot proactively identify and solve problems. Courts instead rely on plaintiffs to bring matters before them and present relevant information, and they then implement and enforce judgments. Courts, in short, are important agents of reform, but they are unable to solve California's water challenges by themselves. This is particularly true where legislation limits the opportunity for independent judicial reform.

Even where courts are not direct reform agents, they can serve important supporting roles. First, courts can provide a valuable forum for negotiating and implementing reforms. After World War II, for example, courts in Southern California provided a forum for establishing effective groundwater management and replenishment districts. Although groundwater users could have voluntarily worked together to establish such districts, groundwater adjudications were a formal means to bring all groundwater users together to negotiate, collect and share relevant data and other information, and examine alternative management options. Courts also could force dissenting groundwater users to accept negotiated agreements and then enforce and oversee the agreements over time. More recently, a federal district court provided the forum in which environmentalists and water users on the San Joaquin River developed a program for restoring environmental flows to the river (Box 9.1). The availability of forums for negotiation, information-sharing, and discussion, as well as for enforcing resulting agreements, is critical to the success of stakeholder processes (Blomquist, Dinar, and Kemper 2010).

9.1

Restoring the San Joaquin River

After completion of Friant Dam on the San Joaquin River in the 1940s to supply water to farmers in the San Joaquin Valley and Tulare Basin, the middle reaches of the river were allowed to go dry, except for a short reach below the dam. As a result, a run of up to 50,000 Chinook salmon went extinct, a clear violation of § 5937 of the Fish and Game Code (Box 1.3). Attorney General Pat Brown declared the Code only advisory and refused to let the Department of Fish and Game sue to keep the river alive. Finally, in 1988, a coalition of environmental groups, led by the Natural Resources Defense Council, filed a lawsuit challenging the right of the Bureau of Reclamation to continue operating the dam without providing water for fish, especially salmon (*Natural Resources Defense Council v. Rodgers*). Eighteen years later, in 2006, the parties finally reached a court-ordered settlement agreement with two major goals: (1) restore and maintain fish populations in "good condition" in 150 miles of the San Joaquin River down to its confluence with the Merced River; and (2) reduce the delivery reduction effects on long-term water contractors that might be affected by the settlement. The settlement established an ambitious schedule to restore Chinook salmon runs and reestablish other fish in the river. The federal and state governments appropriated about $400 million to restore lost channels and provide infrastructure to reduce effects on irrigators. In 2010, the first experimental flows were released from the dam, and major planning efforts were well under way for activities ranging from determining the environmental flow regime to designing new diversions and channels to choosing stocks of fish for reintroduction to appointing a restoration administrator. The post-settlement process has been highly contentious, especially with local farmers, but progress is being made. The first salmon are due to be released into the system by December 31, 2012. The settlement illustrates the potential of lawsuit-disciplined consensus processes to resolve important water management issues, as well as the ability of state laws and policies to "nudge" changes in federal project operations.

The San Joaquin River settlement arose from a lawsuit-disciplined consensus process. Photo by Peter Moyle.

Second, courts can either foster or impede reforms by other branches of government through the constitutional and procedural ground rules that they set. Courts throughout the United States, for example, have helped enable groundwater reform by consistently holding that limitations on pumping do not generally constitute takings of common-law groundwater rights and have assisted efforts to reform federal reclamation practices by holding that the federal government enjoys considerable latitude to change particular policies under federal reclamation contracts (Sax 1990; Thompson 1995; Gray 2002a, 2002b; Sax et al. 2006). Recent decisions holding that restrictions on surface water withdrawals can constitute physical takings for which the government must pay just compensation, by contrast, have created hurdles to increasing environmental flows for endangered or threatened species (Box 7.1). The California Supreme Court's interpretation of the takings protections in the California constitution has similarly made it difficult to abolish or limit riparian rights as most other western states have done (*Long Valley* 1979; Sax et al. 2006). Courts also can affect the ease or difficulty of administrative reforms through decisions dealing with what procedures must be followed under the National Environmental Policy Act or other laws in promulgating reforms and addressing the standing of parties to challenge reforms. The recent decision by a federal district court requiring that agencies comply with the National Environmental Policy Act before complying with a biological opinion issued under the ESA, for example, makes it more difficult to use the ESA to protect environmental flows (Chapter 1).

Mandating and Nudging Local Action

Local agencies often have special advantages in designing and implementing reforms. Local governments historically have held responsibility for many water issues (Chapter 1; Thompson 1997a) and therefore enjoy significant expertise as well as crucial relationships with water users. Decentralized water management can have a variety of advantages—including a greater understanding of local issues and needs; the ability to customize policies to local conditions, constraints, and needs; enhanced input from local resource users and other local members of the public; and the opportunity for experimentation across jurisdictions (Blomquist, Dinar, and Kemper 2010; Anderson and Hill 1997; Thompson 1997a; Lund 2006). The opportunity for experimentation is particularly important where no policy approach is proven and preferable in all situations. States and localities, for example, have adopted varied options in attempting to reduce groundwater overdrafts and nonpoint pollution, promote water conservation, and increase environmental flows (Smith 1986, Sax et al. 2006). By allowing states and localities the freedom to test and compare different approaches, states and the nation benefit from experimentation, comparison, and borrowing (Thompson 1997a).

Local design and implementation of reforms, however, are sometimes inappropriate. State or federal reforms will be needed to address:

- "Spillover effects" or "externalities" where water management in one region affects a broader area—as with groundwater overdraft and downstream impacts of water pollution and flood management decisions (Salzman and Thompson 2010);
- Ethical issues of interest to the general polity, such as the interest of a state or nation in protecting sustainable resources for future generations, or in transparency or equity (Thompson 1997a);
- Economies of scale in addressing an issue in a larger geographic region;
- Fears that local governments will relax environmental standards to attract or retain businesses, leading to a so-called "race to the bottom" (Salzman and Thompson 2010; Stewart 1977);

- Concerns that some interest groups enjoy disproportionate political power at the local level (Blomquist 1991; Ringquist 1993; Thompson 1997a).

Generally, reform is likely to be most effective where agency boundaries match the boundaries of the resource (Blomquist, Dinar, and Kemper 2010; Ostrom 1990). In water, that is typically the watershed. Effective reforms therefore often call for a coordinated effort among local entities in a watershed or creation of a new watershed-wide entity (Goldfarb 1994; Harrison 1980). The key is to ensure coordinated solutions across the watershed (Thompson 1997a). Our recommendation to create regional stewardship authorities reflects this need to improve coordination among the state's many decentralized water and land use planning entities (Chapter 8).

Even where local agencies would be best at designing and implementing reforms, the state or federal government may need to mandate or "nudge" local agencies to act. Local agencies have often not adopted reforms on their own because of political opposition (Leshy 2009). External pressure has commonly been needed for local agencies to act. Groundwater reform is an example. Local water districts and governments might be best at determining how to restrict groundwater usage in a particular area, but the state, which has a strong interest in ensuring that regions manage their water sustainably, may need to force them to act.

Cooperative Federalism

When the state or federal government directly mandates reform at the local level, the critical question is how much authority to delegate to the local agencies. Table 9.1 shows several models of what has become known as cooperative federalism, in which the state or federal government delegates at least some authority to lower levels of government, along with expectations for performance. In all models, the state (or national) government establishes the basic statutory mandate but then delegates varying levels of control to a lower level of government. *Planning mandates*, in which the state (or national) government requires that lower levels of government analyze and address a particular issue (e.g., urban conservation) but does not set specific standards of performance, provide the greatest discretion to the lower levels. Under *standard-driven federalism*, by contrast, the state (or national) government sets minimum performance standards or goals that the lower level of government must meet but leaves the choice of how to meet these standards up to the lower level. In most cases, the state (or national) government also reserves the right to step in and implement the standards if the lower level of government fails to implement them effectively. The lower level of government is also generally responsible for enforcement and often free to set more rigorous standards or goals if it wishes. Finally, under *managerial federalism*, the state (or national) government specifies virtually the entire regulatory program and leaves only the mechanical implementation to the lower level of government.

Table 9.1
Types of cooperative federalism

Approach	Description	Examples
Planning mandates	Higher level of government requires lower level to study and address a problem but does not dictate a specific performance standard	National: Coastal Zone Management Act; nonpoint provisions of the Clean Water Act State: Urban Water Management Planning Act; Senate Bill (SB) 610 and SB 221 ("Show Me the Water" laws); Agricultural Water Management Planning Act
Standard-driven federalism	Higher level of government mandates a particular performance standard or goal (e.g., a specific level of water quality) but then permits lower-level governments to determine how best to implement the standard or goal. If lower-level governments do not meet the standard or goal, higher-level government generally reserves the right to step in	National: water quality standards in the Clean Water Act; ambient air quality standards in the Clean Air Act; Subtitle D of the Resource Conservation and Recovery Act State: outdoor irrigation efficiency standards in landscape ordinances; per capita water use targets
Managerial federalism	Higher level of government sets particular regulatory standards but permits lower-levels of government to implement and manage the standards	National: technology standards in the Clean Water Act State: technology standards for low-flow plumbing

NOTE: For years in which various state legislation cited here was adopted, see Table 2.7.

All three forms of cooperative federalism require two elements. First, the lower level of government must have the expertise and jurisdiction needed to undertake the local tasks, or the state (or national) government must help the lower level of government acquire and develop this expertise and jurisdiction. Second, the lower level of government must have enough funding to carry out its tasks, or the state (or national) government must provide such funding.

Where the general public enjoys significant benefits from a cooperative federalism scheme, centralized funding also is generally more equitable (Blomquist, Dinar, and Kemper 2010).

Nudging

Even where the state or federal government does not wish to directly mandate reform by lower levels of government, it can still usefully nudge reluctant governments toward reform. Nudging simply involves informal pressures or incentives to encourage lower levels of government to do something that they would otherwise probably not do.[3] The federal government, primarily through the Department of the Interior, has often encouraged California and other western states to undertake needed water reforms—even short of the type of cooperative federalism efforts discussed above. For example, in authorizing the Central Arizona Project in 1968, Congress prohibited the Secretary of Interior from delivering water to Arizona until the Secretary of the Interior certified that the state was adequately managing groundwater pumping (Leshy 2009). When Secretary of the Interior Cecil Andrus threatened not to allow Central Arizona Project water to flow in the late 1970s, then-Governor Bruce Babbitt was able to use this threat to help motivate and pass the 1980 Groundwater Management Act (Avery et al. 2007). Twenty years later, pressure from the Department of the Interior, in its role as water master of the Colorado River, helped water users in Southern California agree to the Quantification Settlement Agreement, resolving long-standing disputes over water rights in the Colorado River and enabling a package of large long-term water transfers between the Imperial Irrigation District and Southern California urban water districts (Chapter 6). During the Clinton administration, the Department of the Interior, as manager of the Central Valley Project, helped negotiate the Bay-Delta Accord and bring together farmers, urban water agencies, and environmental organizations to address Delta water issues through the CALFED process (Chapter 1; Rieke 1996). The federal government used the threat of sanctions under the Clean Water Act to bring all parties to the table.

The federal government can continue to nudge California toward effective water reforms. The federal government has various opportunities to influence the

---

3. Thaler and Sunstein (2008) have recently popularized the concept of "nudging." In the academic literature, nudging is used broadly to refer to anything that influences choices. Although much of the emerging literature focuses on the use of social norms, we use the term to refer to the use of power and discretion at one level of government to influence the use of power and discretion at another level.

Federal and state leadership was needed to craft a complex deal to reduce California's use of Colorado River water. Photo by John Locher/ Associated Press.

state's water policies. Through the federal reclamation program, the Department of the Interior runs and manages major irrigation projects in the state. Under *Arizona v. California* (1963), the Department of the Interior also holds significant discretion over delivery of water from the Colorado River. In an era of significant state budget deficiencies, the federal government also could condition federal financial assistance for water management on needed state reforms, or it could provide funding to help states engage in such reforms (Leshy 2009).

The California state government can similarly nudge water districts, counties, cities, and other local governments to engage in necessary reforms. To date, the state has encouraged local reforms by providing financial incentives to local governments—e.g., using the carrot of bond funds to encourage local groundwater management plans, urban water management plans, and integrated water management plans. The state also has significant leverage over local governments through its authority over surface water rights and water quality, and it could use this authority more to promote local reforms and cooperation. The legislature, for example, has encouraged the installation of water meters by threatening to deny new or expanded water supply permits if a utility fails to comply.[4] The state, through the attorney general's office, also could

4. Assembly Bill (AB) 2572 (2004) (§ 529.5 of the Water Code) also requires compliance for eligibility for financial assistance from the state for wastewater treatment projects, water use efficiency projects, and drinking water treatment projects.

be more active in enforcing various laws concerning local agency planning and other actions, which now rely principally on citizen lawsuits for enforcement.[5]

Lower levels of government sometimes can nudge higher levels of government. For example, regional water quality plans have a prominent influence on the relicensing of power plants by the Federal Energy Regulatory Commission (FERC). State water rights administrators can influence the operation and viability of federal water projects and contracts, where they depend on state water rights (*California v. United States* 1978; *United States v. State Water Resources Control Board* 1986). Lawsuits under state Fish and Game Code § 5937 were used to nudge operational changes in the federal Friant Dam under the San Joaquin River restoration settlement agreement (Box 9.1). Similarly, local governments often lobby and become involved in lawsuits aimed at changing state or federal policies. Agitation from local agencies, for example, helped transfer the Kern Water Bank—one of several water banks that became operational in Kern County in the 1990s—from state to local control.

Applying the Approach

Table 9.2 summarizes our assessment of the appropriate actions and roles of different levels of government in some needed areas of California water reform and illustrates the use of cooperative federalism and nudging. Although the state will often need to lead in pursuing reform, other levels of government are important as partners and instigators of reform. Nudging could be effective in several areas. The federal government could use its authority under the beneficial use provisions of the Reclamation Act and under the Clean Water Act, respectively, to pressure the state to institute groundwater management reforms and to implement cap and trade programs for water quality.

In a form of reverse nudging, the state could encourage the federal government to change the administration of the ESA and the CWA to enable more effective ecosystem management in California and more flexible, cost-effective approaches to enforcement of total maximum daily loads (TMDLs) (Chapters 5, 6). State experiments in biodiversity protection (e.g., California's efforts in natural community conservation planning) have often influenced federal reforms (Arha and Thompson 2011). Similarly, the state will need to

5. The attorney general's office has played an active role in encouraging local governments to adopt general plans that take into account the state's greenhouse gas reduction targets by issuing comments on general plans and filing selective lawsuits (Bedsworth and Hanak 2011; http://ag.ca.gov/globalwarming/ceqa.php). It could take similar actions regarding the implementation of water supply and flood planning laws by urban and agricultural agencies and local land use authorities (Hanak 2010).

Table 9.2
Some examples of federal, state, and local roles in reform

Challenge	Federal	State	Regional/Local
Improved groundwater basin and watershed management	Could nudge state to take action	Set performance mandates for local groundwater management and regional integrated watershed approach	Develop and implement basin and watershed plans (including regional stewardship authority governance and activities)
Higher water use efficiency (prices, rate structures)		Set performance mandate for locals	Adopt conservation-oriented rate structures, promote innovations
More flexible water market and grid management	Partner with state in institutional reforms, nudge state reforms	Lead institutional reforms, nudge federal participation	Promote innovations in water marketing
Risk-based flood management	Partner with state in reservoir reoperation	Set new state policy including regulatory standards for locals, lobby federal government to partner in more integrated water supply and flood operations	Implement new risk-based standards
Reconciliation approaches to improve ecosystem function	Align ESA and CWA with reconciliation principles (selective streamsheds, ecosystem function, multiple stressors)	Set new state policy, lobby for federal reforms, experiment with new approaches to help demonstrate value of federal reform, modify state laws to conform to new federal ESA and CWA principles	Partner through regional stewardship authorities for improved ecosystem management
More effective water quality management	Nudge state to implement cap and trade, align CWA for more flexible enforcement of TMDLs	Implement cap and trade for nonpoint sources, lobby for federal reforms on TMDLs	Develop and implement regional water quality plans and cap and trade programs for water quality
Funding for public benefits (planning, ecosystems, system efficiency)		Set new state policy (public goods charge, dam removal fees, etc.)	Establish regional stewardship fees

NOTES: For details on reform actions, see Chapters 5 through 8.

enlist federal cooperation to engage in more integrated water supply and flood management given federal control of flood space in most reservoirs in the state. The federal government also might be nudged into use of more modern risk-based flood policies. The state could also use the reasonable use requirements of the California constitution to pressure the federal government to participate in reforms that improve the efficiency of the water market, including a new water transfer clearinghouse run by a water independent system operator (ISO). Local agencies, similarly, may sometimes need to push the state to institute reforms to improve the efficiency of the water market (although local districts have often been both obstacles and facilitators for water market reform).

Cooperative federalism can help in many important reform areas, including groundwater management, water quality management, conservation-oriented water pricing, integrated watershed management, and risk-based flood management.

Groundwater management

For groundwater management, including integrated management of groundwater and surface water, the state should set performance standards but allow local implementation. State involvement is necessary because unregulated groundwater pumping affects interests beyond the local basin (Chapters 5, 6, 7). Local water agencies, moreover, may feel pressure to take a shorter-term view of groundwater management and resist regulating local water users, even with clear local authority to restrict pumping. Although these considerations call for state performance standards, local entities may be more effective at designing and implementing programs to achieve such standards given their greater knowledge of local conditions and needs.

The state therefore should establish groundwater management standards that encourage and guide local implementation and enforcement. Following the approach used under the federal Clean Air Act and Clean Water Act, local governments would apply to the state for the authority to implement the standards, and the state would review local performance regularly to ensure that the standards are being implemented effectively. Where local governments either do not seek authority or do not use it effectively, the state would undertake enforcement and implementation. Local governments would also be free to set more stringent local groundwater standards.

An important issue in any such system would be how to determine which local entities are authorized to create groundwater management plans. Under a top-down approach, the state (most likely through the SWRCB or its successor) would define the relevant groundwater basins. The state or regional stewardship authorities could delegate local agencies to develop basin groundwater management plans for each basin or allow local counties a set period of time to agree on joint groundwater management plans. Enabling state legislation could provide local agencies with new authority to enact such plans. Under a bottom-up approach, local governments themselves would determine (with guidance from the state) appropriate basin areas to manage, as well as institutional mechanisms for managing them. Under either approach, the state would have authority to develop and implement state groundwater management plans for any defined groundwater area in which local governments have not, within a set period of time, developed an effective management plan and demonstrated their ability to implement the plan. Such a program could be phased in over time, with an earlier time limit for basins with critical groundwater problems.

Where groundwater withdrawals affect surface water outside a basin's physical boundaries, local regulation would need to take these effects into account. To ensure effective integration, jurisdictional boundaries might be expanded to include areas outside the physical basin that are affected. Alternatively, interests outside the basin could be given the right to petition for groundwater restrictions and to protest permitted withdrawals that they believe harm them. Disputes between outside interests and the basin authority could be resolved either by the governing state agency or through judicial appeal. California again could draw on experience with interstate disputes under the Clean Water Act. No state can permit the discharge of pollution if it would violate the water quality standards of a downstream state. Moreover, before issuing pollution permits that might affect a downstream state, states must permit the downstream state to object; the Environmental Protection Agency can veto a permit if it concludes that the proposed discharge would interfere with the downstream state's water quality standards (Salzman and Thompson 2010).

If it is politically impossible to provide for direct state groundwater management where local entities fail to develop adequate groundwater management plans, the state might consider other means to encourage local entities to act. To date, the legislature's primary incentive for local action in water reform has been to make state grants contingent on local compliance. This policy could of course be applied for the development and implementation of adequate groundwater management plans that protect not only other groundwater users but surface water users and the environment. However, other tools may be more compelling, particularly if state bond resources are limited. For example, the legislature could make groundwater users responsible for all damages resulting from overdrafts, including reductions in groundwater quality, subsidence, and damage to groundwater-dependent ecosystems or surface water users. Similarly, the legislature could provide for a reduced levy under the public goods charge, recommended in Chapter 7, where local governments are adequately managing aquifers and therefore reducing the costs that the charge would otherwise need to cover.

Agricultural water quality

As discussed in Chapter 6, today's agricultural dischargers must only monitor their water quality. A next step would be to allow groups of farms (perhaps grouped by river reaches) to agree, as a group, to particular water quality or discharge load limits, under the jurisdiction and enforcement of regional water quality authorities. This type of arrangement would facilitate water quality trading within these groups (much as occurred within the Grasslands Water District for selenium discharges; see Chapter 6). Elaborations might allow water quality load trading across groups. Such trading schemes would add flexibility and local integration to water quality regulations.

Water pricing

State-established water pricing standards have the potential to promote more consistent and effective conservation-oriented rate structures. The state would require that utilities implement conservation-oriented tiered pricing and would conduct periodic rate reviews. The process would provide an impartial technical review of rate structures and give cover to local utilities that face local resistance to more progressive water rates. Water utilities failing to demonstrate an appropriate rate structure could be subject to sanctions for failing to encourage reasonable use by their customers.

Integrated watershed management

State planning mandates are appropriate for instituting more effective integrated watershed management. Our proposal to create regional stewardship authorities would impose two levels of planning requirements: plans of various local water and land use authorities would need to be consistent with the regional integrated water plan developed by the regional stewardship authority, and the regional plan would need to be consistent with state plans developed by the proposed Department of Water Management. As explained in Chapter 8, this approach is similar to the successful use of planning and consistency requirements under the federal Coastal Zone Management Act, the transportation planning provisions of the federal Clean Air Act, and the Delta Stewardship Council. To encourage local initiative, the state could set guidelines for the establishment of these regional authorities and delegate authority to consortia of local agencies willing and able to undertake this broad regional coordinating function.

Flood management

Finally, for flood management, the state could use performance mandates to require that local and regional flood control and land use agencies adopt new risk-based guidelines for new development and planning of flood protection investments. This would build on existing performance standards established in the 2007 flood legislation package but with a more protective, forward-looking orientation.

Facilitating Transition Costs

Reforms can often impose transition costs on stakeholders, leading them to oppose the reforms. If the state were to restrict groundwater overdrafts, for example, at least some existing groundwater users would need to either reduce their water use or find other, probably more expensive, water sources. Such transition costs are not unique to water reforms. Almost every major reform in resource management or environmental regulation creates transition costs. Such transition costs, by generating opposition, often lead to "institutional sclerosis" in which rules remain unchangeable even though reform would benefit society as a whole (Hansmann, Gilson, and Pargendler 2010; Heckelman 2007).

Reform proposals must account for such transition costs for several reasons. First, transition costs are a major cause of political opposition, so addressing transition costs is critical to increasing a reform's chance of succeeding. Second, water users often rely on and make investments based on current water policies. Reforms that neglect legitimate reliance concerns can raise equity issues. Third, by demonstrating to the private market that the government recognizes and accounts for investments made on the basis of existing policies, efforts to reduce or eliminate transition costs can encourage future investment and increase societal wealth (Shavell 2008).

Not every reform generates efficiency and equity concerns, and some level of transition costs is usually considered legitimate and appropriate where a reform promotes social welfare. When Congress passed the Clean Water Act in 1972, for example, no one argued that the act should exempt or compensate companies that were then discharging pollution into the nation's waterways. However, the Clean Water Act subjected existing polluters to laxer standards than new point sources of discharge, and Congress provided financial support to wastewater utilities to undertake the substantial investments needed to meet the new standards (Salzman and Thompson 2010; Misczynski 2009). Whether transition costs need to be addressed in any specific case depends on various factors, including the size of the transition costs, the degree and legitimacy of stakeholders' reliance on existing policies, the importance of the proposed reform to the public welfare, and the political context.[6]

Where the government decides that it must reduce transition costs for political or equitable reasons, a variety of approaches are available. All approaches involve downsides of one form or another, but governments seeking to promote reform have a viable arsenal of mitigation approaches. Here, we summarize some principal approaches to address transition costs for water reforms.[7] The approaches differ in the degree to which stakeholders must bear transition costs and their effect on the reform's effectiveness. The most appropriate approach depends on the circumstances of each reform measure.

Compensation

The most direct method to address transition costs is to fully or partially compensate stakeholders for these costs. The constitutional takings protections are an example of full compensation. Both the federal and state constitutions promise owners of private property that, if a governmental reform constitutes a "taking" of their property as defined and delineated by the courts, they will receive "just compensation." As discussed above, several recent judicial cases have awarded compensation where efforts to protect imperiled fish species have reduced water deliveries (Box 7.1). The constitutions mandate compensation, however, in only a narrow set of situations. Most water reforms, including major shifts in management policies, do not generate legitimate takings claims.

Legislatures, however, may still decide to provide full or partial compensation for the reasons mentioned above, even if the constitution does not require it. The California legislature has chosen to provide at least partial compensation in several settings. For example, to ease the cost of Los Angeles's compliance with the public trust doctrine under the Mono Lake decision, the California legislature in 1989 established a $60 million fund of investment capital to help Los Angeles build water reclamation and conservation facilities to offset its

6. These factors parallel U.S. Supreme Court considerations when reviewing claims that governmental action has "taken" private property for which just compensation is due (e.g., *Penn Central* 1978). The government, however, might decide to reduce transition costs even where private property and thus takings law are not involved.

7. For a general discussion of approaches to address transition costs, see Kaplow (2003) and Hansmann, Gilson, and Pargendler (2010).

Mitigation funds can ease transitions for low-income groups harmed by new water policies. Photo by David McNew/Getty Images.

water losses—although the funding actually supplied to Los Angeles may have been less (d'Estree and Colby 2004).

Compensation typically has the benefit of not undermining the goals of the reform. Funding for reclamation and conservation in Los Angeles, for example, did not undermine the goal of protecting public trust interests in Mono Lake; instead, it promoted the goal by easing implementation of the reforms. The principal disadvantage to monetary compensation is the cost to the public treasury. Compensating stakeholders for the cost of complying with a publicly well-regarded reform also may seem inequitable to the public—simply "buying off" political opposition (Hansmann, Gilson, and Pargendler 2010).

Compensation need not be monetary; it can take other forms less costly to taxpayers. In raising water prices as part of the Reclamation Reform Act of 1982, for example, Congress increased the acreage in a single farm that could receive subsidized Central Valley Project water (Sax et al. 2006). Although farmers faced higher water rates, the increase in acreage provided partial "compensation" for many water users who had been receiving water all along for more acreage and were under legal attack (Kelley 2004).

Compensation may be useful in easing transitions and reducing resistance to new reforms. Congress has established mitigation funds to provide training and assistance for workers affected by trade liberalization as well as forestry workers affected by the Northwest Forest Plan, which protected about 20 million acres of federal land from logging as part of an ecosystem protection effort for the endangered spotted owl and other species.[8] For example, the state might consider compensating Delta farmers for lands that should be flooded, even if permanent flooding is inevitable and if compensation is not legally required (Lund et al. 2010). Similarly, the state might compensate farmers, in the western San Joaquin Valley or elsewhere, who agree to retire their land for water quality concerns or to free up water for use elsewhere.

Rather than providing compensation itself, the government also can encourage or require the beneficiaries of a reform to compensate opponents. For instance, to allay local government concerns that water transfers lower tax receipts and raise social services costs, the state might encourage participants in the water market to create a fund to compensate these entities for the negative third-party effects of water transfers (Chapters 6, 7).[9] Taxing of "windfalls" to compensate for "wipeouts" can be both efficient and equitable (Hagman and Misczynski 1977).

Grandfathering

Another common method to address transition costs is to "grandfather" existing stakeholders (Hansmann, Gilson, and Pargendler 2010). Under grandfathering, existing stakeholders are either exempted entirely from new rules or subject to less strict rules. When the California legislature adopted a permit system for appropriative water rights in 1913, for example, it applied the rules only to new appropriators; existing appropriators did not require a permit for their existing rights (Chapter 1).

Although grandfathering can eliminate or reduce transition costs for existing stakeholders and imposes no costs on the public treasury, it is generally troublesome because grandfathering undermines the goal of the reform itself. By exempting pre-1914 appropriators from permitting requirements, the legislature undermined the goal of keeping track of appropriative rights; to this day, the exact extent of pre-1914 rights remains uncertain (Chapter 7).[10]

8. For evaluations of the trade adjustment assistance, which has been in effect in various forms since the 1940s, see Aho and Bayard (1984) and Richardson (1982). For current information on the program, see www.doleta.gov/tradeact/. On the Northwest Forest Plan, which came into effect in 1994, see Tuchman et al. (1998) and Charnley (2006).

9. Concerns of this nature were raised by Yolo County during the Drought Water Bank of 1991 (Carter, Vaux, and Scheuring 1994). Hanak (2003) describes some of the difficulties parties have had reaching agreement on suitable mitigation programs for fallowing in California.

10. Other objections include disparate treatment among similarly situated individuals or entities and adverse incentives to continue to operate old (highly polluting) technologies (Hansmann, Gilson, and Pargendler 2010) as well as anticompetitive behavior (Ackerman et al. 1999).

Feasibility-Based Implementation

Similar to grandfathering, the government can reduce transition costs by excusing those who find it particularly difficult to comply with a reform from all or part of the new requirements. Under the Safe Drinking Water Act, for example, Congress established health-based standards for all water providers but then excused water supplies from purifying their water beyond levels that were technologically and economically feasible (Salzman and Thompson 2010). The water conservation requirements of the California Urban Water Conservation Council have a similar provision, allowing signatories to avoid implementing any of the identified conservation best management practices that do not meet feasibility or economic criteria. Feasibility-based implementation protects stakeholders from the burden of costs that they cannot feasibly absorb but otherwise allows a reform to move forward. Feasibility-based implementation is generally less disruptive to the goals of a reform than grandfathering but still limits the ability of a reform to achieve its goal.

Delayed Implementation

Another common approach is delayed implementation (Kaplow 2003). Because people tend to discount future costs, delaying the onset of a reform can significantly reduce the current value of future transition costs. The delay also allows more time for integrating the reform into other ongoing activities thus reducing the transition cost. Thus, when the California legislature approved AB 2572 in 2004 requiring that all cities install water meters, it delayed the effective date of the requirement until January 1, 2025, to give utilities time to phase in the costs of meter installment. When Congress has adopted new mileage standards for automobiles, it has similarly delayed the effective date of the standards (Salzman and Thompson 2010). Delayed implementation not only reduces the discounted cost of complying with new reforms but also allows the development of new technology and the phasing in of new investments needed to respond to a reform. Delayed implementation also can allow term-limited legislators to make needed structural changes (such as moving from council to executive agency structures) in the future without losing immediate legislative prerogatives and without incurring opposition from sitting board members and their supporters.

Unfortunately, delayed implementation, like grandfathering and feasibility-based implementation, undermines the goals of the reform, unless the reform is adopted far in advance of the onset of a predicted problem. Whether this drawback is better or worse than grandfathering depends on several factors. For delayed implementation, the benefits of reform are lost only during the period of the delay; once the reform is fully implemented, society enjoys the full benefits, unless irreversible damage has occurred in the meantime. However, all benefits of the reform are generally lost during the period of the delay because the delay typically applies to everyone not just to stakeholders who existed before the reform.

Delayed implementation might be appropriate for a number of the reforms discussed previously, particularly where the reform requires significant advance planning or the development or installation of new technology. For example, the implementation of risk-based flood management should reasonably be delayed to allow time for the development of adequate planning systems (Chapter 6). New conservation standards, which require the adoption of new technologies and behavioral changes, also seem good candidates for delayed implementation.

Phased-In Reforms

A variant on delayed implementation is the gradual phase-in of reforms over time (Kaplow 2003). In the 1972 Clean Water Act, for example, Congress provided for the gradual phase-in of ever-stricter water quality standards, rather than providing for the immediate end of all point sources of pollution (which is a goal of the Clean Water Act) (Salzman and Thompson 2010). Like delayed implementation, phase-ins undermine reform goals in the short run but often to a smaller degree because at least some reform occurs immediately.

A phase-in approach might be particularly appropriate for reducing the transition costs of groundwater reform, particularly where current users have made investments based on groundwater availability and it is not critical to immediately manage groundwater in a particular basin. Other states have phased in their groundwater reforms. When the Arizona legislature adopted its Groundwater Management Act in 1980, for example, it provided for gradual reductions in groundwater pumping in areas of major overdraft, rather than the immediate cessation of all overdrafting (Avery et al. 2007). Texas similarly provided for a stepped reduction in groundwater pumping under the Edwards Aquifer Act of 1993 (Votteler 1998). California might consider both (1) requiring groundwater management first in basins where pumping is causing significant problems for the environment or other ground or surface water users, and (2) allowing local regions to phase in groundwater restrictions rather than requiring immediate cessation of all harmful withdrawals. The danger is that local groundwater users might face incentives to "race for the pump house," or more quickly exploit groundwater, to improve their position when management becomes imposed. The new agricultural water quality program proposed above also seems a good candidate for a phase-in approach.

Regulatory Choice

Regulatory choice permits stakeholders to choose between operating under a reform regime or the preexisting regime. It is particularly appropriate where a reform promises some stakeholders an improved approach but other stakeholders have reasons, generally because of investments or experience, to prefer the preexisting scheme. Governments have often turned to regulatory choice to reduce political opposition to new economic markets and charter systems (Hansmann, Gilson, and Pargendler 2010). In reforming its equity markets, for example, Brazil chose to create a "new market" within its established stock exchange but to end years of political paralysis let businesses choose between the existing and new markets.

Regulatory choice works effectively only where a reform can attract stakeholder adherents and where maintaining a dual system does not undermine reform goals. Regulatory choice might be particularly appropriate for creating an ISO-type structure for water marketing (Chapter 7). For the voluntary transfer clearinghouse model ("ISO-lite"), Central Valley Project and State Water Project contractors would automatically be included, and local water districts would have the option to join. For the broader ISO model, which would operate a bidding system for all water moving through the grid—not just voluntary transfers—contractors and rights holders could have the option to join the full bidding system. Those who prefer the greater flexibility and marketing opportunities of the ISO-type structure could voluntarily participate, whereas others with strong vested interests in the current system could maintain their current contracts and allocations. The electricity ISO includes some regulatory flexibility—by making participation in the ISO optional for public power providers.

Compliance Flexibility

Governments sometimes reduce transition costs by providing compliance flexibility, allowing stakeholders to meet the goals of a reform by whatever means minimize their costs (or local opposition). Cap-and-trade systems are an example of compliance flexibility. Rather than telling all power plants exactly how much they must reduce their sulfur dioxide emissions, for example, the

Clean Air Act Amendments of 1990 cap total emissions and allow power plants that face higher compliance costs to purchase emission allowances from plants with lower reduction costs that are willing to go beyond their minimum reductions (Salzman and Thompson 2010). Similarly, any reform effort in California to reduce water pollution from nonpoint or other sources could help reduce transition costs through a water quality trading system (Chapter 6).

A cap-and-trade system might be particularly appropriate for reducing transition costs where groundwater reform requires that a region reduce current groundwater use (or in any situation where reform reduces supplies for a group of users). Some groundwater users will find it easier and less expensive than others to reduce their use. By allowing groundwater users to trade withdrawal rights, a cap-and-trade system allows users who find it more difficult or expensive to pay for additional rights—minimizing the overall transition costs of the groundwater reduction (Carlson and Satterwaite 2010). For this reason, the Texas legislature provided for groundwater trading when it restricted pumping from the Edwards Aquifer (Votteler 1998). Many adjudicated basins in California also provide for the marketing of groundwater within the basin (Blomquist 1992; *Water Strategist*, various issues).

Another approach to compliance flexibility is a "default rule," under which the government adopts a reform but allows stakeholders to propose alternative approaches that meet the reform goals. Habitat conservation plans (HCPs) under the Endangered Species Act are an example. Although the ESA generally does not permit adverse modifications of the habitat of endangered species, individual landowners or local governments can get permits to modify land and water flows if they design and demonstrate an ability to implement HCPs that will adequately protect the endangered species from extinction (Thompson 1997b).[11]

Combining Approaches

There is no single optimal approach to addressing transition costs. Grandfathering is generally the least effective because it directly and perpetually undermines the reform goal and can create adverse incentives and reduce economic competition. Direct compensation fully preserves the benefits of the reform but can be expensive. All of the approaches discussed above have advantages and disadvantages and are well suited to some reforms but not

11. New charter provisions in the corporate field also frequently use default rules, under which firms can deviate from particular charter provisions (Hansmann, Gilson, and Pargendler 2010).

others. Approaches can also be combined. For example, reductions in groundwater pumping might be phased in over time and combined with markets that permit compliance flexibility, as Texas did with the Edwards Aquifer.

Promoting Reforms

A final question is how to promote reforms. Here we consider three approaches: (1) increasing public understanding of water issues; (2) involving stakeholders; and (3) building consensus.

Public Education

When the public poorly understands a policy issue, providing greater information can help increase public saliency and discussion and thereby encourage reform—either by generating support for a political solution to the issue or by encouraging the public to change its own behavior.

One way to educate the public is through the information that water suppliers provide their consumers. Water suppliers currently must provide consumers only with yearly water quality reports. Unfortunately, the government requires that water suppliers provide so much data and scientific information regarding water quality that few consumers bother to read the reports, and even fewer understand them. A simpler format that focuses on the information of greatest importance would be far more informative to the public.

Consumer reports also could be expanded, in this age of enhanced information technology, to include information on:

- The efficiency of each consumer's water use (e.g., the consumer's total monthly water use, compared to the monthly use a year before and perhaps to the use of average or similar consumers);
- The source(s) of water supplied to the consumer;
- The reliability of the customers' water supply (e.g., vulnerability to drought, development in the supplier's watershed or overdrafting of the source aquifer, risk of earthquakes in the Delta);
- Environmental or socioeconomic effects of the water supply system (e.g., reduced water flows and increased water temperatures in the habitat of endangered or threatened species); and
- Flood inundation likelihood and depth (e.g., the likelihood of flooding at the first and second story levels of the home).

The first category of information could help consumers be wiser users of water resources and is already common for many utilities. The other categories of information would increase Californians' understanding of their water supplies, the challenges of managing those supplies, and their flood risks. Such information, moreover, would encourage water suppliers to address the threats to and effects of their supply systems and, by increasing public understanding, promote public support of reform. For flood risk, this effort could build on the requirements in AB 156, part of the flood legislation package of 2007, which requires that the Department of Water Resources provide Central Valley landowners in areas protected by levees with annual flood risk information; this effort should be extended to other regions of the state (Chapter 6).[12]

Formatting and presentation of such an expanded "Consumer Water Report" would be important. Reports should focus on key information, presented in an understandable format that highlights the most important information. Full reports might be issued every five years, with summary information and updates provided in other years. Reports could link to a website with more complete information. Such public information would be a grassroots extension of existing urban water management plans.

Stakeholders and Interest Groups

Interest groups need to be involved in shaping the reform of California's water policies. An expansion of the interest groups actively involved in water reform efforts in California is likely to aid adoption of effective and sustainable reforms by ensuring a broader perspective. Although businesses have occasionally supported reform efforts (including enactment of the Central Valley Project Improvement Act of 1992, negotiation of the Bay-Delta Accord in 1994, and development of a Model Water Transfer Act in 1996), they could play more prominent and valuable roles than in the past.

Interest groups can provide legislative and administrative bodies with data and information needed to identify, analyze, and develop effective reforms (Sabatier and Whiteman 1985; Lupia and McCubbins 1994). They also can mobilize public support for reforms. Finally, interest groups can sometimes encourage reforms by threatening to file lawsuits. Threats of lawsuits, for example, encouraged agricultural users to accept the acreage and pricing changes in

12. AB 156 (2007) calls for annual notification of flood risk disclosure in areas protected by levees within the area served by the State Plan of Flood Control (principally the Sacramento and San Joaquin Valleys). See Yune (2010) on the initial notifications, which began in September 2010.

the Reclamation Reform Act of 1982 (Kelley 2004) and supplied one of several motivations for the Arizona legislature's support of that state's Groundwater Management Act of 1980 (Avery et al. 2007).

When the legislature fails to address a reform need, interest groups sometimes also are tempted to try to enact reforms through California's initiative process. As discussed in Chapter 2, initiatives have occasionally been important in prior reforms of California water law; interest groups may need to turn to initiatives in the future to enact needed reforms. However, although the voting public remains devoted to the initiative process (Public Policy Institute of California 2008), initiatives have several disadvantages as a method of reform. Initiatives are often long, complex, and poorly drafted, confusing voters. Funding is critical to both qualifying and passing initiatives, putting wealthy interests at an advantage. Because the legislature plays no formal role in the process, initiatives do not benefit from legislative expertise (Center for Governmental Studies 2008). On the other hand, because initiatives do not implement themselves, reticent political officials have significant say over how an initiative is applied and enforced (Gerber et al. 2001). Overall, initiatives often result from a failure of the legislative process to address public concerns and are a poor substitute for effective legislation (Garrett 2005).

Interest groups also can engage in direct reforms without changes in legislation or administrative rules. Nonprofits, for example, can directly protect the environment through market mechanisms or business pressure. In recent years, "water trusts," such as the Oregon-based Freshwater Trust, have adopted a lesson from land trusts and helped protect environmental flows by acquiring water from willing farmers for environmental purposes (Neuman 2004). The Nature Conservancy also is developing a new program to certify water suppliers who manage their watersheds on a sustainable basis, hoping to encourage water suppliers to change their approach to watershed management (The Nature Conservancy 2010). Both programs can improve freshwater conditions without governmental reform.

The business sector also can directly contribute to reforms without governmental action. As major users of water, corporations directly control industrial and commercial water use efficiency (2030 Water Resources Group 2009). Many corporations are seeking to improve their water efficiency, often with benefit to their financial bottom lines, as part of broader sustainability programs (Barton 2010). Corporations are also the principal developers and marketers of new technologies to improve water efficiency or create new water supplies from reuse or desalination.

Public Consensus

Over the past two decades, support has been building for using consensus-based decisionmaking to resolve water issues and other environmental problems (Chapter 1; Kallis, Kiparsky, and Norgaard 2009; Lemos and Agrawal 2006). Proponents argue that consensus processes can reveal new and innovative solutions to apparently intractable problems that better advance the needs of all parties (Crowfoot and Wondolleck 1990; Ingram and Fraser 2006), better focus stakeholders on scientific rather than political issues (Leach, 2006), help change attitudes and behavior (Bobker 2009; Connick and Innes 2003), and create useful long-term relationships among stakeholders and governmental agencies that can prove beneficial in future problem solving (Connick and Innes 2003).

As interest in consensus processes has increased, so has criticism. Some analysts believe that consensus processes allow entrenched interests to block needed reforms or, because of greater sophistication, unduly influence outcomes (Peterson, Peterson, and Peterson 2005). Some argue that consensus processes often undercut rather than promote democratic decisionmaking by excluding marginal, more extreme, or broader but more diffuse public interests (Schilling, London, and Levanos 2009). Others believe that consensus processes diffuse accountability and can permit governmental entities to evade difficult decisions (Hanemann and Dyckman 2009). Even supporters emphasize that consensus processes can be exceptionally time-consuming, delaying needed reforms, making it difficult for some stakeholders to continue participation, and creating a situation incapable of producing solutions to large-scale, complex issues (Crowfoot and Wondolleck 1990). To some observers, the tendency of consensus processes to emphasize agreement tends to sideline more strategic solutions in favor of safer incremental agreements (Kallis, Kiparsky, and Norgaard 2009; Hanak et al. 2010).

Prior consensus processes in the water field suggest that consensus processes have a greater chance of success where opportunities exist for all stakeholders to improve their current position (i.e., in proverbial "win-win" opportunities) than in win-loss situations or where fundamental interests are at stake (van den Belt 2004; Hanemann and Dyckman 2009). A consensus process, for example, is unlikely to produce agreement for peripheral Delta conveyance because, although a new canal or tunnel might benefit the state's economy and environment, it might accelerate water quality losses for some Delta farmers and decrease incentives to subsidize support of the Delta's aging levees (Lund et al. 2010; Madani and Lund 2011). For this reason, consensus processes might work best in addressing small regional issues than large, complex problems such as the Delta (Kallis, Kiparsky, and Norgaard 2009). Consensus processes also are generally most effective where stakeholders have exhausted other means of resolving a problem and have relatively balanced power (Kallis, Kiparsky, and Norgaard 2009).

Prior consensus processes also suggest ways to improve their success:

- **External deadlines.** Consensus processes often work best as part of a governmental decisionmaking process subject to a clear deadline. The governmental process can help force closure and provide an alternative decision route if the consensus process is unsuccessful. The San Joaquin River settlement, for example, was reached under threat of a judicially imposed solution (Box 9.1). Similarly, the Yuba Accord—in which parties agreed to a comprehensive management plan for the river for environment, water supply, and flood management that includes substantial water transfers and groundwater banking—was agreed to under the threat of a water rights decision by the SWRCB that would have caused significant reductions in water availability for human uses (Water Education Foundation 2007).
- **Better ways to meet.** New institutional forums are needed in which parties can gather information and discuss their different views (Norgaard, Kallis, and Kiparsky 2009; Taylor and Short 2009). Consensus processes also can benefit from active facilitation and from mediated modeling of the core problem (van den Belt 2004).
- **Linkages with constituents.** Participating stakeholders must actively communicate with their constituents to ensure their support for any final agreement (Kallis, Kiparsky, and Norgaard 2009).
- **Resources.** External financial support can be helpful, particularly by equalizing resource differences among the parties (Kallis, Kiparsky, and Norgaard 2009).

In the future, consensus processes may be valuable in relicensing a dam or providing for a dam's removal. In both situations, license expirations provide a deadline for action, and the FERC process provides ground rules for discussions. All sides, moreover, enjoy relatively equal bargaining power. Efforts to develop new groundwater management rules also might benefit from consensus negotiations. The issue of groundwater management meets many of the criteria listed above for successful use of consensus processes: It is primarily an economic issue that does not threaten fundamental principles, it can be addressed locally, and failure to manage groundwater can lead to costly adjudications. However, to be successful, groundwater discussions would need a government-imposed deadline and a forum for developing relevant information and discussing options.

Achieving Reforms

Reform is crucial to the sustainability of California's water. And in many cases reform is needed now. The state can ill afford to wait for a crisis to be perceived. Unfortunately, making reform happen is likely to be more difficult than identifying the mix of desirable reforms. It is generally much easier to generate support for incremental reforms than for broadly desirable, but more controversial, strategic reforms. Incremental reforms are generally less threatening to the status quo and so are less likely to face stiff political opposition. However, incremental reforms will often not do the job. Thus, figuring out how to make key reforms happen is essential.

Political opposition is generally the major obstacle to reform. Federal, state, and local agencies typically already enjoy the authority and discretion to pursue needed reforms, without new legislation. California state law includes a variety of broad doctrines, including the reasonable use requirement and the public trust doctrine, that provide means to address many of the state's current water challenges. Many statutes, such as the federal and state Endangered Species Acts, give agencies more leeway for reform than is often assumed. Congress and the state legislature, however, will need to intervene in some cases to encourage or shape reform, establish or clarify agency authority, and provide funding. Congress, for example, may ultimately need to revisit the Endangered Species Act to better align its operation with reconciliation principles, and the state legislature should address the need for better groundwater management. Courts also have a role, not only as the direct source of reform, but as a forum for negotiations (as in the San Joaquin River settlement) and in minimizing legal obstacles to reform.

Achieving strategic reform will require strong leadership from state government as well as federal and stakeholder interests. The concept of cooperative federalism, with authority emanating from either federal or state governments, seems essential to effective long-term water policy for decentralized California water management. The federal government can usefully nudge the state toward reform on such issues as groundwater management, integrated watershed management, improved water markets, and cap-and-trade systems for water quality. The state has an interest in establishing the goals and standards for groundwater, agricultural runoff, water conservation, integrated watershed management, and flood management, but it should leave implementation and enforcement up to local entities when they are willing to step forward.

A key step to reform will be overcoming the opposition of stakeholders worried about transition costs. Grandfathering current stakeholders is often tempting but should be resisted because it typically undermines the goals of the reform. One major weakness of California water policy today stems from the legislature's decisions in 1913 to grandfather preexisting appropriative water rights and to exclude riparian and groundwater rights from the permitting and licensing system of the modern water code. Compensating stakeholders can sometimes be an effective approach, particularly where the beneficiaries of the reform can help fund the compensation. Depending on the particular situation, a variety of other approaches to reducing transition costs, including delayed implementation, regulatory choice, and compliance flexibility, can help reduce reform opposition.

Public education also will be essential in ensuring support for smart reforms both now and in the future. To help improve public understanding of water issues, the state should consider mandating new information reports for water consumers. These reports could cover not only traditional water quality information but also water consumers' own water efficiency; the sources of consumers' water; the reliability of, costs of, and threats to those sources; and local flood risks.

A wide range of strategic and incremental reforms to California water policy is needed over the coming years and decades, and California already has much of the legal framework needed for such reforms. A strategic goal of reforms is to better integrate local, state, and federal interests in water management in ways that allow a very decentralized system of governance to adapt to a wide range of changing conditions. Reforms must often be done incrementally, taking advantage of opportunities imposed by crises and catastrophes, but some major, strategic reforms will require high-level state and federal leadership and preparation.

10 A Way Forward

ISTOCKPHOTO

> There are no secrets to success. It is the result of preparation, hard work, and learning from failure.
>
> Colin Powell, in O. Harari, *Leadership Secrets of Colin Powell*

California is struggling to adapt a water management system—with infrastructure and institutions built for an earlier time—to 21st century conditions, with a changing climate. In this modern era, environmental values have become prominent. The state's population has continued to grow and to urbanize, increasing demands for urban water supply, water quality, and flood protection. The state's economy has evolved and no longer depends as directly on water to generate wealth. Irrigated agriculture, which still consumes the lion's share of water, represents a small fraction of overall employment and economic output, and manufacturing accounts for only a small fraction of total water use. These changes are leading to a rebalancing of water management objectives and approaches.

In recent decades, many federal, state, and local efforts have sought to redress environmental decline, to adjust to the increasing scarcity and unpredictability of water supplies, and to rehabilitate crumbling flood protection infrastructure. But these efforts have proved inadequate. To avoid continued environmental and economic deterioration, California needs to make significant changes in water policy.

Major Crises Await

Without reform, current water policies and institutions virtually guarantee that California will experience five major, protracted water crises involving widespread environmental and economic losses (Chapter 4).

The Sacramento skyline from the Yolo Bypass.

Extinction and Decline of Native Species

California is endowed with a diverse and unique natural environment, with 140 distinct aquatic ecosystems and many fish and other aquatic and riparian species that live nowhere else on the planet. Over the past 150 years, California's native fishes—a broad indicator of aquatic ecosystem health—have lost almost every conflict with economic development. Among the state's 129 native fish species, seven have become extinct, 31 are listed as threatened or endangered under the federal and state Endangered Species Acts (ESAs), and another 69 are in decline and will likely qualify for listing in the future. Only 22 native fish species are reasonably secure (Figure B). The condition of native fish populations has continued to deteriorate, despite decades of well-intentioned but insufficient and poorly coordinated policies to protect them. Efforts to stop these declines now threaten the reliability of water supplies and flood management projects. Yet this deterioration in natural habitat is likely to accelerate with continuing influxes of invasive species and loss of cold water habitat and stream flow from climate warming.

Catastrophic Floods

California's flood management system also has failed to keep up with changing economic, environmental, and social conditions. The state has some of the most flood-prone land in the nation, much of which has been urbanized. In the Central Valley, growing urbanization in floodplains has rendered a formerly prized century-old flood control system inadequate. A major flood in the Sacramento region would endanger thousands of lives and cost tens of billions of dollars in loss of property and economic activity. Unfortunately, recent state efforts to double the urban protection standard in the Central Valley suffer from the same basic weaknesses as federal flood policy. The new standard will promote some strengthening of existing flood defenses but ultimately will increase the economic losses from floods—or flood *risk*—by continuing to encourage population growth and economic activity behind levees. The frequency of large floods is likely to increase with a warming climate, which is already accelerating the pace of winter and early spring runoff, challenging the capabilities of existing flood protection infrastructure. Moreover, the state's new flood policy does not address high-risk flood areas in Southern California and the San Francisco Bay Area.

Water Scarcity

In much of California, water must now be managed every year with an eye toward drought. California has run out of cheap sources of new water and will need to manage water more carefully and more flexibly to satisfy competing demands. In recent decades, progress has been made on several fronts: Water use efficiency has improved, urban wastewater reuse is expanding, a water market has developed to transfer water from economically lower-value uses to higher-value uses, and groundwater banking has expanded the ability to store water in underground aquifers for dry years. But several regions are relying on unsustainable mining of groundwater basins, and the state's water system is still susceptible to prolonged droughts, which could become more frequent. Institutional rigidities and regulatory gaps are hindering the development of groundwater banking and the expansion of the water market—two major tools for better managing water in a semiarid climate with a growing population and dynamic economy.

Deteriorating Water Quality

The passage of clean water legislation in the late 1960s and early 1970s led to a dramatic reduction in water pollution from wastewater and industrial plants. But major nonpoint sources of pollution, such as urban and agricultural stormwater runoff and drainage, remain a serious problem. Meanwhile, new chemical threats have emerged and, with few exceptions, have been largely neglected. Water quality problems compound water scarcity problems by increasing drinking water costs, particularly for small rural communities. Treating wastewater and runoff to meet increasingly high standards is also expensive and often insufficient to protect aquatic species from harm.

Decline of the Sacramento–San Joaquin Delta

All of these problems converge in the Sacramento–San Joaquin Delta—the poster child for California's water woes. Disasters are looming for ecosystems, Delta landowners, and agricultural and urban water users in much of the state (Lund et al. 2010). The Delta's weak levees, which protect local farmland and the channels that convey fresh water to southern Delta export pumps, risk catastrophic failure from earthquakes and floods. Such a failure would draw salt water into the Delta, cutting off water supplies for many months and costing the state's economy billions of dollars. The Delta's ecosystem—stressed by loss of habitat, water diversions, contaminants, and a range of other causes—is witnessing a catastrophic decline in its native species, leading to substantial regulatory restrictions on water exports. Over the longer term, additional pressures on this system from sea level rise, warming temperatures, water pollution, and new invasive species will intensify this deterioration, permanently cutting off water supplies and leaving an impoverished ecosystem, with few traces of its original splendor. The economic costs of a permanent loss of Delta water exports will be especially severe if California's climate becomes drier, as some climate models predict (Chapter 6).

Failing Governance Institutions

The inability to prevent these looming crises reflects major weaknesses in California's current system for governing and funding water management. The highly decentralized nature of most water management—with many hundreds of local and regional agencies responsible for water supply, wastewater treatment, flood control, and related land use decisions—has many advantages but has often resulted in uncoordinated, fragmented water and land use decisions that contribute to chronic groundwater overdraft, impairment of watersheds by a wide range of pollutants, ineffective ecosystem management, and rapid development in poorly protected floodplains. Similar coordination failures among state and federal agencies have led to inefficiencies in reservoir operations, ecosystem management, and water marketing, among others.

In this decentralized system, gaps in the development and analysis of key technical and scientific information are a severe problem; state agencies often lack the resources needed for analysis and sometimes even the authority to gather information from the field. As state and federal agencies have shifted their efforts in recent decades from infrastructure construction to regulation, they have lost much of their former capacity for scientific and technical analysis and strategic planning. Distressed state and local funding systems, as well as increasingly restrictive rules for levying fees and property assessments, have made it difficult to support flood protection, environmental mitigation and pollution control, and state planning and analysis functions. The lack of a strong state technical and scientific program is allowing advocacy-funded "combat science" to take center stage—fueling overly simplistic and wrong-headed, but politically convenient, views of California's water problems and potential solutions (Chapter 2).

Promising Directions for Water Policy

In this book, we have identified a broad and ambitious agenda of reforms for managing California's water. These reforms focus on four mutually reinforcing approaches: (1) reconciling environmental and human water uses through more comprehensive and focused ecosystem management; (2) expanding and integrating the use of portfolio approaches for water supply, water quality, and flood management; (3) enhancing the system's balance and flexibility by strengthening the role of water as a public commodity; and (4) making water management institutions more effective, integrated, and adaptive. Together, these approaches form the basis for a new Era of Reconciliation in water management.

Some elements of this reform agenda build on existing policies and trends, while other elements will require major shifts in policy direction. Similarly, existing laws and regulatory authority are adequate to implement many important reforms, but some will require changes in state and federal laws.

Reconciling Environmental and Human Water Uses

A central task in the new era of water policy and management will be to reverse the decline in California's native aquatic and riparian diversity (Chapter 5). Single-species management under the Endangered Species Acts, which has tended to focus on mitigating individual causes of ecosystem stress, has had little success in protecting ecosystems or preventing new listings. Simply tinkering with current approaches is unlikely to make things much better. Instead, environmental management must focus on improving broad ecosystem function aiming to create better conditions for multiple desirable species and addressing multiple causes of stress to the system. In California's highly altered environment, "reconciliation" approaches—which acknowledge the continued presence of human land and water uses—are likely to have more promise than "restoration" approaches that seek to return ecosystems to an approximation of their native states. In general, the aim should be to maintain a diverse range of functioning ecosystems, while prioritizing areas and actions with the greatest chance of success.

Strategies should include removing or setting back levees in some locations to promote seasonal floodplain inundation, reducing the discharge of contaminants, limiting the introduction of invasive species, and reoperating (and, in some cases, removing) dams to facilitate fish passage and reduce the harmful downstream effects of diversions. In some watersheds, better control of groundwater pumping is essential, because pumping is depleting stream flow. In addition, the state's fish hatchery programs—which have negative unintended consequences for native species—are in dire need of reform.

Although some specialization of streams for environmental purposes may be desirable, these strategies will largely work to improve ecological function

Mono Lake is a reconciled ecosystem, where goals of water supply and ecological management have been balanced. Photo by Image Source/Corbis.

alongside continued human uses of land and water resources. A prime example is the Delta. In a reconciled Delta, dams and water diversions would be reoperated to create a "natural flow regime" that captures or accentuates some of the variability under which native species once thrived, thereby also making conditions less favorable for some invasive species. A peripheral canal or tunnel, diverting water exports around or underneath the Delta, would allow some water exports to continue while ending the disrupting effects of pumping water through the heart of the Delta. Eco-friendly agriculture—with fish-friendly water intakes and better control of harmful chemicals—would continue in much of the Delta, supporting habitat for sandhill cranes and other wildlife, whereas some islands would be allowed to flood, returning to open water habitat. Contaminants from urban wastewater would be reduced, and hatcheries would be managed to lessen competition with wild salmon. Recreational uses of the Delta would increase, but new urban development would be prevented in fragile, low-lying areas. Similar reforms could be made throughout the Sacramento–San Joaquin River system and in California's other watersheds.

Achieving these types of changes will require strategic shifts in the scientific and institutional orientation of aquatic ecosystem management. Although this will be challenging, it can largely be accommodated within existing law. In particular, both the state and federal ESAs allow multispecies, ecosystem-based approaches to mitigation. Large-scale regional habitat conservation plans—such as the one now being developed in the Delta—are an example. And although ESA regulators have tended to focus on single causes of stress, the law is sufficiently flexible to accommodate a broader consideration of actions.

Other environmental laws may need adjustments to be more effective in the face of changing conditions, including climate change. The federal Clean Water Act and the state Porter-Cologne Act prohibit California from allowing water quality to decline in ways that affect existing beneficial uses. But under a reconciliation strategy, the best option may be to adjust to changing conditions. For instance, reimposing variability (in salinity, for example) to suppress invasive species in the Delta would likely harm some current beneficial uses of Delta waters and thus be incompatible with current legislation. In addition, climate warming will make it increasingly difficult to meet water quality standards that depend on temperature, and thus more flexible implementation of rules will be necessary.

Similarly, the state and federal Endangered Species Acts lack provisions for conservation strategies that could allow a listed species to go extinct in the wild as part of a broader effort to protect ecosystems. Yet these types of tradeoffs may become necessary, as some species become so fragile and compromised that costly—and likely futile—efforts to save them may threaten protection of a range of other species. Properly designed and prudently administered, endangered species triage might become needed to allow environmental regulators to focus on integrated ecosystem management and aggregate species recovery.

Expanding and Integrating Portfolios

To better serve both economic and environmental objectives, the management of water supply, water quality, and floods must employ a broader range of tools (Chapter 6). Traditional approaches in all three areas have relied heavily on major public works—dams, levees, conveyances, and treatment plants. Although some new infrastructure will be needed, the era of large-scale infrastructure development is now largely past. New management approaches offer more promise.

Water supply priorities

Water supply management has seen the most progress in portfolio approaches, as numerous nontraditional tools have been tapped to cope with increasingly tight water supplies. Expanded efforts are especially needed in three areas:

- **Urban conservation.** Although per capita urban water use has been falling, California still uses much more water than other economically advanced populations that share a similar climate, such as Australia, Israel, Italy, and Spain. Our modeling results show that a more aggressive conservation strategy—bringing average water use down to about 155 gallons per capita per day (30 percent below 2000 levels)—can significantly reduce demand for Delta exports and lessen the costs of export cutbacks for San Joaquin Valley farm communities. Water rate reform, using tiered rates with variable base allowances, can promote conservation in a flexible and fiscally responsible way.
- **Groundwater banking.** Expanding underground storage can be much more cost-effective than building new surface storage to stretch available water supplies and replace the storage lost by a shrinking Sierra Nevada snowpack. But legal uncertainties over storage rights and ownership of stored water are impeding the development of groundwater banking outside adjudicated basins and special groundwater management districts, concentrated in urban Southern California and Silicon Valley. In many areas, comprehensive basin management is needed to facilitate banking and related water transfers and to limit the harmful environmental effects of pumping.
- **Water transfers.** Water marketing is an equitable way to accommodate the changing economic demands for water, by compensating water rights holders for moving water from low-value uses. Opportunities for market development are still considerable, because many acres of farmland are still planted in low-value crops. But after a decade of rapid growth, the water market has stagnated since the early 2000s. Reasons include cumbersome state procedures for environmental approvals, lack of groundwater basin management in many counties, local resistance to sales involving agricultural land fallowing, and new restrictions on Delta exports. Steps are needed to reduce barriers in all these areas.

Water quality priorities

The primary successes of water quality management have been in reducing pollution from point sources (with treatment before discharge) and removing pollution from drinking water (with treatment before use). Priorities for action should focus on two other key aspects of the portfolio: reducing pollution from nonpoint sources and restricting the use of contaminants:

Some future water demands can be met with new approaches, including recycled water. Photo by Mary Knox Merrill/Christian Science Monitor/Getty Images.

- **Nonpoint pollution sources.** Because treatment is more costly for these diffuse sources, policies have focused on encouraging best management practices to reduce runoff. Quantitative limits on the total maximum daily loads of some pollutants are also being set for some water bodies, to be met jointly by point and nonpoint dischargers. To implement these standards cost-effectively, California should develop pollution trading schemes. Such "cap-and-trade" programs are encouraged under federal law, and they have worked well in the energy sector for some air pollutants. With cap and trade, performance standards can more readily be extended for some problematic types of runoff from farms and urban landscapes, including salts, nitrates, and pesticides.
- **Source control.** Source management of toxic contaminants poses a major challenge for California. Federal efforts are not sufficiently comprehensive. California should pursue its recent Green Chemistry Initiative, to encourage the use of chemicals less harmful to humans and the environment. It should continue to build upon the regulatory model of Proposition 65, the Safe Drinking Water and Toxics Enforcement Act of 1986, which shifts the burden of proof to manufacturers, relies on multiple data sources, and allows private sector enforcement.

Flood management priorities

In its 2007 flood legislation, California broke with federal policy by setting higher protection standards for new development in the Central Valley. But the focus is still largely on improving flood protection infrastructure, using levees and reservoirs to limit the frequency of flooding. To limit California's growing flood risk and the negative environmental consequences of flood infrastructure, new approaches are needed:

- **Flood vulnerability reductions.** To reduce risk, land use planning and regulation should focus on limiting the location of new development in flood-prone areas, improving building codes, and expanding flood insurance requirements to all properties within the 500-year floodplain (current federal requirements apply only to properties in the 100-year floodplain). As with fire hazards, mandatory insurance is the most direct way to reward local communities for their flood management investments and to reduce the losses from inevitable flooding.
- **Locally generated, risk-based investments.** Despite $5 billion in recent state bond funds, California's flood protection system remains woefully underfunded. Higher local contributions are needed, and properties facing higher risk should pay higher fees—a model already used in the Sacramento area. Scarce state and federal investments likewise should be allocated based on cost-effectiveness, which will depend not only on the costs of the investments but also on the value of assets being protected.
- **Environmentally beneficial flood protection.** Approaches should include expanding flood bypass capacity—a strategy used effectively in the early 20th century and largely neglected since then. This approach, which can be both cost-effective and environmentally beneficial, will require compensation of local landowners and local governments for their loss of revenues from forgone development.
- **Statewide focus.** State policy has focused on the Central Valley, where the state operates a large flood control project and faces extensive liability from flood damage. But many areas of California face growing risks from flooding, and state policies to reduce flood risk should be statewide. For instance, the new requirement to provide annual flood risk disclosures to Central Valley residents living behind levees should be extended to all flood-prone regions.

Integrating actions

Many of these actions can be mutually reinforcing, providing multiple benefits. For example, flood bypasses can protect residents from floods, provide valuable habitat, and recharge groundwater basins. Urban conservation can reduce both water demand and polluted runoff. Groundwater banking can expand drought storage and provide reservoir capacity during the flood season. Stormwater capture can reduce water pollution and recharge groundwater basins.

But to work well, many of these actions need to be coordinated across functions that are often managed separately and across broader geographic scales than the boundaries of many existing agencies. Local actions must become better integrated at the scale of groundwater basins and watersheds, and regional actions must become better integrated with statewide objectives for balancing economic and environmental performance.

To achieve this goal, California must move beyond the current voluntary approach to integrated water management, which entices local entities to collaborate in exchange for state bond support for infrastructure projects. This voluntary approach is not very effective, and it is financially unsustainable. Instead, a regional planning and management framework is needed to guide local actions. We propose the creation of regional stewardship authorities (either replacing or supplementing existing regional water quality control boards) to coordinate and focus the supply, quality, flood, and ecosystem management efforts of local entities. These regional authorities could be state institutions (like the regional boards) or delegated consortia of local agencies (similar to the Santa Ana Watershed Project Authority) operating under state authority. This regional framework can foster more systematic and strategic decisions on resource management to benefit the state's residents and its aquatic ecosystems.

Managing Water as a Public Commodity

Successful water management in the new era will require recognition that water is a public commodity, having both economic and broader public values (Chapter 7). Striking a balance among competing uses and objectives is the core principle of managing water as a public commodity. Flexibility—or the ability to adapt—is essential for achieving this balance given continuing demographic, economic, and environmental changes. At its core, California water law—especially the foundational doctrines of reasonable use and the public trust—has remarkable capacity for creating balance and flexibility. Building on these doctrines, a public commodity policy would result in better water

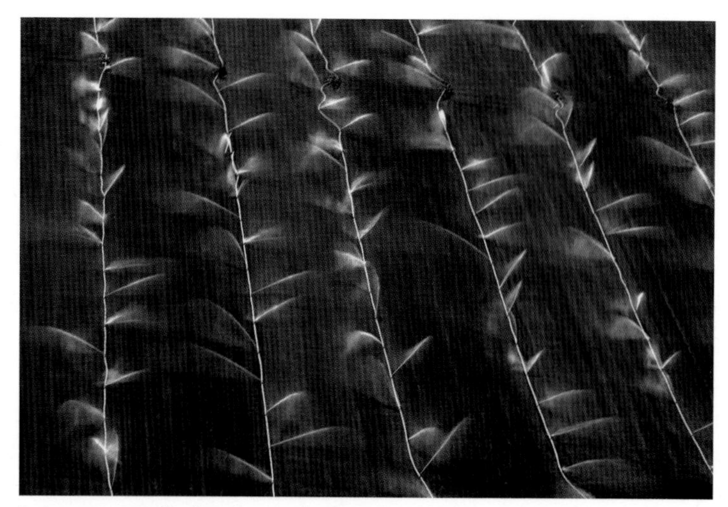

Easing water transfers from lower-value farm uses to higher-value agricultural, urban, and environmental uses is a policy priority. Photo by California Department of Water Resources.

pricing and regulatory decisions, while sustainably funding environmental reconciliation efforts and providing a more adaptable framework for water management for human uses.

The 2009 legislative package on water takes several steps in this direction, including new targets for urban water conservation, new requirements to monitor groundwater levels, and the establishment of a new Delta governance framework to balance human and environmental uses of the Delta. But further reforms are needed:

- **Equal treatment for groundwater.** California's failure to regulate groundwater has harmed fish and aquatic wildlife in related streams, compromised groundwater quality, generated conflicts among water users, and hindered the development of groundwater banking and water marketing. Comprehensive basin management, which treats groundwater and surface water in an integrated, sustainable manner, is needed to improve economic and environmental performance of California's water system. The ideal way to proceed is for the legislature to extend State Water Resources Control Board jurisdiction to all groundwater extraction, and for the board to require that local water districts establish effective basin management protocols. Barring this, the reasonable use doctrine may provide the courts and in some cases the board with the means to move toward more comprehensive management.

- **Streamline and strengthen environmental review of water transfers.** To improve water market efficiency, programmatic environmental assessments should be prepared for potential transfers from regions most likely to sell water to facilitate preapproval of a range of transfer volumes, depending on hydrologic and market conditions. To protect private and public interests, these reviews should consider potential negative effects of transfers that currently require mitigation under state law (i.e., effects on other surface water users), as well as effects on groundwater users and the local economy.
- **Create a water transfer clearinghouse.** California's interconnected water supply grid is a major asset for managing supplies as they become scarcer. But the system is institutionally fragmented, split across state, federal, and local operators. Although cooperative agreements have improved operations, the rules for transferring water from different types of agencies are cumbersome. We propose creating a new clearinghouse, modeled after the independent system operator for the state's electricity grid, to manage the water market in a more integrated and efficient manner.
- **Fund the public goods aspects of water management.** For the foreseeable future, state general funds are unreliable and unsuitable for managing the public aspects of water management. To fund the public goods aspects of water management, including planning, science, and ecosystem management, California should learn another lesson from the electricity sector and introduce a public goods charge on water use. This charge—a small volumetric fee—would also be a more appropriate funding source for regional water projects than general obligation bonds that have been used recently. Specific fees for environmental mitigation, including dam removal and control of contaminants, are also appropriate. Water quality permit fees, which now fund regulatory administration, also should be augmented to support ecosystem management. Fees covering broader purposes than regulatory administration will likely require legislative approval. As noted above, local contributions to flood works will also be needed, ideally on a regional scale (Table 10.1).

Table 10.1
Fee-based funding for modern water management

Public goods charge	Special mitigation fees
Ecosystem reconciliation	Dam removal and mitigation of effects on fish
Regional water supply reliability and infrastructure	Chemical contaminants surcharge
Administration (Department of Water Management, Department of Fish and Game, regional stewardship authorities)	**Water quality permit fees**
Research and development	Ecosystem reconciliation
	Administration (state agencies and regional stewardship authorities)
	Regional and local risk-based flood management fees

Improving Water Governance

Sustainable management of California's fresh water requires not only good policies but also effective, integrated, and adaptive governmental institutions (Chapter 8). Our recommendations call for:

- ▷ **Information and analysis.** Despite its role as one of the centers in the world's information economy, California woefully lags on information and analyses of water use, flows, quality, and costs—essential tools to support modern water management goals. Most information will need to be developed locally and regionally, but the state must ensure that adequate data are collected and made available to policymakers, stakeholders, and the public at large in a usable format.
- ▷ **Integration, coordination, and coherence.** In addition to new regional stewardship authorities to coordinate actions regionally, state water agencies need an overhaul. The State Water Resources Control Board should be merged with the nonproject functions of the Department of Water Resources to form a new Department of Water Management, with responsibilities for water quality, water rights, flood management, and statewide planning. The regional stewardship authorities would report to this new department. The State Water Project should be managed as an independent utility as a public benefit corporation. At the federal level, the National Marine Fisheries Service (now in the Department of Commerce) should be merged with the Fish and Wildlife Service (Department of the Interior) to eliminate unproductive fragmentation of responsibility for the Endangered Species Act.

- **Expert agencies.** To improve the timeliness and scientific underpinnings of policy decisions, the state should move from management through board structures toward greater use of expert agencies. Thus, the functions of the State Water Resources Control Board, whether it remains in its current form or is merged into a new Department of Water Management, should be headed by an appointed state trustee. The responsibilities of the Fish and Game Commission should be limited to setting hunting and fishing regulations, with other responsibilities reassigned to the Department of Fish and Game.
- **Protection of the public trust.** The state should develop structures and mechanisms to ensure that the public trust in water is better protected. For instance, the legislature should create a new public trust advocate, to be located in the new Department of Water Management (or in the existing State Water Resources Control Board). The Department of Fish and Game should retain authority over environmental flows and serve as an independent, environmentally oriented check on the authority of the State Water Resources Control Board to issue and oversee water use permits.
- **Adaptive capacity.** Adaptive capacity is particularly important given the many continuing changes in California's economy, society, and environment. One key institutional issue is to avoid unnecessarily locking in decisions for lengthy periods of time. Permits, licenses, and contracts can limit the government's adaptive capacity when they do not allow for modification during their terms, last for long time periods, and carry a presumption of renewability. Both the state and federal governments should reevaluate whether current terms and conditions for dam licenses, water contracts, and water rights permits should be revised.

Facilitating and Sequencing Reform

Changes to the status quo are never easy and many of the reforms we propose will meet resistance from stakeholders who fear the loss of autonomy or the potential costs of change. Even when reforms would benefit society as a whole, they often impose transition costs on some stakeholders. A new policy to restrict groundwater overdraft, for example, would require at least some existing groundwater users to either reduce their water use or find other, probably more expensive, water sources. However, numerous approaches are available to lessen this resistance and lower the costs of reform (Chapter 9).

Cooperative Approaches

In California's decentralized system, the concept of cooperative federalism—whereby higher levels of government set performance standards for lower levels of government—is essential to effective policy reform. The state has an interest in establishing goals and standards for the management of groundwater, non-point pollution, flood risk, and watershed integration. But these management solutions will benefit from local innovation, achieve greater local buy-in, and be more cost-effective when local entities are allowed to develop implementation and enforcement plans. The state's role should be to set deadlines and guidelines for local compliance, stepping in only where local entities do not step forward. The state can also encourage lower costs for local actors by facilitating the use of flexible compliance tools, such as cap and trade for water pollution management and water markets.

Compensation

Although few water policy changes legally require compensation from the government, compensation may be warranted to facilitate some economically and environmentally beneficial reforms. For water marketing, more attention should be devoted to mitigating economic harm to third parties in regions exporting water—including workers who may become unemployed and local governments that may incur higher social service costs and lower tax receipts. This is of particular concern when water is made available by taking farmland out of production—one of the main ways to achieve net water savings in agriculture. Mitigation is not legally required in these cases, but an equitable water policy should encourage buyers and sellers to fund programs to address significant negative local effects resulting from major transfers. Compensation also may be appropriate to ease transitions for Delta landowners facing island flooding. And, as noted above, local governments (in addition to affected landowners) also should be compensated for forgone tax revenues as part of new flood easements. In general, compensation should be funded by beneficiaries rather than the government, to limit burdens on public budgets.

Flexible Timing

Some elements of this reform agenda are urgent, but not every reform to California water policy needs to be immediate. In some cases, waiting may produce valuable information or new technologies or save on administrative expenses. Waiting for better information on whether the future climate will be wetter or drier before building new surface storage is an example, because new storage is expensive and will have little added value in a drier climate with less water available to fill reservoirs (Chapter 6). Urgent actions are those that help to avoid irreversible losses (as with species protection) or that help avoid catastrophic costs to the economy (as with the Delta or with development in floodplains).

This temporal flexibility can help lower transition costs for stakeholders. For groundwater management, phasing in reforms (focusing initially on regions with the most severe problems) may be appropriate. Delayed implementation is another transition tool. For instance, even though efforts should start immediately to limit floodplain development and to improve building codes, the implementation of risk-based flood management should reasonably be delayed to allow time for the development of adequate planning systems. New conservation requirements also seem good candidates for delayed implementation, to allow time for new technologies and habits to become familiar.

Acting Now to Avert Crisis

Although not all reforms need to happen immediately, California's leaders should act now to launch a reform agenda that prepares California for contemporary and future conditions. Without bold action, California will be subjected to a succession of protracted water crises. Crises have motivated most water reforms in California's history. But by the time a crisis strikes, political positions may have become too entrenched to overcome, many of the best management options may be precluded or difficult to implement, and costs may be greater.

Even with measures to reduce costs to stakeholders and to ease transitions, the reforms outlined here will not be easy. But California possesses strong foundations for implementing a bold agenda of reforms to meet the needs of changing times. The state has opportunities to significantly reduce urban water use without reducing quality of life and to equitably and responsibly transition some water from low-value agricultural activities. Diverse, flexible strategies are available for improving water quality and reducing flood risk in environmentally responsible ways. These actions will be costly in the short term but will pay off many times over by enabling the economy and society to thrive and by more effectively safeguarding California's unique natural environment. Change is never easy, but Californians need to have the courage and foresight to create a sustainable and prosperous water future.

Glossary

Adjudicated basin	A groundwater basin (or aquifer) where all rights to use groundwater have been determined in a judicial proceeding following a trial or settlement.
Anadromous fish	Fish that spend most of their life in the ocean but spawn and often rear their young in fresh water (e.g., salmon, steelhead trout).
Appropriative rights (also, rule of prior appropriation)	Rights to use water based on actual amount used, having a priority of right based on the date use began. Unlike riparian and overlying rights, there are no land-based restrictions on the place of use of appropriative rights. See Box 1.1.
Beneficial use	The basis, measure, and limit of water rights in California. Water must be put to a beneficial purpose, and the quantity used cannot exceed what is reasonable (taking into account other potential beneficial uses of the water). What is a beneficial use can change over time in response to changed conditions.
Conjunctive use	The joint management of surface water and aquifers.
Correlative rights	The principal basis for allocating water among overlying groundwater rights holders in times of shortage or other conflict. Water is allocated on a shared basis, rather than on the principle of priority of use.
Evapotranspiration	Movement of water from the earth's surface to the atmosphere, from evaporation of water from soil and water bodies as well as transpiration from plants.
Fishery	A collective capture activity by humans for fish or shellfish, usually for food or sport, such as a salmon fishery or steelhead fishery.

Gross water use (or "applied" water use)	The water delivered to a home, business, or farm—not all of which is consumed. Some gross water use—such as excess irrigation water and discharges from wastewater treatment plants—flows to streams, lakes, or aquifers and is available for reuse. See Box 2.1.
Net water use (or "consumptive" water use)	The part of gross water use that is unavailable for reuse, including water consumed by people or plants, embodied in manufactured goods, or evaporated into the air ("evapotranspiration"), and return flows of water discharged into saline or contaminated waters or groundwater basins ("nonrecoverable flow"). See Box 2.1.
Nonpoint source pollution	Pollution from diffuse sources, such as agricultural runoff or stormwater.
Overlying rights	Rights to use groundwater based on ownership of land overlying an aquifer, based on common law.
Pelagic fish	Fish that live their whole life in open water, above the bottom; these include the delta smelt, longfin smelt, and striped bass.
Point source pollution	Pollution discharged from a pipe, channel, or other discrete point of conveyance, e.g., industrial or wastewater treatment plants.
Pre-1914 rights	Appropriative surface water rights established before the adoption of the modern Water Code. Pre-1914 rights do not require a permit or license from the State Water Resources Control Board.
Prescriptive rights (also, prescriptive use)	A water right created by prescriptive use—i.e., by unlawful use for five consecutive years without permission of the true water rights holder. Prescriptive rights cannot be asserted against the state where the user has not obtained an appropriative right to the water.

Public trust doctrine	The legal recognition that the state retains continuing supervisory control over all its navigable waters and the lands beneath them and must protect the public's common interest in them for navigation, commerce, fishing, recreation, preservation, and scientific study, except in the rare situation where the state has abandoned its rights consistent with those purposes. Explicitly held in California to apply to rights in flowing waters. See Box 1.2.
Pueblo rights	Exclusive water rights of cities that were once pueblos under Spanish and Mexican dominion to waters within their borders needed for their residents and for municipal purposes.
Reasonable use doctrine	The use of water rights in a manner that does not result in waste, is efficient, and considers the reasonable demands for water of competing riparian water users. What is a reasonable use may change over time as conditions change. See Box 1.4.
Residual risk	The level of risk remaining after measures have been taken to mitigate risk (e.g., risk remaining after reinforcement of flood protection levees).
Riparian rights	Rights to use surface water based on ownership of land fronting on a river, based on common law. See Box 1.1.
Safe yield	The quantity of water that can be extracted each year from an aquifer on a renewable basis.

References

2030 Water Resources Group. 2009. *Charting Our Water Future: Economic Frameworks to Inform Decision-Making.* Available at www.mckinsey.com/App_Media/Reports/Water/Charting_Our_Water_Future_Full_Report_001.pdf.

Ackerman, F., B. Biewald, D. White, T. Woolf, and W. Moomaw. 1999. "Grandfathering and Coal Plant Emissions: The Cost of Cleaning Up the Clean Air Act." *Energy Policy* 27: 929–40.

Acreman, M., and M. J. Dunbar. 2005. "Defining Environmental River Flow Requirements—A Review." *Hydrology and Earth System Sciences* 8: 861–76.

Adams, L., et al. 2010. *Draft Biennial California Climate Action Team Report.* Available at www.climatechange.ca.gov/adaptation/.

Adams, S. M., ed. 2002. *Biological Indicators of Ecosystem Stress.* Bethesda, MD: American Fisheries Society.

Aho, C. M., and T. O. Bayard. 1984. "Costs and Benefits of Trade Adjustment Assistance." In *The Structure and Evolution of U.S. Trade Policy*, ed. R. E. Baldwin and A. O. Krueger (Chicago: University of Chicago Press).

Allen, R. G., M. Tasumi, A. Morse, and R. Trezza. 2005. "A Landsat-Based Energy Balance and Evapotranspiration Model in Western U.S. Water Rights Regulation and Planning." *Irrigation and Drainage Systems* 19(3–4): 251–68, doi:10.1007/s10795-005-5187.

Allen, R. G., M. Tasumi, A. Morse, R. Trezza, J. L. Wright, W.G.M. Bastiaanssen, W. Kramber, I. Lorite, and C. W. Robinson. 2007. "Satellite-Based Energy Balance for Mapping Evapotranspiration with Internalized Calibration (Metric)—Applications." *ASCE J. of Irrigation and Drainage Engineering* 133(4): 395–406.

Alpers, C. N., M. P. Hunerlach, J. T. May, and R. L. Hothem. 2005. "Mercury Contamination from Historical Gold Mining in California." U.S. Geological Survey Fact Sheet 2005-3014.

Anderson, J., et al. 2008. "Progress on Incorporating Climate Change into Management of California's Water Resources." *Climatic Change* 87 (Suppl 1): 91–108.

Anderson, M. K. 2005. *Tending the Wild: North American Knowledge and the Management of California's Natural Resources.* Berkeley, CA: University of California Press.

Anderson, P., N. Denslow, J. E. Drewes, A. Olivieri, D. Schlenk, and S. Snyder. 2010. *Monitoring Strategies for Chemicals of Emerging Concern (CECs) in Recycled Water. Recommendations of a Science Advisory Panel.* Sacramento, CA: State Water Resources Control Board. Available at www.swrcb.ca.gov/water_issues/programs/water_recycling_policy/recycledwater_cec.shtml.

Anderson, T. 1983. *Water Crisis: Ending the Policy Drought.* Washington, DC: Cato Institute.

Anderson, T. L., and P. J. Hill. 1997. "Environmental Federalism: Thinking Smaller." In *Environmental Federalism*, ed. T. L. Anderson and P. J. Hill (Lanham, MD: Rowman & Littlefield Publishers, Inc.), xi–xix.

Anderson, T. L., O. R. Burt, and D. T. Fractor. 1983. "Privatizing Groundwater Basins: A Model and Its Application." In *Water Rights: Scarce Resource Allocation, Bureaucracy, and the Environment*, ed. T. L. Anderson (San Francisco: Pacific Institute for Public Policy Research), 223–48.

Arax, M., and R. Wartzman. 2005. *The King of California.* New York: Public Affairs.

Archibald, S., and M. E. Renwick. 1998. "Expected Transaction Costs and Incentives for Water Market Development." *Natural Resource Management & Policy* 15: 95–107.

Archibald, S. O., et al. 1992. "An Economic Analysis of Water Availability in California Central Valley Agriculture: Phase II Draft Report." Stanford, CA: Center for Economic Policy Research.

Arha, K., and B. H. Thompson. 2011. *Biodiversity Federalism*. Washington, DC: Resources for the Future Press.

Arizona v. California. 1963. 373 U.S. 546.

Arizona v. California. 1964. 376 U.S. 340 (decree).

Arizona v. California. 2006. 547 U.S. 150 (final consolidated decree).

Arthington, A. H., R. J. Naiman, M.W.E. McClain, and C. Nillson. 2009. "Preserving the Biodiversity and Ecological Services of Rivers: New Challenges and Research Opportunities. *Freshwater Biology* 55: 1–16.

Association of California Water Agencies. 2002. *Water Supply and Development: A User's Guide to California Statutes Including SB 221 (Kuehl) and SB 610 (Costa)*. Sacramento, CA: McCormick, Kidman, and Behrens.

Association of State Dam Safety Officials. 2005. *Dam Safety in California*. Available at http://damsafety.org.

Avery, C., C. Consoli, R. Glennon, and S. Megdal. 2007. "Good Intentions, Unintended Consequences: The Central Arizona Groundwater Replenishment District." *Arizona Law Review* 49: 339–59.

Awerbuch, S. 1993. "The Surprising Role of Risk in Utility Integrated Resource Planning." *Electricity Journal* 6(3): 20–33.

Bain, J. S., R. E. Caves, and J. Margolis. 1966. *Northern California's Water Industry: The Comparative Efficiency of Public Enterprise in Developing a Scarce Natural Resource*. Baltimore, MD: Resources for the Future, Johns Hopkins Press.

Baldassare, M., et al. 2000–2010. *PPIC Surveys on Californians and Their Environment*, San Francisco: Public Policy Institute of California.

Baldwin v. County of Tehama. 1994. 36 Cal. Rptr. 2d 886, 889 (Cal. Ct. App.).

Balian, E. V., C. Lévêque, H. Segers, and K. Martens. Eds. 2008. "Freshwater Animal Diversity Assessment." *Hydrobiologia* 595: 1–637.

Baltz, D. M., and P. B. Moyle. 1993. "Invasion Resistance to Introduced Species by a Native Assemblage of California Stream Fishes." *Ecological Applications* 3: 246–55.

Barakat & Chamberlain, Inc. 1994. *The Value of Water Supply Reliability: Results of a Contingent Valuation Study of Residential Customers*. Sacramento: California Urban Water Agencies.

Barnett, T. D., D. W. Pierce, H. G. Hidalgo, C. Bonfils, B. D. Santer, T. Das, G. Bala, A. W. Wood, T. Nozawa, A. A. Mirin, D. R. Cayan, and M. D. Dettinger. 2008. "Human-Induced Changes in the Hydrology of the Western United States." *Science* 319: 1080–83.

Barnett-Johnson, R., C. B. Grimes, C. F. Royer, and C. J. Donohoe. 2007. "Identifying the Contribution of Wild and Hatchery Chinook Salmon (*Oncorhynchus tshawytscha*) to the Ocean Fishery Using Otolith Microstructure as Natural Tags." *Canadian Journal of Fisheries and Aquatic Sciences* 64: 1683–92.

Barstow v. Mojave Water Agency. 2000. 23 Cal. 4th 1224, 5 P.3d 853, 99 Cal. Rptr. 2d 294.

Barton, B. 2010. *Murky Waters? Corporate Reporting on Water Risk—A Benchmarking Study of 100 Companies*. Washington, DC: Ceres.

Bates, M. 2010a. "Energy Use in California Wholesale Water Operations: Development and Application of a General Energy Post-Processor for California Water Management Models." Master's thesis, University of California, Davis.

Bates, S. 2010b. "California State Water Project Governance Options." Review Draft. Missoula, MT: University of Montana, Center for Natural Resources and Environmental Policy.

Bedsworth, L., and E. Hanak. 2011. "Defining Roles of Different Levels of Government on Climate Change: The Case of California." In *Sustainable Business Practices: Challenges, Opportunities, and Practices*, ed. George Basile, James Hershauer, and Scott G. McNall (Santa Barbara, CA: Praeger Press).

Beechie, T. J., D. A. Sear, J. D. Olden, G. R. Pess, J. M. Buffington, H. Moir, P. Roni, and M. M. Pollock. 2010. "Process-Based Principles for Restoring River Ecosystems." *Bioscience* 60: 209–22.

Bennett, W. A. 2005. "Critical Assessment of the Delta Smelt Population in the San Francisco Estuary, California." *San Francisco Estuary and Watershed Science* 3(2). Available at http://repositories.cdlib.org/jmie/sfews/vol3/iss2/art1/.

Benson, L., et al. 2002. "Holocene Multidecadal and Multicentennial Droughts Affecting Northern California and Nevada." *Quaternary Science Reviews* 21: 659–82.

Bhaskar, A., and J. C. Beghin. 2009. "How Coupled Are Decoupled Farm Payments? A Review of the Evidence." *Journal of Agricultural and Resource Economics* 34(1).

Bish, R. L. 1982. *Governing Puget Sound*. Seattle, WA: Washington Sea Grant.

Black and Veatch. 2004. *California Wastewater Charge Survey*. Irvine, CA: Management Consulting Division.

Black and Veatch. 2006. *California Water Charge Survey*. Irvine, CA: Management Consulting Division.

Blandford, D., and T. Josling. 2007. "Should the Green Box Be Modified?" International Food and Agriculture Trade Policy Council. Available at www.agritrade.org/Publications/green_box.html.

Blomquist, W. 1991. "Exploring State Differences in Groundwater Policy Adoptions, 1980–1989." *Publius* 21: 105–15.

Blomquist, W. 1992. *Dividing the Waters: Governing Groundwater in Southern California*. San Francisco: ICS Press.

Blomquist, W., A. Dinar, and K. E. Kemper. 2010. "A Framework for Institutional Analysis of Decentralized Reforms in Natural Resource Management." *Society and Natural Resources* 23: 620–35.

Blomquist, W., E. Schlager, and T. Heikkila. 2004. *Common Waters, Diverging Streams: Linking Institutions and Water Management in Arizona, California, and Colorado*. Washington, DC: Resources for the Future Press.

Bobker, G. 2009. "The Means Do Not Justify the Ends: A Comment on CALFED." *Environmental Science and Policy* 12: 726–28.

Bouse, R. M., C. C. Fuller, S. Luoma, M. I. Hornberger, B. Jaffe, R. E. Smith. 2010. "Mercury-Contaminated Hydraulic Mining Debris in San Francisco Bay." *San Francisco Estuary and Watershed Science* 8(1).

Boyd, J., and S. Banzhaf. 2006. "What Are Ecosystem Services? The Need for Standardized Environmental Accounting Units." Discussion Paper 06-02. Washington, DC: Resources for the Future.

Brauman, K. A., G. C. Daily, T. K. Duarte, and H. A. Mooney. 2007. "The Nature and Value of Ecosystem Services: An Overview Highlighting Hydrologic Services." *Annual Review of Environment and Resources* 32: 67–98.

Breetz, H. L., K. Fisher-Vanden, L. Garzon, H. Jacobs, K. Kroetz, and R. Terry. 2004. *Water Quality Trading and Offset Initiatives in the U.S.: A Comprehensive Survey.* Hanover, NH: Dartmouth College.

Brekke, L. D., E. P. Maurer, J. Anderson, M. D. Dettinger, E. S. Townsley, A. Harrison, and T. Pruitt. 2009. "Assessing Reservoir Operations Risk Under Climate Change." *Water Resources Research*, W04411, doi:10.1029/2008WR006941.

Brennan, D. 2006. "Water Policy Reform in Australia: Lessons from the Victorian Seasonal Water Market. *The Australian Journal of Agricultural and Resource Economics* 50: 403–23.

Bromirski, D., R. E. Flick, and D. R. Cayan. 2003. "Storminess Variability Along the California Coast: 1858–2000." *Journal of Climate* 16(6): 982–93.

Brookes, A. 1988. *Channelized Rivers; Perspectives for Environmental Management.* Chichester, UK: John Wiley & Sons.

Brown. L. R. 2000. "Fish Communities and Their Associations with Environmental Variables, Lower San Joaquin River Drainage, California." *Environmental Biology of Fishes* 57: 251–69.

Brown L. R., and M. L. Bauer. 2009. "Effects of Hydrologic Infrastructure on Flow Regimes of California's Central Valley Rivers: Implications for Fish Populations." *River Research and Applications* 26(6): 751–65.

Brown, L. R., and P. B. Moyle. 1997. "Invading Species in the Eel River, California: Successes, Failures, and Relationships with Resident Species." *Environmental Biology of Fishes* 49: 271–91.

Brown, L., and P. B. Moyle. 2004. "Native Fishes of the Sacramento–San Joaquin Drainage, California: A History of Decline." In *Historical Changes in Large River Fish Assemblages of the Americas*, ed. J. N. Rinne, R. M. Hughes, and B. Calamusso (Bethesda, MD: American Fisheries Society Symposium 45), 75–98.

Brown L. R., C. A. Burton, and K. Belitz. 2005. "Aquatic Assemblages of the Highly Urbanized Santa Ana River Basin." *American Fisheries Society Symposium* 47: 263–87.

Brown, L. R., W. Kimmerer, and R. Brown. 2009. "Managing Water to Protect Fish: A Review of California's Environmental Water Account, 2001–2005." *Environmental Management* 43: 357–68.

Brown, L. R., P. B. Moyle, and R. M. Yoshiyama. 1994. "Status of Coho Salmon (*Oncorhynchus kisutch*) in California." *North American Journal of Fisheries Management* 14: 237–61.

Brown, S. J., and D. S. Sibley. 1986. *The Theory of Public Utility Pricing*, Cambridge, UK: Cambridge University Press.

Brunke, H., R. Howitt, and D. Sumner. 2005. "Future Food Production and Consumption in California Under Alternative Scenarios." *California Water Plan Update 2005*, Vol. 4—*Reference Guide.* Sacramento, CA: Department of Water Resources.

Buchanan, W. 2010. "Previous Money Unspent as Leaders Urge New California Water Bond." *San Francisco Chronicle*, August 1.

Burtraw, D., D. A. Evans, A. Krupnick, K. Palmer, and R. Toth. 2005. "Economics of Pollution Trading for SO2 and NOx." Discussion Paper 05-05. Washington, DC: Resources for the Future.

Cain, B., and T. Kousser. 2004. *Adapting to Term Limits: Recent Experiences and New Directions.* San Francisco: Public Policy Institute of California.

Calder R.S.D., and K. A. Schmitt. 2010. "Role of Detection Limits in Drinking Water Regulation," *Environmental Science and Technology,* doi:10.1021/es101417u.

CALFED. 1996. *Workshop 5 Information Packet: Draft Alternatives.* CALFED Bay-Delta Program. Sacramento, CA.

CALFED. 2006. *Comprehensive Evaluation of Water Use Efficiency.* CALFED Bay Delta Program. Sacramento, CA.

California Air Resources Board. 2008. *Climate Change Scoping Plan, a Framework for Change.* Pursuant to AB 32. Available at www.arb.ca.gov/cc/scopingplan/document/adopted_scoping_plan.pdf.

California Department of Finance. 2007. *Population Projections for California and Its Counties 2000–2050.* Sacramento, CA.

California Department of Finance. 2010. *E-4 Population Estimates for Cities, Counties and the State, 2001–2010, with 2000 Benchmark.* Sacramento, CA.

California Department of Fish and Game. 1997. *California Central Valley Wetlands and Riparian GIS (wetrip).* Available at ftp://ftp.dfg.ca.gov/BDB/GIS/Wetlands/Central_Valley_Wetlands_and_Riparian_GIS/.

California Department of Fish and Game. 2008. *California Aquatic Invasive Species Management Plan.* Available at www.dfg.ca.gov/invasives/plan.

California Department of Fish and Game. 2010a. DRAFT Quantifiable Biological Objectives and Flow Criteria for Aquatic and Terrestrial Species of Concern Dependent on the Delta. September 22.

California Department of Fish and Game. 2010b. NCCP Summary Table. July. Available at www.dfg.ca.gov/habcon/nccp/.

California Department of Forestry and Fire Protection. 2002. Multi-Source Land Cover Data. Available at http://frap.cdf.ca.gov/data/frapgisdata/download.asp?rec=fveg02_2.

California Department of Water Resources. 1995a. *California's Groundwater—Salinas Groundwater Basin.* Bulletin 118—Basin number 3-4. Sacramento, CA.

California Department of Water Resources. 1995b. *Delta Atlas.* Sacramento, CA.

California Department of Water Resources. 1998. *California Water Plan Update,* Bulletin 10-98, Sacramento, CA.

California Department of Water Resources. 2003. *California's Groundwater.* Bulletin 118-03. Sacramento, CA.

California Department of Water Resources. 2005a. *Flood Warnings: Responding to California's Flood Crisis.* Sacramento, CA.

California Department of Water Resources. 2005b. *California Water Plan Update.* Bulletin 160-05. Sacramento, CA.

California Department of Water Resources. 2006. *Progress in Incorporating Climate Change into Management of California's Water Resources.* Sacramento, CA.

California Department of Water Resources. 2009. *California Water Plan Update*. Bulletin 160-09. Sacramento, CA.

California Energy Commission. 2005. *California's Water–Energy Relationship*. Report CEC-700-2005-011-SF. Sacramento, CA.

California Energy Commission. 2009. *The Future Is Now: An Update on Climate Change Science Impacts and Response Options for California*. Report CEC-500-2008-071. Sacramento, CA.

California State University, Chico. 2003. *The Central Valley Historic Mapping Project*. Chico, CA: Department of Geography and Planning and Geographic Information Center.

California Tribal Water Summit Regional Tribal Water Plenary. 2009. *California Water Plan Update 2009: Greater Kern, Kings, Tule, and South Central Valley Waters*, a summary of Regional Tribal Water Plenary Meeting, Sacramento, CA.

California Urban Water Agencies. 1991. *Cost of Industrial Water Shortages*. San Francisco: Spectrum Economics, Inc.

California v. FERC. 1990. 495 US 490.

California v. United States. 1978. 438 U.S. 645.

Cappaert v. United States. 1976. 426 U.S. 128.

Carey, L., D. Sunding, and D. Zilberman. 2001. "Transactions Costs and Trading Behavior in an Immature Water Market." *Environment and Development Economics* 7: 733–50.

Carlson, S., and W. Satterwaite. 2010. "Weak Portfolio Effect in a Collapsed Fish Population Complex." Unpublished manuscript.

Carolan, M. S. 2005. "One Step Forward, Two Steps Back: Flood Management Policy in the United States." *Environmental Politics* 16: 36–51.

Carter, H. O., H. J. Vaux, and A. F. Scheuring. 1994. *Sharing Scarcity: Gainers and Losers in Water Marketing*. University of California, Davis: Agricultural Issues Center.

Casitas Municipal Water District v. United States. 2009. 543 F.3d 1276 (Fed. Cir. 2008), petition for rehearing denied, 556 F.3d 1329.

Catskill Mountains Chapter of Trout Unlimited v. City of New York. 2001. 273 F.3d 481 (2d Cir.).

Cayan, D. R., S. A. Kammerdiener, et al. 2001. "Changes in the Onset of Spring in the Western United States." *Bulletin of the American Meteorological Society* 82(3): 399–415.

Cayan, D. R., E. P. Maurer, M. D. Dettinger, M. Tyree, and K. Hayoe. 2007. "Climate Change Scenarios for the California Region." *Climatic Change* 87(1): S21–S42.

Cayan, D. R., P. D. Bromirsk, K. Hayhoe, M. Tyree, M. D. Dettinger, and R. E. Flick. 2008. "Climate Change Projections of Sea Level Extremes Along the California Coast." *Climatic Change* 87(1): S57–S73.

Center for Governmental Studies. 2008. *Democracy by Initiative: Shaping California's Fourth Branch of Government*. 2nd ed. Los Angeles, CA.

Chadderton, W. L., D. J. Brown, and R. T. Stephens. 2004. "Identifying Freshwater Ecosystems of National Importance for Biodiversity." Discussion document. Wellington, NZ: Department of Conservation.

Charnley, S. 2006. "The Northwest Forest Plan as a Model for Broad-Scale Ecosystem Management: A Social Perspective." *Conservation Biology* 20(2): 330–40, doi:10.1111/j.1523-1739.2006.00388.x 2006.

Chen, W-H., K. Haunschild, J. R. Lund, and W. Fleenor. 2010. In press. "Current and Long-Term Effects of Delta Water Quality on Drinking Water Treatment Costs from Disinfection Byproduct Formation." *San Francisco Estuary and Watershed Science.*

Chevron, U.S.A., Inc. v. Natural Resources Defense Council. 1984. 467 U.S. 837.

Chung, F., et al. 2009. *Using Future Climate Projections to Support Water Resources Decision Making in California.* Report CEC-500-2009-052-F. Sacramento, CA: California Energy Commission.

Churchill, R. K. 2000. "Contributions of Mercury to California's Environment from Mercury and Gold Mining Activities; Insights from the Historical Record." *Assessing and Managing Mercury from Historic and Current Mining Activities.* San Francisco: Environmental Protection Agency, S35–S48.

Clemmens, A. J., R. G. Allen, and C. M. Burt. 2008. "Technical Concepts Related to Conservation of Irrigation and Rainwater in Agricultural Systems." *Water Resources Research* 44, W00E03, doi:10.1029/2007WR006095.

Cohen A. N., and J. T. Carlton. 1998. "Accelerating Invasion Rate in a Highly Invaded Estuary." *Science, New Series* 279(5350): 555–58.

Colby, B., J. Thorson, and S. Britton. 2005. *Negotiation Tribal Water Rights.* Tucson, AZ: University of Arizona Press.

Connell, C., 2009. "Bring the Heat, but Hope for Rain—Adapting to Climate Warming in California." M.S. thesis, University of California, Davis.

Connick, S., and J. Innes. 2003. "Outcomes of Collaborative Water Policy Making: Applying Complexity Thinking to Evaluation." *Journal of Environmental Planning and Management* 46: 177–97.

Connor, J. 2010. *Principles for Economically Efficient and Environmentally Sustainable Water Markets During Operative Droughts: The Australian Experience.* Policy note 01-1110. Riverside, CA: University of California, Water Science and Policy Center. Available at http://wspc.ucr.edu/PN_01_1110_Drought.pdf.

Cooley, H., J. Christian-Smith, P. H. Gleick, M. J. Cohen, and M. Heberger. 2010. *California's Next Million Acre-Feet: Saving Water, Energy, and Money.* Oakland, CA: Pacific Institute.

Cordova, J. 1994. "Mexico." In *The Political Economy of Policy Reform*, ed. J Williamson (Washington, DC: Institute for International Economics).

Crowfoot, J. E., and J. M. Wondolleck. 1990. *Environmental Disputes: Community Involvement in Conflict Resolution.* Washington, DC: Island Press.

Dahl, T. E., and G. I. Allord. 1997. "History of Wetlands in the Conterminous United States." U.S. Geological Survey Water-Supply Paper 2425, Washington, DC. Available at http://water.usgs.gov/nwsum/WSP2425/.

Daily G., S. Polasky, J. Goldstein, P. M. Karieva, H. A. Mooney, L. Pejchar, T. H. Ricketts, J. Salzman, and R. Shallenberger. 2009. "Ecosystem Services in Decision Making: Time to Deliver." *Frontiers in Ecology and Environment* 7(1): 21–8.

Das, T., H. G. Hidalgo, M. D. Dettinger, D. R. Cayan, D. W. Pierce, C. Bonfils, T. P. Barnett, G. Bala, and A. Mirin. 2009. "Structure and Detectability of Trends in Hydrological Measures over the Western United States." *Journal of Hydrometeorology* 10, 871–892, doi:10.1175/2009jhm1095.1.

Das, T., M. D. Dettinger, D. R. Cayan, and H. G. Hidalgo. Submitted. Potential Increase in Floods in California's Sierra Nevada Under Future Climate Projections, San Diego, CA: Scripps Institute.

de Alth, S., and K. Rueben. 2005. "Infrastructure Financing in California." Occasional paper, San Francisco: Public Policy Institute of California.

Deltacommissie. 2008. "Working Together with Water: A Living Land Builds for Its Future." The Netherlands.

Delta Vision Blue Ribbon Task Force. 2008. *Delta Vision Strategic Plan*. Available at deltavision.ca.gov/StrategicPlanningProcess/StaffDraft/Delta_Vision_Strategic_Plan_standard_resolution.pdf.

DeShazo, J. R., and J. Freeman. 2005. "Public Agencies as Lobbyists." *Columbia Law Review* 105(80): 2217–2309.

d'Estree, T. P., and B. G. Colby. 2004. *Braving the Currents: Evaluating Environmental Conflict Resolution in the River Basins of the American West*. Norwell, MA: Kluwer Academic Publishers.

Dettinger, M. D. 2005. "From Climate-Change Spaghetti to Climate-Change Distributions for 21st Century California." *San Francisco Estuary and Watershed Science* 3(1). Available at http://repositories.cdlib.org/jmie/sfews/vol3/iss1/art4.

Dettinger, M. D., D. R. Cayan, M. K. Meyer, and A. E. Jeton. 2004. "Simulated Hydrologic Responses to Climate Variations and Change in the Merced, Carson, and American River Basins, Sierra Nevada, California, 1900–2099." *Climatic Change* 62: 283–317.

Dettinger, M. D., H. Hidalgo, T. Das, D. Cayan, and N. Knowles. 2009. *Projections of Potential Flood Regime Changes in California*. Report CEC-500-2009-050-D. Sacramento, CA: California Energy Commission.

Dinar, A. 2000. "Political Economy of Water Pricing Reforms." In *The Political Economy of Water Pricing Reforms*, ed. A. Dinar (New York: Oxford University Press).

Disco, C., and J. van der Ende. 2003. "Strong, Invincible Arguments? Tidal Models as Management Instruments in Twentieth-Century Dutch Coastal Engineering." *Technology and Culture* 44: 502–35.

Division of Ratepayer Advocates. 2010. *Welcome to the Division of Ratepayer Advocates*. Available at www.dra.ca.gov/dra/.

Division of Water Resources. 1930. *State Water Plan 1930*, Bulletin 25, Sacramento, CA: California Department of Public Works.

Dobes, L. 2008. "Getting Real About Adapting to Climate Change: Using 'Real Options' to Address the Uncertainties." *Agenda* 15(3): 55–69.

Doppelt, B., M. Scurlock, C. Frissell, and J. Karr. 1993. *Entering the Watershed: A New Approach to Save America's River Ecosystems*. Covelo, CA: Island Press.

Doremus, H., and A. D. Tarlock. 2003. "Fish, Farms, and the Clash of Cultures in the Klamath Basin." *Ecology Law Quarterly* 30: 279–350.

Doremus, H., and A. D. Tarlock. 2008. *Water War in the Klamath Basin*. Washington, DC: Island Press.

Doyle, M. W., and D. G. Havlick. 2009. "Infrastructure and the Environment." *Annual Review of Environment and Resources* 34: 349–73.

Draper, A. J., "Implicit Stochastic Optimization with Limited Foresight for Reservoir Systems." 2001. Ph.D. dissertation. University of California, Davis.

Dubrovsky, N. M., C. R. Kratzer, L. R. Brown, J. M. Gronberg, and K. R. Burow. 1998. "Water Quality in the San Joaquin–Tulare Basins, California, 1992–95." U.S. Geological Survey Circular 1159.

Duit, A., and V. Galaz. 2008. "Governance and Complexity—Emerging Issues for Governance Theory." *Governance: An International Journal of Policy, Administration, and Institutions* 21: 311–35.

Eagles-Smith, C. A., T. H. Suchanek, A. E. Colwell, N. L. Anderson, and P. B. Moyle. 2008. "Changes in Fish Diets and Mercury Accumulation in Clear Lake, California: Effects of an Invasive Planktivorous Fish." *Ecological Applications* 18(8) (Suppl): A213–A226.

Easterling, W. E., Jr., B. H. Hurd, and J. B. Smith. 2004. *Coping with Global Climate Change: The Role of Adaptation in the United States.* Washington, DC: Pew Center on Global Climate Change.

Eigenraam, C.J.J. 2006. "Optimal Safety Standards for Dike-Ring Areas." No. 62, CPB Netherlands Bureau for Economic Policy Analysis, The Hague, The Netherlands.

Elkind, S. S. 1998. *Bay Cities and Water Politics: The Battle for Resources in Boston and Oakland.* Lawrence, KS: University Press of Kansas.

Ellis, A. W., G. B. Goodrich, and G. M. Garfin. 2010. "A Hydroclimatic Index for Examining Patterns of Drought in the Colorado River Basin." *International Journal of Climatology* 30: 236–55.

Environmental News Service. 2009. "Dry California Sucks Up Federal Water Recycling Dollars." July 6.

Environmental Working Group. Undated. Farm Subsidy Database. Available at http://farm.ewg.org.

Environmental Working Group. 2004. *California Water Subsidies: Large Agribusiness Operations—Not Small Family Farmers—Are Reaping a Windfall from Taxpayer-Subsidized Cheap Water,* Washington, DC.

EPA Science Advisory Board. 2009. *Valuing the Protection of Ecological Systems and Services: A Report of the EPA Science Advisory Board.* Washington, DC.

Epanchin, P. N., R. A. Knapp, and S. P. Lawler. 2010. "Nonnative Trout Impact an Alpine-Nesting Bird by Altering Aquatic-Insect Subsidies." *Ecology* 91: 2406–15.

Fairbank, Maslin, Maullin, Metz & Associates. 2010. Key Findings from Recent Opinion Research on Attitudes Toward Water Conservation in California. Memo to the Association of California Water Agencies from Dave Metz and Shakari Byerly, June 1.

Faunt, C. C., ed. 2009. *Groundwater Availability of the Central Valley Aquifer, California.* U.S. Geological Survey Professional Paper 1766. Sacramento, CA.

Federal Energy Regulatory Commission. 2004. *Handbook for Hydroelectric Project Licensing and 5 MW Exemptions from Licensing.* Washington, DC. Available at www.ferc.gov/industries/hydropower/gen-info/handbooks/licensing_handbook.pdf.

Feyrer, F., M. L. Nobriga, and T. R. Sommer. 2007. "Multi-Decadal Trends for Three Declining Fish Species: Habitat Patterns and Mechanisms in the San Francisco Estuary, California, USA." *Canadian Journal of Fisheries and Aquatic Sciences* 64: 723–34.

Field, E. H., T. E. Dawson, K. R. Felzer, A. D. Frankel, V. Gupta, T. H. Jordan, T. Parsons, M. D. Petersen, R. S. Stein, R. J. Weldon II, and C. J. Wills. 2008. *The Uniform California Earthquake Rupture Forecast,* Version 2 (UCERF 2). U.S. Geological Survey Open File Report 2007-1437. Reston, VA.

Fissekis, A. D. 2008. "Climate Change Effects on the Sacramento Basin's Flood Control Projects." Master's thesis, University of California, Davis.

Fleckenstein, J., M. Anderson, G. Fogg, and J. Mount. 2004. "Managing Surface Water-Groundwater to Restore Fall Flows in the Cosumnes River." *Journal of Water Resources Planning and Management* 130(4): 301–10.

Fleenor W. E., E. Hanak, J. R. Lund, and J. F. Mount. 2008. *Delta Hydrodynamics and Water Salinity with Future Conditions. Technical Appendix C: Comparing Futures for the Sacramento San Joaquin Delta.* San Francisco: Public Policy Institute of California.

Fleenor, W. E., W. Bennett, P. Moyle, and J. Lund. 2010. "On Developing Prescriptions for Freshwater Flows to Sustain Desirable Fishes in the Sacramento–San Joaquin Delta." University of California, Davis: Center for Watershed Sciences.

Florsheim J. L., J. F. Mount, and A. Chin. 2008. "Bank Erosion as a Desirable Attribute of Rivers." *BioScience* 58(6): 519–29.

Fogg, G. E., and E. M. LaBolle. 2006. "Motivation of Synthesis, with an Example of Groundwater Sustainability." *Water Resources Research* 42: W03S05, doi:10.1029/2005WR004372.

Folke, C., T. Hahn, P. Olsson, and J. Norberg. 2005. "Adaptive Governance of Social-Ecological Systems." *Annual Review of Environmental Resources* 30: 441–73.

Food and Agricultural Organization of the United Nations. n.d. AQUASTAT online database. Available at www.fao.org/nr/water/aquastat/main/index.stm.

Freeman, A. M. 2003. *The Measurement of Environmental and Resource Values: Theory and Methods.* 2nd ed. Washington, DC: Resources for the Future.

Galloway, D. L., D. R. Jones, and S. E. Ingebritsen. 1999. *Land Subsidence in the United States.* U.S. Geological Survey Circular 1182.

Galloway, G., et al. 2007. *A California Challenge—Flooding in the Central Valley.* Independent Review Panel Report to the California Department of Water Resources. Available at www.water.ca.gov/news/newsreleases/2008/101507challenge.pdf.

Garner, E. L., and J. N. Willis. 2005. "Right Back Where We Started From: The Last Twenty-Five Years of Groundwater Law in California." *McGeorge Law Review* 36(2): 413.

Garrett, E. 2005. "Hybrid Democracy." *George Washington Law Review* 73: 1096–1130.

Garry, T. 2007. "Water Markets and Water Rights in the United States: Lessons from Australia." *Macquarie Journal of International and Comparative Environmental Law* 4: 23–60.

Genius, M., E. Hatzaki, E. M. Kouromichelaki, G. Kouvakis, S. Nikiforaki, and K. P. Tsagarakis. 2008. "Evaluating Consumers' Willingness to Pay for Improved Potable Water Quality and Quantity." *Water Resources Management* 22(12): 1825–34.

Georgakakos, K. P., and N. Graham. 2008. "Potential Benefits of Seasonal Inflow Prediction Uncertainty for Reservoir Release Decisions." *Journal of Applied Meteorology and Climatology* 47(5): 1297–1321.

Gerber, E. R., A. Lupia, M. D. McCubbis, and D. R. Kiewiet. 2001. *Stealing the Initiative: How State Government Responds to Direct Democracy.* Upper Saddle River, NJ: Prentice Hall.

Gilbert, G. K. 1917. "Hydraulic-Mining Debris in the Sierra Nevada." U.S. Geological Survey Professional Paper 105.

Gillilan, D. M., and T. C. Brown. 1997. *Instream Flow Protection: Seeking a Balance in Western Water Use.* Covelo, CA: Island Press.

Gleick, P. H., D. Haasz, C. Henges-Jeck, V. Srinivasan, G. Wolff, K. K. Cushing, and A. Mann. 2003. *Waste Not, Want Not: The Potential for Urban Water Conservation in California.* Oakland, CA: Pacific Institute for Studies in Development, Environment, and Security.

Glibert, P. M. 2010. "Long-Term Changes in Nutrient Loading and Stoichiometry and Their Relationships with Changes in the Food Web and Dominant Pelagic Fish Species in the San Francisco Estuary, California," *Reviews in Fisheries Science* 1064–1262 18(2): 211–232.

Goldfarb, W. 1994. "Watershed Management: Slogan or Solution?" *Boston College Environmental Affairs Law Review* 23: 483–509.

Gordon, T. 2004. *The Local Initiative in California.* San Francisco: Public Policy Institute of California.

Gordon, T. 2010. "California Budget." In *California 2025: Planning for a Better Future.* San Francisco: Public Policy Institute of California.

Governor's Commission to Review California Water Rights Law. 1978. *Final Report.* Sacramento, CA: State of California.

Graham, N. E., and M. K. Hughes. 2007. "Reconstructing the Mediaeval Low Stands of Mono Lake, Sierra Nevada, California, USA." *The Holocene* 17(8): 1197–1210.

Gray, B. E. 1989. "In Search of Bigfoot: The Common Law Origins of Article X, Section 2 of the California Constitution." *Hastings Constitutional Law Quarterly* 17: 225–69.

Gray, B. E. 1994a. "The Modern Era in California Water Law." *Hastings Law Journal* 45: 249–308.

Gray, B. E. 1994b. "The Market and the Community: Lessons from California's Drought Water Bank." *Hastings West-Northwest Journal of Environmental Law and Policy* 1: 17–45.

Gray, B. E. 1996. "The Shape of Transfers to Come: A Model Water Transfer Act for California." *Hastings West-Northwest Journal of Environmental Law and Policy* 4: 23–59.

Gray, B. E. 2002a. "The Property Right in Water." *Hastings West-Northwest Journal of Environmental Law and Policy* 9: 27–28.

Gray, B. E. 2002b. "Takings and Water Rights." *Annual Proceedings of the Rocky Mountain Mineral Law Foundation* 48(23).

Gray, B. E. 2004. "Dividing the Waters: The California Experience." *Hastings West-Northwest Journal of Environmental Law and Policy* 10: 141–51.

Great Oaks Water Co. v. Santa Clara Valley Water District. 2010. No. 1-05-CV053 142 (Santa Clara Supr. Ct. February 3).

Gregory, S., H. Li, and J. Li. 2002. "The Conceptual Basis for Ecological Responses to Dam Removal." *Bioscience* 52: 713–23.

Griffin, K., G. Leventis, and B. McDonald. 2010. "Implementing a Public Goods Charge for Water." Policy and Planning Division Staff White Paper, California Public Utilities Commission. Available at www.cpuc.ca.gov/PUC/emergingissues/.

Groundwater Replenishment System. Undated. Website. Available at www.gwrsystem.com.

Gumprecht, B. 1999. *The Los Angeles River.* Baltimore, MD: John Hopkins University Press.

Guo, Y. C., S. W. Krasner, S. Fitzsimmons, G. Woodside, and N. Yamachika. 2010. *Source, Fate, and Transport of Endocrine Disruptors, Pharmaceuticals, and Personal Care Products in Drinking Water Sources in California.* Final Project Report NWRI-2010-02. Fountainside, CA: National Water Research Institute.

Haddad, B. A. 2000. *Rivers of Gold.* Washington, DC: Island Press.

Hagman, D. G., and D. J. Misczynski. 1977. *Windfalls for Wipeouts: Land Value Compensation and Capture.* Washington, DC: American Planning Association.

Hall, D. C. 1996. "Calculating Marginal Cost for Water Rates." In *Advances in the Economics of Environmental Resources: Marginal Cost Rate Design and Whole Sale Water Market*, ed. D. C. Hall (Greenwich, CT: JAI Press), 77–94.

Hall, D. C. 2000. "Public Choice and Water Rate Design." In *The Political Economy of Water Pricing Reforms*, ed. A. Dinar (New York: Oxford University Press), 189–212.

Hall, D. C. 2009. "Politically Feasible, Revenue Sufficient, and Economically Efficient Municipal Water Rates." *Contemporary Economic Policy* 27(4): 539–54.

Hall, M. 2010. "The Importance of Improved Groundwater Management in Sustainable Water Management for California's People and Ecosystems." Written testimony for the Little Hoover Commission on California Water Governance, The Nature Conservancy. Available at www.lhc.ca.gov/studies/activestudies/watergovernance/HallJan10.pdf.

Hallegatte, S. 2009. "Strategies to Adapt to an Uncertain Climate Change." *Global Environmental Change* 129: 240–47.

Hamilton, J. B., G. L. Curtis, S. M. Snedaker, and D. K. White. 2005. "Distribution of Anadromous Fishes in the Upper Klamath River Watershed Prior to Hydropower Dams—A Synthesis of the Historical Evidence." *Fisheries* 30: 10–20.

Hanak, E. 2003. *Who Should Be Allowed to Sell Water in California? Third-Party Issues and the Water Market.* San Francisco: Public Policy Institute of California.

Hanak, E. 2005a. "Stopping the Drain: Third-Party Responses to California's Water Market." *Contemporary Economic Policy* 23(1): 59–77.

Hanak, E. 2005b. *Water for Growth: California's New Frontier.* San Francisco: Public Policy Institute of California.

Hanak, E. 2008. "Is Water Policy Limiting Residential Growth? Evidence from California." *Land Economics* 84(1): 31–50.

Hanak, E. 2009a. "Decentralized Growth Planning: Evaluating Water Utility Performance." Unpublished paper.

Hanak, E. 2009b. *Paying for Infrastructure: California's Choices.* San Francisco: Public Policy Institute of California.

Hanak, E. 2010. "Show Me the Water Plan: Urban Water Management Plans and California's Water Supply Adequacy Laws." *Golden Gate University Environmental Law Review* 4(1).

Hanak, E. In press. California's Water Market: Lessons from the Field." In *Permit Trading in Different Applications,* ed. B. Hansjürgens, R. Antes, and M. Strunz (London: Routledge).

Hanak, E., and C. Dyckman. 2003. "Counties Wresting Control: Local Responses to California's Statewide Water Market." *University of Denver Water Law Review* 6(2): 494.

Hanak, E., and E. Barbour. 2005. "Sizing Up the Challenge: California's Infrastructure Needs and Tradeoffs." In *California 2025: Taking on the Future*, ed. E. Hanak and M. Baldassare (San Francisco: Public Policy Institute of California), 113–156.

Hanak, E., and M. Davis. 2006. "Lawns and Water Demand in California." *California Economic Policy* 2(2). San Francisco: Public Policy Institute of California.

Hanak, E., and J. Lund. 2008. *Adapting California's Water Management to Climate Change.* San Francisco: Public Policy Institute of California.

Hanak, E., L. Bedsworth, S. Swanbeck, and J. Malaczynski. 2008. *Climate Policy at the Local Level: A Survey of California's Cities and Counties.* San Francisco: Public Policy Institute of California.

Hanak, E., J. Lund, A. Dinar, B. Gray, R. Howitt, J. Mount, P. Moyle, and B. Thompson. 2010. "Myths of California Water—Implications and Reality." *West-Northwest Journal of Environmental Law and Policy* 16(1).

Hanemann, W. M. 1992. "Natural Resources Damages for Oil Spills in California." In *Natural Resource Damages in Law and Economics*, ed. Kevin M. Ward and John W. Duffield (New York: John Wiley & Sons).

Hanemann, M., and C. Dyckman. 2009. "The San Francisco Bay-Delta: A Failure of Decision-Making Capacity." *Environmental Science and Policy* 12: 710–25.

Hansmann, H., R. Gilson, and M. Pargendler. 2010. "Regulatory Dualism as a Development Strategy: Corporate Reform in Brazil, the U.S., and the EU." Stanford Law and Economics Olin working paper, No. 390.

Harou, J. J., and J. R. Lund. 2008. "Ending Groundwater Overdraft in Hydrologic-Economic Systems." *Hydrogeology Journal* 16(6): 1039–55.

Harou, J. J., M. Pulido-Velazquez, D. E. Rosenberg, J. Medellin-Azuara, J. R. Lund, and R. E. Howitt. 2009. "Hydro-Economic Models: Concepts, Design, Applications, and Future Prospects." *Journal of Hydrology* 375(3–4): 627–43.

Harou, J. J., J. Medellin-Azuara, T. Zhu, S. K. Tanaka, J. R. Lund, S. Stine, M. A. Olivares, and M. W. Jenkins. 2010. "Economic Consequences of Optimized Water Management for a Prolonged, Severe Drought in California." *Water Resources Research* 46: W05522, doi:10.1029/2008WR007681.

Harrison, D. C. 1980. "Basinwide Perspective: An Approach to the Design and Analysis of Institutions for Unified River Basin Management." In *Unified River Basin Management*, ed. R. M. North, L. B. Dworsky, and D. J. Allec (Minneapolis, MN: American Water Resources Association), 427–37.

Harter, T., H. Davis, M. C. Mathews, and R. D. Meyer. 2002. "Shallow Groundwater Quality on Dairy Farms with Irrigated Forage Crops," *Journal of Contaminant Hydrology* 55: 287–315.

Healey, M., M. Dettinger, and R. Norgaard. 2008. "New Perspectives on Science and Policy in the Bay-Delta." In *The State of Bay-Delta Science*, ed. M. Healey, M. Dettinger, and R. Norgaard (Sacramento, CA: CALFED Science Program), 1–18.

Heberger, M., H. Cooley, P. Herrera, P. H. Gleick, and E. Moore. 2009. *Impacts of Sea-Level Rise on the California Coast.* Report CEC-500-2009-024-F. Sacramento, CA: California Energy Commission.

Heckelman, J. C. 2007. "Explaining the Rain: The Rise and Decline of Nations After 25 Years." *Southern Economics Journal* 74: 18–33.

Heinz Center for Science, Economics, and the Environment. 2002. *Dam Removal: Science and Decision-Making.* Washington, DC.

Helfman, G. S. 2007. *Fish Conservation.* Covelo, CA: Island Press.

Herminghaus v. Southern California Edison. 1926. 200 Cal. 81, 252 P. 607.

Hewitt, J., and M. Hanemann. 1995. "A Discrete-Continuous Choice Approach to Residential Water Demand Under Block Rate Pricing." *Land Economics* 71(2): 173–92.

Hidalgo, H., D. Cayan, and M. Dettinger. 2005. "Sources of Variability of Evapotranspiration in California." *Journal of Hydrometeorology* 6: 3–19.

Hidalgo H. G., T. Das, M. D. Dettinger, D. R. Cayan, D. W. Pierce, T. P. Barnett, G. Bala, A. Mirin, A. W. Wood, C. Bonfils, B. D. Santer, and T. Nozawa. 2009. "Detection and Attribution of Stream Flow Timing Changes to Climate Change in the Western United States." *Journal of Climate* 22, doi:10.1175/2009JCLI2470.1, 3838–55.

Hoagland, R. 2010. "Least-Cost Planning Simulation Model," Draft. Sacramento, CA: California Department of Water Resources, Division of Statewide Integrated Water Management.

Hobbs, B. F. 1995. "Optimization Methods for Electric Utility Resource Planning." *European Journal of Operational Research* 83(1): 1–20.

Holling, C. S. 1978. *Adaptive Environmental Assessment and Management.* Chichester, UK: Wiley Interscience.

Hollinshead, S. P., and J. R. Lund. 2006. "Optimization of Environmental Water Account Purchases with Uncertainty." *Water Resources Research* 42(8): W08403.

Howard, J., and M. Merrifield. 2010. *Mapping Groundwater Dependent Ecosystems in California. PLoS ONE* 5(6): e11249, doi:10.1371/journal.pone.0011249.

Howard, J., and C. Revenga. 2009. "California's Freshwater Biodiversity in a Continental Context." *Science for Conservation Technical Brief Series.* San Francisco: The Nature Conservancy of California.

Howitt, R. E. 1995. "Malleable Property Rights and Smooth-Pasting Conditions." *American Journal of Agricultural Economics* 77: 1192–98.

Howitt, R., J. Medellin-Azuara, and D. MacEwan. 2009. *Measuring the Employment Impact of Water Reductions.* University of California, Davis: Department of Agricultural and Resource Economics and Center for Watershed Sciences. Available at http://swap.ucdavis.edu.

Huffaker, R. 2008. "Conservation Potential of Agricultural Water Conservation Subsidies." *Water Resources Research* 44, W00E01, doi:10.1029/2007WR006183.

Hundley, N., Jr. 2001. *The Great Thirst. Californians and Water: A History.* Berkeley: University of California Press.

Hurlbert, A. H., T. W. Anderson, K. K. Sturm, and S. H. Hurlbert. 2007. Fish and Fish-Eating Birds at the Salton Sea: A Century of Boom and Bust. *Lake and Reservoir Management* 23: 469–99.

Imperial Irrigation District. 1984. *Alleged Waste and Unreasonable Use of Water.* Water Rights Decision Number 1600, Sacramento, CA: California Water Resources Control Board.

Imperial Irrigation District and San Diego County Water Authority. 2007. *Settlement Agreement Resolving Present and Future Disputes Under Sections 14.5 and 18.1 of the Revised Fourth Amendment to the IID/SDCWA Conserved Water Transfer Agreement.*

Ingram, H., and L. Fraser. 2006. "Path Dependency and Adroit Innovation: The Case of California Water." In *Punctuated Equilibrium and the Dynamics of U.S. Environmental Policy,* ed. R. Repetto (London: Yale University Press), 78–110.

In re Long Valley Creek Stream System. 1979. 25 Cal. 3d 339, 599 P. 2d 656, 158 Cal. Rptr. 350.

Intergovernmental Panel on Climate Change. 2007. "Climate Change 2007—Impacts, Adaptation and Vulnerability." *Contribution of Working Group II to the Fourth Assessment Report of the IPCC.* Available at www.ipcc.ch/ipccreports/ar4-wg2.htm.

Irwin v. Phillips. 1855. 5 Cal. 140.

Isenberg, A. 2005. *Mining California: An Ecological History.* New York: Hill and Wang.

Israel, M., and J. R. Lund. 1995. "Recent California Water Transfers: Implications for Water Management." *Natural Resources Journal* 35: 1–32.

Jacobs, J., G. Freeman, J. Grygier, D. Morton, G. Schultz, K. Staschus, and J. Stedinger. 1995. "SOCRATES: A System for Scheduling Hydroelectric Generation Under Uncertainty." *Annals of Operations Research* 59: 99–133.

James, L. A. 2005. "Sediment from Hydraulic Mining Detained by Englebright and Small Dams in the Yuba Basin." *Geomorphology* 71: 202–26.

Jenkins, M. W. 1992. "Yolo County, California's Water Supply System: Conjunctive Use Without Management." University of California, Davis: Department of Civil and Environmental Engineering.

Jenkins, M. W., and J. R. Lund. 2000. "Integrated Yield and Shortage Management for Water Supply Planning." *Journal of Water Resources Planning and Management* 126(5): 288–97.

Jenkins, M. W., J. R. Lund, and R. E. Howitt. 2003. "Economic Losses for Urban Water Scarcity in California." *Journal of the American Water Works Association* 95(2): 58–70.

Jenkins, M. W., J. R. Lund, R. E. Howitt, A. J. Draper, S. M. Msangi, S. K. Tanaka, R. S. Ritzema, and G. F. Marques. 2004. "Optimization of California's Water System: Results and Insights." *Journal of Water Resources Planning and Management* 130(4): 271–80.

Jevrejeva, S., J. C. Moore, and A. Grinsted. 2008. "Relative Importance of Mass and Volume Changes to Global Sea Level Rise, *Journal of Geophysical Research* 113, D08105, doi:10.1029/2007JD009208.

Johnston, R., J. R. Lund, and P. Craig. 1995. "Capacity Allocation Methods for Reducing Traffic Congestion." *Journal of Transportation Engineering* 121(1): 27–39.

Kahrl, W. 1982. *Water and Power.* Berkeley: University of California Press.

Kallis, G., M. Kiparsky, and R. Norgaard. 2009. "Collaborative Governance and Adaptive Management: Lessons from California's CALFED Water Program." *Environmental Science and Policy* 12: 631–43.

Kaplow, L. 2003. "Transition Policy: A Conceptual Framework." *Journal of Contemporary Legal Issues* 13: 161–209.

Karkoski, J., and T. Young. 2000. "Green Evolution: Are Economic Incentives the Next Step in Nonpoint Source Pollution Control?" *Water Policy* 2: 151–73.

Katz v. Walkinshaw. 1903. 141 Cal. 116, 135, 74 P. 766.

Kelley, R. 1989. *Battling the Inland Sea.* Berkeley: University of California Press.

Kelley, A. 2004. "Federal Reclamation Law." *Waters and Water Rights* 4.

Kendall, M. 2011. In press. "Drought and Its Role in Shaping Water Policy in Australia. In *Drought in Arid and Semi-Arid Environments: A Multi-Disciplinary and Cross-Country Perspective,* ed. K. Schwabe, J. Albiac, J. Connor, R. Hassan, and L. Meza-Gonzalez (Berlin: Springer).

King, R. 2005. *Federal Flood Insurance.* Washington, DC: Congressional Research Service Report for Congress, The Library of Congress. Available at www.fas.org/sgp/crs/misc/RL32972.pdf.

King Moon, L. 2009. Testimony to the Little Hoover Commission Hearing on State Water Governance. Sacramento, CA: Little Hoover Commission.

Kiparsky, M., and P. H. Gleick. 2005. "Climate Change and California Water Resources." In *The World's Water 2004–2005,* ed. P. G. Gleick (Washington, DC: Island Press), 157–88.

Klemes, V. 2000a. "Sensitivity of Water Resource Systems to Climatic Variability." In *Common Sense and Other Heresies: Selected Papers on Hydrology and Water Resources Engineering,* ed. V. Klemes (Cambridge, Ontario: Canadian Water Resources Association).

Klemes, V. 2000b. "Design Implications of Climate Change." In *Common Sense and Other Heresies: Selected Papers on Hydrology and Water Resources Engineering,* ed. V. Klemes (Cambridge, Ontario: Canadian Water Resources Association).

Kletzing, R. 1988. "Imported Groundwater Banking: The Kern County Water Bank—A Case Study," *Pacific Law Journal* 19(4): 1225–66.

Knapp, R. A., K. R. Matthews, and O. Sarnelle. 2001. "Resistance and Resilience of Alpine Lake Fauna to Fish Introductions." *Ecological Monographs* 71: 401–21.

Knowles, N., and D. R. Cayan. 2002. "Potential Effects of Global Warming on the Sacramento/San Joaquin Watershed and the San Francisco Estuary," *Geophysical Research Letters* 29(18).

Knowles, N., and D. R. Cayan, 2004. "Elevational Dependence of Projected Hydrologic Changes in the San Francisco Estuary and Watershed." *Climatic Change* 62(1/3): 319–36.

Knowles, N., M. D. Dettinger, and D. R. Cayan. 2006. "Trends in Snowfall Versus Rainfall for the Western United States." *Journal of Climate* 19: 4545–59.

Kondolf, G. M. 1998. "Lessons Learned from Stream Restoration Projects in California." *Aquatic Conservation: Marine and Freshwater Systems* 8: 39–52.

Kuby, M. J., W. F. Fagan, C. S. ReVelle, and W. L. Graf. 2005. "A Multiobjective Optimization Model for Dam Removal: An Example Trading Off Salmon Passage with Hydropower and Water Storage in the Willamette Basin." *Advances in Water Resources* 38: 845–55.

Kuduk, C. A., and S. J. Anders. 2006. *Following California's Public Goods Charge: Tracking Contributions and Expenditures of the Renewable Energy Program and the PIER Program.* San Diego: University of San Diego School of Law, Energy Policy Initiatives Center.

Lackey, R. T., D. H. Lach, and S. L. Duncan, eds. 2006. *Salmon 2100: The Future of Wild Pacific Salmon.* Bethesda, MD: American Fisheries Society.

la Farré, M., S. Perez, L. Kantiani, and D. Barceló. 2008. "Fate and Toxicity of Emerging Pollutants, Their Metabolities and Transformation Products in the Aquatic Environment," *Trends Anal. Chem.* 27(11): 991–1007.

Landis, J. D., and M. Reilly. 2002. *How We Will Grow: Baseline Projections of California's Urban Footprint through the Year 2100.* Project Completion Report, Berkeley: University of California, Institute of Urban and Regional Development, Department of City and Regional Planning.

Leach, W. D. 2006. "Theories About Consensus-Based Conservation." *Conservation Biology* 20: 573–75.

Lee, K. N. 1993. *Compass and Gyroscope: Integrating Science and Politics for the Environment.* Covelo, CA: Island Press.

Legislative Analyst's Office. 1996. *Understanding Proposition 218.* Sacramento, CA.

Legislative Analyst's Office. 2008. *California's Water: An LAO Primer.* Sacramento, CA.

Legislative Analyst's Office. 2010. *Liquid Assets: Improving Management of the State's Groundwater Resources.* Sacramento, CA.

Leidy, R. A., and P. B. Moyle. 1998. "Conservation Status of the World's Fish Fauna: An Overview." In *Conservation Biology for the Coming Decade*, ed. P. A. Fiedler and P. M. Karieva (New York: Chapman and Hall).

Lemos, M. C., and A. Agrawal. 2006. "Environmental Governance." *Annual Review of Environment and Resources* 31: 297–325.

Leshy, J. 2009. "Notes on a Progressive National Water Policy." *Harvard Law and Policy Review* 3: 133–59.

Letey, J. 2000. "Soil Salinity Poses Challenges for Sustainable Agriculture and Wildlife." *California Agriculture* 54(2): 43–48.

Letey, J., G. J. Hoffman, J. W. Hopmans, S. R. Grattan, D. Suarez, D. L. Corwin, J. D. Oster, L. Wu, and C. Amrhein. In press. "Evaluation of Soil Salinity Leaching Requirement Guidelines," *Agricultural Water Management.*

Lettenmaier, D. P., and D. P. Sheer. 1991. "Climatic Sensitivity of California Water Resources." *Journal of Water Resources Planning and Management* 117(1): 108–125.

Leung, B., D. M. Lodge, D. Finnoff, J. F. Shogren, M. A. Lewis, and G. Lamberti. 2002. "An Ounce of Prevention or a Pound of Cure: Bioeconomic Risk Analysis of Invasive Species." *Proceedings of the Royal Society B* 269: 2407–13.

Lightfoot, K. G., and O. Parrish. 2009. *California Indians and Their Environment.* Berkeley: University of California Press.

Lindley, S. T., C. Grimes, M. S. Mohr, W. Peterson, J. Stein, J. T. Anderson, L. W. Botsford, D. L. Bottom, C. A. Busack, T. A. Collier, J. Ferguson, J. C. Garza, A. M. Grover, D. G. Hankin, R. G. Kope, P. W. Lawson, A. Low, R. B. MacFarlane, K. Moore, M. Palmer-Zwahlen, F. B. Schweig, J. Smith, C. Tracy, R. Webb, B. T. Wells, and T. H. Williams. 2009. *What Caused the Sacramento River Fall Chinook Stock Collapse?* Report to the Pacific Fishery Management Council. Portland, OR.

Little Hoover Commission. 1990. *Report on Fish and Game Commission and Department of Fish and Game.* Sacramento, CA.

Little Hoover Commission. 2005. *Still Imperiled, Still Important.* The Little Hoover Commission's Review of the CALFED Bay-Delta Program. Sacramento, CA.

Little Hoover Commission. 2009. *Clearer Structure, Cleaner Water: Improving Performance and Outcomes at the State Water Boards.* Sacramento, CA.

Little Hoover Commission. 2010. *Managing for Change: Modernizing California's Water Governance.* Sacramento, CA.

Littleworth, A. L., and E. L. Garner. 2007. *California Water II.* Point Arena, CA: Solano Press Books.

Lodge, D. M., S. L. Williams, H. J. MacIssaac, K. R. Hayes, B. Leung, S. H. Reichard, R. N. Mack, P. B. Moyle, M. Smith, D. A. Andow, J. T. Carlton, and A. McMichael. 2006. "Biological Invasions: Recommendations for U.S. Policy and Management." *Ecological Applications* 16: 2035–54.

Long Valley Creek Stream System. 1979. 25 Cal. 3d 339, 599 P. 2d 656, 158 Cal. Rptr. 350.

Los Angeles v. San Fernando. 1975. 14 Cal. 3d 199, 537 P. 2d 1250, 123 Cal. Rptr.

Luers, A. L., and S. C. Moser. 2006. "Preparing for the Impacts of Climate Change in California: Opportunities and Constraints for Adaptation." White Paper. Sacramento, CA: California Climate Change Center, State of California.

Lund, J. R. 2002. "Floodplain Planning with Risk-Based Optimization," *Journal of Water Resources Planning and Management* 128(3), 202–7.

Lund, J. R. 2006. "Most Excellent Integrated Water Management from California." *Proceedings of the 2006 Conference on Operations Management.* Reston, VA: American Society of Civil Engineers.

Lund, J. R., and M. Israel. 1995a. "Optimization of Transfers in Urban Water Supply Planning." *Journal of Water Resources Planning and Management* 121(1): 41–8.

Lund, J. R., and M. Israel. 1995b. "Water Transfers in Water Resource Systems." *Journal of Water Resources Planning and Management* 121(2): 193–205.

Lund, J., E. Hanak, W. Fleenor, R. Howitt, J. Mount, and P. Moyle. 2007. *Envisioning Futures for the Sacramento–San Joaquin Delta.* San Francisco: Public Policy Institute of California.

Lund, J. R., E. Hanak, W. E. Fleenor, J. F. Mount, R. Howitt, B. Bennett, and P. B. Moyle. 2010. *Comparing Futures for the Sacramento San Joaquin Delta.* Berkeley: University of California Press and Public Policy Institute of California.

Lupia, A., and M. D. McCubbins. 1994. "Who Controls Information and the Structure of Legislative Decision Making." *Legislative Studies Quarterly* 19: 361–84.

Lusk, B. 2008. "Local Entity Completes Its Work," *The Imperial Valley Press*, May 17.

Lux v. Haggin. 1886. 69 Cal. 255, 10 P. 674.

Maass, A. A. 1951. *Muddy Waters, the Army Engineers and the Nation's Rivers*. Cambridge, MA: Harvard University Press.

MacDonald, G. M. 2007. "Severe and Sustained Drought in Southern California and the West: Present Conditions and Insights from the Past on Causes and Impacts." *Quaternary International* 173–174: 87–100.

Madani, K., and J. R. Lund. 2009. "Modeling California's High-Elevation Hydropower Systems in Energy Units." *Water Resources Research* 45: W09413, doi:10.1029/2008WR007206.

Madani, K., and J. R. Lund. 2010. "Estimated Impacts of Climate Warming on California's High/Elevation Hydropower," *Climatic Change* 102(3–4): 521–38.

Madani, K., and J. R. Lund. 2011. "California's Sacramento–San Joaquin Delta Conflict: From Cooperation to Chicken." Working paper. University of California, Davis: Center for Watershed Sciences.

Magurran, A. E. 2009. "Threats to Freshwater Fish." *Science* 325: 1215–16.

Mann, M. E., Z. Zhang, M. K. Hughes, R. S. Bradley, S. K. Miller, S. Rutherford, and F. Ni. 2008. "Proxy-Bed Reconstructions of Hemispheric and Global Surface Temperature Variations over the Past Two Millenia." *PNAS* 105(36): 13252–57.

Marchetti, M. P., and P. B. Moyle. 2001. "Effects of Flow Regime on Fish Assemblages in a Regulated California Stream." *Ecological Applications* 11: 530–39.

Marks v. Whitney. 1971. 6 Cal. 3d 251, 491 P.2d 374, 98 Cal. Rptr. 790.

Marvin-DiPasquale, M. C., J. L. Agee, C. McGowan, R. S. Oremland, M. Thomas, D. Krabbenhoft, and C. C. Gilmour. 2000. "Methyl-Mercury Degradation Pathways: A Comparison Among Three Mercury-Impacted Ecosystems," *Environmental Science and Technology* 34: 4908–16.

Maurer, E. P., I. T. Stewart, C. Bonfils, P. B. Duffy, and D. Cayan. 2007. "Detection, Attribution, and Sensitivity of Trends Toward Earlier Streamflow in the Sierra Nevada." *Journal of Geophysical Research* 112, D11118, doi:10.1029/2006JD008088.

McKinsey & Company. 2007. *Reducing U.S. Greenhouse Gas Emissions: How Much at What Cost?* U.S. Greenhouse Gas Abatement Mapping Initiative Executive Report.

McPhee, J. 1989. *The Control of Nature*. New York: Farrar, Strauss and Giroux.

Medellin-Azuara, J., R. E. Howitt, J. R. Lund, and E. Hanak. 2008a. "The Economic Effects on Agriculture of Water Export Salinity South of the Delta." *Technical Appendix I: Comparing Futures for the Sacramento San Joaquin Delta* (San Francisco: Public Policy Institute of California).

Medellin-Azuara, J., J. J. Harou, M. A. Olivares, K. Madani-Larijani, J. R. Lund, R. E. Howitt, S. K. Tanaka, M. W. Jenkins, and T. Zhu. 2008b. "Adaptability and Adaptations of California's Water Supply System to Dry Climate Warming." *Climatic Change* 87(1): S75–S90.

Metropolitan Water District of Southern California. 2010. *Integrated Resources Plan 2010 Update*, Report Number 1373. October.

Millennium Ecosystem Assessment. 2005. *Ecosystems and Human Well-Being: The Assessment Series*. Washington, DC: Island Press.

Miller, G. 2010. "In Central California, Coho Salmon Are on the Brink." *Science* 327: 512–13.

Miller, J. D., H. D. Safford, M. Crimmins, and A. E. Thode. 2009. "Quantitative Evidence for Increasing Forest Fire Severity in the Sierra Nevada and Southern Cascade Mountains, California and Nevada, USA." *Ecosystems* 12: 16–32.

Milly, P.C.D., J. Betancourt, M. Falkenmark, R. M. Hirsch, Z. W. Kundzewicz, D. P. Lettenmaier, R. J. Stouffer. 2008. "Stationarity Is Dead: Whither Water Management?" *Science* 319: 573–74.

Misczynski, D. 2009. "Fixing the Delta: How Will We Pay for It?" San Francisco: Public Policy Institute of California.

Monterey County Water Resources Agency. 2001. *Draft Environmental Impact Report/ Environmental Impact Statement for the Salinas Valley Project*. Salinas, CA.

Moore, M., A. Mulville, and M. Weinberg. 1996. "Water Allocation in the American West: Endangered Fish Versus Irrigated Agriculture." *Natural Resources Journal* 36: 319–57.

Morel F.M.M., A. M. Kraepiel, and M. Amyot. 1998. "The Chemical Cycle and Bioaccumulation of Mercury." *Annual Review of Ecology and Systematics* 29: 543–66.

Moser, S., G. Franco, S. Pittiglio, W. Chou, and D. Cayan. 2009. *The Future Is Now: An Update on Climate Change Science Impacts and Response Options for California*. Report CEC-500-2008-071. Sacramento, CA: California Energy Commission.

Mote, P. W., A. F. Hamlet, M. P. Clark, and D. P. Lettenmaier. 2005. "Declining Mountain Snowpack in Western North America." *Bulletin of the American Meteorological Society* 86(1): 39–49, doi:10.1175/BAMS-86-1-39.

Mount, J. F. 1995. *California Rivers and Streams: The Conflict Between Fluvial Process and Land Use*. Berkeley: University of California Press.

Mount, J. 2007. "Sea Level Rise and Delta Planning." Memo from the CALFED Independent Science Board to Mike Healey, CALFED Lead Scientist, September 6. Available at http://calwater.ca.gov/science/pdf/isb/meeting_082807/ISB_response_to_ls_sea_level_090707.pdf.

Mount, J. F., and R. Twiss. 2005. "Subsidence, Sea Level Rise, and Seismicity in the Sacramento–San Joaquin Delta." *San Francisco Estuary and Watershed Science* 3(5). Available at http://repositories.cdlib.org/jmie/sfews/vol3/iss1/art5.

Moyle, P. B. 2002. *Inland Fishes of California*. Berkeley: University of California Press.

Moyle, P. B., and W. A. Bennett. 2008. "The Future of the Delta Ecosystem and Its Fish." *Technical Appendix D: Comparing Futures for the Sacramento–San Joaquin Delta*. San Francisco: Public Policy Institute of California.

Moyle, P. B., and J. Ellison. 1991. "A Conservation-Oriented Classification System for California's Inland Waters." *California Fish and Game* 77: 161–80.

Moyle, P. B., and R. A. Leidy. 1992. "Loss of Biodiversity in Aquatic Ecosystems: Evidence from Fish Faunas." In *Conservation Biology: The Theory and Practice of Nature Conservation, Preservation, and Management*, ed. P. L. Fiedler and S. A. Jain (New York: Chapman and Hall), 128–69.

Moyle, P. B., and M. P. Marchetti. 2006. "Predicting Invasion Success: Freshwater Fishes in California as a Model." *Bioscience* 56: 515–24.

Moyle, P. B., and J. F. Mount. 2007. *Homogenous Rivers, Homogenous Faunas: Proceedings of the National Academy of Sciences* 104: 5711–12.

Moyle, P. B., and P. J. Randall. 1998. "Evaluating the Biotic Integrity of Watersheds in the Sierra Nevada, California." *Conservation Biology* 12: 1318–26.

Moyle, P. B., and G. M. Sato. 1991. "On the Design of Preserves to Protect Native Fishes." In *Battle Against Extinction: Native Fish Management in the American West,* ed. W. L. Minckley and J. E. Deaco (Tucson: University of Arizona Press), 155–69.

Moyle, P. B., and J. E. Williams. 1990. "Biodiversity Loss in the Temperate Zone: Decline of the Native Fish Fauna of California." *Conservation Biology* 4(3): 275–84.

Moyle, P. B., and R. M. Yoshiyama. 1994. "Protection of Aquatic Biodiversity in California: A Five-Tiered Approach." *Fisheries* 19: 6–18.

Moyle, P. B., W. A. Bennett, W. E. Fleenor, and J. R. Lund. 2010. "Habitat Variability and Complexity in the Upper San Francisco Estuary." *San Francisco Estuary and Watershed Science* 8(3).

Moyle, P. B., P. K. Crain, K. Whitener, and J. F. Mount. 2003. "Alien Fishes in Natural Streams: Fish Distribution, Assemblage Structure, and Conservation in the Cosumnes River, California, USA." *Environmental Biology of Fishes* 68: 143–62.

Moyle, P. B., J. A. Israel, and S. E. Purdy. 2008. *Salmon, Steelhead, and Trout in California: Status of an Emblematic Fauna.* University of California, Davis: Center for Watershed Sciences. Available at http://watershed.ucdavis.edu/.

Moyle P. B., J.V.E. Katz, and R. Quiñones. 2010. *Rapid Decline of California's Native Inland Fishes.* Working Paper 7. University of California, Davis: Center for Watershed Sciences. Available at http://watershed.ucdavis.edu/pdf/Moyle%20CA%20fish%20status-WP.pdf.

Moyle, P. B., H. W. Li, and B. A. Barton. 1986. "The Frankenstein Effect: Impact of Introduced Fishes on Native Fishes in North America." In *Fish Culture in Fisheries Management,* ed. R. H. Stroud (Bethesda, MD: American Fisheries Society), 415–26.

Moyle, P. B., M. P. Marchetti, J. Baldrige, and T. L. Taylor. 1998. "Fish Health and Diversity: Justifying Flows for a California Stream." *Fisheries* 23(7): 6–15.

Moyle, P. B., R. Quiñones, and J. Katz. 2010. *Fish Species of Special Concern of California.* 3rd ed. Sacramento, CA: California Department of Fish and Game.

Mumley, T. E., L. Shoemaker, J. Craig, J. Koenig, and G. Golliday. 2003. "Comprehensive Guidance for Managing California's Impaired Waters." *Proceedings of the Water Environment Federation* 32: 1039–70.

Murray-Darling Basin Authority. 2008. *Guide to the Proposed Basin Plan.* Canberra, AU: Australian Government.

National Audubon Society v. Superior Court. 1983. 33 Cal. 3d 419, 658 P. 2d 709, 189 Cal. Rptr. 346.

National Conference of State Legislatures. 2010. *Initiative States Ranked in Order by Use.* Available at www.ncsl.org/Default.aspx?TabID=21238.

National Marine Fisheries Service. 2010. *Recovery Plan for the Evolutionarily Significant Unit of Central California Coast Salmon,* Washington, DC.

National Research Council. 1995. *Science and the Endangered Species Act.* Washington, DC: National Academy Press.

National Research Council. 1996. *Upstream: Salmon and Society in the Pacific Northwest.* Washington, DC: National Academy Press.

National Research Council. 2004. *Endangered and Threatened Fishes of the Klamath River Basin: Causes of Decline and Strategies for Recovery.* Washington, DC: National Academies Press.

National Research Council. 2005. *Valuing Ecosystem Services: Toward Better Environmental Decision-Making.* Washington, DC: National Academies Press.

National Research Council. 2008. *Hydrology, Ecology, and Fishes of the Klamath River Basin.* Washington, DC: National Academies Press.

National Research Council. 2010. *A Scientific Assessment of Alternatives for Reducing Water Management Effects on Threatened and Endangered Fishes in California's Bay Delta.* Washington, DC: National Academies Press.

National Surface Transportation Infrastructure Financing Commission. 2009. *Paying Our Way: A New Framework for Transportation Finance.* Washington, DC: U.S. Department of Transportation.

National Water Commission. 2009. *Australian Water Markets Report 2008–2009.* Canberra, AU: National Water Commission, Australian Government.

National Water Initiative. 2004. *Intergovernmental Agreement on a National Water Initiative.* Canberra, AU: National Water Commission, Australian Government.

National Water Research Institute. 2009. *Managing Contaminants of Emerging Concern in California.* Technical Report 600, California Ocean Science Trust, National Water Research Institute, San Francisco Estuary Institute, Southern California Coastal Water Research Project. Fountain Valley, CA: National Water Research Institute. Available at www.sccwrp.org/ResearchAreas/RelatedPublications.aspx?id=b19861d8-3ab5-40a1-a520-f6f2818bf230.

National Wildlife Federation v. Gorsuch. 1982. 693 F.2d 156 (D.C. Cir.).

Needham, J., D. Watkins, J. R. Lund, and S. Nanda. 2000. "Linear Programming for Flood Control on the Iowa and Des Moines Rivers." *Journal of Water Resources Planning and Management* 126(3): 118–27.

NERA Economic Consulting. 2008. *Competitive Electricity Markets: The Benefits for Customers and the Environment.* White Plains, NY: NERA Economic Consulting. Available at www.nera.com/extImage/PUB_CompetitiveElectricityMarkets_Feb2008.pdf.

Neuman, J. C. 2004. "The Good, the Bad, the Ugly: Ten Years of the Oregon Water Trust." *Nebraska Law Review* 83: 432–84.

Nishikawa, T., A. J. Siade, E. G. Reichard, D. J. Ponti, A. G. Canales, and T. A. Johnson. 2009. "Stratigraphic Controls on Seawater Intrusion and Implications for Groundwater Management, Dominguez Gap Area of Los Angeles, California, USA." *Hydrogeology Journal* 17: 1699–1725.

Noble, R. T., S. B. Weisberg, M. K. Leecaster, C. D. McGee, J. H. Dorsey, P. Vainik, and V. Orozco-Borbon. 2003. "Storm Effects on Regional Beach Water Quality Along the Southern California Shoreline," *Journal of Water and Health* 1(1): 23–32.

Norgaard, R. B., G. Kallis, and M. Kiparsky. 2009. "Collectively Engaging Complex Socio-Ecological Systems: Re-Envisioning Science, Governance, and the California Delta." *Environmental Science and Policy* 12: 644–52.

North Coast Regional Water Quality Control Board. 2010a. *Action Plan for the Klamath River TMDLs Addressing Temperature, Dissolved Oxygen, Nutrient and Microcystin Impairments in the Klamath River in California and Lost River Implementation Plan.*

North Coast Regional Water Quality Control Board. 2010b. *Final Staff Report for the Klamath River Total Maxiumum Daily Loads (TMDLs) Addressing Temperature, Dissolved Oxygen, Nutrient, and Microcystin Impairments in California.* Available at www.swrcb.ca.gov/northcoast/water_issues/programs/tmdls/klamath_river/.

Norton, B. G. 1987. *Why Preserve Natural Variety?* Princeton, NJ: Princeton University Press.

Null, S. E. 2008. *Improving Managed Environmental Water Use Efficiency: Shasta River Flow and Temperature Modeling.* Ph.D. dissertation, University of California, Davis.

Null, S., and J. R. Lund. 2006. "Re-Assembling Hetch Hetchy: Water Supply Implications of Removing O'Shaughnessy Dam." *Journal of the American Water Resources Association* 42(4): 395–408.

Null, S. E., E. Bartolomeo, J. R. Lund, and E. Hanak. 2011. "Managing California's Water: Insights from Interviews with Water Policy Experts." Technical appendix to *Managing California's Water.* Available at www.ppic.org/content/pubs/other/211EHR_appendix.pdf.

Null, S. E., M. L. Deas, and J. R. Lund. 2010. "Flow and Water Temperature Simulation for Habitat Restoration in the Shasta River, California." *River Research and Applications* 26: 663–81.

Null, S. E., J. H. Viers, and J. F. Mount. 2010. "Hydrologic Response and Watershed Sensitivity to Climate Warming in California's Sierra Nevada." *PLoS ONE* 5(4): e9932, doi:10.1371/journal.pone.0009932.

Null, S. E., J. H. Viers, M. L. Deas, S. K. Tanaka, and J. F. Mount. Submitted. "Stream Temperature Sensitivity to Climate Warming in California's Sierra Nevada: Impacts to Coldwater Habitat." *Climatic Change.*

Nyman, L., ed. 1999. *River Jhelum, Kashmir Valley: Impacts on the Aquatic Environment.* Solna, SWE: SWEDMAR.

Olmstead, S. M., W. M. Hanemann, and R. N. Stavins. 2007. "Water Demand Under Alternative Price Structures." *Journal of Environmental Economics and Management* 54(2): 181–98.

O'Neill v. United States. 1995. 50 F.3d 677 (9th Cir.).

Opperman, J., G. Galloway, J. Fargione, J. Mount, B. Richter, and S. Secchi. 2009. "Sustainable Floodplains Through Large-Scale Reconnection to Rivers." *Science* 326: 1487–88.

Orang, M. N., J. S. Matyac, and R. L. Snyder. 2008. "Survey of Irrigation Methods in California in 2001." *Journal of Irrigation and Drainage Engineering* 4(1): 96–100.

Orlob, G. T. 1991. "San Joaquin Salt Balance: Future Prospects and Possible Solutions." In *The Economics and Management of Water and Drainage in Agriculture,* ed. A. Dinar and D. Zilberman (Boston, MA: Kluwer), 143–67.

Ostrom, E. 1990. *Governing the Commons: The Evolution of Institutions for Collection Action.* Cambridge, UK: Cambridge University Press.

Pacific Coast Federation of Fishermen's Associations v. National Marine Fisheries Service. 2001. 253 F.3d 1137 (9th Cir.).

Pajaro Valley Water Management Agency v. Amrhein. 2007. 150 Cal. App. 4th 1364, 59 Cal. Rptr. 3d 484.

Palmer, R. N., and J. R. Lund. 1986. "Drought and Power Production." *Journal of Water Resources Planning and Management* 112(4): 469–84.

Palmer, M. A., C. A. Reidy Liermann, C. Nilsson, M. Florke, J. Alcamo, P. S. Lake, and N. Bond. 2008. "Climate Change and the World's River Basins: Anticipating Management Options." *Frontiers in Ecology and the Environment* 6, doi:10.1890/060148.

Palmieri, A., F. Shah, and A. Dinar. 2001. "Economics of Reservoir Sedimentation and Sustainable Management of Dams." *Journal of Environmental Management* 61: 149–63.

Palo Alto Utilities Department. 2010. "Bay Area Water Supply and Conservation Agency Activities Update," Memo to the Utilities Advisory Commission, April 7.

Parr, D., and J. Parr. 2009. "California Tribal Water Rights." Briefing Paper prepared for the 2009 California Tribal Water Summit.

Paterno v. State of California. 2003. 113 Cal. App. 4th 998, 6 Cal. Rptr. 3d 854.

Pechman, C. 2007. *California's Electricity Market: A Post-Crisis Progress Report*. San Francisco: Public Policy Institute of California.

Peck, J. C. 1980. "Kansas Groundwater Management Districts." *Kansas Law Review* 29: 51–92.

Pejchar, L., and K. Warner. 2001. "A River Might Run Through It Again: Criteria for Consideration of Dam Removal and Interim Lessons from California." *Environmental Management* 28: 561–75.

Penn Central Transportation Co. v. New York City. 1978. 438 U.S. 104.

People v. Gold Run Ditch & Mining Co. 1884. 66 Cal. 138, 4 Pac. 1152.

Perry, C., P. Steduto, R. G. Allen, and C. M. Burt. 2009. "Increasing Productivity in Irrigated Agriculture: Agronomic Constraints and Hydrological Realities." *Agricultural Water Management* 96(11): 1517–24.

Peterson, M. N., M. J. Peterson, and T. R. Peterson. 2005. "Conservation and the Myth of Consensus." *Conservation Biology* 19: 762–67.

Phelps, C. E., N. Y. Moore, and M. H. Graubard. 1978. *Efficient Water Use in California: Water Rights, Water Districts, and Water Transfers*, R-2386-CSA/RF. Santa Monica, CA: RAND Corporation.

Phelps, C. E., M. H. Graubard, D. A. Jaquette, A. J. Lipson, N. Y. Moore, R. Shishko, and B. Wetzel. 1978. *Efficient Water Use in California: Summary*. R-2385-CSA/RF. Santa Monica, CA: RAND Corporation.

Pierce, D. W., T. P. Barnett, H. G. Hidalgo, T. Das, C. Bonfils, B. D. Santer, G. Bala, M. D. Dettinger, D. R. Cayan, A. Mirin, A. W. Wood, and T. Nozawa. 2008. "Attribution of Declining Western U.S. Snowpack to Human Effects." *Journal of the American Meteorological Society* 21: 6425–44.

Pisani, D. 1984. *From the Family Farm to Agribusiness: The Irrigation Crusade in California, 1850–1931*. Berkeley: University of California Press.

Poff, N. L., and D. D. Hart. 2002. "How Dams Vary and Why It Matters for the Emerging Science of Dam Removal." *Bioscience* 52: 659–68.

Poff, N. L., J. D. Allen, M. B. Bain, J. R. Karr, K. L. Prestegaard, B. D. Richter, R. E. Sparks, and J. C. Stromberg. 1997. "The Natural Flow Regime: A Paradigm for River Conservation and Restoration." *BioScience* 47: 769–84.

Pohl, M. M. 2003. "American Dam Removal Census: Available Data and Data Needs." In *Dam Removal Research*, ed. W. L. Graf (Washington, DC: Heinz Center), 29–39.

Poland, J. F., B. E. Lofgren, R. L. Ireland, and R. G. Pugh. 1975. *Land Subsidence in the San Joaquin Valley, California, of 1972*. U.S. Geological Survey Professional Paper 437-H. Washington, DC.

Presley, G. 2011. "California's Natural Community Conservation Planning Program: Saving Species Habitat Amidst Rising Development." In *The Endangered Species Act and Federalism: Effective Conservation Through Greater State Commitment*, ed. K. Arha and B. Thompson (Washington, DC: Resources for the Future Press).

Public Policy Institute of California. 2008. "Californians and the Initiative Process." Just the Facts. Available at www.ppic.org/content/pubs/jtf/JTF_InitiativeJTF.pdf.

Public Utility Commission of Oregon. 2010. Final Order No. 10-364 in the matter of Pacificorp, dba Pacific Power, Application to implement the Provisions of Senate Bill 76, entered 09-16-2010.

Pulido-Velázquez, M., M. W. Jenkins, and J. R. Lund. 2004. "Economic Values for Conjunctive Use and Water Banking in Southern California." *Water Resources Research* 40(3): W03401, doi:10.1029/2003WR002626.

Quay, R. 2010. "Anticipatory Governance: A Tool for Climate Change Adaptation." *Journal of the American Planning Association* 76(4): 496–512.

Quiñones, R. M., B. N. Harvey, A. P. Wintzer, M. Klasson, M. A. Evans, J. D. Kiernan, and P. B. Moyle. 2011. *Potential Effects of Dam Removal on Anadromous Salmonids in California*, Working Paper. University of California, Davis: Center for Watershed Sciences.

Ragatz, R. 2011. "California's Water Futures: How Water Conservation and Varying Delta Exports Affect Water Supply in the Face of Climate Change." Master's thesis. University of California, Davis.

Rajagopalan, B., K. Nowak, J. Prairie, M. Hoerling, B. Harding, J. Barsugli, A. Ray, and B. Udall. 2009. "Water Supply Risk on the Colorado River: Can Management Mitigate? *Water Resources Research* 45, W08201, doi:10.1029/2008WR007652.

Recycled Water Task Force. 2003. *Water Recycling 2030: Recommendations of California's Recycled Water Task Force.* Sacramento, CA: California Department of Water Resources.

Renwick, M. E., and R. D. Green. 2000. "Do Residential Water Demand Side Management Policies Measure Up? An Analysis of Eight California Water Agencies," *Journal of Environmental Economics and Management* 40: 37–55, doi:10.1006/jeem.1999.1102.

Ribaudo, M. O. 2009. "Non-Point Pollution Regulation Approaches in the US." In *The Management of Water Quality and Irrigation Technologies,* ed. J. Albiac and A. Dinar (London: Earthscan), 83101.

Ribaudo, M. O., and C. J. Nickerson. 2009. "Agriculture and Water Quality Trading: Exploring the Possibilities." *Journal of Soil and Water Conservation* 64: 1–7.

Richardson, J. D. 1982. "Trade Adjustment Assistance Under the United States Trade Act of 1974: An Analytical Examination and Worker Survey." In *Import Competition and Response,* ed. J. N. Bhagwati (Chicago: University of Chicago Press).

Richardson, S. D. 2009. "Water Analysis: Emerging Contaminants and Current Issues," *Analytical Chemistry* 81: 4645–77.

Richter, B. D., J. V. Baumgartner, R. Wigington, and D. P. Braun. 1997a. "How Much Water Does a River Need?" *Freshwater Biology* 37: 231–49.

Richter, B. D., D. P. Braun, M. A. Mendelson, and L. L. Master. 1997b. "Threats to Imperiled Freshwater Fauna." *Conservation Biology* 11: 1081–93.

Rieke, E.A. 1996. "The Bay-Delta Accord: A Stride Toward Sustainability." *University of Colorado Law Review* 67: 341–69.

Ringquist, E. J. 1993. *Environmental Pollution at the State Level: Politics and Progress in Controlling Pollution.* Armonk, NY: Sharpe.

Rolston, H., III. 1994. *Conserving Natural Value.* New York: Columbia University Press.

Roos-Collins, R. 2009. "Modernizing the Water Rights System." Testimony before the Little Hoover Commission, Sacramento, CA.

Rosenberg, D., R. Howitt, and J. Lund. 2008. "Water Management with Water Conservation, Infrastructure Expansions, and Source Variability in Jordan." *Water Resources Research* 44, doi:10.1029/2007WR006519.

Rosenberg, D. E., T. Tarawneh, R. Abdel-Khaleq, and J. R. Lund. 2007. "Modeling Integrated Water-User Decisions in Intermittent Supply Systems," *Water Resources Research* 43(7).

Rosenzweig, M. L. 2003. *Win-Win Ecology: How the Earth's Species Can Survive in the Midst of Human Enterprise*. New York: Oxford University Press.

Rounds, S. A., and A. B. Sullivan. 2009. *Review of Klamath River Total Maximum Daily Load Models from Link River Dam to Keno Dam, Oregon*. Washington, DC: U.S. Geological Survey.

Rounds, S. A., and A. B. Sullivan. 2010. *Review of Revised Klamath River Total Maximum Daily Load Models from Link River Dam to Keno Dam, Oregon*. Washington, DC: U.S. Geological Survey.

Rueben K. S., and P. Cerdán. 2003. *Fiscal Effects of Voter Approval Requirements on Local Governments*. San Francisco: Public Policy Institute of California. Available at www.ppic.org/main/publication.asp?i=377.

Ryan, H. F., and M. A. Noble. 2007. "Sea Level Fluctuations in Central California at Subtidal to Decadal and Longer Time Scales with Implications for San Francisco Bay, California." *Estuarine, Coastal and Shelf Science* 73: 538–50.

Sabatier, P., and D. Whiteman. 1985. "Legislative Decision Making and Substantive Policy Information: Models of Information Flow." *Legislative Studies Quarterly* 10: 395–421.

Sacramento Area Flood Control Agency. 2008. *Development Fee Program: Comparative Risk Analysis*. Sacramento, CA: David Ford Consulting Engineers. Available at www.safca.org/assessments/documents/SAFCADeveloperFee_benefits01292008.pdf.

Salzman, J., and B. H. Thompson, Jr. 2010. *Environmental Law and Policy: Concepts and Insights*. New York: Foundation Press.

San Diego County Water Authority. 1997. *Water Resources Plan*. San Diego, CA.

Sanstad, A., H. Johnson, N. Goldstein, and G. Franco. 2009. *Long-Run Socioeconomic and Demographic Scenarios for California*. Report CEC-500-2009-013-F, Sacramento: California Energy Commission.

Santer, D., and T. Nozawa. 2009. "Detection and Attribution of Stream Flow Timing Changes to Climate Change in the Western United States." *Journal of Climate* 22, doi:10.1175/2009JCLI2470.1, 3838–3855.

Sax, J. L. 1990. "The Constitution, Property Rights and the Future of Water Law." *University of Colorado Law Review* 61: 257–82.

Sax, J. L. 2003. "We Don't Do Groundwater: A Morsel of California Legal History." *University of Denver Water Law Review* 6: 269–317.

Sax, J. L., B. H. Thompson, Jr., J. D. Leshy, and R. H. Abrams. 2006. *Legal Control of Water Resources*. 4th ed. St. Paul, MN: Thomson/West.

Scheierling, S. M., R. A. Young, and G. E. Cardon. 2006. "Public Subsidies for Water-Conserving Irrigation Investments; Hydrologic, Agronomic, and Economic Assessment," *Water Resources Research* 42, W03428, doi:10.1029/2004WR003809.

Schilling, F., J. K. London, and R. Levanos. 2009. "Marginalization by Collaboration: Environmental Justice as a Third Party in and Beyond CALFED." *Environmental Science and Policy* 12: 694–709.

Schindler, D. E., R. Hilborn, B. Chasco, C. P. Boatwright, T. P. Quinn, L. A. Rogers, and M. S. Webster. 2010. "Population Diversity and the Portfolio Effect in an Exploited Species." *Nature* 465: 609–13.

Schneider, A. 1977. "Groundwater Rights in California." Staff Paper No. 2, Governor's Commission to Review California's Water Rights Law.

Schwartz, J. 2010. "New Orleans Levees Nearly Ready, But Mistrusted." *New York Times*, August 24. Available at www.nytimes.com/2010/08/24/us/24levee.html.

Scott, J. M., D. D. Goble, L. K. Svancara, and A. Pidgorna. 2006. "By the Numbers." In *The Endangered Species Act at Thirty*: Vol. 1, *Renewing the Conservation Promise*, ed. D. D. Goble, J. M. Scott, and F. W. Davis (Washington, DC: Island Press), 36–44.

Sharp, R., and B. Walker. 2007. *Power Drain: Big Ag's $100 Million Subsidy*. Washington, DC: Environmental Working Group.

Shoups, G., J. Hopmans, C. Young, J. Vrugt, W. Tanji, and S. Panday. 2005. "Sustainability of Irrigated Agriculture in the San Joaquin Valley, California." *Proceedings of the National Academy of Sciences* 102: 15352–15356.

Semiat, R. 2008. "Energy Issues in Desalination Processes." *Environmental Science and Technology* 42(22): 8193–8201.

Shavell, S. 2008. "On Optimal Legal Change, Past Behavior, and Grandfathering." *Journal of Legal Studies* 27: 37–85.

Sinclair Paint Co. v. State Board of Equalization, 1997. 15 Cal. 4th 866.

Smith, P. 1986. "Coercion and Groundwater Management: Three Case Studies and a 'Market' Approach." *Environmental Law* 16: 797–882.

Sommer, T. R., W. C. Harrell, M. Nobriga, R. Brown, P. B. Moyle, W. J. Kimmerer, and L. Schemel. 2001. "California's Yolo Bypass: Evidence That Flood Control Can Be Compatible with Fish, Wetlands, Wildlife and Agriculture." *Fisheries* 58(2): 325–33.

Sommer, T., C. Armor, R. Baxter, R. Breuer, L. Brown, M. Chotkowski, S. Culberson, F. Feyrer, M. Gingras, B. Herbold, W. Kimmerer, A. Mueller-Solger, M. Nobriga, and K. Souza. 2007. "The Collapse of Pelagic Fishes in the Upper San Francisco Estuary." *Fisheries* 32: 270–77.

South Florida Water Management District v. Miccosukee Tribe of Indians, 2004. 541 U.S. 95.

Stanley, E. H., and M. W. Doyle. 2003. "Trading Off: The Ecological Effects of Dam Removal." *Frontiers in Ecology and the Environment* 1: 15–22.

State Water Resources Control Board. 2003. "Amount of Water Held by Water Rights," Handout at stakeholder meeting. Sacramento, CA: State Water Resources Control Board, November 6 (cited in *California Farm Bureau Federation v. State Water Resources Control Board* 2007, Appendix).

State Water Resources Control Board. 2010a. "Groundwater Quality Data Report—Tulare County Focus Area." Draft. Groundwater Ambient Monitoring and Assessment (GAMA), Domestic Well Project, Sacramento, CA.

State Water Resources Control Board. 2010b. Development of Flow Criteria for the Sacramento–San Joaquin Delta Ecosystem. Appendix B: Water Supply Modeling. Draft report, July. Sacramento, CA.

State Water Resources Control Board. 2010c. "Draft Text of Proposed Regulations: Russian River Frost Protection." Available at www.swrcb.ca.gov/waterrights/water_issues/programs/hearings/russian_river_frost/.

State Water Resources Control Board. 2010d. *Total Maximum Daily Load Program, Background and Information*. Available at www.swrcb.ca.gov/water_issues/programs/tmdl/background.shtml#current.

Stewart, R. 1977. "Pyramids of Sacrifice? Problems of Federalism in Mandatory State Implementation of National Environmental Policies." *Yale Law Journal* 86: 1196–1272.

Stine, S. 1994. "Extreme and Persistent Drought in California and Patagonia During Medieval Time." *Nature* 369: 546–49.

Stockton East Water District v. United States. 2009. 583 F.3d 1344 (Fed. Cir.).

Stokstad, Erik. 2007. "Feared Quagga Mussel Turns Up in Western United States." *Science* 315(5811): 453.

Suchanek, T. H., P. J. Richerson, R. A. Zierenberg, et al. 2008. "The Legacy of Mercury Cycling from Mining Sources in an Aquatic Ecosystem: From Ore to Organism." *Ecological Applications* 18: 12–28.

Suddeth, R., J. F. Mount, and J. R. Lund. 2010. "Levee Decisions and Sustainability for the Sacramento San Joaquin Delta." *San Francisco Estuary and Watershed Science* 8(2). Available at www.escholarship.org/uc/item/9wr5j84g.

Sugihara, N. G., J. W. Wagtendonk, K. E. Shaffer, J. Fites-Kautman, and A. E. Thode, eds. 2006. *Fire in California's Ecosystems.* Berkeley: University of California Press.

Tanaka, S. K., T. Zhu, J. R. Lund, R. E. Howitt, M. W. Jenkins, M. A. Pulido, M. Tauber, R. S. Ritzema, and I. C. Ferreira. 2006. "Climate Warming and Water Management Adaptation for California." *Climatic Change* 76(3–4): 361–87.

Tanaka, S. K., C. Buck, K. Madani, J. Medellin-Azuara, J. Lund, and E. Hanak. In press. "Economic Costs and Adaptations for Alternative Regulations of California's Sacramento–San Joaquin Delta." *San Francisco Estuary and Watershed Science.*

Taylor, K., and A. Short. 2009. "Integrating Scientific Knowledge into Large-Scale Restoration Programs—The CALFED Bay-Delta Program Experience." *Environmental Science and Policy* 12: 674–83.

Taylor, M.F.J., K. F. Suckling, and J. J. Rachlinski. 2005. "The Effectiveness of the Endangered Species Act: A Quantitative Analysis." *Bioscience* 55: 360–67.

Teitz, M. B., C. Dietzel, and W. Fulton. 2005. *Urban Development Futures in the San Joaquin Valley.* San Francisco: Public Policy Institute of California.

Thaler, R. H., and C. R. Sunstein. 2008. *Nudge: Improving Decisions About Health, Wealth, and Happiness.* New Haven, CT: Yale University Press.

Tharme, R. E. 2003. "A Global Perspective on Environmental Flow Assessment: Emerging Trends in the Development and Application of Environmental Flow Methodologies for Rivers." *River Research and Application* 19: 397–441.

"The Land and Environment Court of NSW, Annual Review 2009." 2010. State of New South Wales, Sydney, AU.

The Nature Conservancy. 2010. *Freshwater Conservation: What We Do—Protecting Watersheds and Water Supplies for Cities.* Available at www.nature.org/initiatives/freshwater/strategies/watersheds.html.

Thomas, G. 2001. *Designing Successful Groundwater Banking Programs in the Central Valley: Lessons from Experience.* Berkeley, CA: Natural Heritage Institute.

Thompson, B. H., Jr. 1990. "Judicial Takings." *Virginia Law Review* 76: 1449–1544.

Thompson, B. H., Jr. 1993. "Institutional Perspectives on Water Policy and Markets." *California Law Review* 81: 671–764.

Thompson, B. H., Jr. 1995. "Takings and Water Rights." In *Water Law: Trends, Policies, and Practice,* ed. K. Carr and J. Crammond (Chicago: American Bar Association Section of Natural Resources, Energy, and Environmental Law).

Thompson, B. H., Jr. 1997a. "Water Federalism: Governmental Competition and Conflict over Western Waters." In *Environmental Federalism,* ed. T. L. Anderson and P. J. Hill (Lanham, MD: Rowman & Littlefield Publishers, Inc.), 175–224.

Thompson, B. H., Jr. 1997b. "The Endangered Species Act: A Case Study in Takings & Incentives." *Stanford Law Review* 49: 305–80.

Thompson, B. H., Jr. 2000. "Markets for Nature." *William and Mary Environmental Law and Policy Review* 25: 261–77.

Thompson, B. H., Jr. 2006. "Managing the Working Landscape." In *The Endangered Species Act at Thirty,* Vol. 1, *Renewing the Conservation Promise,* ed. D. D. Goble, J. M. Scott, and F. W. Davis. (Washington, DC: Island Press).

Thompson, B. H., Jr. 2010. "Facilitating Adaptation to Climate Change: Themes for Law and Policy." Stanford Law School Working Paper.

Thompson J. 1957. *Settlement Geography of the Sacramento–San Joaquin Delta, California.* Ph.D. dissertation, Stanford University.

Thompson, L. C., D. R. Purkey, M. I. Escobar, C. M. Mosser, and P. B. Moyle. Submitted. "Climate Change Adaptations to Prevent Loss of Aquatic Ecosystem Service. Part 2. Case Study for Chinook Salmon in California." *Journal of Water Resources Planning and Management.*

Town of Antioch v. Williams Irrigation District. 1922. 188 Cal. 451, 205 P. 688.

Truan, M. A. 2004. "Spatiotemporal, Multiscale Gradient Analysis of Longitudinal Community Structure and Habitat Relationships for Plants, Birds, and Small Mammals in Two Shredded Riparian Ecosystems, Central Valley." Ph.D. dissertation, University of California, Davis.

Tuchman, E. T., K. P. Connaughton, L. E. Freedman, and C. B. Moriwaki. 1998. *The Northwest Forest Plan: A Report to the President and Congress.* Washington, DC: Office of Forestry and Economic Assistance, U.S. Department of Agriculture.

Tulare Lake Basin Water Storage District v. United States. 2001. 49 Fed. Cl. 313.

United States v. New Mexico. 1978. 438 U.S. 696.

United States v. State Water Resources Control Board [Racanelli]. 1986. 182 Cal. App. 3d 82, 227 Cal. Rptr. 161.

URS Corporation and J. R. Benjamin and Associates. 2009a. *Delta Risk Management Strategy (DRMS) Phase 1 Risk Analysis Report,* prepared for the California Department of Water Resources.

URS Corporation and J. R. Benjamin and Associates. 2009b. *Delta Risk Management Strategy (DRMS) Phase 2 Evaluation of Delta Risk Management Strategies Report Preliminary,* prepared for the California Department of Water Resources.

U.S. Bureau of Reclamation. 2008. *Upper San Joaquin River Basin Storage Investigation.* Plan Formulation Report. Sacramento, CA.

U.S. Department of the Interior. 1990. *San Joaquin Valley Drainage Program.* Final Draft Report. Sacramento, CA: California Resources Agency.

U.S. Environmental Protection Agency. Undated (a). *Assessment Data for the State of California Year 2004.* Washington, DC.

U.S. Environmental Protection Agency. Undated (b). *Contaminant Candidate List.* Available at www.epa.gov/ogwdw000/ccl/ccl3.html.

U.S. Environmental Protection Agency. Undated (c). National Pollutant Discharge Elimination System Permit Program Regulations, 40 C.F.R. § 122.3(i).

U.S. Environmental Protection Agency. Undated (d). *Water Quality Handbook*, Chapter 4: *Antidegradation*. Washington, DC.

U.S. Environmental Protection Agency. Undated (e). *Water Quality Regulations*, 40 C.F.R. §§ 131.1–131.22.

U.S. Environmental Protection Agency. Undated (f). Contaminants of Emerging Concern. Available at http://water.epa.gov/scitech/cec/.

U.S. Environmental Protection Agency. 2004. *Water Quality Trading Assessment Handbook: Can Water Quality Trading Advance Your Watershed Goals?* Washington, DC.

U.S. Environmental Protection Agency. 2008. *Clean Watersheds Needs Survey*. Washington, DC.

U.S. Environmental Protection Agency. 2009. *Drinking Water Infrastructure Needs Survey and Assessment*. Washington, DC.

U.S. Fish and Wildlife Service. Undated. *National Wetland Inventory. Classification of Wetlands and Deepwater Habitats of the United States*, FWS/OBS-79/31. Washington, DC. Available at www.fws.gov/wetlands/.

U.S. Geological Survey. 2009. "Groundwater Availability of the Central Valley Aquifer, California." Professional Paper 1766, U.S. Department of the Interior.

U.S. Government Accountability Office. 2009. *Options for Enhancing the Effectiveness of the Toxic Substances Control Act*. Report GAO-09-428T. Available at www.gao.gov/products/GAO-05-458.

van Dantzig, D. 1956. "Economic Decision Problems for Flood Prevention." *Econometrica* 24(3): 276–87.

van den Belt, M. 2004. *Mediated Modeling: A System Dynamics Approach to Environmental Consensus Building*. Washington, DC: Island Press.

Vaux, H. J. 1986. "Water Scarcity and Gains from Trade in Kern County, California." In *Scarce Water and Institutional Change*, ed. K. Frederick (Washington, DC: Resources for the Future), 67–101.

Vaux, H. J., and R. E. Howitt. 1984. "Managing Water Scarcity—An Evaluation of Interregional Transfers." *Water Resources Research* 20(7): 785–92.

Vermeer, M., and S. Rahmstorf. 2009. "Global Sea Level Linked to Global Temperature." *Proceedings of the National Academy of Sciences*, doi:10.1073/pnas.0907765106.

Vicuna, S., R. Leonardson, M. W. Hanemann, L. L. Dale, and J. A. Dracup. 2008. "Climate Change Impacts on High Elevation Hydropower Generation in California's Sierra Nevada: A Case Study of the Upper American River." *Climatic Change* 87(1): 123–37.

Vine, E. 2008. *Adaptation of California's Electricity Sector to Climate Change*. San Francisco: Public Policy Institute of California. Available at www.ppic.org/content/pubs/report/R_1108EVR.pdf.

Voortman, H. G., and J. K. Vrjiling. 2004. "Optimal Design of Flood Defence Systems in a Changing Climate." *HERON* 49(1): 95–94.

Vörösmarty, C. J., P. Green, J. Salisbury, and R. B. Lammers. 2000. "Global Water Resources: Vulnerability from Climate Change and Population Growth." *Science* 289(5477): 284–88.

Votteler, T. H. 1998. "The Little Fish That Roared: The Endangered Species Act, State Groundwater Law, and Private Property Rights Collide over the Texas Edwards Aquifer." *Environmental Law* 28: 845–77.

Walker, B., and D. Salt. 2006. *Resilience Thinking: Sustaining Ecosystems and People in a Changing World.* Covelo, CA: Island Press.

Walker, R. A., and M. J. Williams. 1982. "Water from Power: Water Supply and Regional Growth in the Santa Clara Valley." *Economic Geography* 58(2): 95–119.

Ward, F. A., and M. Pulido-Velazquez. 2008. "Water Conservation in Irrigation Can Increase Water Use." *Proceedings of the National Academy of Sciences* 105(47): 18215–20.

Water Education Foundation. 2007. *The Lower Yuba River Accord: From Controversy to Consensus.* Sacramento, CA: Water Education Foundation.

Water Strategist. Various issues. Claremont, CA: Stratecon, Inc.

Weiser, M. 2005. "New Orleans Flooding 'Wake-Up Call' for Capital." *Sacramento Bee.* August 31.

Welch, A. H., D. B. Westjohn, D. R. Helsel, and R. B. Wanty. 2000. "Arsenic in Ground Water of the United States—Occurrence and Geochemistry." *Ground Water* 38(4): 589–604.

West J. M., S. H. Julius, P. Kareiva, C. Enquist, J. J. Lawler, B. Petersen, A. E. Johnson, and M. R. Shaw. 2009. "U.S. Natural Resources and Climate Change: Concepts and Approaches for Management Adaptation." *Environmental Management* 44: 1001–21.

White, G. F. 1945. "Human Adjustment to Floods: A Geographical Approach to the Flood Problem in the United States." Research paper no. 29. Chicago: University of Chicago, Department of Geography.

White, R. 1995. *The Organic Machine: The Remaking of the Columbia River*, New York: Hill and Wang.

Wichelns, D., and D. Cone. 2006. "A Water Transfer and Agricultural Land Retirement in a Drainage Problem Area." *Irrigation and Drainage Systems* 20: 225–45.

Wichelns, D., L. Jouston, and D. Cone. 1997. "Economic Analysis of Sprinkler and Siphon Tube Irrigation, with Implications for Public Policy." *Agricultural Water Management* 32: 259–73.

Wilkinson, R. 2000. Methodology for Analysis of the Energy Intensity of California's Water Systems and an Assessment of Multiple Potential Benefits Through Integrated Water-Energy Efficiency Measures." Santa Barbara: University of California, Environmental Studies Program.

Williams, J. G. 2006. "Central Valley Salmon: A Perspective on Chinook and Steelhead in the Central Valley of California." *San Francisco Estuary and Watershed Science* 4(3): Article 2. Available at http://repositories.cdlib.org/jmie/sfews/vol4/iss3/art2.

Williamson, J., ed. 1994. *The Political Economy of Policy Reform.* Washington, DC: Institute for International Economics.

Williamson, K. J., and B. P. May. 2005. Homogenization of Fall-Run Chinook Salmon Gene Pools in the Central Valley of California, USA." *North American Journal of Fisheries Management* 25: 993–1009.

Winters v. United States. 1908. 207 U.S. 564.

Woodall, D. L., and J. R. Lund. 2009. "Dutch Flood Policy Innovations for California." *Journal of Contemporary Water Research and Education* 141: 45–59.

Woodruff v. North Bloomfield Mining Co. 1884. 18 F. 753 (C.C. Cal.).

Woody, C. A., R. M. Hughes, E. J. Wagner, T. P. Quinn, L. H. Roulson, L. M. Martin, and K. Griswold. 2010. "The Mining Law of 1872: Change Is Overdue." *Fisheries* 35: 321–31.

Worster, D. 1985. *Rivers of Empire: Water, Aridity, and the Growth of the American West*. New York: Pantheon Books.

Yarnell, S., J. Viers, and J. Mount. 2010. "Ecology and Management of the Spring Snowmelt Recession." *Bioscience* 60: 114–27.

Yoshiyama, R. M. 1999. "A History of Salmon and People in the Central Valley Region of California." *Reviews in Fisheries Science* 7: 197–239.

Yoshiyama, R. M., and P. B. Moyle. 2010. "Historical Review of Eel River Anadromous Salmonids, with Emphasis on Chinook Salmon, Coho Salmon and Steelhead." Working paper, University of California, Davis.

Yoshiyama, R. M., F. W. Fisher, and P. B. Moyle. 1998. "Historical Abundance and Decline of Chinook Salmon in the Central Valley Region of California." *North American Journal of Fisheries Management* 18: 487–521.

Yoshiyama, R. M., E. R. Gerstung, F. W. Fisher, and P. B. Moyle. 2000. "Chinook Salmon in the California Central Valley: An Assessment." *Fisheries* 25(2): 6–20.

Yoshiyama, R. M., E. R. Gerstung, F. W. Fisher, and P. B. Moyle. 2001. "Historical and Present Distribution of Chinook Salmon in the Central Valley." In *Contributions to the Biology of Central Valley Salmonids,* ed. R. Brown (*CDFG Fish Bulletin* 179), 71–176.

Young, M. D. 2009. "Non-Point Pollution Control: Experience and Observations from Australia." In *The Management of Water Quality and Irrigation Technologies,* ed. J. Albiac and A. Dinar (London: Earthscan), 103–16.

Young, M. D. 2010. "Environmental Effectiveness and Economic Efficiency of Water Use in Agriculture: The Experience of and Lessons from the Australian Water Reform Programme." In *Sustainable Management of Water Resources in Agriculture*. Organisation for Economic Co-operation and Development. Available at www.oecd.org/water.

Yune, H. 2010. "DWR Notices Remind Residents of Flood Risk." *Marysville Appeal-Democrat,* September 20.

Zhu, T., J. R. Lund, M. W. Jenkins, G. F. Marques, and R. S. Ritzema. 2007. "Climate Change, Urbanization, and Optimal Long-term Floodplain Protection." *Water Resources Research* 43(6): W06421, doi:10.1029/2004WR003516.

About the Authors

Ariel Dinar is a professor of environmental economics and policy and a director of the Water Science and Policy Center, Department of Environmental Sciences, University of California, Riverside. He teaches and conducts research on the economics of water resources and the environment, regional water resource management, policy and strategic behavior, and climate change and water resources.

Brian E. Gray is a professor of law at the University of California, Hastings College of Law, San Francisco. His academic writings and professional work have focused on various aspects of water policy, including instream flow protection, water transfers, federal reclamation reform, endangered species, groundwater management, and water rights and environmental regulation. He has served as chair of the California State Bar's Committee on the environment and has been a consultant to a variety of state and federal agencies. He also has appeared before the California Supreme Court and the U.S. Court of Appeals in cases involving the Wild and Scenic Rivers Act, reclamation reform and takings, the Central Valley Project Improvement Act, and the CALFED Bay-Delta Program.

Ellen Hanak is a senior fellow at the Public Policy Institute of California. Her career has focused on the economics of natural resource management and agricultural development. At PPIC, she has launched a research program on water policy and has published reports and articles on water marketing, water and land use planning, water conservation, infrastructure planning, climate change, and management of the Sacramento–San Joaquin Delta. Before joining PPIC in 2001, she held positions with the French agricultural research system, the President's Council of Economic Advisers, and the World Bank.

Richard Howitt is a professor and department chair of agricultural and resource economics at the University of California, Davis. He teaches both graduate and undergraduate courses in resource economics, economic theory, and operations research. His current research interests include constructing disaggregated economic modeling methods based on maximum entropy estimators, testing the allocation of water resources by market mechanisms, and developing empirical dynamic stochastic methods to analyze changes in investments and institutions. He serves on advisory boards for the California Department of Water Resources and the U.S. Academy of Sciences.

Jay Lund is the Ray B. Krone Professor of Environmental Engineering and director of the Center for Watershed Sciences at the University of California, Davis. He specializes in the management of water and environmental systems. His research has included system optimization studies for California, the Columbia River, the Missouri River, and other systems for climate change adaptation, water marketing, water conservation, system reoperation, and integrated water management. He served on the Advisory Committee for the 1998 and 2005 issues of the *California Water Plan Update* and is a former editor of the *Journal of Water Resources Planning and Management*.

Jeffrey Mount is a professor in the Geology Department at the University of California, Davis. His research and teaching interests include fluvial geomorphology, conservation and restoration of large river systems, floodplain management, and flood policy. He holds the Roy Shlemon Chair in Applied Geosciences at UC Davis and is the founding director of the UC Davis Center for Watershed Sciences.

Peter Moyle has been studying the ecology and conservation of freshwater and estuarine fish in California since 1969. He has authored or coauthored over 180 scientific papers and nine books. He is a professor of fish biology in the Department of Wildlife, Fish, and Conservation Biology at the University of California, Davis, and is associate director of the UC Davis Center for Watershed Sciences.

Barton "Buzz" Thompson is the Robert E. Paradise Professor in Natural Resources Law at Stanford Law School and the Perry L. McCarty Director of the Woods Institute for the Environment at Stanford University. He also serves as Special Master for the United States Supreme Court in *Montana v. Wyoming*. His research focuses on the role of law, institutions, and markets in effective water management, as well as the law of regulatory takings and biodiversity protection. He is a member of the Science Advisory Board for the U.S. Environmental Protection Agency and served on the Technical Review Panel for the California Environmental Water Account.

Index